*Varieties of
Psychopathological Experience*

Carney Landis, 1897–1962

CARNEY LANDIS

Late Professor of Psychology,
Columbia University,
and Chief Research Psychologist,
New York State Psychiatric Institute

Edited by
FRED A. METTLER

Departments of Anatomy and Neurology,
College of Physicians and Surgeons,
Columbia University

VARIETIES OF
Psychopathological Experience

HOLT, RINEHART AND WINSTON

New York, Chicago, San Francisco,
Toronto, London

Acknowledgments

Grateful acknowledgment is made to Mr. Helmut Gruber and Mr. George Gourevitch, for their assistance in the task of translating material from the German and the French, respectively.

Acknowledgment is made to the following named authors and publishers for permission to reprint excerpts from the material noted below:

George Allen and Unwin Ltd., London, and F. Pastorelli, G. Stuart, and J. Vincent, for F. Pastorelli's (1936) *The Glorious Bondage of Illness*, G. Stuart's (1953) *Private World of Pain*, and J. Vincent's (1948) *Inside the Asylum*.

The Association for the Advancement of Psychoanalysis, New York, for K. Horney's "Finding the real self," Vol. IX (1949), in *The American Journal of Psychoanalysis*.

Archives of Neurology and Psychiatry, Chicago, and S. Cobb, W. Freeman, and D. J. Sullivan for W. Lennox and S. Cobb's (1933) "Epilepsy" (Vol. 30); W. Freeman and J. M. Williams' (1953) "Hallucinations in Braille" (Vol. 70); D. J. Sullivan's (1948) "Insulin subshock (subcoma) treatment of psychoses and psychoneuroses" (Vol. 59); and A. Angyal's (1936) "Phenomena resembling lilliputian hallucinations in schizophrenia" (Vol. 36).

American Journal of Orthopsychiatry, New York, for Anonymous' (1940) "Insulin and I" (Vol. 10).

American Psychiatric Association, New York, and the *American Journal of Psychiatry* for E. Bryan's (1933) "A study of forty cases exhibiting neologisms" (Vol. 13); J. Lang's (1938) "The other side of hallucinations" (Vol. 94); and J. Lang's (1939) "The other side of hallucinations" (Vol. 96).

American Psychological Association, Washington, D.C., for T. Alper's (1948) "An electric shock patient tells his story" (*J. abnorm. soc. Psychol.* 43); Anonymous'

(1955) "An autobiography of a schizophrenic experience" (*J. abnorm. soc. Psychol.* 51); C. Berry's (1916) "Obsessions of normal minds" (*J. abnorm. Psychol.* 11); P. Janet's (1906) "On the pathogenesis of some impulsions" (*J. abnorm. Psychol.* 1); and A. Kampmeier's (1907) "Confessions of a psychasthenic (*J. abnorm. Psychol.* 2).

Annales Medico-Psychologiques, Paris, for A. Starobinski's (1921) "Un cas de psychose maniaque dépressive à un jour d'alternance" (Ser. 11, Vol. 1).

The Aquarium Publishing Co., Norristown, Pa., for R. Bucke's (1901) *Cosmic Consciousness: A Study in the Evolution of the Human Mind.*

Bobbs-Merrill Company, Inc., Indianapolis, for R. Dahl's *Breakdown* (copyright 1959 by Robert E. Dahl).

The Bodley Head Ltd., London, and M. Harrison, for M. Harrison's (1941) *Spinners Lake.*

Brain, London, for R. Efron's (1956) "The effect of olfactory stimuli in arresting uncinate fits" (Vol. 79) and J. Hughlings-Jackson's (1889) "On a particular variety of epilepsy ('intellectual aura'): One case with symptoms of organic brain disease" (Vol. 11).

British Medical Journal, London, for E. Anderson's (1938) "A clinical study of states of 'ecstasy' occurring in affective disorders" (Vol. 1).

British Medical Association and the publishers of the *Journal of Neurology and Psychopathology*, for R. C. Turnbull's (1921) "A case of catatonia" (Vol. 2); and H. Devine's (1921) "An expiation process in a case of schizophrenia" (Vol. 2).

The British Psychological Society, London, for Anonymous' (1931) "The asylum environment" (Vol. 10) and A. Lewis' (1934) "The psychopathology of insight" (Vol. 14), in the *British Journal of Medical Psychology.*

Chilton Books, Philadelphia, for Anonymous' *The Philosophy of Insanity* (copyright 1947 by Chilton Books).

The Clarendon Press, Oxford, for T. Traherne's (1910) *Traherne's Poems of Felicity* (ed. from the ms. of H. I. Bell).

Crown Publishers, Inc., 419 Park Avenue South, New York, for L. Freeman's *Fight Against Fears* (copyright 1959 by Lucy Freeman).

Peter Davies Ltd., London, and Thomas Hennell for T. Hennell's (1938) *The Witnesses.*

Dawson's of Pall Mall, London, for D. Schreber's (1955) *Memoirs of My Nervous Illness* (ed. and translated by I. Macalpine and R. A. Hunter).

Dodd, Mead & Co., New York, for M. Rutherford's (1885) *The Autobiography of Mark Rutherford.*

E. P. Dutton & Co., Inc., New York, and H. C. Brown, for H. C. Brown's (1937) *A Mind Mislaid.*

Exposition Press, Inc., New York, for W. Moore's (1955) *The Mind in Chains.*

Faber and Faber Ltd., London, and F. Karinthy and M. Channing-Pearce, for F. Karinthy's (1939) *A Journey Round My Skull;* Nicodemus (1942) *Midnight Hour;* and Anonymous' (1932) *I Lost My Memory: The Case as the Patient Saw It.*

Farrar, Straus & Company, Inc., New York, for J. Custance's (1952) *Wisdom, Madness and Folly* (copyright 1952 by John Custance) and F. Peters' *The World Next Door* (copyright 1949 by Fritz Peters).

Fudge & Co. Ltd., London, for M. Hamilcar's (1910) *Legally Dead.*

Funk & Wagnalls, New York, and L. Jayson for L. Jayson's (1937) *Mania.*

Grune & Stratton, Inc., New York, and M. Sechehaye for M. Sechehaye's (1951) *Autobiography of a Schizophrenic Girl.*

Harcourt, Brace & World, Inc., New York, and T. S. Eliot and S. W. and J. T. Pierce for T. S. Eliot's (1936) *Collected Poems, 1909–1935* and S. W. and J. T. Pierce's (1929) *The Layman Looks at Doctors.*

Harper & Row, Publishers, New York, and A. T. Boisen and J. Cary for A. T. Boisen's (1936) *The Exploration of the Inner World* and J. Cary's (1958) (edited by Ruth N. Anshen) *Art and Reality: Ways of the Creative Process*.

David Higham Associates, Ltd., London, and Margiad Evans for M. Evans' (1952) *A Ray of Darkness* (published by Arthur Barker).

Holt, Rinehart & Winston, Inc., New York, for W. James' (1890) *The Principles of Psychology*.

International Journal of Psycho-Analysis, London, for E. Sharpe's (1940) "Psycho-physical problems revealed in language: An examination of metaphor" (Vol. 21).

Johnson Publications Ltd., London, for J. Custance's (1954) *Adventure into the Unconscious*.

S. Karger, Basel/New York, for E. Straus' (1938) "Ein Beitrag zur Pathologie der Zwangserscheinungen," in *Monatsschrift für Psychiatrie und Neurologie* (Vol. 98).

The Lancet, London, for *Disabilities and How to Live with Them* by the Editors of *Lancet* (1952).

J. B. Lippincott Co., Philadelphia, and L. McCall for L. McCall's (1947) *Between Us and the Dark*.

Macmillan Company, New York, and J. Oliver for J. Oliver's (1928) *Fear: The Autobiography of James Edwards*.

The Master and Fellows of Magdalene College, Cambridge, for A. Bensen's (1912) *Thy Rod and Thy Staff*.

The Editors of the *Bulletin of the Menninger Clinic* and K. Menninger, R. Fraser, and W. Sargent for permission to publish from K. Menninger's "We hardly know we are alive" (Vol. 18, copyright 1954 by The Menninger Foundation) and R. Fraser and W. Sargent's (1940–1941) "The subjective experiences of a schizophrenic illness: Personal records written at the end of the illness by some patients who were treated with insulin."

Meredith Press, 60 East 42nd Street, New York, for W. E. Leonard's *The Locomotive-God* (copyright 1927 by The Century Co., 1942 by D. Appleton-Century Co., Inc.).

The Newman Press, Westminster, Maryland, for St. John of the Cross' (Juan de Yepes') (1953) "Dark night of the soul," in *The Complete Works of St. John of the Cross* (Vol. 1).

W. W. Norton & Company, Inc., 101 Fifth Avenue, New York, and A. Forel for A. Forel's (1937) *Out of My Life and Work*.

Physicians Postgraduate Press, New York, for S. Brock and B. Wiesel's (1942) "Derealization and depersonalization: Their occurrence in organic and psychogenic states," in *Diseases of the Nervous System* (Vol. 3).

Presses Universitaires de France, Paris, for E. Lombard's (1923) "Quelques impressions après une commotion," in *J. Psychol. norm. path.* (Vol. 20).

The Psychiatric Quarterly, Utica, for J. R. Blalock's (1936) "Psychology of the manic phase of the manic-depressive psychoses" (Vol. 10); F. Cohen's (1956) "The relationship between delusional thinking and hostility—A case study" (Vol. 30); E. Dearborn's (1950) "Time out for death" (Vol. 24); M. Hayward and J. Taylor's (1956) "A schizophrenic patient describes the action of intensive psychotherapy" (Vol. 30); B. Karpman's (1953) "Dream life in a case of schizophrenia" (Vol. 27); P. Milici's (1937) "Graphocatharsis in schizophrenia" (Vol. 11); P. Milici and C. Von Salzen's (1938) "Situational schizophrenia" (Vol. 12); and B. Pollock's (1937) "Schizophrenic thought" (Vol. 11).

Psychiatry (*Journal of the Study of Interpersonal Processes*) for Anonymous' (1952) "Recovery from a long neurosis," pp. 162–177 (Vol. 15); A. T. Boisen's

(1942) "The form and content of schizophrenic thinking," pp. 24–26 (Vol. 5); A. T. Boisen's (1947) "Onset in acute schizophrenia," p. 160 (Vol. 10); J. Kindwall and E. Kinder's (1940) "Postscript on a benign psychosis," pp. 529–531 (Vol. 3); J. Lang's (1939) "The other side of the affective aspects of schizophrenia," pp. 197–199 (Vol. 2) and J. Lang's (1940) "The other side of the ideological aspects of schizophrenia," pp. 389–393 (Vol. 3).

The *Psychoanalytic Quarterly*, New York, for I. Glauber's (1949) "Observations on a primary form of anhedonia."

The *Psychoanalytic Review*, New York, for R. Clark's (1946) "Cosmic consciousness in catatonic-schizophrenia" (Vol. 33).

G. P. Putnam's & Coward-McCann, New York, and P. Hackett and E. Krauch for P. Hackett's *The Cardboard Giants* (copyright 1952 by Paul Hackett) and E. Krauch's *A Mind Restored: The Story of Jim Curran* (copyright 1937 by Elsa Krauch).

Random House, Inc., New York, and M. Ward for permission to publish from M. Ward's *The Snake Pit* (copyright 1946 by Mary Jane Ward).

Routledge & Kegan Paul, Ltd., London, and J. Leuba and J. MacCurdy for J. Leuba's (1929) *The Psychology of Religious Mysticism* and J. MacCurdy's (1925) *The Psychology of Emotion: Morbid and Normal.*

The Royal Medico-Psychological Association, London, for Anonymous' (1917) "Insanity from the patient's point of view," in *J. ment. Sci.* (Vol. 63); Anonymous' (1925) "The mental patient as he feels himself," in *J. ment. Sci.* (Vol. 71); S. Bockner's (1949) "The depersonalization syndrome: Report of a case," in *J. ment. Sci.* (Vol. 95); W. Dawson's (1909) "An autograph account of a case of sane hallucinations due to alcohol and atropin," in *J. ment. Sci.* (Vol. 55); H. Manning's (1882) "Moral insanity: Case of homicidal mania," in *J. ment. Sci.* (Vol. 28); M. Nolan's (1928) "Hallucinations and sanity," in *J. ment. Sci.* (Vol. 74); H. Osmond and A. Hoffer's (1958) "The case of Mr. Kovish," in *J. ment. Sci.* (Vol. 104); W. Roberts' (1960) "Normal and abnormal depersonalization," in *J. ment Sci.* (Vol. 106); R. Rowe's (1914) "The importance of disturbances of the personality in mental disorders," in *J. ment. Sci.* (Vol. 60); and E. Stengel's (1943) "Further studies on pathological wandering (fugues with the impulse to wander)," in *J. ment. Sci.* (Vol. 89).

Chas. Scribner's Sons, New York, and G. Santayana and L. P. Smith for G. Santayana's (1920) *Little Essays Drawn from the Writings of George Santayana* (Ed. by L. P. Smith).

Simon and Schuster, Inc., New York, and R. Nijinsky (Ed.) for permission to publish from R. Nijinsky's (1936) *The Diary of Vaslav Nijinsky* (copyright 1936 by Simon and Schuster, Inc.).

The Society for Psychical Research, London, for H. Sidgwick's (1894) *Report on the Census of Hallucinations* (Vol. 10).

Springer Verlag, Berlin, for K. Beringer and W. Mayer-Gross' (1925) "Der Fall Hahnenfuss; Ein Beitrag zur Psychopathologie des akuten schizophrenen Schubs," in *Z. ges. Neurol. Psychiat.* (Vol. 96); F. Fischer's (1929) "Zeitstruktur und Schizophrenie," in *Z. ges. Neurol. Psychiat.* (Vol. 121); R. Gaupp's (1942) "Zur Lehre von der Paranoia," in *Z. ges. Neurol. Psychiat.* (Vol. 174); Haveroch's (1913) "Uber die Storungen des Ichtums," in *Z. ges. Neurol. Psychiat.* (Vol. 19); K. Rychlinski's (1896) "Ein Fall hallucinatorisch-periodischer Psychose," in *Arch. Psychiat. Nervenkr.* (Vol. 28); F. Schwab's (1919) "Selbstschilderung eines Falles von schizophrener Psychose," in *Z. ges. Neurol. Psychiat.* (Vol. 44); and W. Winkler's (1948) "Das Oneiroid (zur Psychose Alfred Kubins)," in *Arch. Psychiat. Nervenkr.* (Vol. 181).

Jack Vickers, for L. Jefferson's (1947) *These Are My Sisters.*

x————Acknowledgments

The Viking Press, Inc., New York, and E. Coleman and W. E. Leonard, for E. Coleman's (1930) *The Shutter of Snow* and W. E. Leonard's (1925) *Two Lives, A Poem.*

A. P. Watt & Son, London, as literary agents to the Owner of the Copyright, to the Owner of the Copyright and to Victor Gollancz, Ltd., for E. Raymond's (1946) *The Autobiography of David.*

C. A. Watts & Co. Ltd., London, for Anonymous' *The Maniac* (1932), and to E. Thelmar.

The Wayne State University Press, Detroit, for O. Diethelm's (1930) "Disturbance of vision and consciousness in petit-mal attacks," in *Human Biology* (Vol. 11).

John Wiley & Sons, Inc., New York, for J. Zubin's (1948) "Objective studies of disordered persons," a chapter in T. Andrews' *Methods of Psychology.*

The Williams & Wilkins Co., Baltimore, for S. Arieti's (1950) "Autistic thought," in *J. nerv. ment. Dis.* (Vol. 111); C. W. Littman's (1953) "Hallucinations of physical duality in migraine," in *J. nerv. ment. Dis.* (Vol. 111); T. Rathmell and K. Corrin's (1940) "Retrospective study of a case involving homicide," in *J. nerv. ment. Dis.* (Vol. 91); G. Weickhardt and K. Langenstrass' (1947) "Psychosynthesis of amnesia," in *J. nerv. ment. Dis.* (Vol. 105); W. Woods' (1938) "Language study in schizophrenia," in *J. nerv. ment. Dis.* (Vol. 87); and M. Zeifert's (1940) "Metrazol remission in severe obsession-compulsion neurosis of five years' duration," in *J. nerv. ment. Dis.* (Vol. 92).

Editor's Foreword

Varieties of Psychopathological Experience occupied the final years of Carney Landis' life, and the manuscript had been submitted to the publisher at the time of the author's death on March 4, 1962.* Laura Landis, Professor Landis' widow, has provided the impetus and means for carrying forward those inevitable adjustments and revisions which publication requires. Suggestions as to the nature of certain of these has been made by Professor Rosenzweig of the Department of Psychology, Washington University, St. Louis 30, Missouri, and by Professor Theodore R. Sarbin of the Department of Psychology, University of California, Berkeley 4, California, and the editor is particularly indebted to Professors H. E. and K. King, of the University of Pittsburgh, who were of major assistance in determining the final form of the manuscript.

Over the millennia, and from country to country, psychotic persons have tended to behave and express themselves in ways which tend to fall into definite

* W. A. Hunt, 1962. Carney Landis: 1897–1962. *Amer. J. Psychol.* 75:506–509. W. A. Hunt, 1962. Carney Landis: (1897–1962). *Amer. J. Psychiat.* 119:390–392.

patterns. Without regard for theories of causation these patterns have exhibited relatively little change with respect to variation in culture or geographic location or the passage of time. Thus, the Greek of classic times who was agitated by the belief that his body was disintegrating after the fashion of a sand castle subjected to the action of water, and who feared bodily injury from falling oil cruets, has his modern counterpart. The words and idioms may change but the pattern of distress is repetitive through the ages. Psychiatrists come to recognize such particular patterns of behavior and complaints in much the same way that the botanist gradually comes to recognize exotic plants—through the opportunity of gaining familiarity with them. The reaction of inexperienced persons, when first subjected to a psychotic's account of his condition, is likely to be one of distress (or, perhaps, amusement), which may be accompanied by considerable fatigue because considerable effort has to be expended in the attempt to detect any logic which may be involved. Ultimately, one becomes aware that patients' accounts of their condition fall into particular patterns which are not so easily characterized by forms of logic as by types of affective distress or, more particularly, subjective happenings. Once one becomes aware that certain particular forms of abnormal experience are repetitive, their frequency becomes apparent and the broad outlines of the ways in which these experiences appear, and are combined, become evident. The observer is then able to detect similarities and differences which allow him to recognize particular accounts as characteristic of abnormalities of a particular type and to anticipate a particular course of further development.

The present collection serves the purpose of introducing the reader to a broad, and particularly well expressed, sample of such abnormal experiences—experiences which it might take even a psychiatrist with a large practice a very long time indeed to gain.

There will no doubt be those who, upon reading Professor Landis' book, will regret that he did not see fit to organize his material in accordance with one or another theoretical interpretation. Landis makes it plain that he deliberately avoided doing this in order to avoid a doctrinaire approach which would cast the raw material within a dated frame of reference. Obviously individual readers will interpret the material contained herein according to their own points of view but, for Landis, the important job was to make the raw material available to the reader.

A tabulation of the cases according to current diagnostic classification has been prepared by Dr. Humphry Osmond, Director of the New Jersey Bureau of Research in Neurology and Psychiatry, and appears in association with the index.

Two chapters in Landis' original manuscript have been omitted in order to keep the book within the limits of size set by the publisher. One was entitled "Mystical and Religious Experience" (originally Chapter 9, 74 pages) and the other "Sex and Sexuality" (originally Chapter 16, 35 pages of manuscript). In general, the burden of the latter was that the sexual experiences of most psychotics are rather sparse. The chapter on mystical experiences contains some interesting material and the manuscript of it, as well as of the chapter on sex, has been turned over to Dr. Osmond with a view toward subsequent publication elsewhere.

Since Professor Landis' death there have appeared various repetitions of the principles which his illustrative material displays. Experience with hallucinogens has been considerably expanded, but the editor could see no advantage in including additional samples of principles which have been adequately illustrated by Landis. It is to be doubted whether any new expressions of psychopathological experience will emerge in the foreseeable future. In some areas (such as the field of conversion hysterias, sensory disregard, paradoxical sensory projection) Landis' coverage is sketchy or even deficient, but it may be doubted whether any extensive body of autobiographical material relating to these less common areas is available (people with conversion hysterias are not likely to be sufficiently sophisticated to attempt coherent written accounts of their conditions) and it was a requirement of Landis' that any description which he included should be autobiographic.

New York   Fred A. Mettler, M.D.
July 1964

Preface

Abnormal psychology deals with human behavior and mental experiences that seem unusual, unreasonable, or in one or another way distinct from the ordinary psychology of everyday life. Traditionally the subject matter consists of descriptions that have been written by observers of this unusual behavior. For the most part these observers have been psychiatrists, neurologists, physicians, or psychologists who have been responsible for the care and treatment of the mentally deranged. The observers of abnormal behavior have over several centuries derived a fairly systematic organization of those behavioral phenomena that are readily observable. The real difficulty in the organization of the phenomena of abnormal psychology derives from the subjective experience that each individual person undergoes during the episode of abnormality. Every individual finds that he lacks the words and the phrases in his everyday vocabulary which seem necessary to communicate his experience to others. There exist and have existed for the past three centuries textbooks that adequately cover the objective behavioral phenomena of abnormal psychology, but descriptions of the nature of the "inner" experience that went on during an episode that others have called a psychosis, a neurosis, or an epileptic seizure are hard to come by.

The material which follows consists of a selection of excerpts published by persons who were trying to describe such inner experiences during a deranged episode. A choice had to be made of the fashion in which the material was to be presented. I could have brought together selections of materials that in some way resembled each other and called this material "Readings in Subjective Psychopathology." However, since more or less obvious themes ran through the collected material I chose to organize and present this experiential material in the fashion of a textbook. It has seemed to me that with a minimum of theory this experiential material lent itself to a "textbook" form of organization which fits the common-sense psychology of everyday life.

Very few persons have ever read an autobiographical account of anyone who has lived through a period of insanity. I have read approximately two hundred books that were autobiographical accounts descriptive of the experience and about an equal number of journal articles that were first-hand accounts of deranged experience. In all of these there were not more than five or six cross references, or in other words, very few sufferers had ever read or heard of a similar account. About ten of these autobiographical accounts had introductions by physicians or friends who certified to the accuracy of the objective account and said that the document was unique.

There has been some tendency on the part of theorists in psychoanalysis to ignore the literal meaning of what psychotic persons say about themselves. Certainly one cannot accept the statement of a patient who says he sees snakes to prove that snakes are present when no one else can see them. However, there appears to be no reason to reject the statement that, as far as the patient is concerned, he does see snakes. Elaborate theories have been developed to explain that what patients say should be reinterpreted to mean something other than what the words convey. It takes a great deal of experience to reinterpret what people say and if attention is focused upon theory instead of the accounts patients give of their distress there is a real danger that their condition will be misinterpreted. Among the first steps in finding out what is wrong with a patient is the determination of what he has to say about his subjective experience.

CARNEY LANDIS

Contents

xviii———*Contents*

*Varieties of
Psychopathological Experience*

A cloud seen from far off, lit by a fair light, becomes a thing of beauty, of wonder and aspiration. But when one enters the cloud another face of things is seen; and he who is within longs for clear air and sunshine.

(*Hennell*, 1938, p. 3)

CHAPTER 1

Introduction

The cloud of insanity seen from without usually stimulates the imagination. The nature of the experience in this cloud has, indeed, been the source of much speculation, expressed in art, science, fiction, biography, and poetry. A few persons who found themselves enveloped by such a cloud have recorded and published accounts of this unusual experience. They agree that the experience was unpleasant, difficult to describe, and, for each, a terrifying and unique experience for which he knew no precedent. While cloud-enveloped, each longed to escape into the familiar clear air and sunshine of normal experience.

My object in this venture is the collection of some of the personal descriptions of abnormal experience published by persons who have lived through a period of mental derangement. Reports of the subjective experience while on the "inside looking out" have been assembled and will constitute the basis of this presentation. My essential concern will be psychological in the traditional use of the term: that is, pertaining to activities and reflections of the mind. To the best of my knowledge there is no previous comprehensive collection of first-hand accounts of the experiences of those who have lived through one or more episodes of mental derangement.

Collection of Autobiographical Material

Since no bibliographical reference list pertinent to this sort of material is available, hundreds of books and bound journals that might contain relevant descriptions of first-hand experience were reviewed. In order that we might have at least a partial representation of similar material published in German and French, I secured the assistance of two psychologists, one born in Germany, whose native tongue was German, and a second born in France, whose native tongue was French. Each systematically searched through the German and French psychiatric journals published between 1830 and 1950. Whenever they encountered an autobiography of a psychotic person, this autobiography was translated into English so that the context and meaning of the account could be preserved as nearly as possible. Portions of this translated material have been used in the following accounts.

I have retained and cited a fair number of accounts where the author explicitly stated, "I am not now, nor was I ever insane." I have also made use of records in which the author never expressed an opinion of his own sanity, but the record provided clear evidence that others believed he was at some time insane. With documents of these last two categories, the retention and use of the material depended on the character of the contents. Records were used from those cases where, had I been able to confront the individual with all the facts and asked the question, "Were you ever insane, or were you ever in such a disturbed state of mind that you could not have defended yourself against the allegation of insanity, had it been urged?", the truthful answer would have had to be, "I might have been insane at that particular time."

This collection of excerpts should enable the reader to gain some appreciation of the qualities of inner life that other human beings have experienced when they (as well as the observers who contemplated such bewildered sufferers) have said, "This is insanity." The self-descriptions of such inner mental lives constitute the basic material out of which the subjective psychopathology I shall present has been organized.

In the collection of this subjective material, certain very arbitrary criteria have been employed for inclusion or exclusion of any particular record. Only published (book or journal) prima facie autobiographical material has been included. Not all autobiographical records are written in the first person ("I did this"), some are cast in the third person ("He did that"). It is quite possible that some of the material cited may have been edited and altered in part by someone other than the person who originally had the experience. The related excerpts are reproduced verbatim. Unless specially noted, the material has not been paraphrased; neither has the meaning of any excerpt been knowingly distorted by omission of pertinent material. Throughout the presentation, excerpts have been included only when two or more reports of the phenomenon in question, supplied by different persons, seemed to be comparable. It should be explicitly stated that no opportunity was available to ask any individual whose account was utilized any direct questions.

Examples of Psychopathological Reports

It might be possible to define and delimit those areas in the private mental life of another person that include severe psychopathological experiences. It seemed preferable to illustrate by relevant autobiographic descriptions rather than to attempt to define many of the terms that will be employed. For example, it seemed easier to accept the concept of perceived insanity without further attempts to derive a precise definition.

An anonymous patient published in 1856 the following account of his own period of insanity.

In [sane] consciousness we may suppose the soul resides in its normal state. . . . In the rational mind no ideas of external things or their relations are allowed to enter which do not correspond with realities: thus truth and reason are maintained. But when insanity takes place, this harmonious confederation is broken up and each becomes a petty sovereignty independent within itself. A unity of action is lost, the perceptive faculties become careless, the gates are thrown open, and any gigantic fantasy may walk boldly in and usurp the seat of government! . . . The ideas of space and time, which are the fundamental conditions of all thought in rational minds, become confused, or wholly lost. . . .

The first symptom of insanity in my own case was want of sleep. . . . The very consciousness of the fact that I needed repose, and my efforts to obtain it, only aggravated my excitement, and my brain grew every day more disturbed. At last I began to imagine that the final dissolution of all things was coming on, thus transferring the tumult in my own mind to external nature. . . .

I was lying in an upper room in the house . . . and as I looked out at the dreary weather, everything conspired to favor this delusion. The window curtains were parted so that the space through which the light came in was in the form of a steep lattice-roof, such as I remember in the old pictures of the ark. Here I obtained a short repose, but the pursuing fiend found me again, and drove me abroad through boundless space. Then every muscle and nerve seemed wrought to the utmost tension, and I imagined that the world was again dissolved into chaos, and that all living things had perished, but I had found out the great secret of Nature, and through me the universe was to be reconstructed. I thought that I was the living, intelligent principle of electricity, and that I had power to call into my own person all the electric fluid in the world, and thus I was to give life again to my friends and others. . . . I thought all the telegraph wires in the United States were employed in conducting the fluid into my body, and this gave me unnatural strength. I thought I was moving by some attraction towards the sun, and that there, in the opaque center of the great luminary, I should at last find an eternal rest and rejoin my friends and kindred. But these periods of intense excitement were followed by great nervous prostration, and then I would seem to lose again all my powers. . . .

At this time I was very violent, and struggled fiercely with my attendants; finally, getting no repose, and finding that I saw my friends no more, I despaired of getting back again, and thought myself a comet—the living intelligent head of a comet—flying through space with inconceivable velocity, and passing far beyond the confines of the habitable universe, thus leaving my friends hopelessly behind me. I lost all sense of time and space. A whizzing and careering through trackless solitudes, a sense of rapid and lonely motion, at an incalculable rate, and a sinking of the heart in utter despair, are all I can recollect. (Anon., 1856a, pp. 30; 32; 34)

This description of the beginning of a psychotic period is representative of many similar accounts. The sufferer began with insomnia that led on to a state of mental confusion and uncontrollable turmoil. His memory of the passing events became faulty; his orientation in space and time, defective. He never seemed to consider that his confusion might be a medical problem. He speaks of a "pursuing fiend," of having found "the great secret of Nature," and the acquisition of the ability to "give life again to my friends," to impart ideas of a mystical or religious nature. Other than the difficulty with insomnia, his description was not related to events or ideas that are part of the natural physical world.

A second excerpt may be taken from Custance's autobiography, *Wisdom, Madness and Folly* (1952), which is a rather remarkable account of the author's many attacks of mania and depression, together with his attempt to create out of his experiences a philosophy of insanity. His descriptions are very lucid. I will draw on Custance's account at many points in the following chapters. In telling of his experience during an episode of depression he wrote as follows.

I seem shut into myself, withdrawn from real contact with the outer world as also from contact with God; the sun does not really shine, the trees and fields are not really green; I am shut in with my thoughts, always of a depressing and melancholy nature. This sense of isolation, of being cut off from God, one's fellows and the world, seems to me to be the paramount feature underlying the whole state. . . .

Moral tension returns in full force. I am haunted by a sense of guilt; my conscience gives me no rest, even when there do not seem to be any particularly grievous sins upon it. Whatever I am doing I feel I ought to be doing something else. I worry perpetually about my past sins and failures; not for a moment can I forget the mess I seem to have made of my life. However I may pray for and think of forgiveness, no forgiveness comes. Eventually the terrors of Hell approach (Custance, 1952, p. 61)

This lament is typical of those which have been recorded by patients suffering from melancholia. The feelings of self-condemnation, of having sinned, and of isolation are central. No amount of reassurance or explanations indicating that the feelings have no basis in fact, provides consolation to the sufferer.

In contradistinction to this pathological condition of melancholia is the state of mania. To illustrate this contrast an additional excerpt from Custance, in which he was trying to describe his experience in the Universe of Bliss (his term), may be cited.

In connection with the delusions of grandeur and drive for power should be noted the peculiar sensation . . . reminiscent of the cat tribe. I first noted it in the padded cell at Brixton while in a state of acute mania. I saw a series of visions which impelled on my consciousness a strong sense of destiny and leadership. I imagined myself a sort of lion destined to conquer the world, and in conformity with this delusion paced interminably round and round my cell on the balls of my feet with a sense of extraordinary muscular looseness or suppleness . . .

The only other association of that particular sensation which comes to my mind is the rather incongruous one of jazz music. In the manic state this sometimes gives rise to similar sensations, though in this case my movements tend to be rather faster and the phantasy is not so much one of being a lion or tiger as a savage dancing a war-dance.

Another symptom is the ability to see visions in the form of illusions, that is to say distortion of visual images. This power is proportionate to the acuteness of the mania. At the present time I am seeing no visions. In periods of acute mania they can appear almost like a continuous cinema performance, particularly if there are any complicated and variable light-patterns with which my optical mechanism can play the necessary tricks. These visions generally appear on the walls of my room, if these are shiny enough to reflect light. They are infinitely varied, and bear a close relation to the processes of thought passing in my mind at the time. They are obvious products of the Unconscious, which in this state is of course largely in control of my mind . . .

With visions are associated dreams. When in the state of acute mania it is not always easy to separate the two. There is a very close correlation between dreams and waking thoughts and imaginings. I wake up and my mind carries on the same train of thought which has been begun in a dream. I go to sleep and go on dreaming about the subjects I have been thinking about. This is presumably to be expected since both dreams and the visions and trains of thought in mania are governed by the Unconscious. . . .

That concludes, I think, this rather overlong catalogue of the features and symptoms of the manic state as I have experienced it. It may sound a delightful condition. Perhaps it would be if it were not such a nuisance to others and did not so easily change into its opposite. (Custance, 1952, pp. 55–57; 58; 59)

Both the content and the style of this excerpt should be noted. The inner experience of the maniacal patient is confused by distractability, press of activity, and changeable themes of thought. It is one of the very few varieties of psychopathology that is ever reported by patients to be, in any sense, pleasurable or pleasant. But, as Custance said, it is not truly delightful.

Another description of still another variety of the inner life of the distraught or deranged personality may be cited: the condition known as a phobic neurosis. This excerpt comes from the autobiography of W. E. Leonard, a well-known Professor of English at the University of Wisconsin. He wrote an account of his life published under the title of *The Locomotive-God*, a document often quoted by psychologists. This excerpt is illustrative of a profound phobic state.

My central dominating phobia [is one] of distance. . . . But the *form* of itself will lack adequate motivation for consciousness. So the mind feigns motivation. . . . With the knowledge I now have of the real causes, the spells of diffused terror have apparently become negligible as long as I am in good physical tone. . . . I always knew that the terror was without adequate motivation. I could only say; as soon as I get a certain distance from home. . . . I am overwhelmed with a feeling of insecurity, of terror that I can't get back. The truest statement of the conscious content is this: I am in a terror of the seizure of terror; and I fear seizure at a given distance. . . .

For the emotion in the distance-phobia, as for the emotion in all others, there have been clearly defined degrees of intensity. Let me assume I am walking down University Drive by the Lake. I am a normal man for the first quarter of a mile; for the next hundred yards I am in a mild state of dread, controllable and controlled: for the next twenty yards in an acute state of dread, yet controlled; for the next ten, in an anguish of terror that hasn't reached the crisis of an explosion; and in a half-dozen steps more I am in as fierce a panic of isolation from help and home and of immediate death as a man overboard in mid-Atlantic or on a window-ledge far up in a sky-scraper with flames lapping his shoulders. . . . My phobic seizures at their worst approach any limits of terror that the human mind is capable of in the actual presence of death in its most horrible forms. (Leonard, 1939, pp. 321–322)

There can be no doubt concerning the central theme of Leonard's disorder—*fear,* an unreasonable and uncontrollable fear that was essentially a fear of death. Leonard thought he had traced the origin of the fear to a childhood experience of being frightened by a locomotive plus diffuse ideas of the malevolence of God, but having traced the fear back to its origin in his childhood experience, he remained unable to achieve a reasonable state of self-control.

These four samples of psychopathological experience convey some idea of the nature and major varieties of derangement with which we shall deal in the chapters that follow.

Divergent Attitudes

The excerpts just given serve as a basis for the recognition of the basic difference between two general social attitudes toward the phenomena of derangement. Most men have been inclined to believe that a psychotic person has lost or misused his mental faculties so that his disordered mind can no longer function adequately. This loss or misuse is generally attributed to the idea that in the person's past he has disregarded the moral, ethical, and religious standards of healthy existence. Since most normal individuals believe that they are masters of their own minds, souls, and destinies, it follows that the regaining of a lost mind, or the rehabilitation of a misused mind, should be facilitated by removing the bewildered person from free society, affording him asylum, where, with the support of moral guidance, he may regain self-control and the proper use of his mind. Such, in essence, is the common sense belief of most persons, including most of those who are, or who have been, mentally ill at one time or another.

A smaller fraction of mankind believes and attempts to demonstrate that almost all deranged persons are actually sick or diseased in the same sense that a person who has cancer is sick or diseased. This smaller fraction of mankind avers that a deranged person should be placed under the care and supervision of properly trained medical specialists so that they may use their skill in the application of the healing arts and sciences in the treatment and care of such mentally disturbed persons. This smaller fraction of society would also insist that the ultimate decision as to whether an individual is sane or insane is not a matter to be determined by either a general social group, by legal authorities, or by the judiciary, but one that should be established by medically trained specialists whose judgments would depend, insofar as possible, on medical considerations. To summarize these two attitudes: most individuals will say when trying to deal with a deranged person, "He is obviously insane, he is a sinner, he must repent"; but a smaller fraction of the general public will say, "He is sick; physicians should attempt to assist him in the recovery of his health."[*]

If no more than twenty-five or thirty persons out of each thousand individuals in the general population are acutely deranged at any time during their entire life-span, then the number of such persons that any one of us will encounter during any five-year span of our own lifetime will be limited. Unless one makes a direct effort or has special opportunities, he will not have first-hand acquaintance with more than a very few

---

[*] A recent appraisal of the *Popular conceptions of mental health* has been published by J. C. Nunnally, Jr. (1961, New York: Holt, Rinehart and Winston, Inc.), which assesses these concepts in more detail than we have done here but with the same general conclusions.

persons during the period of their acute derangement. Since our chances of such acquaintanceship is limited, our knowledge of what it might be like is even more limited.

Consider again the four illustrative excerpts I have cited. First, it may be noted that each of these patients emphasized spiritual phenomena or religious feelings as the most prominent features of the experience. Second, these persons complained of the fear of death; while a third complaint revolved about the loss of personal self-control. Each patient did mention a few physical symptoms, such as insomnia, increased muscular tension, perceptual distortion, or a run-down physical state. None intimated that his disturbed state of mind seemed to him to be a problem which demanded medical attention. It is these first-hand considerations—the leading complaints of the patients—that give rise to and maintain the common-sense belief that insanity is related to sin and guilt.

What then gives support to the more modern belief that deranged states of mind are primarily medical problems which should properly be part of the general field of medicine? There are two major reasons. The first is that during the past half century, medical and biological research has devised methods of treatment which have solved the problems of approximately a quarter of the miscellany of deranged patients who were confined in mental hospitals in 1900. (Some of these methods were "rational," in that the isolation of the relationship between cause and cure was established; others were "irrational" in that no such relationship has been established between the therapy and the cure—for example, electric convulsive therapy.) Second, the methods of psychotherapy have produced improvement or cure in many persons who were suffering from the milder forms of neurosis and occasionally have been helpful among patients suffering from psychosis.

Unfortunately, "moral therapy," which was fashionable during the nineteenth century, and "pastoral counseling," which has more or less replaced the older moral therapy during the twentieth century, cannot point to any tabulated record of therapeutic success. Many patients continue to seek a therapy that somehow seems to be related to the problems that seem so vital to their mental turmoil, and the procedures employed by physicians may be resented by the deranged patients themselves, who find the methods inappropriate for the relief of their mental ferment.

Physicians are legally licensed and accorded many special privileges by society. Their license is given because they have participated in a special course of training which has acquainted them with the body of knowledge relevant to the art of healing, knowledge, that has been accumulated over the past centuries and that constitutes today the disciplines of medicine, surgery, psychiatry, and psychotherapy. Physical medicine and surgery are comprised of arts, skills, and factual material.

Psychiatry dealing as it does with mental phenomena, is at present based largely on speculative hypotheses plus the actual demonstration of the behavior of mentally ill patients. Actually, there have existed, and continue to exist, divisions of interest and knowledge between physicians, surgeons and psychiatrists so that communication among the three specialties is far from satisfactory. It is possible that the worst break in communication exists between the deranged patient and some asylum or mental hospital medical practitioners.

As an example of the difficulty of communication between such ordinary hospital doctors and a deranged patient, we may cite the following excerpt from Hennell's autobiography, *The Witnesses*. Hennell, an artist, had been mentally disturbed for some time and had protested against the lack of intelligent care as well as the unenlightened treatment he had received. Finally, two members of the hospital staff interviewed him. The following is Hennell's account of their conversation.

Two doctors approach for conversation: they wish to ascertain my progress and present mental condition; and thus they introduce the subject:

Dr. Craugasides:　We understand that you are conscious of audible voices which utter words that excite you, or move you to behave violently and irresponsibly. Is this so? What are these voices and do you believe in their reality?

Myself:　Yes, sir; I hear voices distinctly, even loudly; they interrupt us at this moment. It is more easy for me to listen to them than to you; I can more easily believe in their significance and actuality, and they do not ask questions.

Dr. Embásichytros:　How can you say that these hallucinations are more real than ourselves? You must realize that you are talking unreasonably.

Myself:　There is more sympathy between my own experience of nature and these voices, which seem to be the voices of nature, than between my acquired rationalization of experience and that which seems to be yours; and therefore I say that their unfinished forms are truer than your conventional views.

Dr. C.:　But surely you do not mean to shut yourself up from society by paying attention to these delusive ideas. Surely you wish to be cured of them, and to return well to your parents. Do you not? What is the nature of these voices?

Myself:　They assume the nature of all those objects through which they speak—whether they speak out of walls, from ventilators, or in the woods and fields.

Dr. E.:　Dear me, this is very interesting: and what do they say?

Myself:　Sometimes they speak secretly and guardedly: and then I want to listen and make sense of their meaning, for it is outside myself, and I only partly understand it.

Dr. C.:　And what do they ever say that you do understand?

Myself:　Sometimes they are provoked or tormented, and then they cry out, "Fight the fools!" "Why don't you beat these bloody swindlers?" or "You have to fight the doctor!"—Punch, you know (I added by way of explanation) had to kill the doctor as well as the hangman.

As the two mental practitioners went away, I fancied in their expressions the signs of pained disapproval: presently it was made clear to me that by accurate definition I had not improved my case. To dispute with men whose credit and superior qualifications of mind depend on basically opposite axioms to one's own is a more vain recourse than straw applied to smother a fire. (Hennell, 1938, pp. 181–183)

Actually, this interview was an attempt on the part of the physicians to evaluate whether Hennell was well enough to be transferred to another institution where close confinement was not required. The excerpt illustrates the point of the difference between the ideas of a mentally disturbed patient and the physicians in charge of his care. Note that Hennell said: "There is more sympathy between my own experience of nature and these voices . . . than that which seems to be yours," which is to say that he was convinced of his own ideas even though the doctor had just told him that he was talking irrationally.

Many psychiatrists with years of clinical experience would react after hearing such a conversation with a mental patient in much the same way that these doctors did. The psychiatrist has become acquainted with certain appropriate questions and the expected answers, which are, so far as he is concerned, relevant. Every practicing clinical psychiatrist learns to listen by a method of selective attention to the recital of the symptoms and complaints of psychotic patients. Indeed, every educated person uses selective attention in reacting to the words and behavior of all persons with whom he comes in contact. The point is that the verbal productions, the accounts of experience which are made by psychotics, are diverse, differing from time to time and from person to person, and the fact that the expressions used seem to be repetitious does not mean that the one who has listened has any real understanding of the information which the patient has attempted to convey.

Selective Factors in the Choice of Material

It is noteworthy that many deranged persons have written that they did not have words or phrases which would adequately describe their feelings or their experiences, but even so, they did continue with their descriptions in the evident hope that readers would comprehend their accounts, even if the words and phrases were not particularly appropriate. A selective factor which operated in my choice of illustrative excerpts grew out of the fact that the material sought and used had to be fairly lucid and presented in literate fashion. I undoubtedly favored those records that were both clearly descriptive and succinct enough to be easily quoted. For example, a record that stated, "I became very excited and was taken to the hospital," would not be cited unless it also gave a descriptive statement of the subjective experience during the excitement.

A second selective element derives from the system of thought that readers may be accustomed to using. If one is accustomed to the use of mystical and religious phrases and descriptions, the reports of mental patients may seem only slightly misleading; but if the reader has been trained in medical and biological terminology alone, the descriptions given by deranged persons may convey but little sense.

Most present-day psychiatrists and clinical psychologists have been trained to attend to reports that may be interpreted in the psychoanalytic frame of reference. Only when one turns back over half a century to the psychology of William James does one find a systematic viewpoint that will readily accommodate the *phenomenological* reports the deranged patient commonly uses. For example, one finds in James' (1890) *Principles of Psychology* (Vol. 2) such chapter headings as "The Stream of Thought," "The Perception of Time," "Imagination," "The Perception of Reality," and "Will." In James' *The Varieties of Religious Experience* (1902) one finds chapters entitled "The Reality of the Unseen," "The Divided Self," "Conversion," "Saintliness," and "Mysticism." The phenomenological reports of patients who experienced periods of mental derangement during the eighteenth, nineteenth, and twentieth centuries have been largely concerned with topics that are covered by subject headings of the sort that James organized.

Starting about 1930, one finds some reports by patients that do employ certain psychodynamic phrases and concepts current in modern psychiatry in the descriptions of their experiences. The use of the phraseology of these concepts, however, does not mean that the patient has accepted the viewpoint.

To summarize, I am aware that selective factors operated in the choice of the material which composes the main body of the autobiographical accounts which have been utilized. Considering the nature of the description of the experiences, I can only say that I think I was aware of the more obvious selective factors and have tried to guard my comments accordingly.

Grouping of the Material

It should be made explicit that the selected excerpts were originally randomly gathered, photostated, and grouped according to no self-evident system. Since the material that constitutes the text consists for the most part of descriptive excerpts taken from autobiographical accounts, the method of classification and the use of the material may be clarified as examples are cited. The following is taken from an account that a very disturbed patient wrote for the benefit of his therapist.

I went out of my head and wrote to my sister that I was crazy. The voices told me that I was and that they were going to kill me. The Devil offered me unlimited power if I would do his bidding. He said he would give me half of hell to rule over when I died. He would under no condition let me go to heaven because I knew too much about him and would put him out of business. I was supposed to rule the world and wipe out civilization. There was a new force by which the mind of man could be controlled. It came from another planet, and it manifested itself through me. (Fodor, 1945, p. 382)

This excerpt was classified as being an example of *onset* (went out of my head); *voices* (voices told me); *being persecuted* (going to kill me); *demons* (the Devil); *mysticism* (mind of man could be controlled); *power* (unlimited power); *revelation* (He said he would give me); and so on. The most startling statement, which caught my immediate attention, was, "I wrote to my sister that I was crazy," while the description of his experience does seem to justify his statement. There is no single part of this excerpt that is particularly obscure or unclear. Anyone reading this excerpt should be able to understand what this patient said about himself and, to a certain extent, sympathize with the delusional and mystical experiences that troubled him.

As a second example, let us take the description published more than a century ago (1854) by a recovered mental hospital patient who was attempting to characterize his asylum experiences.

The first thing I remember which seems to savor of insanity was a presentment of some great evil which was to befall me, either in my own person, or to those nearest and dearest to me. . . I fancied that if I was to leave home for a while I should find something to banish trouble. I left my parents to spend the winter among friends and relatives, yet the grim phantom of coming evil haunted my slumbers, and I found, like Noah's dove, no rest for the sole of my foot. I was ashamed to tell my friends the fears which tormented me, and at length became so weary of myself that life seemed a burden. I dreaded to pass a grave yard, it would cause a faintness, and deathly sensations to see a coffin, or read of young persons who had recently died. I struggled against these fantasies, but I grew thin and pale, lost strength rapidly, and my friends became alarmed. I could not eat, food was repulsive. I could not sleep quietly, for in dreams I saw my father drowning, my little brother dying, and I arose each morning pale and haggard. Society had no charms for me, the faces of my former associates became almost repulsive, and I sought in the solitude of my room for relief by looking in my Bible in a haphazard manner, for some particular verses to speak comfort. . . I read the Bible and Commentaries from morning till night. I wept, I prayed, but no comforter came, reason tottered on its throne. . . . I was insane, and every step of my journey home only increased the evil. (Anon., 1854a, p. 48)

This excerpt was classified as an example of *fear* and *self-reference* (presentiment of great evil which was to befall me), *death fear* and *dread* (I dreaded to pass a graveyard), *onset* and *melancholia* (no comforter came, reason tottered on its throne), and so forth.

The classified excerpts were sorted so that all material relevant to the selected topics could be separately indexed. Each grouping was then further examined so that they might be combined into more generalized headings. After some "cutting and fitting" the material was organized under twenty-two more general headings that constitute most of the chapters that follow.

As I have said, the excerpts are cited verbatim and each excerpt illustrates more or less precisely the ideas which it seemed to me that the patient was attempting to convey. I have inserted, between the excerpts, explanations, condensations, generalizations, cross references, and comments of my own, together with other relevant material. Each chapter will begin with an Introduction, which is, in effect, a stage setting, furnishing the ground on which the "figure" of the excerpts may stand out for the reader to scrutinize. Each chapter will conclude with a Discussion, in which an attempt will be made to clarify—and, if possible, unify—the figure-ground relationships that have been presented.

Psychological Organization

Almost all the excerpts presented are taken from the published accounts of deranged persons who had no more than common sense to guide their exposition. The abnormal experience was, for the majority of sufferers, quite new and unique. Only a handful of excerpts could be drawn from the records of persons who had had more than one episode of derangment, who had even read or heard of the experiences that other deranged sufferers had had, or had read the explanations that any authority had offered.

The concepts of the *Stream of Conscious Thought* and *Consciousness of Self* as they were formulated by William James have served as a basis for the explanatory schemes I have adopted on several occasions in the chapters to follow. My use of either of these organizational concepts has been tentative and illustrative only.

In dealing with many of the excerpts I have come upon accounts where the patient stated or implied that one part of his mental life seemed to proceed in an independent fashion which was more or less critical of the remainder of his mental life as it was occurring at any particular time. This phenomenon or experience has been well expressed in a line of verse by Kipling: "Stood by an' watched myself behaving like a bloomin' fool." Another poet spoke of the experience that occurred just before her epileptic seizures as, "When the being tries to laugh it off, to leave it behind, to walk irresponsibly away."

This divided self has gone by many names and has had a wide variety of characterizations in various languages, systems of thought, and systems of psychology. James recognized it as a function of self-consciousness; McDougall spoke of it as the self-regarding tendency; in his earlier theorizing, Freud called it the psychic censor. Various patients, whose descriptions I will cite, speak of "part of myself," "my better judgment," "the essential me," and so forth. Some have gone so far as to speak of a dwarf that dwells just behind the eyes, who tries to regulate their behavior.

In an attempt to gain a certain degree of uniformity of characterization of such a mental process, I will adopt a new name to designate this process or function. Since it does have, among other qualities, the properties of *Essential Discrimination* among *Intellectual* processes and also deals with *Traces of Recall*, I will speak of it as the EDITOR process, which accompanies the stream of conscious thought.

The EDITOR process continues during almost all one's waking existence, functioning in the observation, comparison, recording, recalling, and interpreting of all that goes on in the major stream of one's mental existence. The remainder of the stream of conscious thought may rush by in a tumultuous fashion while the EDITOR process acts to classify parts of it as usual or unusual, commonplace or startling, tranquil or disturbing, and either under or beyond voluntary control.

The duration and degree of the fragmentation of the stream of conscious thought, together with disturbances in environmental circumstances, may be so intense or prolonged that the EDITOR function may become confused, unclear, and even "unconscious." When this occurs, the EDITOR process may give rise to such conclusions as, "I have lost control of my mind," or "I am insane." The degree, duration, and circumstances that must occur before such a mental self-judgment may be made are most various.

The topics of this chapter have been touched on in only a superficial fashion. There is a large library of material in philosophy, psychology, medicine, and literary speculation that is relevant to many of the subjects raised. The purpose of my discussion is not to evaluate, praise, or condemn any system of classification of the behavior disorders or viewpoint as to their possible origin. Rather, I wish to present the accounts of those persons who have experienced at one or another period of their life some variety of mental derangment so that each individual may speak for himself with the greatest possible clarity. Such systematic organization on the part of the reporters as does occur in these individual reports, I will refer to as being *common sense*.

SUMMARY

The following text will be concerned with the nature of subjective experience commonly called psychopathological. The varieties of psychopathological experience encompass a wide range of qualities of human mental life, varying from extremely agitated manic madness to mildly annoying trancelike states. The common qualities these pathological states possess are, (1) a disturbance in thought process, (2) an uncertain emotional feeling state, and (3) some degree of apprehension about one's ability to control voluntarily one's thoughts and actions.

A primary concept in the presentation of this material concerns the nature of the stream of conscious thought that occurs during these episodes of unusual experience. I have found the psychological framework presented by William James to be very useful for the better comprehension of the autobiographical records of psychopathological experience.

There are two general attitudes society has held regarding the phenomena of psychopathology. The first and more generally accepted attitude, really part of common sense, is that these abnormal experiences are causally related to guilt and sin. The second attitude, which has much more relation to present-day scientific thought, is that mental pathology is a disease process in the same sense that tuberculosis or high blood pressure are disease processes. If mental aberrations are basically forms of disease, then these unusual phenomena belong in the realm of medicine. The fact that practically every modern institution which is dedicated to the care of persons who suffer from one or another form of psychopathology is called a hospital and is under medical supervision is evidence of the prevalence of the second attitude. Most mental hospitals have an admission service where acutely disturbed patients receive, as a routine measure, adequate medical care and treatment. But, if the mental status of the patient does not improve during the initial months of medical care and treatment, the person is usually moved to the chronic or "back-ward" section of the institution, where custodial care constitutes the therapeutic effort and from which effort not too many recoveries result. The result of the interaction of these two attitudes, sin and disease, is that society at large continues to suspect and distrust anyone who has suffered from either prolonged or acute periods of marked psychopathological experience. Almost every individual hesitates to admit having lived through such abnormal experiences—not that there was any doubt in his mind about the occurrence, but because the very fact of the public admission of having experienced a period of unsound mind raises fears, doubts, and questions in the minds of his fellow men, which questions usually bear more on his ethics and morality than on his health.

Many problems arise regarding social status and social interaction as they are related to psychopathology. But for the most part these questions will not be the concern of either my presentation or my conclusions. In essence, I will present the viewpoint that relates the primary psychological difficulties and complaints that regularly appear in the patients' reports of their individual experiences. The social considerations are only secondary features to the personal experience. Almost every autobiography I have read that has recounted the experience of a deranged mind devoted a great amount of space to the symptoms, complaints, and treatment of the individual's fellow patients. These interpersonal reactions and comparisons were important to each patient, but the personal complaints related to the subjective experience of each individual constitute my primary concern.

The words and phrases that any individual used were limited by his working vocabulary. For example, an examining physician once asked a patient, "Are you bothered by stolen thoughts?" To this question the patient replied, "Oh, so that's what you call them," and then went on to describe this experience in great detail.

The next three chapters (Chapters 2, 3, and 4) will deal with the beginning, the course, and the recovery from mental derangement. For the most part, the emphasis in these particular chapters will be on the temporal course of abnormal experience. The qualitative nature of the phenomena will be dealt with in Chapters 5 through 19. Chapters 20 and 21 will present a few speculative conclusions drawn from the material that has been presented.

So the last connected and coherent thing in my thinking gave way—and the Madness filling me rejoiced. Because at last there was nothing to stay it, it shouted and exulted with a noise that tore my throat out, charging through me till it nearly dragged the life out of me. Part of my mind stood there and took in the whole situation, yet could do nothing about it. The thing that was raging did not seem wrong to me then—but the rightest thing in the world—a magnificent accomplishment.

(*Jefferson*, 1947, p. 231)

CHAPTER 2

The Onset of Psychopathological States

INTRODUCTION

What experiences must a person have before he will say to himself, "I am mad"? Anyone may observe the behavior or listen to the remarks of another and privately think to himself, "That man is crazy!" Such an observation may be a considered judgment, or it may be a semifacetious bit of byplay, meaning only that the person in question is somewhat peculiar, at least from the standpoint of the observer. My present inquiry is not directed to the question, "Is that man insane?", but to the question, "What experiences must a man have before he will say to himself, 'I am really losing my mind' or 'I must have gone mad'?" It is not unusual to think that overwhelming emotion, excessive fatigue, or profound physical illness might lead one to think, "This is driving me crazy; unless things become easier, I'll lose my mind." But how does one recognize that such a change has actually taken place?

If a person had been ill, lapsed into unconsciousness, and finally awakened to find himself locked in a mental hospital, he would necessarily wonder what he had done or said which had convinced others that he was so disturbed that he had to be taken to an asylum. Then he may ask himself, "Am I crazy?" If he has never been mad before what aspects of his mental experience will convince him of his own madness?

The behavior or speech that leads others to have a person committed to an institution or certified as insane are, for the most part, concerned with threats or attempts that seem to endanger the life and safety of some person or persons, including the individual in question. Anyone may exhibit peculiar behavior, express odd ideas, and speak in a queer fashion, but as long as he does not threaten or attempt to do anything which may threaten his own safety or that of those about him little is ordinarily done to restrict his freedom of action. Common sense and social tolerance hold that almost any sort of peculiar speech or behavior may occur, but only when such behavior occurs which endangers life or security does it precipitate social action. In general, present-day society holds that loss of prudent self-control is the distinguishing mark of insanity.

The convincing realization of one's own madness is to a large extent conceived in this same general frame of reference. When one says, "I have lost my self-control; I am no longer master of my own mind" or "There are strange ideas, experiences and actions that I have and that I should be able to direct or modify but that I cannot control"; then one starts doubting one's own sanity.

Effects of the Realization of One's Loss of Self-Control

Any person may have times when he realizes that his mind is confused, that he is overwhelmed by emotion, or that his thought processes are not normal. None of these states is pleasant or desirable, yet if in the background one continues to believe, "I could control myself if I would only summon my reserve strength," there is no necessary recognition of the possibility of derangement. Only when one's efforts at maintaining self-control fail and continue to fail, does the real question of one's sanity enter into consciousness.

The awareness of losing self-control or the feeling of being a puppet responding to forces and experiences that one cannot direct or modify is quickly associated with a variety of acute emotions, particularly with despair and a growing sense of hopelessness. Beyond the mere recognition of the lack of self-control, one realizes the implication that this loss may be, and in all probability is, the loss of sanity. In our social relationships, we have been taught from childhood that insanity constitutes not only a human failure but a personal disgrace, and an unwholesome reflection on the reputation of one's family and even of one's friends. We may also have been imbued with the idea that insanity is due to sinfulness, evil ways, immorality, or lack of respect for God and religion. Indeed, many believe that mental illness may be the consequence of almost any sort of socially disapproved behavior or thought, a disgrace second only to conviction of a major crime.

To convey some idea of the devastating effect of the subjective realization of madness I will cite an account taken from Jane Hillyer's autobiography, *Reluctantly Told.* Jane Hillyer was a young school teacher who became more and more fatigued toward the end of the school year until she reached the point of physical collapse. She was taken to a hospital where she became delirious. During one of the first nights in the hospital, she awakened and stumbled in terror to a mirror where she saw her image, an episode she later described as follows.

I knew definitely that the figure in the mirror was mad. *I* was mad. I have never learned words with which to describe the sensations accompanying that realization. I seemed dual; struggling against the truth, crying out against fate, pleading, praying; and at the same time, cool and almost surgical in my analysis of the situation. I probed to find the cause; I reckoned the factor of fatigue, long continued fever, strain, tension; I checked my recent behaviour and the accompanying drives and emotions. Yes, that explained it all. I was mad. Again I looked at the mirrored figure. It seemed all eyes. I called it by name. "Do you know," I said, "do you know that you are insane? Do you know what that means? Do you know they won't trust you any more? They can't. You may not work in the fall. You will disappoint them all. Do you know what it is like to be mad? That *thing* will get stronger and stronger. Some day it will *be* you. . . . If you had listened and rested and stayed out of doors and done the thousand things they advised, you might not be insane now? . . . Every one will know soon. They will shut you up. . . . Do you know it's *you* that's mad, you, and not any one you are reading about? . . . Yes, I know; I know; . . . I know it's me that's mad. (Hillyer, 1926, pp. 14–15)

The desolating effect of such a realization, the critical attitude of the EDITOR function toward the remainder of the self, the regret at not having followed advice, and the final admission of failure, all are presented in sharp focus. In one sense, as long as self-criticism persists, the patient may legitimately continue to insist that he is not yet completely insane. But if self-criticism and self-control are both absent, then, at some later time, the patient can only say, "I must have lost my mind."

Circumstances Commonly Said to Lead to Lunacy

There are several internal and external circumstances that the general public commonly considers as constituting an adequate basis for explaining the beginning of a period of mental derangement. It is generally believed (without too much factual evidence) that physical illness may so "weaken the mind" that self-control is endangered and may be in time completely lost. It is also believed that emotional turmoil, excessive physical stress, great fatigue (either physical or mental), and prolonged lack of sleep, will likewise "weaken the mind" and lead to mental disintegration. Although it is true that both physical illness and excessive stress and strain are often present at the start of a mental disease, it is usually impossible to ascertain whether or not such circumstances did play a major causal role.

PHYSICAL ILLNESS

Since physical illness may involve periods of unconsciousness and delirium, many afflicted persons consider that the appearance of any psychopathological disorder is no more than an additional feature of an existent physical disease. The following account illustrates this point. It was written in a letter sent to an asylum superintendent by a patient who had recovered from a mental illness and returned home.

In the fall of 1839, I was much exposed, and laboured exceedingly hard, which brought on an attack of fever, that seemed to spend its force principally in my head. I also had a severe cough, and at one time spit blood. As the fever increased, I experienced a kind of stupor and derangement of mind. In this state I had the most singular dreams, or visions of things. One peculiar thought that entered my mind was, that my body was divided into four parts; the legs being cut off at the knees, and my head and breast severed from the body, which appeared to me to be real and true; and I suffered great anxiety as to how the parts of my body should be re-united, and made to grow together again. A physician was employed, and he ordered plasters to be applied to my ancles, and a blister to my breast, and one on the top of my head, and gave me several emetics; and the pain of all these, and the distress of the fever in my head, was enough to render the strongest man, with the best constitution in the world, senseless and delirious.

I continued in this condition some time, sometimes pretty sensible, and at others indifferent to what presented itself before me. At length, through the advice of some friends, I believe I was taken to your asylum. . . . At this time, I entertained the opinion of having just landed in the city of Rome . . . I was induced to entertain the belief of its being a house used by the Roman Catholics . . . I thought it was a monastery. I also thought that the land in front of the building was . . . used by them for the interment of the dead. . . . I thought I was brought here to be scourged, and taken through purgatory. After that, I concluded it was a kind of a fort for the protection of the people of the country . . . and we were suffering the unpleasant consequences of war. . . . These, and a great many other curious and singular notions . . . I entertained during the winter and spring, and until I began to get better. (Anon., 1850a, pp. 472–473)

A similar account of delirium and stupor was written by a young man who had just finished his college studies and was "in a great anxiety of mind, and in an unwise melancholy" which he attributed, in part, to the recent, premature death of his father. While still dwelling in his college quarters, he contracted a sore throat and became increasingly feverish.

Here I believe my derangement began . . . My mind felt an uncommon shock! I fancied myself at death's door—I called in advisers—I was in a dreadful state of agitation, but alas! nothing appeased the storm begun. I had been ordered to lie in bed some days . . . I foolishly thought (being deranged) that if I quitted my bed, I should quit my pains also. The time arrived when I was to rise, my clothes were placed at hand, I sat up in a pensive mood, and delayed stirring. The attendant approached and said . . . "What John, not stirring, for shame." . . . I made no reply, but fiddled with my clothes, and began to talk wildly . . . I had very strange notions; I thought I had no longer a claim to be a man, I thought I was big with young pigs—in a word, I thought when I was getting up, that I was delivered of them. . . . When I had risen, I was conducted to an arm chair, and here I had a lucid interval of restored reason. . . . As soon as I had been up a short time I felt a return of my disorder and I called aloud for assistance . . . They placed the table near me, and on it placed a pillow, on which I might recline my arm. [I thought that] around me sat some scholars who seemed to jeer and to talk silently against me; to crack nuts, and laugh, so that I really believed I had assumed the face of a pig. (Knight, 1827, pp. 144–146)

Both the preceding accounts agree with the commonly held belief regarding circumstances that lead to insanity. Prolonged physical and emotional excitement (here attendant on the death of a parent), induced physical exhaustion and illness, low despondent spirits, feverish illness, and unrestrained imagery caused by fever, all are thought to lead to an "unhinged mind." This notion seems most comprehensible in common sense. Whether accounts of this sort are factual, or whether they are "screen memories," following the event of mental derangement, is impossible to say. (A "screen memory" is a fictional account of circumstances that may have occurred, but for which no true memory trace remains.) They do constitute, however, acceptable rationalizations for most persons and seem to become partial explanations for the afflicted individual. As long as no one seems to have any certain knowledge with respect to the real cause of the person's mental illness, any explanation that seems plausible acts to console, in some part, the overwhelming terror of the realization, "I am mad" or "I was a lunatic."

FATIGUE AND EXHAUSTION

Other circumstances mentioned by some patients in their description of the beginning of their madness is excessive fatigue (which sleep and rest do not allay), increasing fearfulness mixed with melancholia, and hopelessness. The major complaint is exhaustion and an unfounded sadness which seems to increase until it is beyond self-control. Some fragments from the very moving and illustrative account by Lenore McCall in her autobiography, *Between Us and the Dark*, may be assembled as follows.

In the Spring of that year I was tired; quite definitely I knew that. I had gone through a long period of great strain . . . I was tired out, so tired that I did not seem to be able to make the effort to carry on from day to day. So tired that there seemed to be no enthusiasm left within me for anything. . . .

That year when we arrived [at our summer home], it was not the same . . . But you can't expect a miracle, I thought. . . . Give yourself time. You'll be all right in a few days. When you're rested physically then your zest for everything will be restored. I know now in retrospect that I had already turned off the broad, sunlit road of my normal life and had taken the first steps along that tortuous highway [of madness] . . . I was heading for that realm of darkness, that land of half-lights and weird shadows, the world of the mentally ill. . . .

The middle of September came; it was time to close [our summer home] and to return to the city. . . . But I could not assemble my thoughts. My mind would not focus upon the job at hand and I discovered that I lacked the impetus to get on with it. . . . I sat down and, without any warning, I burst into tears. . . . Depression far deeper and more pronounced than that of the early summer . . . took possession of me. Moreover, the seed of an idea was germinating in my mind; the hopelessness, the unreasonable quality of it appalled me. . . .

I knew by this time that my mind was affected and, to me, this was shameful. It was a bitter disgrace that must be concealed if possible and fought to the last ditch. If some part of my body had been misbehaving, I would have gone immediately to the best specialist available. But because my brain was the offender I could not bring myself to enlist aid from any source.

I had reached the point of knowing that my mind was affected through a realisation that I was no longer able to make the most trivial decision. Gradually I was losing the power to direct my mind along straight and logical channels. Little things which, in the recording of them, appear unimportant began to assume gigantic proportions because of my inability to handle them. . . .

I'll fight this thing, I've got to. I'm young; I won't give up. There's never been anything so far that I couldn't handle in my life and I won't let this get me. In answer came that other voice within me, that voice that was like an alter ego and that was becoming so familiar. All right, you've been fighting now for several months and what have you proved? You're going down and down every day, slipping away, with nothing to hold on to. . . .

The end came abruptly a week later, a week that bore every characteristic of a nightmare. Although I still inhabited the world I had always known, my mind and spirit had definitely crossed the border into that land of unreality, of shadows in which I was to live for five years. . . .

Henry [my husband] looked at me for a brief second. "Anne, what is it that you don't want anyone to find out?" "That I'm mad." There, it's out. I've said it, I thought, through terror and confusion. I've tried not to tell, but I couldn't hold out any longer. (McCall, 1947, pp. 3–4; 6–7; 10; 11–12; 22; 30)

There are many similar accounts to the above, which relate how fatigue, mental confusion, the loss of self-control, feelings of desolation, the feeling of being out-of-touch with reality, the growth of an unfounded panic, all lead up to the point of collapse in an undeniable psychosis. As a usual thing, the patient attributes part of the distress to some physical weakness or failure, but at the same time, he implies that he is aware that he is rapidly losing control over his mental processes and that he should —but cannot—control his own mind.

PAIN, TENSION AND INSOMNIA

In addition to physical illness and exhaustion, many descriptive accounts of the beginning of a prolonged abnormal mental experience tell of unaccustomed painful sensations, feelings of tension, and periods of insomnia. The sufferer is fully aware of the pain and inner tensions but cannot convince himself that they constitute a sufficient explanation for the experiences which follow. In the same way he may complain of sleeplessness, despite being so physically exhausted that he would ordinarily have had no difficulty in sleeping soundly. Graves, who was a very intelligent journalist, described in his extraordinary autobiography, *The Eclipse of a Mind,* the onset of the first of his many periods of overt insanity in the following way.

I began to collapse shamefully under fear and rather real pain. Failing to sleep one night—my memory is a little obscure as to the details—I experienced many nervous sensations amounting to pain. I would try to lie down, in a hotel room or on a boardwalk bench, and find myself dragged up to movement, and to fear of the causation of these nerve sensations. . . . It was the first time in my life that I had encountered the full impact of neurotic sensation. Hitherto in my life pain—or the approach to pain—had been associated with a definite physical cause. The habitual reaction was one of looking for causation, and thereafter removing it. . . . For a while I simply could not lie still at the onset of sensations. . . .

In thus describing the neurasthenic sensations which in 1919 bordered on pain I have already done about the best I can. The single most noticeable effect among these was a sense of pressure around the head, of weight, of resistance to any collected attempt to think. Over the body surface I would occasionally have a sensation as though my structure was inclosed in a straitjacket, and occasionally on dropping into a doze I would be pulled out of sleep by my own convulsive movements. My stock of self-control was inadequate to resist the combination of actual pain and fear about causes. For a period of days, per-haps weeks, I was simply on the verge of uncontrollable fear. . . .

After dark, the first night on the deserted beach walk, I can remember arising from bed after failing to go to sleep and walking in the night, occasion-ally dog-trotting, with some notion of getting enough physical tiredness to sleep —and then would draw another white night. The insomnia was the chief symp-tom which scared me out of my senses. The iron-cap-around-the-head sensation, plus tautened nerves all over the body, was coaxing me toward barely restrained hysteria. (Graves, 1942, pp. 144–145)

In essence, the experience described by Graves was a "neurotic" or obscure sensation of pain, coupled with tension and unreasonable fear. The sleeplessness, when physical fatigue should have led to sleep, and the realization that his usual self-control had ceased to function drove him to what he termed "hysteria." The associated mental confusion, unclear memory, and rather senseless behavior seemed to him, later, to be secondary.

A more succinct account of a similar pain–tension–sleeplessness experience, likewise preceding an insane episode, was published in the same hospital report from which the excerpt relating to physical illness was drawn. It was written by the wife of a frontier farmer, to whom she was devoted. Her husband, she relates, had injured his shoulder, so that she was at that time working with him in the fields, assisting in clearing the land. She goes on to say that the onset of her illness was very sudden.

On a certain day, while engaged in the field, I was suddenly struck almost blind, and felt an uncommon stiffness in the back of my neck, accompanied with a drawing down of the skin over my eyes and forehead, and the sensation of tight cords passing through my head. It was some time before I felt able to return to the house, and attend to my domestic duties. I had lost much sleep for two or three weeks previous to this attack, and felt troubled in my mind on account of our difficulties in getting along in the world. On the following night I was greatly distressed, and thought somebody was coming to kill me. I could not go to sleep, and, by morning, I believe I was completely deranged. I continued out of my head for three or four months, and suffered much distress and anxiety of mind, from the apprehension that I was to be killed. (Anon., 1850a, pp. 465–466)

In this instance, though the first symptoms might suggest the possibility of sunstroke, the ensuing events were in no way associated with sunstroke. The pain–tension–sleeplessness picture was of the nature that is often typical of the onset of insanity. The main value of this description lies in the fact that it was furnished by an uneducated, simple-minded woman who realized the existence of her derangement and was later able to recall some of the details relevant to the beginning of her illness.

The circumstances that are commonly said to precede an episode of mental derangement, namely, physical illness, fatigue, and exhaustion, or pain, tension, and insomnia, may very well represent the preliminary conditions that occur before any actual psychopathological symptoms become apparent. But there is no good or convincing evidence that these circumstances, of themselves, either *cause* or are the *necessary* forerunners of mental derangement.

Prominent Complaints and Conditions at the Onset

Not all psychopathological episodes are alike in their qualitative, quantitative, or temporal aspects. However, they are similar in that most mental patients in describing the beginning of their illness complain of having been overwhelmed by peculiar unpleasant feelings which they could no longer control and which seemed to them to be unreasonable, without an adequate basis in known fact. Such unpleasant inner states may begin slowly or the inner state may spring up quite suddenly.

GRADUAL VS SUDDEN ONSET

In the citations I have given thus far, the symptoms leading to the breaking point, as related by Jane Hillyer and Lenore McCall, were part of a gradual process, extending over several months; on the other hand, the onset of the derangement of the frontier farm wife, as well as that of the university student, was sudden.

Paul Hackett, whose autobiography, *The Cardboard Giants*, very vividly tells of his derangement, suffered from an acute episode that led to his hospitalization, for a period of several years. He tells in his book that the central fear during his derangement was the idea that all the world, including himself, was under the control of an evil power, the *Mind*. In retrospect, it seemed to him that this evil had been in the background of his awareness for many years, though only occasionally did the specific idea become acute.

I tried to remember when I first knew the world was controlled by this evil force, the Mind, but I could not remember. It may have been when I was little, watching bright-colored leaves burn and smoke, or it might have been when I watched so many close to me die and heard the shovels of wet dirt striking on the coffins, or it might have been when I watched myself from a height doing evil when I meant to do good. When it started, I could not remember. I remembered only that my knowledge meant that the evil force would destroy me and mine and that I was near the end; that for years I had been pitched beyond pitch of anxiety and dread and fear, and that I now felt the pain exploding in my head and the dull grip of pain in the back of my neck, and that I could not fight any longer, or watch any longer, or hope any longer. . . . I let down my guard and slept. The Mind could have struck at me. The fear and terror washed over me like a wave. . . . I had the sensation of falling and something of walking in a dark room. . . . I let myself fall. (Hackett, 1952, pp. 4–5)

Insofar as he was personally concerned, the *evil Mind* did finally overwhelm him. Despite occasional periods of lucidity when he felt he had partially regained his self-control, he realized that he had become insane, even though, at first, he was quite disoriented and not fully aware of that which had happened to him.

In contrast to Hackett's experience of gradually being overwhelmed by an outside evil influence, the following account describes a more sudden and dramatic onset of abnormality. This account is taken from the autobiography, *The Life of the Rev. Mr. Geo. Trosse*, published in 1714. Trosse related that he was the son of well-to-do parents who had indentured him to several business concerns during his early manhood. During his indenture, he said, he learned little and became to some degree a drunkard and a wastrel. Finally, on one occasion, having arrived at the city of Exeter, he endorsed a note of a certain Major against the advice of his family. Somewhat disturbed by his foolish action, he drank heavily before retiring for the night in a room at the local tavern.

I then waking, and being alone in the Chamber, fancy'd I heard some *rushing kind of Noise*, and discern'd something at the *Bed's-Foot* like a *Shadow;* which I apprehended to have been a *Spirit.* Hereupon, I was seiz'd with *great Fear* and *Trembling*, rose in Haste, went forth into the *Outer-Chamber* in great *Consternation*, and walk'd up and down in it as one *amaz'd*. . . . The *Devil*, who in our Blindness and Presumption hurries us upon *rash* and foolish *Actions*, knows how in a Time of *Trouble* to set them home, with such Aggravations, as utterly to sink & distract us.

While I was thus walking up and down, hurried with these worldly disquieting Thoughts, I perceiv'd a *Voice* (*I heard it plainly*) saying unto me, *Who art thou?* Which, knowing it could be the Voice of *no Mortal*, I concluded was the *Voice of GOD*, and with Tears, as I remember, reply'd, *I am a very great Sinner, LORD!* Hereupon, I withdrew again into the *Inner-Room*, securing and barring the Door upon me, I betook my self to a *very proper* and *seasonable Duty*, namely, *Secret Prayer;* performing it with some kind of *Conscience* towards *GOD*, and with Hopes to receive some *Good* at his Hands, (which I *never* did all my Life-time *before*). But it was an *impudent* and *proud Prayer:* For I *pray'd* in *my own Strength* . . .

For while I was praying upon my Knees, I heard a Voice, as I fancy'd, as it were just behind me, saying, *Yet more humble; Yet more humble;* with some Continuance. And not knowing the Meaning of the *Voice*, but undoubtedly concluding it came from GOD, I endeavour'd to comply with it. Considering that I kneel'd upon something, I remov'd it; and then I had some kind of Intimation given me, that that was what was requir'd. Thus I kneel'd upon the Ground: But the *Voice* still continu'd, *Yet more humble; Yet more humble*. In Compliance with it I proceeded to pluck down my *Stockings*, and to kneel upon my bare *Knees:* But the same *awful Voice* still sounding in mine Ears, I proceeded to pull off my *Stockings*, and then my *Hose*, and my *Doublet;* and as I was thus uncloathing my self, I had a strong internal Impression, that all was well done, and a full Compliance with the Design of the *Voice*. . . .

At length, standing up before the Window, I either *heard a Voice*, which bid me, or *had a strong Impulse*, which excited me, to *cut off my Hair;* to which I reply'd, *I have no Scissors*. It was then hinted, that *a Knife would do it;* but I answer'd, *I have none.* Had I had one, I verily believe, this *Voice* would have gone from my *Hair* to my *Throat*, and have commanded me to *cut it:* For I have all Reason to conclude, that the Voice was the Voice of *SATAN*, and that his Design was, to *humble* me as *lowest HELL:* But the Absence of a *proper Instrument* prevented it. (Trosse, 1714, pp. 46–48)

Seemingly, this experience started suddenly. In such circumstances, the uncertainty of the individual as to whether it is the voice of God or of the Devil is not uncommon. But some of the phrases Trosse used in this account are worth noting, since similar expressions appear often in the descriptions of psychopathological experience. For example: "rushing kind of noise," "seized with great fear," "a voice (I heard it plainly)," "then I had some kind of intimation," "it was then hinted," and so forth, are typical of the way in which many patients attempt to give verbal expression to their unusual inner experience.

Whether the beginning of a psychotic episode, like that of Trosse, is attributed by the patient to the action of good or evil influences depends both on the nature of the inner experience and on the attendant circumstances. If the experience is one of fear, or if it is intimated that the hallucinatory voice is that of a Devil, or if the surrounding circumstances have no elements suggestive of good, then the sufferer may at once conclude that he has become the victim of evil forces.

When reading an account such as this, one usually wonders why the sufferer so unquestioningly obeyed the "imaginary" orders and commands. Trosse said that he had been a wastrel, irreligious, self-willed, and disrespectful of authority; yet when voices and ideas were thrust upon him, though he was uncertain as to their angelic or demoniacal source, he complied with their orders and without question. Furthermore, he notes that had he possessed a knife, he would probably have cut his throat. The oddity of these sudden experiences is the unquestioning submission of the individual to commands or suggestions that are subjectively experienced as coming from without.

FEAR

Simple *uncomplicated* feelings of fear or anxiety, occurring as the first or leading complaint at the very beginning of a psychopathological episode, are not common. Only those persons whose accounts are usually labeled as phobic neuroses dwell on fear as their primary complaint. In *The Autobiography of David* ————, the author, who suffered for many years from an acute and disabling agoraphobia (fear of open places), gives a good description of this particular type of simple fear.

But it was in Arran, according to my sisters, that I first showed signs of a fear of open spaces. I was going through a field with two white horses in it and became so frightened of the open space that I had to be picked up and carried across it. But on this occasion, no doubt, it was the horses which made me afraid rather than the space itself. The first real attack occured some time later. I was trying to climb Ben Vahren, and halfway up I was suddenly seized with what would now be called agoraphobia. The immense vastness of the scene, the great, lonely granite boulders, the mighty, towering, precipitous ravines, and far off across the blue mist, where sky and sea seemed to meet, . . . produced in me a sense of immensity, a feeling of being lost, of being a minute particle without any habitation or place to rest in a menacing material universe which offered no means of coming into its heart. I started to run as this feeling grew—running from what I could not guess. I only knew that I seemed to be poised on the edge of some eternal mystery which I could not understand or fathom, and that I did not belong to it, but belonged to some other dearer and nearer company. After running some time, the feeling left me a little, and I was able to make my way along the bed of a stream overhung with scarlet rowans from the mountain ash growing along the banks. (Raymond, 1946, p. 42)

Whether slight or severe, the fear that accompanies the beginning of a mental breakdown is usually complicated by feelings of depression, unreality, ideas of persecution, and the like. For example, a certain patient cited by Rychlinski said that his abnormality began when he was a college student living in a city away from home. He was informed of his mother's sudden death, and being summoned home, he started his journey by railway coach. He was calm at first, but suddenly an idea came to him that he might catch a cold. He then thought that a cold might provoke a mental illness of the particular variety to which his family was prone. He tried at first to divert such thoughts by reading a newspaper.

While I read I also looked at my travelling companions in the car and was especially struck by the presence of two passengers with iron poles, for it appeared to me that they were watching me. I made an effort not to yield to the fear to which I succumbed upon seeing the two unknown passengers, by directing my attention solely to the newspaper, but it was useless . . . my thoughts were occupied with something entirely different and with such tension that I began to reflect about how far my thoughts would be able to reach if they were not subdued by reason; from this the thought came to me how frightfully large and powerful are the questions which disquiet man. . . . The thought about an abnormality of my mind flashed before me several times; I fought with the ghost of an illness which I feared; calling my whole will power for aid. I wanted to ask passing people for a way in which I could meet my new misfortune. The optical illusions persecuted me. . . . The facial expressions of the people involved took on a horrible form; it appeared to me as if I saw ghosts who stray about with pale, pale yellow and fire-red faces; it appeared to me, that I was surrounded by persons who have arisen from the grave, that in movement their lips assumed an oblong shape; that the space of their mouths represented a dark gorge, which had something demonically-devilish about it. Since I was inclined to believe in the actuality of these hallucinations, I assumed then that I also did not live any longer, and that I had found myself in the other world. (Rychlinski, 1896, pp. 628–630)

The panic and illusions overcame him so quickly that he lost consciousness. The next thing he recalled was being aroused when the train reached a railway station where he was to change trains. The panic, delusions, and lapses of consciousness continued over several days, and he was finally committed to a mental hospital by the authorities.

Note the difference between the roles of fear at the onset of this disturbance and in the accounts given by David. For David, fear first overwhelmed him as a pure panic state with no real justification or logical reason; for the student the account indicates that a panic started that seemed at the time to be partly justified by the attendant circumstances and by his knowledge of his hereditary predisposition.

MELANCHOLIA

In most of the autobiographical descriptions cited so far concerning the beginning of a mental episode, mention has been made of a pervasive feeling of despair and loss of hope; in short, feelings akin to melancholia. The account of Lenore McCall may be called to mind. Her melancholic experiences were marked by a growing sense of hopelessness and desolation, which persisted in spite of all her efforts to gain control of her painful experiences by seeking new interests and activities. It will be recalled that in other descriptions each individual seemed to realize the lack of an adequate basis for his unusual feelings and behavior, but could not achieve control of his thoughts and feelings. Almost every patient emphasizes this feeling of hopelessness as a primary disturbance. However, close scrutiny of the accounts indicates that the feelings became truly unusual or abnormal only when the patient realized that the experience had passed beyond his self-control.

An illustrative description of a sudden onset of melancholia has been selected from *The Autobiography of Mark Rutherford.* He said that he had hitherto been a normal young man when the episode occurred.

Towards morning I got into bed, but not to sleep; and when the dull daylight of Monday came, all support had vanished, and I seemed to be sinking into a bottomless abyss. I became gradually worse . . . and my melancholy took a fixed form. I got a notion into my head that my brain was failing, and this was my first acquaintance with that most awful malady, hypochondria. I did not know then what I know now, although I only half believe it practically, that this fixity of form is a frequent symptom of the disease, and that the general weakness manifests itself in a determinate horror, which gradually fades with returning health. For months—many months, this dreadful conviction of coming idiocy or insanity lay upon me like some poisonous reptile with its fangs driven into my very marrow, so that I could not shake it off. It went with me wherever I went, it got up with me in the morning, walked with me all day, and lay down with me at night. I managed somehow or other to do my work, but I prayed incessantly for death; and to such a state was I reduced that

I could not even make the commonest appointment for a day beforehand. The mere knowledge that something had to be done agitated me and prevented my doing it. (Rutherford, 1885, pp. 36–37)

In this account the experience was one of being overwhelmed by lethargy and feelings of hopeless despair, so much so that there seemed no point in the person's attempting to summon his reserve strength so that he might fight what he felt was a hopeless battle. The melancholic man is quite unable to *will* any quality of hope back into his mind; in this inability lies the core of his distress.

In essence, melancholia and phobia are feeling states that seem to have no necessary essential external reference. Both states are experienced as having some *future* temporal reference, rather than being concerned with either the present or the past. The core of both experiences seems to arise from within the body itself, in the same sense that a blush arises from within. Either condition is commonly dealt with as one which would be more comfortable if only circumstances would permit some reasonable explanation for its presence. The mark of abnormality lies in the fact that these feelings cannot be controlled or diverted. Hence the sufferer says to himself, "Something has happened inside my mind; it is not essentially related to the outside world; I know I should be able to drive such thoughts and feelings out of my mind, but this I cannot do."

FEELING OF BEING UNDER OUTSIDE CONTROL

This disturbance consists of a feeling or conviction of having been thrust, either gradually or suddenly, under the sway of unknown and unnatural outside influences. The individual loses control over his thoughts, together with his usual ability to recognize the direction of his mental processes. The sufferer may even feel that he has lost his own personality, as well as the hitherto taken-for-granted capacity to channel his thinking appropriately. This commanding external influence may appear to be good or evil, angelic or demoniacal, personal or impersonal, specific or cosmic. In addition to its general imperative quality, its potency may extend to affect the person's plasticity of thought, sometimes so completely that the ordinary course of thought becomes impossible. The realization that he is no longer a free agent with normal self-control and self-responsibility is so confusing and unreal that the sufferer may quite quickly become aware of his disability, but will only occasionally conclude, "I am mad."

DIVINE POWER The way in which the feeling of becoming controlled by a Divine Power can lead to irrational self-surrender is aptly illustrated by the following portion of a transcript of a conversation between Boisen, a hospital chaplain, and a patient. The patient's monologue relates to events which led to his first hospitalization.

I must give it to you in order. You can't understand unless we go back to the beginning 13 years ago. You must know how the whole thing started, how I made a sort of bet with God.

I was at a Socialist meeting one night. A man there spoke of Jesus and of his giving his life for others. He asked if there were not many others who would be willing to do that.

That night I was thinking about what the Socialist speaker said and that I would gladly give my life for my family alone. In the night I was waked up and a voice said, "You must be put to the test to see if you will really give up your life." It seemed as though God were right in front of me and the voice seemed to be God's voice, and words from the Bible came into my head. I began to feel very nervous. It seemed as though something was getting into me. I did not tell my wife. I felt she would not understand. I got up and ran out into the street in my underwear. Of course, that was a very strange thing to do, but it was just like the old Greek who found out how to weigh a ship. He was in his bathtub at the time the idea came to him, but he got so excited that he got up and ran out without anything on. You get an idea so big it just carries you away . . .

About a week after that I was sent to the hospital. After that dream I was nervous. I had a feeling like when they bind up your arm and give you a blood test. I was sort of filled up. It was a queer feeling—something you don't understand what it is. I had the feeling that there were two sides and that I had to go to one side or the other in order to get salvation. (Boisen, 1947, p. 160)

It is worth noting that in this account and in many other similar ones the experiences seem to the patient to be only partially related to his previous thoughts and life history. Patients who come under an outside influence say that they "became thoughtful" and then subsequently feel that they are being directed or controlled by some outside force; voices and visions may occur, and though they *know* that the voices or visions may be unreal, they never doubt the orders but obey without question. Even after recovery it is rare for such a patient to doubt the verity of the occurrence or the unique meaning of his experience. Their interpretation of the meaning of the event is not that of having lost their mind, but rather of having been chosen for some divine mission. This revelation usually carries with it an unshakable conviction of the truth of the experience, a conviction that may continue for the remainder of their lives.

EVIL OR DEMONIACAL POWER   An instance of demoniacal influence was related by the writer of an anonymous letter to the editor of a journal, giving the details of the beginning of his auditory hallucinations, which he was sure constituted the work of the Devil.

As I was taking a quiet walk one evening about six years ago, in the outskirts of the metropolis, I suddenly experienced the sensations of the sound of apparently human voices. There was no human being on the spot, but as the sounds were those of conversation between one person and another or others, I endeavoured to trace their origin: such an attempt was ineffectual. A boy came within sight, amusing himself in some ruinous buildings at a distance— the sounds appeared to proceed from him. I called and ran to him, but being alarmed he speedily made his exit. The language then appeared to emanate from some fowls; I knew these birds incapable of producing such sounds, and entertained myself by thinking on the marvellous stories in the "Arabian Nights" and in our Indian transmigratory tales, and then reasoned that persons in a cottage not far from the fowls might possibly, by ventriloquism, have deceived me. I approached the cottage, and watched it a considerable time; the voices then seemed to be those of persons in the interior of it, but no one appeared at the windows, and some labourers passing by I walked away. The voices then evidently came from these men, gradually becoming more and more indistinct, until I lost them momentarily. The words used were, "Who is he?—What is he?—Do you know who he is?" The responses were, "He is the Devil's own—He is Satan's own." Shouts of laughter and derision and questions of doubt afterwards succeeded. (Anon., 1854b, pp. 262–263)

These demoniacal voices continued to disturb him for over six years. They were so demanding and omnipresent that he was forced to retire from his occupation. They did not gain full control of his behavior so that he was never adjudged insane, nor did he ever consider that he had lost his mind, despite his inability to control the intrusive ideas. In the letter he also said that after approximately seven years the voices quieted down so that they could be ignored, but he remained convinced that he suffered from demoniacal possession.

COSMIC INFLUENCES Another variety of the experience of an overpowering outside force directing thoughts and actions is the belief that one has somehow come into possession of a vast amount of knowledge of the Universe and its meaning—the feeling of having achieved "cosmic consciousness." This experience usually sets in rather suddenly and carries with it an unquestionable conviction that in some mysterious fashion one has been given the key to all Divine knowledge of the meaning of Heaven and life. On the person's shoulders is usually placed the responsibility of his own salvation and the salvation of his family, his group, his nation, in fact all mankind. He may suddenly conceive that, in one way or another, he has come into possession of a full understanding of the world and its meaning; that somehow the key to universal understanding has become available to him.

In a more sophisticated person, the onset of this experience is similar to the one described in the following account, written by a psychiatric social service worker:

A few weeks before my illness I began to regress into success daydreams somewhat similar to, though not quite as naive and grandiose, as those I had had during early adolescence. I was puzzled by this tendency, though not greatly alarmed because it hardly seemed that my daydreaming self was a part of my adult ethical self. At the onset of panic, I was suddenly confronted with an overwhelming conviction that I had discovered the secrets of the universe, which were being rapidly made plain with incredible lucidity. The truths discovered seemed to be known immediately and directly, with absolute certainty. I had no sense of doubt or awareness of the possibility of doubt. In spite of former atheism and strong anti-religious sentiments, I was suddenly convinced that it was possible to prove rationally the existence of God. (Anon., 1955, p. 679)

When this occurred she said that she began to write, in a compulsive fashion, an essay on cognition. After her recovery from the psychosis, she found parts of the essay among her notes. Some portions of the essay were quite lucid, while other parts were incoherent and full of symbolic sexual content. Her cosmic thoughts quickly developed into the idea that she had an exclusive religious mission to accomplish, and although she struggled consciously against these overwhelming Messianic delusions, she continued to have a feeling of burdensome responsibility for the world, which persisted throughout the entire period of her illness.

The phenomenon of firm belief in the subjective experience of divine revelation of all knowledge can also manifest itself in persons who are in no sense insane. For example, about a century ago, when chloroform and ether were first introduced, a great deal of "social" experimentation took place and records of their occasional odd effects on some normal persons reached publication. The English poet Symonds reported his experience during and following chloroform anesthesia. He was so moved that he published a pamphlet on the subject. This was included in his biography, from which the following excerpt has been taken.

After the choking and stifling of the chloroform had passed away, I seemed at first in a state of utter blankness: then came flashes of intense light, alternating with blackness, and with a keen vision of what was going on in the room round me, but no sensation of touch. I thought that I was near death; when, suddenly, my soul became aware of God, who was manifestly dealing with me, handling me, so to speak, in an intense personal present reality. I felt Him streaming in like light upon me, and heard Him saying in no language, but as hands touch hands and communicate sensation, "I led you. I guided you; you will never sin, and weep, and wail in madness any more; for now, you have seen me." My whole consciousness seemed brought into one point of absolute conviction; the independence of my mind from my body was proved by the phenomena of this acute sensibility to spiritual facts, this utter deadness of the senses; Life and Death seemed mere names, for what was there then but my soul and God, two indestructible existences in close relation, I could reason a little, to this extent that I said: "Some have said they were convinced by miracles and spirit-rapping, but my conviction is a real new sense." I also felt God saying, "I have suffered you to feel sin and madness, to ache and be abandoned, in order that now you might know and gladly greet Me. Did you think the anguish of the last few days and this experience you are undergoing were fortuitous coincidences?" I cannot describe the ecstasy I felt. Then as I gradually awoke from the influence of the anesthetics, the old sense of my relation to the world began to return, the new sense of my relation to God began to fade. I suddenly leapt to my feet on the chair where I was sitting, and shrieked out, "It is too horrible, it is too horrible, it is too horrible," meaning that I could not bear this disillusionment. . . . To have felt for that long dateless ecstasy of vision the very God, in all purity and tenderness and truth and absolute love, and then to find that I had after all no revelation, but that I had been tricked by the abnormal excitement of my brain [was most distressing]. (Symonds, 1895, pp. 78–80)

This description is qualitatively very similar to some which have been written by mental patients or, indeed, to some of the revelations of cosmic consciousness recorded by religious mystics. Symonds had experienced mystical states during adolescence and early manhood, but maintained that they were neither as vivid nor as detailed as the one released by the anesthesia.

OUTSIDE PERSECUTORY POWER Ideas of persecution, usually expressed by an inner compulsion to fight back and conquer the persecutor, constitute one of the main characteristics of the condition of *paranoia*. They are, however, not restricted to this particular diagnostic category. Persecutory delusions are not infrequent phenomena and are associated with a wide range of mental abnormalities. Generally speaking, these feelings of being persecuted are not prominent at the beginning of a mental breakdown, but more commonly developed during the course of illness. Examples of a very rapid onset of this state can be found, the rapidity indicating that such systems may at times occur and develop in an independent fashion. For example, Dr. K. A. Menninger published the account of a patient who wrote as follows.

I knew it for seven or eight months before it came. I felt this thing coming on. The first thing I noticed was when I was shopping I had a feeling as if everything was leaving me including my mind. *I began to think that the world was against me and I was losing out everywhere.* I began to think my husband was unfaithful, that he was being taken away or that he was going to leave me, that he was lying to me and that they were all in a gigantic plot against me.

All the time I was scared to death they would find out. I would be deluded like that for a time and then at another time I would be aware of the fact that it was false but then I was so terrified with the thought of losing my mind that I could think of nothing else. . . .

People noticed that I didn't talk plain. They frequently spoke of it, but I tried to hide it and tell them that they were mistaken. I really noticed it myself, however, and that it was another sign that my mind was going. Throughout these six or eight months things grew more and more muddled, but every day I had the terrible fear which I supposed was the realization that I was losing my mind and that sooner or later it would be found out. Why, one day when I got mixed in trying to say something, my daughter said in a joking way, "Mother is getting nutty, isn't she?" This almost broke my heart, and I was so disturbed and terrified that I left the table and went to my room.

And then I was really changing so in disposition. I was unkind to everyone, irritable, disagreeable, no love in my heart—why, I wasn't even civil. The last night, I remember, before everything went black, during the episode when I thought I had been struck on the head—it was as if someone had given me a blow with a club in the back of my head and after that I can remember nothing definitely until everything suddenly got clear on the day I came home from the hospital. (Menninger, 1924, p. 30)

It should be noted that this patient emphasized the fact that while she was shopping she "began to think that the world was against me." She stated that the sense of being the object of persecution started suddenly, without a period of prior development. I have found accounts written by other patients who have made similar statements.

Ideas of persecution differ from the phobias and melancholias, in that they seem to carry an immediate outside reference, usually expressed by some direct statement as, "People are talking about me." One may be possessed by fear or hopelessness without having anything, or anyone, to which the fear or despair is necessarily related. Emotionally, the feeling of being persecuted seems to carry with it an essence of compulsion directed against someone or something. It is not a floating state of anger without any immediate external reference. Originally, the feeling of persecution may not be specifically directed, leaving some existing doubt as to the certainty of its truth. However, this period of doubt is short-lived, and soon thereafter the patient can no longer entertain any doubt about the essential truth of the persecutory delusions. No further objective evidence will shake his certainty. The firm inner belief in the delusion is just as complete and sincere as is the inner conviction of the truth of religious conversion.

Phenomena That Are Especially Disturbing

The preceding section dealt with the more prominent complaints and conditions that occur at the beginning of a psychotic attack. We pass on now to several additional phenomena that are of themselves not specific to a particular pattern of derangement, but that quite frequently occur and are very distressing to the patient.

HALLUCINATIONS

Unusual feeling states for which the patient finds difficulty in evincing an adequate cause and which fail to yield to ordinary methods of self-control are always disturbing. When the world about one begins to provide auditory or visual experiences that no one else can hear or see, and for which all the guiding standards of everyday life provide few, if any, trustworthy reference points, then one indeed has a basis for doubting one's sanity. Scattered among the descriptions of the onset of psychopathological experience, already given in this chapter, are examples of sensory distortions that have acted to produce and enhance confusion among deranged persons. The sounds of rushing noises, strange optical illusions, moving shadows, buzzings and hissings, are all experiences for which no good explanation could be given by patients; yet they could be partly explained as misinterpretations due to distracted attention, poor observation, or the like. Such illusions are disturbing, but they do not actually serve to lead the person to "doubt his own senses."

However, to suddenly *hear* a clear voice distinctly speaking in a sensible fashion, when no one is present, or *meet* a stranger with whom one has a sensible conversation and then to see that stranger disappear into thin air before one's very eyes, are occasions directly contrary to ordinary perceptual experience. Such experiences may lead to an immediate doubt of one's own sanity. This type of hallucinatory phenomena may be illustrated by the following citation taken from L. M. Jayson's *Mania*. It is in no way an unusual description to find in the autobiographies of the insane.

Seated on a steamer chair on the boardwalk of Coney Island, I heard the voice for the first time. It was, I remember distinctly, a rough, deep bass voice that did not belong to my brother who was sitting quietly in the chair next to mine, nor to the middle-aged gentleman with whom I'd just picked up a talking acquaintance.

It was a voice without any body at all. But it was as positive and persistent as any voice I had ever heard. It said slowly, "Jayson, you are worthless. You've never been useful, and you've never been any good."

I shook my head, unbelievingly, trying to drive out the sound of the words, and as if I had heard nothing, continued to talk with my neighbor.

"You know," I said to him, in what I tried to make an off-hand manner, "it's a funny thing how many prescriptions you can get from people about curing the blues and how little any of them help." . . .

He was nodding sympathetically, and I remember thinking it funny how blurred and misty his face looked—as if it were miles off—when suddenly, clearer, deeper, and even louder than before, the deep voice came at me again, right in my ear this time, and getting me tight and shivery inside.

"Larry Jayson, I told you before you weren't any good. Why are you sitting here making believe you're as good as any one else when you're not? Whom are you fooling?"

The sounds were so clear and so loud, I knew that pretty soon the people next to me would hear them. So I got up, and started walking slowly away, down the stairs of the boardwalk to the stretch of sand below . . . I waited until the voice came back, the words pounding in this time, not the way you hear any words, but deeper, as though all parts of me had become ears, with my fingers hearing the words, and my legs, and my head, too.

"You're no good," the voice said slowly, in the same deep tones. "You've never been any good or use on earth. There is the ocean. You might just as well drown yourself. Just walk in, and keep walking." As soon as the voice was through, I knew, by its cold command, I had to obey it. (Jayson, 1937, pp.1–3)

Jayson did walk on into the ocean, beyond his depth, and then struggled against the lifeguards who came to his rescue. They turned him over to the police, who, in turn, took him to the psychiatric division of a large hospital.

Notice that the voice was perceived as clear and distinct, outside the hearer and disembodied (that is, he did not see anyone, he only heard a voice). What he heard were orders that admitted no argument. Further, he heard not only with his ears, but with his entire body. He *had* to obey the voice. When such an experience occurs the hearer is overwhelmed and usually obeys without question. Jayson's experience was very similar to that of the Rev. Mr. Trosse, whose account I cited earlier.

At the onset of mental derangement the hearing of voices is a more common experience than the seeing of visions. Man is fundamentally a "visual" animal, that is to say visual experience is prepotent among the sensory qualities. For this reason most persons are able to experience visual illusions with somewhat flexible mental mechanisms that permit their thought processes to compensate, after a fashion, for most visual distortions. For this reason, if for no other, visions are not as disturbing to most individuals as are voices. Usually, visions are reported as having something of a dreamlike quality, which is, of itself, not too frightening. An example, written by Winkler's patient, Kubin, may aid in clarifying this point.

With still a heavy heart I roamed about the town and in the evening entered a variety show because I was looking for an indifferent and yet noisy environment in order to equalize an *inner pressure* which became steadily stronger. There, something psychically very unusual and decisive for me happened, which even today I don't completely understand, although I have thought about it a great deal. Namely, as the small orchestra began to play, my whole surroundings suddenly appeared to be *clearer* and *sharper*, as if seen in another light. In the faces of those sitting around me I suddenly saw peculiar *animal-human* qualities; all sounds were singularly strange, separated from their cause; it sounded to me like a scornful, groaning, droning common language, which I could not understand but which still clearly seemed to have a *ghostly* inner meaning. . . . And then, suddenly, I was overcome by a whole *cascade of visions* of black and white pictures—one cannot depict the *thousand-fold riches* with which my imagination dazzled my eyes. I quickly left the theatre because the music and the many lights now disturbed me. I strayed aimlessly through the dark streets and was thereby *overcome*, being plainly assaulted by a dark power which conjured up strange animals, houses, landscapes, grotesque and frightful situations in my mind. I felt *indescribably well and uplifted in my enchanted world* and when I became tired I entered a small tea room. Here, too, everything was unusual throughout. Immediately upon entering it seemed to me as if the waitresses were *wax dolls* driven by God knows what mechanism and as if I had surprised the few guests—which appeared to me just as unreal as shadows—at *satanic occupations.* The whole background with the organ and the bar were *suspicious* like a false front which was only to hide the real secret—presumably a dimly lit, stall-like, *bloody cavern.* (Winkler, 1948, p. 140)

Many accounts of the experiences at the beginning of a derangement such as the above, emphasize auditory disorders and the over-all unpleasant feeling state. The patient, Kubin, seems to have been more impressed by the perceived visual changes, and yet said that he felt strangely well and uplifted. Both the sounds and sights seemed unreal, but for some reason he was not particularly frightened.

Auditory hallucinations may be accompanied by the perception of visual images, so that we often find a patient relating how he held a conversation with a person whom no one else ever saw. The following dialogue which Davidson held with a stranger, in fact, constituted the onset of the first abnormal mental episode he experienced. In his autobiography, *Remembrances of a Religio-Maniac,* from which we will quote repeatedly, he told how, on a particular day while playing tennis, he had left the court to retrieve some stray balls that had gone into a neighboring field. At the gate just outside the court, he met a man, a stranger, who said he was a doctor. They introduced themselves and held several minutes of quite meaningful conversation, finally shaking hands when they parted. Davidson then collected the tennis balls and started back toward the court.

After I had retraced my steps a short distance, I turned round, as one often will, in order to have another look at a person who has impressed one greatly. I had just noticed that the stranger's shoulders were particularly square, and that he held himself straight and well, when he turned quickly towards his left, sprang off the ground into the air, and was gone, almost as if he had flown in pieces. The impression made upon me for the second was that he had deliberately sprung upwards into something that immediately hid him from view, like a diver diving into water, not at all like smoke vanishing into air, and I confess that for an instant the thing looked uncanny, almost diabolical. I looked carefully rubbed my eyes, and looked again, but could see no more of him. (Davidson, 1912, p. 34)

Although mystified by this strange encounter and the person's disappearance, he never doubted the reality of the stranger. He spoke about this stranger to his tennis partner, who told him that he (Davidson) had, in fact, wandered about picking up tennis balls but had at no time met any person in the field. His partner also said that she had heard him talking to himself, a bad habit which he should overcome. Quite angrily, Davidson completely rejected his partner's remarks, insisting on the truth and reality of his experience. He described the stranger in some detail. He recalled their conversation and was sure that he had felt the stranger's hand when he had shaken it. During the next couple of weeks Davidson had several further encounters with both men and women "who weren't there," but since these persons changed in appearance while he was talking with, or looking at them, he was less certain about the reality of these chance-met strangers. Only after he had been placed in the custody of a mental hospital did he finally realize that his original experience had been unreal and was indeed the starting incident of his insanity.

An allegedly autobiographical account, *Operators and Things*, written under the pseudonym of Barbara O'Brien (1958) is in style and content quite different from the usual description of hallucinatory experiences that commonly involve ideas of persecution and religion, accompanied by fearful astonishment. In contrast, Miss "O'Brien's" description resembles modern science-fiction more than any other we have encountered.* This unusual account begins with details of both visual and auditory hallucinations, although the auditory experiences were at all times better developed and more organized than were the visual ones. The content of these hallucinations is very different from that of most patients, but the effect of the voices was just as compelling for Miss "O'Brien" as it was for any other deluded patient whose statements we have reviewed. Miss "O'Brien," says she left a good position, her home, and friends and started wandering across the country via Greyhound buses, simply because the voices told her to do so.

The phenomena of hallucinations are so varied and so compelling in the life of mental patients that I shall return to the topic of hallucinations in greater detail in Chapter 6.

Unreality

Another frequent phenomenon that is most distressing and astonishing to mental patients is one they refer to as a feeling of unreality. This condition is usually reported as developing during the *course* of the psychosis and is not prominent at the *beginning*. However, in Marguerite Sechehaye's *Autobiography of a Schizophrenic Girl* the author cites the patient's (Renee) vivid description of her earliest experience with feelings of unreality, which occurred when she was five years old. Since her psychotic difficulties did start at this early age and continued (so far as the

---

* When this book was first published the editor attempted to verify its validity. Mail to both publisher and author remained unanswered. More recently mail addressed to Arlington Books (30 Arlington Street, Cambridge 40, Mass., the 1959 and last known address on file with the Copyright Office of The Library of Congress) has been consistently returned marked "Moved, not forwardable" by the postal service. In the editor's opinion *Operators and Things* should not be accepted at face value until something more tangible can be learned about the circumstances that gave rise to its writing and publication.

record goes) until after the age of twenty, her experience may be accepted as one of the few recorded examples of feelings of unreality being manifested at the beginning of a psychosis.

> I remember very well the day it happened. We were staying in the country and I had gone for a walk alone as I did now and then. Suddenly, as I was passing the school, I heard a German song; the children were having a singing lesson. I stopped to listen, and at that instant a strange feeling came over me, a feeling hard to analyze but akin to something I was to know too well later—a disturbing sense of unreality. It seemed to me that I no longer recognized the school, it had become as large as a barracks; the singing children were prisoners, compelled to sing. It was as though the school and the children's song were set apart from the rest of the world. At the same time my eye encountered a field of wheat whose limits I could not see. The yellow vastness, dazzling in the sun, bound up with the song of the children imprisoned in the smooth stone school-barracks, filled me with such anxiety that I broke into sobs. I ran home to our garden and began to play "to make things seem as they usually were," that is, to return to reality. It was the first appearance of those elements which were always present in later sensations of unreality: illimitable vastness, brilliant light, and the gloss and smoothness of material things. I have no explanation for what happened, or why. (Sechehaye, 1951, pp. 3–4)

Various patients use different words, phrases, and analogies to describe the feeling of unreality they experience. It is, however, always said to be unpleasant, distressing, and fearful, probably because the individual feels an inner change that is somehow very undesirable. I will return to these phenomena in Chapter 17.

Denial of Insanity

In my search for autobiographies of the insane I have found more than a dozen books written by individuals who had been held, committed, or certified as insane and institutionalized in some mental hospital, and who, nevertheless protested that at no time had they actually been insane. In general, these persons apparently undertook the writing of their autobiographies in order to prove that their alleged insanity had been a mistake and that they had been subjected to unjustified imprisonment. Their accounts usually depict much the same circumstances and complaints that actually led to the beginning of their derangement and are quite similar to those of persons who did realize and admit their pathology. Those who denied insanity may or may not have admitted that they had at some time been confused and deluded, but, in general, insisted that they had really been persecuted and that their complaints of ill-treatment were fully justified.

An example of such a dubious mental state was given by Marcia Hamilcar in her account, *Legally Dead.*

I had for some weeks previously to Christmas been very despondent, and the future loomed blackly before me . . . but I had no delusions . . . I had, as it were, lost the proportion of things; my mind was out of joint, and I was physically too exhausted to right it myself, or to reason myself into a saner condition . . . I twisted the most innocent of actions into subjects for the deepest remorse. (Hamilcar, 1910, pp. 88–90)

She continued by describing in some detail the physical and mental abuse suffered at the hands of her sister, the matron of a nursing home, and the attendants at an asylum. We cannot ascertain whether these descriptions are completely factual, although she denied that she was, or ever had been, insane. Miss Hamilcar's autobiography unfortunately does not provide very much information concerning her inner mental life. Essentially, she tells how she had had a period of melancholia, marked by slight mental confusion and periods of self-accusation, whereupon she had been sent by her sister to a nursing home and had there been subjected to partial starvation and other forms of cruelty. She firmly believed in her denial of insanity, that there had ever been any true psychopathology, but gives no evidence of having known what the criteria of insanity might be.

In his book *My Experiences in a Lunatic Asylum*, "A Sane Patient," the pseudonymous Merivale, described in detail his depression, hypochondria, and mental confusion, which he said had been precipitated by the death of a relative and was followed by several empty months during which he had no regular work to occupy his time and interest. Finally, he lapsed into a state of semiconsciousness and delirium, at which time he was placed in a lunatic asylum where, during a period of excitement, he attacked an attendant. Later his health steadily improved and he was discharged from the asylum. He subsequently wrote his book, in which he made the following statement.

I deny distinctly, deliberately, categorically, that I have ever been insane; and I say that the fancies of delirium or hypochondria are as clearly to be distinguished from those of madness as midday from midnight, on a very little close observation, by every honest and unselfish mind. To send them to an asylum for treatment is the best way to turn them to insanity. I have been perfectly frank about my "delusions," for I remember them all, as had I been mad I should not. A man may doubt if he is in his mind or no; he cannot doubt whether or not he has been. (Merivale, 1879, p. 88)

This citation presents several interesting points. The writer admits to having been mentally confused, depressed, and at times excited and deluded, yet insists that he was never insane. His criterion for insanity is a curious one—the ability to recall—for had he been insane, he said, he would not have remembered his delusions. Since, as he says, he did remember everything, he concludes that he could not possibly have been insane. By the patient's own account, however, his behavior justifies the judgment of the authorities concerning his mental status. That he never realized his own derangement is clear, but the facts he related certainly argue against his own conclusions.

By no means have all the persons who denied their psychosis supplied as much material, relevant to the fact, as did both Hamilcar and Merivale. It is possible that some denials are bona fide and that some individuals may have been unjustifiably accused of insanity, but the autobiographical accounts indicate that such occurrences were not very common.

DISCUSSION

We must depend on the subjective reports of experiences as they have been related by those persons who have lived through them. It is apparent that at the earliest stage of the abnormality, almost every person regards his own psychotic experience as something that has never happened to any human being before. Only after hospitalization do most mental patients realize, by virtue of the environment, that there are other individuals whose experiences seem to be quite as disturbing as their own. Most psychotics are bewildered and confused when they first have such unusual experiences, while the confusion, of itself, adds to the subjectively perceived abnormality. All persons have difficulties in finding the appropriate words and phrases to describe their experiences. At the beginning, they do not know or have available many of the necessary descriptive expressions that are commonly utilized by mental patients. If one considers these difficulties, then the patients' problems become more apparent as to the outstanding psychological changes that the patient is trying to convey in narrating how the derangement began.

Essentially, each patient seems to be trying to say, "Something new, different, terrifying and indescribable is happening or has happened to my mind. Things seem unreal and indescribable; I can't control them; they frighten me; something makes me do things that I don't want to do but I can't help myself; new feelings, ideas and thoughts come to my mind; I don't really know how to tell you what it's like."

After surveying many autobiographical descriptions, I conclude from the reports of the subjective experience that two major considerations occupy the patient's mind at the onset of the psychopathological experience; first, the realization of the loss of adequate self-control, and second, the attempt, usually not too successful, to explain these experiences to himself.

The ordinary growth of the mind from birth through adolescence is the period of organization of subjective feelings, sensations, and memories, so that one becomes accustomed to the multiple interconnections of events in the world as well as to the subjective feeling states that usually go with the various circumstances. It is a process of mental growth, proceeding from the childish phase of fearful surprise and astonishment to a commonplace familiarity with anticipated causes and effects. One may not really comprehend the causes and effects but one frequently has, through experience, built up a series of seemingly adequate and logical explanations. These serve to protect oneself from the knowledge of the present and the fear of possible consequences in the future. This total process is commonly considered to be characteristic of normal mental growth between birth and mid-, or late, adolescence.

If, after the age of sixteen or seventeen, an individual has experiences that he has never had or heard about previously, he is surprised and astonished. One has become "adjusted" to one's world, which seems so familiar that one considers that all ordinary relationships are *real* and lawful. Now an unusual experience occurs; something must be changed in one's own private life. No one else shares these new experiences or feelings. In fact, a person who attempts to communicate such experiences to others is most apt to be told, "That's crazy. You'd better forget such things and put them out of your mind." But one knows this unusual experience cannot be forgotten or controlled. If it continues, then one may, in time, come to agree with the idea of madness. This realization is all the more convincing if one finds that ordinary explanations or rationalizations are inadequate and only serve to alarm, rather than to pacify, oneself and others.

In brief, the experiences at the beginning of a psychopathological episode are usually recounted in terms of the realization of the inability to exercise self-control and to find a basis for an adequate self-explanation. These experiences, which are new ("this never happened to me before") and practically unheard of, come to govern the individual's mental life. The psychopathological experiences are neither simple nor pleasant and are almost invariably difficult to describe.

A lunatic appears insensible, but he is, perhaps the most alive of any mind to ridicule, and to the contemptibleness of his state. But he is, as I may say, unconsciously alive to it. He does not acknowledge his own feelings, because his mind is deeply engrossed in painful and excruciating conflicts; he is already troubled by a thousand horrible and fanciful ideas of danger; the victim of inward and preternatural sarcasm, contumely, and derision. But he acts strangely, from what he suffers unacknowledged and not understood by himself. (Perceval, 1838, pp. 205–206)

CHAPTER 3

The Course of
Mental Derangement

INTRODUCTION

The course of a psychopathological episode encompasses the experiences that occur between the realization of mental derangement (or the realization that one has been placed under some form of guardianship) and the inner feeling that one has more or less completely recovered one's self-control and sanity. The experiences and behavior during such a period are extremely variable.

For more than 2,000 years, mankind has tried to organize the mental phenomena of derangement into an orderly and meaningful pattern. No classification has ever been very satisfactory. A few groupings or systematic generalizations, such as melancholia, mania, paranoia, and dementia, do characterize certain of the major varieties of aberrant experience, but by no means do they include all the phenomena that must be considered. Most patients do not follow any single or well-defined course of abnormal events. For example, the course of an attack of melancholia may vary markedly among patients or from time to time in the same patient.

As we have seen in the previous chapter, the sufferer has end-less difficulty in describing his experiences, while the onlooker finds it equally difficult to understand what the sufferer is trying to convey. During the course of an episode the patient may be out of contact with his immediate environment; much of his perceptual world may be distorted and his feelings and thought processes confused. After his recovery he may be able to recall most of his experience, or his memories may be very incomplete. He may recall that he was overwhelmed by a nameless fear or that he seemed to be in an ecstatic dreamlike state. Usually, the only certain statement he can make about the course of the episode is that he could no longer adequately control his thoughts and behavior. Though he may recall various incidents, he knows that he, himself, could not start, stop, regulate, or direct either his feelings or his behavior, or even the course of his own stream of thought. He may later report that there were periods during which he was lucid and sane, and other moments during which he lapsed into unconsciousnes or into dreamlike states.

Memory for the Intervals of Insanity

A report made by a patient following the acute phase of his illness may give the observer an idea of the fragmentary and dreamlike quality of memories of this kind. The following soliloquy is taken from a record made by Boisen, chaplain at the hospital where the patient in question was undergoing psychiatric treatment. (This report is a continuation of the account of the patient on page 31.) The soliloquy concerns two episodes separated by a three-year interval.

In the hospital [the first time] I was put in a strait jacket. The first night I had a dream. I seemed to be crucified, and the whole room was full of devils. They were trying to hurt me, but I was full of power. You see I was in a delirium. I dreamed I was dead. I dreamed I was lying in the grave just like Jesus did.

In about three days my mind came back, and I was released at the end of three weeks. I got along very well after that. I had steady work and there was nothing to worry about. During the last three years work had been scarce and there has been plenty of time to think. No, I had not been thinking much about religion. My wife was told at the hospital that the trouble came from reading the Bible; so I put the Bible in the attic. I didn't want to make her nervous. And I didn't go to church.

The last attack began when something told me to go and get the Bible. I had started then to pray to God. I had been feeling lonesome and I had it in my mind that there is a God. Then it came to me that I had a second install-ment to pay. I had to finish paying my bet with God. I came then into a state of fear. Something said to me, "Are you willing to commit suicide?" And it was just like I had to do it. I turned on the gas. That was for my wife. Then I slashed my wrists, one for one daughter and the other for the other daughter. But everything I have done before came to a good end, and I have the feeling that this will too. I just felt that I had to do it to keep my promise. I have the feeling now that I am a new man. . . .

No, I didn't hear anything. It's just like when you sit and think. Something comes to you. Sometimes it comes quick just like something talk to you. I suppose it comes from God. I can't see any other explanation.

Yes, I did say when this came on it was just like I hypnotized myself. When I talk with a doctor, I talk about self-hypnotizing. A doctor understands that. He don't understand about religion.

Did I think of myself as Christ? Yes, I guess I did. That was before I understand. You get happy and you wake up and think you are it. You get puzzled as to who you are. (Boisen, 1947, p. 160)

In this citation the patient tells of the first episode as if it were the memory of a dream or delusion during the course of which he had lost his mind. Undoubtedly, there was much more that had happened than he was able to remember while conversing with Boisen. Of the second episode, he mentioned little about the onset of his illness or the details of his suicidal attempt. This period seems to be followed by a lapse of memory before any connected, conscious series of events could be recalled. What he did recall, as told in the final portion of this excerpt, is related to either the beginning or the end of the period of acute illness. The course itself seems to have been more or less dreamlike.

Many reports written by patients about the experiences and outstanding events of their mental illness are either too fragmentary or too extensive to be adapted to our purpose. Since most of these autobiographies deal with the course of psychotic processes, I will select and discuss typical and succinct citations concerning particular conditions, bearing in mind that there are endless variations among any and all of these states.

Melancholia

In Chapter 2 I cited a portion of Lenore McCall's description of the onset of her profound passive depression, which lasted several years. Interestingly, she, like many melancholic patients, was certain that she had lost her mind and that her brain was rotting away. Actually, there does seem to have been a state of mental confusion and a slight loss of memory. In recalling her first several months of hospitalization, she characterized her state at that time as follows.

I slid down into the deepest depression and most of my waking hours were spent in weeping. As usual I made a pattern of all my movements to avoid confusion and one of the upholstered chairs, that one which had its back to the bay windows and faced the door, became my special post. There I sat hour after hour, dissolved in bitter tears and racked by sobs. I wept for my lost world, wept in fear and horror, wept because I could see nothing ahead for me but life in this hospital. (McCall, 1947, pp. 100–101)

She continued in her withdrawn despondent state for several years, taking little interest in her surroundings and, in general, avoiding friendships with other patients or with her nurses. She was so engrossed with her own troubled thoughts that she did not notice many things in her environment.

Benson, a lecturer and author of inspirational books, suffered for about a year from an acute depression. In an introductory chapter in his book, *Thy Rod and Thy Staff*, he described this period of his life as follows.

Neurasthenia, hypochondria, melancholia—hideous names for hideous things—it was these, or one of these. The symptoms, a persistent sleeplessness, a perpetual dejection, amounting at times to an intolerable mental anguish; the mind perfectly unclouded and absolutely hopeless. I tried rest-cures, medicines, treatment of all kinds, waters, hypnotism. There was a month of travel, during which the lights of life seemed to be going out one by one. I . . . toiled faithfully about to see beautiful things, till the whole became unutterably hideous to me, and I sickened for home; then came an attempt to return to work, and another collapse; and then came the worst experience of all, when I went for some careful treatment to a nursing home in the suburbs of London. . . .

I used to wake, morning by morning, in my pleasant room, and hear the drowsy twittering of birds in the great planetree, the upper boughs of which were on a level with my window, and wonder half-bewildered where I was; till the old horror rushed back into the mind, the dread of I knew not what, the anguish of life thus strangely interrupted, perhaps never to be resumed. . . . I think that the worst hour of my whole illness came to me there, on a sunny morning full of life and light, when I walked on the high Common with all its wide rolling views, . . . condemned to suffer a pain of which each minute seemed an eternity, in which dread, disgust, repugnance, and dreariness seemed all entwined in one sickening draught . . .

After six months of these miseries I went back to my work—it would have been perhaps better if I had never left it—and struggled on, just able to get through my daily engagements, but without the slightest interest in anything. . . . Many doctors . . . could really do little for me except reassure me that there was nothing organically wrong. The illness is not, I think, dangerous to life, except in so far as the perpetual desire for rest on any terms, even on terms of death itself, must inevitably make the sufferer dwell upon the thought of self-destruction; but my natural vitality, or my imagination, or perhaps my cowardice, saved me to a great extent from ever entertaining this purpose. (Benson, 1912, pp. 1–6)

In this excerpt Benson has set forth the leading complaints of many melancholic sufferers. There are few, if any, physical disabilities. Also, there is usually little in the environment to which the sufferer can point that would justify the utter hopelessness, the lethargy, the dreariness, and the thoughts of self-destruction from which he suffers. Benson's phrase, "The mind perfectly unclouded and absolutely hopeless," conveys the essential tone of the dilemma of the melancholic person.

H. C. Brown, the founder of The Museum of the City of New York, who underwent a period of agitated depression, spoke of the symptoms in his book, *A Mind Mislaid*. Notice that, unlike Benson, his negativism was directed outwards in a fashion which affected his interpersonal relationships.

I do not now recall that I was ever muddled in my thoughts, but I certainly suffered from a depressed state of mind that was so severe as to make me utterly indifferent to muddles or no muddles. In that state you seldom speak to anyone, and then only to snarl. A constant state of hostility would perhaps define the attitude . . .

I do not now recall any time when I did not think clearly. I am conscious of the fact that I did not care to talk to anyone and that it annoyed me to have anyone attempt to enter into conversation with me. I was perfectly aware at all times of everything that was going on around me and do not recall a single moment when I was confused or didn't know what I was doing. I do know that I was simply sick of living, that nothing interested me. (Brown, 1937, pp. 74; 77)

Just as the phobic patient is tenaciously obsessed with fear, so is the melancholic patient almost continuously obsessed with a meaningless despair. Life, for him, has lost all meaning and all goal. His mind is clear, but there seems to be no point in trying either to attend or to respond to things going on about him. Some melancholic patients will walk almost continuously throughout all of their waking hours; others will play cards or chess in an endless fashion, trying to keep their minds occupied with routine matters in order to dismiss the feeling of despair. Such patients are potentially suicidal. Having lost all personal hope and zest, it seems clear to them that to continue to live can be no more than a burden to themselves and a nuisance to relatives and friends.

Mania

Since a fair number of persons who suffer from periods of depression or melancholia also experience episodes of mania, there is often a tendency to consider mania as a mental condition opposite to that of melancholia. Unfortunately, as far as any theory of opposites is concerned, the descriptions of the course of mania cannot be diametrically contrasted to those of melancholia. The following account, written by one of Dr. E. C. Reid's cases about 1910, provides some idea of the subjective experience of mania; the patient was a hospital charge nurse, who wrote the following after her recovery.

I [began by having] an indescribable nervous feeling. . . . My nights were sleepless. . . . The blood seemed to be carried to my brain in such quantities that the skull was too small to contain the brain enclosed therein. The feeling of emptiness gave way to a sensation of fullness and pressure. It seemed as though the condition of cerebral anemia had given place to one of congestion. By beating my head against the floor and walls I believed that I loosened up the sutures and gave the brain a chance to expand. It certainly gave me relief. On two occasions a slight [nose bleed] seemed to relieve the pressure and clear my thinking processes. This confirmed my theory of cerebral congestion. . . . The muscles which heretofore [during the period of depression] had refused to respond to stimuli now refused to remain at rest. To keep physically quiet was an utter impossibility. The strain of trying to keep still was fast wearing me out. I would lie in bed and jump up and down on the springs; I would make numerous excuses to go for a drink and to the toilet, simply to be doing something. My thought processes which hitherto had been retarded, and their expression difficult, now began to flow with lightning rapidity. Thoughts crowded into my mind too rapidly for expression. Talking was the greatest relief imaginable. . . .

Words fail to describe the feeling of relief I experienced when I was at last placed in a strong room at my own request. To be alone, to be shut off from the observation of the anxious and the curious, to be free to act and talk in any way my distorted fancy dictated was relief unspeakable. . . . I was not told a hundred times a day that I *must* keep quiet. I talked, laughed, cried, sang, shouted and danced to my heart's content. The living up of all attempt at self-control brought the needed rest and sleep. The condition of my mind for many months is beyond all description. My thoughts ran with lightning-like rapidity from one subject to another. I had an exaggerated feeling of self-importance. All the problems of the universe came crowding into my mind, demanding instant discussion and solution—mental telepathy, hypnotism, wireless telegraphy, Christian science, women's rights, and all the problems of medical science, religion and politics. . . . Every article of clothing and bedding . . . I immediately tore into shreds . . . I felt like a person driving a wild horse with a weak rein, who dares not use force, but lets him run his course . . . Although my egotism was unbounded, yet I never for one moment was happy. . . .

The sensation of physical pain which I endured is beyond my powers of description. Every afternoon I was seized by the most violent paroxysm of pain which racked every nerve in my body. The alimentary system throughout felt as though it were one rotten mass . . . At times during the night the spinal cord would be drawn up so tightly that it seemed like a violin string about to snap. My head would be drawn back and I would rest on my head and heels. . . . The two things I could not endure were restraint and observation. (Reid, 1910, pp. 613–617)

In addition to all these distressing complaints, this patient told of many sensory and motor illusions, delusions, and a few hallucinations. She could not control her thoughts or her behavior. During these periods of elation she never felt fatigue. At times, she was overwhelmed by senseless fear or pointless anger. At other times she seemed convinced that she had come under the control of some outside power. During the months before this manic episode she had endured a profound period of depression that had been marked by difficulty in thinking, lethargy, hopeless despair, and mental suffering. In contrast to the depression, her manic experience was marked by a leading characteristic, the press-of-activity, as it is in most patients. There was also an inability to do any concentrated thinking, plus a wide variety of aches and pains.

The two major peculiarities of mania are the experience of rather brief periods of *elation* and prolonged periods of *press-of-activity*. Another name for the press-of-activity is the flight-of-ideas. Most other aspects of manic experience are changeable and changing; aggressive to timid, confident to despairing, courageous to fearful, happy to unhappy, never-felt-better to full of pain and suffering. The mania starts during the course of a day or so, runs its course over a period of days to several months, and then slowly tapers off through a period that is designated as one of hypomania.

Patients who have lived through periods of both mania and melancholia uniformly say that melancholia is by far the more painful and mentally exhausting. Hopeless, dejected despair, which itself does not threaten one's life, is still much more abhorrent than the rush and pressure of the flight-of-ideas, even though the manic may, at times, have the feeling of losing complete touch with his ordinary personality and with reality.

Paranoia

There are persons who insist that many events which have happened or are happening in the world are directed toward themselves, or have direct personal reference to themselves—usually in some harmful way—which interpretation is rejected by their associates as being delusional. These individuals are said to be suffering from paranoia or paranoid ideas. The paranoid patient rarely regards himself as insane. He maintains that his mind is as clear and logical as anyone else's and likewise insists that there is nothing wrong with his perceptual or volitional mental processes. Formerly, some of these individuals were said to be suffering from monomania, that is, their disturbance was thought to be related to only a limited number of specific topics. In this field of limited aberration, the observations of others and the conviction of the patient as to the correctness of his knowledge and his interpretation of objective circumstances come into sharp disagreement. No amount of demonstration, argument, or negative evidence shakes the paranoid (or monomaniac) person's convictions that support his delusional system of thought.

The course of a systematic paranoid delusion was well described in Courtney's publication, *The Autobiography of J.G.R.*

I call attention to a great crime, which has hardly its equal in history. . . . Fate, however, is fickle and deceitful. A conspiracy was inaugurated against me, unparalleled by anything heard of before. It was conducted by cunning and unscrupulous emissaries or agents who considered me a means by which they could extort money from wealthy people.

So cunning is their work that no one can ever find them out. . . . The question must naturally arise: How in all the world is it possible that such a conspiracy, which is a real mockery of all human and divine laws, could exist . . . for fully ten years, and in a civilized commonwealth at that? . . .

It is a custom in this country to use . . . the services of private detectives who are heartless and unscrupulous, who will ruin a man if they can only profit by it. . . . They organized themselves into a permanent, regular corps of observation, watching all my steps and doings by day and night, and succeeded in running and keeping me down. . . .

I was often kept in a state of stupor, which deprived me of power of acting and thinking. Often had I been wondering why I did not do what I ought to have done or the reverse, and what it was that could cause such a condition. They must have given me internally some chemical mixtures, and I have reason to believe that also hypnotism or something similar was brought into use against me. I remember distinctly, for instance, that one evening when, on a visit in the Catskill Mountains during the summer, I tried to get up in order to join a party, I was powerless to do it. I have often been trying to greet some person or speak to him, but as if my arms and tongue were paralyzed, I was not able to take off my hat or to utter a single word. I soon observed that I was closely watched by agents. I was given to understand from different sides that the proprietor of the hotel would have liked me to marry his daughter. . . . I declined the offer.

[Later] on some business, I once met some gentlemen in an office on Broadway, but suddenly one of these crafty emissaries or agents caused chemical odors to penetrate into the room. Owing to this mean trick I began to stammer like a drunken man, and was unable to utter a distinct word or grasp a single thought. Thus, this time again my plan for building up a future for myself was shamelessly destroyed by the combined effects of these agents. Now, wherever I go, these diabolical agents are following me. They not only injure me in business, but are molesting every one who may come in contact with me. They place chemical odors in every room where I may be. The effects of these odors upon my system are as numerous as they are painful. Now and then I lose, almost, my consciousness, and with the utmost efforts can keep my eyes open. Often, again, I experience a feeling as if my whole body was pierced with needles. At night, especially, these merciless agents pour such chemical odors or gases into my room that I have a choking sensation, and I am unable to breathe. Pain seems to squeeze my eyes out of the sockets, and visions arise before me. (Courtney, 1901, pp. 141–145)

J.G.R. went on to tell how he was forced to leave one job after another, to move to new communities, to appeal to the police for aid, and even to publish a circular describing the conspiracy, all to no avail. Finally, he wrote a letter to the District Attorney stating that he would shoot some prominent person unless he was given police protection. Again, he obtained no response, so he did shoot a clergyman on Fifth Avenue, wounding but not killing him. He was then arrested and the case was brought to trial. "But alas, I was simply declared insane." As far as his statement goes, it indicates that no satisfactory evidence was ever given by the patient which in any way convinced the police or anyone else that a conspiracy existed, or that anyone was attempting to damage him in any way. But this delusion so obsessed him that it came to govern his whole life and led him to attempt a murderous attack on an innocent man.

Acute Schizophrenic Episodes

Kraepelin first defined the group of mental disorders called dementia praecox, that is, a process which starts early in life (in the twenties) and in at least two thirds of the cases, leads to dementia. Some years later, Bleuler made a more detailed study of patients in this condition, and proposed the more knowledgeable name *schizophrenia*, which means a shattering or fragmentation of the individual's mental life. There is no single leading complaint that marks the onset or course of the derangement. There are, if one is to judge from the reports of schizophrenic patients, several rather common patterns of experience, but each patient's experiences change in character during the course of the disorder, so that one cannot confidently predict or ascertain what his complaints and behavior will be from one day to the next.

A common variety of schizophrenia revolves about a peculiar disorder of a religious nature that usually bears little or no relation to the religious beliefs held by the individual before the onset of the episode. A. T. Boisen had experienced several schizophrenic periods during his college days. Later, while serving as a Presbyterian minister, he had an acute psychotic episode from which he recovered. After his recovery he continued his education and finally became chaplain of a large mental hospital. Because of his interest in the subject, his own subjective experience, and his training, he investigated many varieties of schizophrenic phenomena. For example, he queried many patients about the course of their religious experiences during schizophrenia. From the information thus obtained, he later formulated the following generalized account of the usual course of such religious experiences.

In the initial stages, schizophrenic thinking follows a fairly definite pattern. After a period of preoccupation and sleeplessness, ideas begin to come as though from an outside source. This dynamism is a normal one. It is known as the "inspiration," or the "automatism," and may be defined as the idea or thought process which after a period of incubation darts suddenly into consciousness. In the case of the schizophrenic, because of the depth of the emotional stirring and the intensity of the concentration, such ideas come surging in with peculiar vividness. They seem to him entirely different from anything he had ever thought or dreamed before. He assumes therefore that they come from a superhuman source. He thinks God is talking to him, or perhaps the devil is on his trail. In any case he feels himself in the realm of the mysterious and uncanny. All the accepted bases of judgment and reasoning are gone. He does not know what to believe. His state is one of utter perplexity regarding the very foundations of his being. "Who am I?," "What is my role in life?," "What is this universe in which I live?," become for him questions of life and death. Very commonly his eyes are opened to the fact that he is more important than he had ever dreamed. It "comes to him," or "something tells him" that a great responsibility has been resting upon him, and that his failure has brought untold misery to those whom he loves. Perhaps the entire world has been hanging in the balance, its fate dependent upon him. He has failed and it [the world] is about to be destroyed, but there may yet be a chance to save it. To do so he must sacrifice his own life. The readiness to make that sacrifice is commonly followed by a sense of being identified with God or with Christ. It may come to him that he is about to be re-born, or that he has lived before in previous incarnation. Such ideas are common in the acute phases of schizophrenia.

In other cases the patient sees no way out. The situation is utterly hopeless. He himself is to die, or perhaps he is dead, with nothing to hope for but rebirth. In such cases the picture is one of deep depression or stupor.

In other cases ideas of mysterious hostile forces are dominant. Ideas that evil forces are at work and that great danger is impending are common in all types, but when the attitude is one of bitterness, when there is a tendency to transfer blame and to nurse grievances and suspicions the outlook for recovery is not good. (Boisen, 1942, pp. 24–25)

This statement of Boisen's differs from most of the excerpts I have cited thus far, in that it constitutes a generalization drawn from many interviews with patients, and, although Boisen had himself lived through such an episode, he has evaluated and reported the experiences of other individuals in addition to his own. His generalization is related not to the course of all varieties of this disorder, but only to those in which a religious theme has dominated the experience. There are few accounts available where such religious experiences are related in such a logical or systematic fashion. It is more common for a patient to produce an illogical and confused statement with respect to his religious mental processes during the course of such an episode. More often, the content of such reports resembles the following written by Beringer's patient Hahnenfuss.

It seems as if all people were *one* picture and only an *illusion* which is perceived in the scattered *multitude*. Hasn't that which I am presently experiencing been present for countless times and doesn't it strive to again take part in a remembrance? Isn't that which one calls *history* a process of constantly re-turning—I don't want to say the same but similar things? There is no reality, but only the *spirit*. For what is material no one knows, but what spirit is no one doubts who has experienced it. The whole connection which holds this breathing spiritual world together is the bond of harmony. You have but to join a community, in a personal, free union, and you are a member. But the hitch, which develops wherever success seems to be certain, and which continues the *chain* of *deceit*, is the *sin* of malice. (Beringer and Mayer-Gross, 1925, p. 212)

Just exactly what ideas this patient was trying to express is far from clear. That his ideas are associated with thoughts of the spirit, disturbances of perception, and notions of sin seems plausible. It is also probable that such meditations form part of that experience termed by Boisen, "He does not know what to believe. His state is one of utter perplexity." The pathological concern with religious topics; the period of thoughtfulness; the period of revelation and religious convictions; the feelings of uncertainty regarding the meaning of existence; the vague accusations and guilt feelings; the notion of having committed some unknown but unpardonable sin; the grievances and suspicions—all these mark the course of many schizophrenic episodes.

Some patients emphasize in their account of their feelings that the world and its creatures have become unreal; this sense of unreality is often connected with a feeling typified by "I am no longer myself"—that is, a sense of depersonalization. Frequently included in the patient's complaint is that of having somehow come under an overwhelming outside influence which may be either good, evil, or impersonal. This external power, whatever its nature, usually can control the sufferer's actions, thoughts or utterances, and does so in the most unpredictable and inconvenient ways. Most disturbing to many of these patients are auditory hallucinations. Generally speaking, schizophrenic patients fall under two groups, a large group made up of those who hear voices and a much smaller one composed of those who never hear them but who usually complain of stolen thoughts and long memory gaps. Auditory hallucination is considered by many to practically establish a diagnosis of schizophrenia.

The following portion of a description of the course of a psychotic episode was related by Renee, the schizophrenic girl whose *Autobiography* was previously quoted. In the following she speaks of the feeling of fear.

It was New Year's when I first experienced what I called *Fear*. It literally fell on me, how I know not. . . . Suddenly Fear, agonizing, boundless Fear, overcame me, not the usual uneasiness of unreality, but real fear, such as one knows at the approach of danger, of calamity. . . . I remained unaware of the basis for the fear which from then on came over me at any moment of the day. (Sechehaye, 1951, pp. 13–14)

Often this profound *fear* is unattached to any external object, as in the example of Renee, but in others the fear may be actually attached to some impending event, object, or person. Whether attached or unattached, the feeling itself is probably one and the same, in essence a fear of death, although not specifically recognized as such.

Another account of the agony of fear and suffering experienced during the course of a psychotic episode was related by a convalescent patient, a young lady, in a letter to her parents published in 1847.

Since my stay here, I have suffered more than tongue can tell or pen can write. I thought when they were bringing me here, it was taking me to judgment, there to meet my final sentence of "depart from me ye cursed to everlasting flames." When I ascended to the chapel on the sabbath day, I thought it was the judgment hall of Christ, and that it was a temporary platform built over the infernal abyss, where the evil spirits were congregated together.

For six long months I remained deprived entirely of reason, and nearly deaf and blind at times, and subject to the greatest agony of body and mind, and a burning inflammation on my brain; sleeping on beds of fire at night, and eating food and taking medicine three times a day, which seemed to add to my torments. But I will not distress you longer. . . . Suffice it to say, that my reason has returned, and with it my health. (Anon., 1846–1847, pp. 342–343)

The puzzling phenomena of feelings of unreality and depersonalization will be dealt with at greater length in Chapter 17. A description of this common psychotic experience, as related by a patient of Minkowski's, may be given here, to illustrate the way in which these phenomena occur during the course of an acute phase of schizophrenia.

Everything that surrounds me is immobile. . . . and that immobility is in myself. Things present themselves singly, each one by itself, without evoking anything else. Certain things that should form a recollection, evoke a great number of thoughts, produce an isolated picture. They are understood rather than felt. It is the same as a pantomime. Pantomimes that play around me but I do not enter in them, I remain outside. I have my judgment, but I lack the instinct of life. . . . I have lost contact with all kinds of things. The idea of the value of difficult things has disappeared. . . . An absolute fixity surrounds me. I have still less mobility for the future than for the present and the past. . . . I see the future as a repetition of the past. (Minkowski, 1926, pp. 561–562)

This account was given by an agonized, fearful patient who spent most of her time in bed, inert, and when she did move about she was said to have offered the sad appearance of a mechanical doll.

An example of the feeling of an outside "Strength" which controlled one of Devine's patient's thoughts and actions with torturing, fearful, unreal voices, was recounted in the following terms.

He has gathered from my brain everything I have ever done or remembered. . . . He is entirely engrossed in my thoughts—a listener informing himself of what I think. He reprimands me for all I have thought or done in a kind of parental authority. It is the role of the *elderly-father-bishop* rolling about in my brain. It is as if my childhood were a book. They tear out the pages, as it were, and accuse me of them all. He gets all these things from me; he weighs me down with my own knowledge. Their talk is a kind of tyranny. Their attitude is one of vicious mastery—they say they are greater than God. They like to punish; they will punish for anything I did in my youth. It is simple wilfulness; a whimsical capriciousness, not proper punishment, but just a delight in punishing. He says it is just his will to punish. He keeps me terror bound as if life would terminate in about an hour. He strikes me quite capriciously. He is the sort of person who loves to strike without reason. He is vindictive and revengeful, a mixture of villainy and cunning. He annoys me for the joy of it; it is semi-brutal attitude, misused strength. They control me viciously. He has a cantankerous will against me; he is a *continuer* of corrections; a *getter* into vicious states; a *brain trailer* to see how long I can stand him; a pernicious authority correcting me as if I were a child of three; a delighter in dislocating things; a seller of me; a blackmailer; a lover of punishment. He is not a creator but a destroyer—a lover of slighting sex moralities. It is a domination and brutality. (Devine, 1921, pp. 226–227)

The torturing voices and ideas he describes kept this patient in mute terror and fear of his life. The "Strengths" used all his thoughts and memories as a basis for guilt-producing accusations, which they told him would bring certain punishment as a later consequence. Not only were the accusations most unpleasant, but the continuous threats aroused in him the fear and apprehension of brutality still to be inflicted. Accusing voices of this sort are commonplace during the course of many schizophrenic episodes.

Lack of insight during the course of any mental disorder refers to the incorrect evaluations the individual attaches to himself and his place in the world. For example, in his famous autobiography, *Memoirs of My Nervous Illness,* Judge Schreber wrote as follows.

I wish to add another point in connection with God's inability to understand the living human being as an organism and to judge his thinking correctly, which has in many ways become important to me. I can put this point briefly: *everything that happens is in reference to me.* Writing this sentence, I am fully aware that other people may be tempted to think that I am pathologically conceited; I know very well that this tendency to relate everything to oneself, to bring everything that happens into connection with one's own person, is a common phenomenon among mental patients. But in my case the very reverse obtains. Since God entered into nerve-contact with me exclusively, I became in a way for God the only human being, or simply the human being around whom everything turns, to whom everything that happens must be related and who therefore, from his own point of view, must also relate all things to himself. (Schreber, 1955, p. 197)

The quality of defective insight is not easy to define or delimit, but this excerpt from Schreber's *Memoirs* should give the reader an idea of what is meant by lack of insight. A statement such as Schreber's could be made and published only by either an acutely psychotic patient or a very egotistical fanatic.

The course followed by schizophrenic psychoses is usually very complex. Not all patients exhibit all the characteristic symptoms with equal intensity. Many individuals who have lived through such an affliction have finally recovered; afterwards they have maintained that their mental state during the episode was quite different and distinct from any other condition they had ever experienced. There does seem to be one (or more) peculiar and unique feeling state that does underlie most of the basic disturbance during an acute schizophrenic episode. This is usually characterized as a *senseless unreal fear, mixed with religious ideas and feelings of hostility* toward the world about them. There can be no doubt that schizophrenic patients suffer in an overwhelming and practically continuous fashion during all their waking hours.

At the present time, it is estimated that about 60 per cent of schizophrenic patients regain some degree of lucidity for some period of their life history, after the disease has once reached a chronic phase. The suffering does seem to become less agonizing as time goes by, so that the chronic patient comes to be characterized as a "burned out dement" for the remainder of his life. His thoughts are confused, his expressiveness limited, and little is known of his mental life, since he loses, to a large extent, his ability to communicate with others.

Dementia

Dementia—loss of mind—is usually a terminal state reached after one or more periods of acute mental disturbance. From this condition, there is little or no expectation that the patient will ever recover any part of the clarity of mind which marked his status before its onset. The varieties of dementia are largely defined by the nature and course of the disorder that existed prior to the development of the loss of mind.

Only very few documents were found that give any idea of the inner life of the chronic, demented mental patient. From them I have selected part of a letter written by a chronic schizophrenic patient to Dr. K. Menninger.

Dear Dr. M—, *Re* pts. in seclusion rooms after thirty years or so of incurable schizophrenia who like to smash beds, etc.: We people have a constant terrific craving for eye-hand, eye-foot, eye-ear and foot-ear coordination. Our whole desire is in *touch.* This sense is more than touch sensitivity of the blind. . . . Only speech centers and those associated with it still intact . . .

Long ago they took materials away in occupational therapy because I ruined them. Well, I am like the picture of your patient in a recent magazine sitting on floor, head bowed.

Recommendations: Paste large squares of flowered wallpaper with scotch tape on walls of seclusion rooms and give pencils to trace around flowers with. Let them toss oranges also for eye-hand coordination even if costly and messy inside seclusion rooms. Singing and screaming releases the fierce energy in us. Please don't put us in packs. The need for constant movement is accentuated in the demented. . . .

We no longer take in anything on television or radio. All of our energy has gone from the brain into the body which must move, move, move. . . . We hardly know that we are alive at all after *years* of shock treatment and all the rest. Pray for our death. (Menninger, 1954, pp. 17–18)

This patient's psychosensory activities were reduced mainly to touch, movement, and speech (not necessarily organized speech). For her, vision and audition had seemingly become inadequate methods of keeping in contact with the world.

In many persons of advanced age there is an irreversible loss of mental capabilities to such a degree that they become incoherent and incomprehensible in their speech. What, if anything, remains of their mental life beyond scraps and fragments is impossible to learn directly from them.

DISCUSSION

Individual patients have used many different analogies in describing the course of mental illness. Several patients have said that the memory of the experience might be compared to one's recollection of a railway trip. The analogy suggests that before the episode began one's everyday experiences might be said to have been similar to the witnessing of the constantly changing scenery from the car window. All the sights and sounds seemed familiar and normal. The entire experience seemed real even though the sights and sounds were new. One's feelings seemed quite properly associated with the passing scene and the accompanying circumstances. And depending on circumstances one may have felt the experience to be pleasant or unpleasant; one may have been angry or fearful, the anger or fear somehow seeming appropriate to the occasion.

Then, to continue the analogy, more or less suddenly one was surrounded by an unsteady darkness plus a great deal of unfamiliar noise because the train had entered a tunnel. The feelings changed sharply; strange unreality displaced familiar reality. Since little that seemed real could be seen, there were but few incidents that could be fixed in mind beyond those associated with the passing of time. Later, the train came out of the tunnel. The real visual world returned; the volume of surrounding noise was vastly diminished. The scenery again seemed real and easy to fix in mind. During the progress of such a journey, one may have gone through several tunnels, each of which gave rise to these quite definite subjective alterations in both sensory and emotional experience.

One who has never lived through a period of mental derangement seldom has the need or desire to ponder on what normality and sanity are like—since he has never passed through any but this realm. If such a normal man ever comes to think about the problems of psychopathology, his ideas are apt to be somewhat fantastic. Since he believes that the world about him is real, he is also quite certain that he can, within reasonable limits, guide and control his own, likewise real, thoughts and feelings. He believes that existence sets its normal goals and purposes, he himself having almost always consciously and voluntarily been able to direct his behavior and thoughts in line with these purposes. The only way in which he can escape everyday reality and purpose is by imagination or by dwelling on ideas that are obviously fantastic. All this seems apparent; this is the way he has found life, and it seems to him that most human beings have, or should have, approximately the same basic experiences that he has had.

If the ordinary normal man ever considers what the experience of insanity is likely to be, he is more apt to refer to the processes of imagination or to the acquisition of peculiar ideas, which he believes are characteristic of the disease. He is, of course, only regarding certain aspects of someone's peculiar speech or behavior and hence is merely referring to the person's "weaknes of mind," his unrestrained emotions and lack of self-control.

But the fact is that insanity generally occurs in persons who have hitherto been at least relatively sane. All the phenomena I have cited as constituting the subjective worlds of mental derangement have been related by hitherto apparently sane persons, persons who are bewildered and confused by "something" that has happened to them that is beyond their control. To the patient the experience is often, as Perceval said (in the chapter heading), one of the worst aspects of his disturbed state; he acts strangely as a result of what he suffers and does not understand. In addition, the experience of the patient carries with it a personal meaning and significance that is very different from those gained by the observers.

For example, Schreber suffered for years from the "bellowing-miracle," which he described and mentioned repeatedly in his *Memoirs*.

In my own person the advent of the bellowing-miracle when my muscles serving the processes of respiration are set in motion by the lower God . . . in such a way that I am forced to emit bellowing noises, unless I try very hard to suppress them; sometimes this bellowing recurs so frequently and so quickly that it becomes almost unbearable and at night makes it impossible to remain in bed; . . .

All these phenomena happen hundreds of times every day; I must have observed them in the course of years tens of thousands if not hundreds of thousands of times with exactly the same regularity. I have repeatedly pointed to the reason. Every time my thinking activity ceases God instantly regards my mental powers as extinct, the desired destruction of my reason (the "dementia") achieved and the possibility of a withdrawal thus brought about. (Schreber, 1955, pp. 165–166)

Before his illness, Schreber had been the Presiding Judge of the Supreme court of the German state of Saxony; a man of dignity, intelligence, and responsibility. He was adjudged insane and held in a mental hospital for more than seven years. Toward the end of this period the acute symptoms subsided and he wrote his own petition to the court asking to be discharged from hospital custody, and this petition was acted on favorably. The superintendent of the asylum wrote for the court a statement of Schreber's conditions as he knew it. Concerning the bellowing he said as follows.

Outwardly most disturbing have been for a long time what the patient himself calls attacks of bellowing, that is to say the uttering of partly inarticulate sounds, partly threats and imprecations against imaginary disturbers of his well-being. . . . These noisy outbursts occur completely automatically and in a compulsive manner against the patient's will. Though he is able to repress them, if not always at any rate for a time through lively speech, making music fortissimo, and some other tricks, they sound not only throughout the greater part of the day from his living room and in the garden, causing considerable annoyance to his environment, but even at night they can often be heard for hours, causing intolerable disturbance of peace and quiet in the whole department; he sometimes even shouts down into the town without regard. Recently especially these vociferations have become very noisy, and how the patient himself suffers thereby, how helpless and powerless he feels against these "miracles" and is forced to the most nonsensical counter-actions. (Schreber, 1955, p. 281)

The point I wish to make with these two citations is that Schreber's behavior (bellowing) had vastly different significances for the sufferer and for an outsider. For Schreber, the bellowing, though disturbing both to himself and others, was a divine miracle brought forth by God himself and hence not to be questioned. For the outsider, the bellowing was a disturbance of the peace, a behavior that society need not tolerate.

As has been repeatedly pointed out, psychotic experiences are almost always so new and unique that the individual concerned may not have at hand the proper words or phrases with which to communicate to others the precise nature and quality of his inner life. Everything occurring in his psychological world seems new, disconnected, frightening, and somehow unreal. Since the sufferer finds himself plunged into a confused whirlwind of inescapable experience, he can do no other than be frightened and emotionally overwhelmed. There is little chance for him to note carefully the meaningful connections between events. That some patients have been able to reconstruct their experiences during an acute psychotic episode is in itself a rather remarkable feat.

Little is known about the accuracy and completeness of the process of registration of conscious experience in everyday life. It is known that there are very great individual differences in the accuracy and number of evoked memory traces. Those remembrances that seem most detailed and unified we tend to accept. Very frequently, disconnected, illogical, incoherent reports we either distrust or simply disregard as unintelligible. In the realm of psychopathology, we are compelled to give credence to those accounts that seem, at least in part, to have elements or organizational patterns in common with those related by other patients. The more frequently we hear or read descriptions that have a fair number of commonly found elements, the more we come to accept such a pattern and the likelihood of its truth. However, mere similarity in the reports of the memoirs of deranged episodes is at best not a very good criterion; but being the main standard which we have set ourselves, we can do no other than abide by it.

In summarizing this chapter, I call attention to the fact that I have provided descriptions largely in the form of excerpts from accounts written by persons who have lived through a somewhat extended period of psychopathology. I have given examples picked from the more common patterns of symptoms and complaints. I have not tried to carry any analysis or explanation of the experiental material beyond that which seemed fairly self-evident. Lastly, I have considered the difficulties that attend the mnemonic reconstruction of the period of abnormality, from the standpoint both of the sufferer and of the observer. I trust that my form of presentation will make these autobiographical descriptions, as well as those in following chapters, somewhat more comprehensible to the reader and that they will assist him in evaluating the phenomena I have abstracted from the entire series of accounts. It must be borne in mind that any single facet we consider, such as hallucinations or phobias, actually is part of a matrix of the total life experiences that occur at the same time and in that one individual.

*It is a matter of great difficulty if not impossible, to declare
that a lunatic is radically cured and not liable to relapse;
or to decide whether the state of lucidity which he appears
to enjoy, is not a lucid interval which may very probably be
followed by a fresh attack.*

(Millingen, 1840, p. 146)

CHAPTER **4**

Lucid Interval;
Relapse; Recovery

INTRODUCTION

Having sketched the beginning and the course of an
episode of mental abnormality, we may pass on to consideration of the ways in which such incidents end.
The termination of a psychopathological episode need
not correspond subjectively to the evaluation made by
outside observers. As we have seen, the realization of
one's derangement depends in large part on self-recognition of one's loss of voluntary control while in a world
of disorganized perceptions and unusual feelings.
From the patient's personal standpoint, the course of
derangement is marked by the experience of an overwhelming emotional turmoil, associated with difficulties in thinking and with confused perceptual
processes, all of which have passed beyond ordinary
self-control. Consequently, the patient often says that
he became an irresponsible puppet. The confused
mental state is frequently mixed with long periods
of which no memories can ever be recalled and
which, for convenience, we may call in this context
periods of unconsciousnes.

The chain of events that are associated with the

termination of a derangement may be roughly grouped as lucid intervals, relapses, and recovery. These terms refer to rather generalized descriptive processes, with a great deal of overlap both in verbal usage and in the phenomena involved.

Lucid Interval

The circumstance known as a *lucid interval* has often been reported by mental patients as having occurred at one or more periods during their illness. The patient who has been existing in his own confused and disorganized inner world, more or less unaware of his surroundings, comes suddenly or gradually into full contact with his environment, thus experiencing a period that is called a lucid interval. He now recognizes himself and his surroundings and feels that he has regained his sanity. Usually, the lucid interval breaks the course of the illness rather abruptly and may last from a few moments to several days. The relapse into confusion and disorganization following a lucid interval may be either sudden or slow. These periods of subjective normality may or may not be externalized to the extent of being recognized by others. Actually, lucid intervals do not necessarily constitute a perfect restoration of sanity, but each is a break in the "nightmare" to such an extent that the patient is able to comprehend and to act with such perception, awareness, and judgment as to make his behavior seem rational, at least to himself.

An example of a brief flash of lucidity is described by John Perceval in one chapter of his autobiographical *Narratives* as follows.

> Having no books, no occupation, nothing to do but to look out the window, or read the newspaper, I was again excited by my spirits to waltz round the room; in doing this . . . I caught the reflection of my countenance in the mirror, I was shocked and stood still; my countenance looked round and unmeaning: I cried to myself, "Ichabod!* my glory has departed from me," then I said to myself, what a hypocrite I look like! So far I was in a right state of mind; but the next thought was, "how shall I set about to destroy my hypocrisy"; then I became again lunatic. Then I resumed my waltzing. (Perceval, 1838, p. 90)

During the acute period of his illness, which lasted about a year, Perceval was, as he realized both then and later, quite insane, convinced that he was completely under the control of spirits and devils. These outer forces not only directed his behavior and thoughts but also stole his thoughts, altering the course of his actions and speech, substituting acts and remarks which, he realized (at times), were quite inappropriate. The short-lived moment of lucidity seemed to him as though the outside

---

* *Ichabod* = Where is thy glory (*Hebrew*).

control had somehow ended for a few seconds, so that for a brief flash he was again a reasonable being.

Another illustration of this phenomenon, in this instance interrupting a period of acute agitated madness, was given by a woman journalist in her pseudonymous autobiography, *The Maniac*. The lucid interval was described as follows.

The doctor, two nurses, Mrs. W., and my eldest brother—all these attended me during those days. Not one of them did I ever see or become conscious of. Then one night I opened my eyes. . . . I was fully conscious, and I believed then—and think the same now—I was sane (for the time being). I cannot describe how ill I felt. I had a horrible sensation of sinking fast. I remembered all that had happened, and I thought—"I have been in frenzies of madness. Now I am dying." . . . I did not speak to the nurse . . . I died and passed utterly away. . . .

A second time, late one evening, I awoke—*sane*. Again I was experiencing that horrible sensation of sinking fast—of dying. . . . I thought—"I am sane now; and I really cannot die like this" . . . I said to the nurse—"Nurse! Please bring me my writing-case, and all my letters and papers—I want to burn them." She answered, "I can't bring them now." . . . I said nothing more. I lay there . . . and finally went out. (Anon., 1932a, pp. 106–107; 115–117)

This woman's lucid experiences, like those of Perceval, were related as being transient periods of sanity that interrupted, so to speak, the course of the insanity. Only the patient was aware of these flashes, which lasted a few seconds and during which the confusion seemed to vanish. Had even a keen observer been present, it is doubtful that he would have noted anything indicative of the patient's period of lucidity.

A comparable episode was reported by an anonymous patient as an experience similar to that of awakening from sleep in a strange room, and, like any ordinary sleeper, he was first occupied by the problem of orienting himself.

I was admitted . . . in the summer of 1918 on an emergency order. I have no memory at all of arrival. I stayed there nine weeks. My first clear memory is of awakening suddenly one night in pitch darkness and hearing a woman's voice calling in agony. I answered, "stay where you are and I'll come and help." I jumped out of bed and tried in vain to find a light. I then felt all around the room, and to my horror discovered that it was very small, and I could find no door, door handle, window or aperture of any kind . . . I felt like a trapped animal and was overcome by fear, and entirely forgot the woman in distress to whose assistance I had tried to go. A long period followed in which I got to know this room well. . . . During this time I must have steadily refused to face the awful reality of which this room was the outward and visible sign. (Anon., 1931, p. 347)

In this instance, the lucid interval was a sharp awakening from sleep as well as from a state of insanity, which was followed by a lapse.

Sometimes recognition of the world in such an instance seems to depend on some factor of "unconscious memory." For example, Jane Hillyer was able to orient herself without any conscious recollection of many of the details of the previous circumstances of her acute disturbance.

So far as recollection goes, I never got back to my room . . . I "came to" . . . in a new place. Again I did not recall how I happened to be there, but by some process, a sort of unconscious registering of incident, I knew positively the moment I sensed anything, that I was where I had never been before, and also that I was up very high. This was true. I had been moved to a "worse" ward on the top floor of the building . . . In another bed was another heap of blanket, with a touseled head barely visible in the dark. "Who are you any-way?" I asked . . . "What are you doing in my room?" . . . The heap moved, mumbled something and looked up. . . . "Oh, I know," I said [recognizing her]. . . . The room moved a little as if it were gradually slipping into that all-enveloping nothingness. (Hillyer, 1926, pp. 73–74)

This description, like some of those above, indicates that the patient was fairly well oriented at the very onset of the lucid interval. With other patients it apparently takes a little while before they are able to orient themselves.

The ending of a period of acute excitement and confusion was described by Hackett in the following terms.

Then it stopped. The wild racing red hand carrying the tumbling thoughts stopped one night in the night. When I awoke I knew I was in a hospital. I listened to the sounds in the room, some snoring, some laughing, a muffled voice in the far corner. I looked out the window across the courtyard to the other buildings and watched the green quilt formed by the lighted windows in the dark. I tried to remember what had happened. . . .

I wanted to write a note to Marie and let her know I was all right. I decided to wait until morning. . . . When I awoke, I looked at the others as though I was seeing them for the first time. . . . At breakfast, I looked around the hall. . . . That fellow's name was Jack Hayden. . . . He slept next to me. (Hackett, 1952, pp. 57–58)

This description of lucidity and gradual orientation probably illustrates the more common type of return to conscious self-realization and control. Since it is like a gradual awakening from sleep, the patient is not too impressed, and hence specific instances of this variety are not often mentioned in retrospective accounts.

The descriptions of lucid intervals cited thus far have referred to short periods of time. The distinction between a lucid interval and a period of temporary recovery, which may continue for hours or weeks, is quite arbitrary. Turnbull published the following account as an example of a lucid interval that lasted approximately forty hours. The patient in question was a World War I veteran who had been hospitalized since March 1917. His case record indicated that between 1918 and

1921 he had been almost continuously in a mute, negativistic attitude and a rigid posture. Shortly after midnight on January 11, 1921, he suddenly awakened in the hospital dormitory and for the first time spoke to the night attendant, saying that he was dizzy and asked to be allowed to go to the lavatory. He then asked to see a medical officer. When interviewed by the physician the next morning, he gave the following account of his awakening.

I dreamt I was in a billet in Acle in bed, in a double bed, with Sergt. A. A batman named A.C. used to sleep in the other bed on the other side of the room, and I saw in my dream that his bed was vacant. I called out, "Where's A?" This seemed to wake me. A young man in a blue suit came and asked me what was the matter, and I asked him where I was. [When examined he seemed to be mentally normal, except that he had no memory of his long hospitalization. During the morning he wrote the following letter to a relative.]

I am writing this note after, it appears, three years' oblivion. I can recollect things from the beginning of the war as far as March, 1917—the remainder is a blank. I awoke last night and discovered I was a patient in the above institution . . . The attendants tell me I have not spoken a word since being here until last night, when I came to myself. I am thankful to be able to say that I am now quite *compos mentis.* . . . Just a rough outline of my doings since we left England on July 25, 1915:

We embarked on the transport "S————" at Devonport on July 23, 1915, and sailed on the night of the 25th . . . [He recounted the details of his adventures in the Near East where he took part in the Gallipoli expedition and the subsequent Near East warfare and how he succumbed to illness, was invalided back to England, and hospitalized there in December 1916, finally being sent to a reserve batallion at Wendover.

I was taken queer while there, partly, I've no doubt, due to the extreme change of climate . . . I entered a motor ambulance in the middle of March, 1917, and to the best of my knowledge had a smash up. From that time until January, 1921, is absolutely a blank. This is my history from July 15, 1915, and I hope that you will endeavour to obtain my release from this institution as soon as possible. (Turnbull, 1921, pp. 154–156)

During the following twenty-four hours the patient remained in an apparently normal condition. On the second day, however, it was noticed that he was becoming taciturn and dreamy, a condition which grew more pronounced until by evening, he had relapsed into the same mute, constrained catatonic stupor which had marked his behavior during the previous years.

Many former catatonic patients have fairly accurate memories of the events which occurred around them during their period of apparent stupor. Turnbull's patient was exceptional, in that the period of lucidity started with a return to consciousness and sanity which seemed complete in every way, except for a total absence of recall for the preceding period of forty-six months.

Lucid intervals are puzzling in terms of almost any theory or system that may be advanced to clarify the phenomena of psychopathology. From the recorded accounts of the course of psychoses, the general impression is gained that during mental disease all cognitive processes are disorganized and confused, being mixed with unusual and unreal feeling states and all of this coupled with a lack of voluntary self-control. Then the confusion vanishes, clarity appears rapidly or abruptly. The sufferer has no doubt that he is again sane (*compos mentis*) and in a state of self-control. Very few forms of physical disease ever remit so abruptly.

In one sense, a lucid interval is the reverse of a memory lapse. The lucid interval appears as part of the main stream of normal consciousness, bounded temporarily by periods of confusion or blankness. In contrast, a memory lapse is a blank or highly confused period, bounded on either end by the normal stream of consciousness.

Relapse

Relapse means the return into a state of mental derangement after a period of more or less normal sanity. Neither the cessation nor return of the aberrant mental symptoms need be complete. The recurrence of the psychopathological symptoms may or may not follow the same sort of course followed originally at the onset of the illness. The beginning of a relapse may be rapid or slow. There may or may not be attendant circumstances that offer some sort of an explanation for the relapse.

The patient whose first lucid interval (finding himself in a locked room) was cited above, described his gradual relapse following the lucid interval as follows.

I cannot be definite about the relapse, but it seemed to me that from the time I came into this room I became steadily clearer, that is to say, I noticed what I was doing, was conscious of everyone who came in contact with me, and of the daily routine of meals, etc. Consciousness of external reality was only occasional in the first period [before the lucid interval], and patchy in the second, while it seems to me that except for a short time it was continuous (apart from sleep) in the third period. During what I call the relapse, I got out of bed and did a symbolic dance that gave me some emotional satisfaction. At another time I felt I was getting telepathic communication from the other patients and was afraid, and I felt alarmed by dreams going on in my room independently, as it seemed, while I believed I was sitting up in bed wide awake watching. I also became curiously emotional when I heard that an elderly patient had escaped; in some unexplained way I believed my fate was involved in hers. (Anon., 1931, pp. 356–357)

This patient said that he suspected his relapse to be somehow associated with the realization, during the lucid interval, of the fact that he had been certified as a lunatic and would have to live with this stigma the rest of his life. This suspicion may have served the patient as a rationalization, but it is still questionable whether the realization of his lunacy had anything to do with the relapse itself.

A description of a rather slow relapse process was given by Jane Hillyer.

In the next few weeks all that was normal fled very quickly. "She is getting worse every day," they reported. I was. One of the chief signs lay in the weakening of all inhibitions. That which makes an individual moral, decent, considerate, modest, kind, had gone—it had snapped. Except for short intervals of complete and painful lucidity, I had receded into some dim twilight such as the caveman may have known. Primitive impulses had their way. The result was more insidious because almost always there was a hint of the "watcher," the "censor" left, just enough to gloat over the show, not enough to control or in any way size up the situation. This led to a studied devilishness at times, rather worse than mere torrential violence, or primitive naturalness; there was sometimes an element of semi-conscious display. (Hillyer, 1926, p. 41)

The mention in this account of the role of the *watcher* or *censor*, that is, an EDITOR process, is worth noting, particularly since she said that the censor portion of her consciousness seemed to gloat over the show. Ordinarily, this sort of experience is recounted in terms that indicate that the EDITOR merely notes what is happening.

In general, a relapse is the return to a deranged condition which is more or less similar to that suffered before the period of lucidity. The following account is taken from the account cited by T. G. Alper of a young patient who had suffered through three complete cycles of depression–normality–mania–normality. It is illustrative of a rapid relapse into what was, for him, a new pattern of mental symptoms.

I knew the game, knew it cold, . . . nothing could surprise me [about the experience of a manic-depressive psychosis]. But in March 1944 at one of the Friday afternoon hospital dances I had a new experience. I began to "hear voices." There was a great deal of conversation, noise, and general confusion. But suddenly every noise, every word was aimed at *me*. Everything that was being said, was being said about me. Everything that was being done, was being done because of me. For a short time I did my best to cope with this unusual situation. I tried to answer every remark . . . but in a short time it overwhelmed me. I knew something was radically wrong, and I told the attendant . . . that I must see the doctor immediately. We started back to the ward together. On the way it slowly dawned on me that it would be impossible to see the doctor in my present "disturbed condition" . . . I have no recollection of the following two weeks. (Alper, 1948, p. 203)

His last recollection of this incident was running down a long corridor to try to get to a favorite attendant. The period of the following memory lapse was, he said, the only time during the three years of his illness that remained vague, confused, and distorted. He had previously experienced maniacal periods and periods of depression. After two weeks of this schizophrenic excitement, he again became lucid.

Clifford Beers suffered from an acute psychosis that he described in his well-known book *A Mind That Found Itself.* The onset of his psychosis was very slow, covering a period of several years, during which he suffered from inner tension and an obsessing fear that he was developing epilepsy. Finally, he attempted suicide by dropping from a fourth floor window, but suffered no other damage than broken feet and ankles. In the hospital he became obsessed with the idea that his suicidal attempt had been a criminal offense. He imagined himself surrounded by police and by spies and as a defense retreated into a mute, stuporous condition for several months. One day he smuggled a letter out of the hospital to his brother asking the latter to come to visit him. Beers has described how this led to his rapid shift from profound delusion to lucidity.

The very instant I caught sight of my letter in the hands of my brother, all was changed. The thousands of false impressions recorded during the seven hundred and ninety-eight days of my depressed state seemed at once to correct themselves. Untruth became Truth. My old world was again mine. That gigantic web woven by an indefatigable yet tired imagination, I immediately recognized as a snare of delusions, in which I had all but hopelessly entangled myself. That the Gordion knot of mental torture should be cut and swept away by the mere glance of a willing eye is like a miracle; . . . My memory during this [deluded] phase might be likened to a photographic film, seven hundred and ninety-eight days long. Each impression seems to have been made in a negative way and then, in a fraction of a second, miraculously developed and made positive. . . .

After two years of silence I found it no easy matter to carry on with my brother a sustained conversation. . . . During the first few hours I seemed virtually normal. I had none of the delusions which had previously oppressed me; nor had I yet developed any of the expansive ideas, or delusions of grandeur, which soon began to crowd in upon me. So normal did I appear while talking to my brother that he thought I should be able to return home in a few weeks; and, needless to say, I agreed with him. But the pendulum, as it were, had swung too far. . . . Comparatively, sane and able to recognize the important truths of life, I was yet insane as to many of its practical details. . . . At first I seemed to live a second childhood. I did with delight many things which I had first learned to do as a child . . . to eat and walk, and now how to talk. . . . In short, I [relapsed] into that abnormal condition which is known to psychiatrists as "elation." (Beers, 1908, pp. 79–80; 83–84)

Beers' account, like that of the World War I veteran cited previously, illustrates how a patient may have an interval of lucidity or sanity and then fall back into a different set of symptoms and abnormal mental experiences. Usually, it is practically impossible for a person who has suffered from systematic delusions, like those which Beers described, to free himself of the conviction that at least part of the delusional system had a basis in fact. Beers, as he says, found all his delusions and his conviction of their truth wiped away in a most miraculous way. And then he passed on into an agitated and elated mental state.

Recovery

The description of the recovery from psychopathological experiences differs widely from one person to another. According to some, the abnormal experience gradually fades, becoming less intrusive and demanding, although remnants of abnormality may linger as a part of awareness for long periods. At the other extreme the entire pathological experience may somehow be cut off sharply and never recur. Persons who have had repeated psychotic episodes are in a position to compare their own experiences during and at the end of successive episodes. Graves, who experienced five or more acute psychotic episodes (both mania and depression), made the following observations about his experiences.

In the last two hospitalizations, there was no prolonged period of real strain, though some emotional conflict; no serious seizure by the dementia affect appeared, though conduct bordered upon it momentarily. Nevertheless, the last two confinements were associated with immensely more mental deterioration, in the sense that the cultured and habitual outlook of the conscious mind was abandoned without much of a struggle, merely with a little imbecile rationalization of the esoteric theories that it was necessary to embrace to justify the delusion. The hallucination incidents were sufficently depersonalized so that the personality surveying them always retained a question as to their reality. That is to say, the hallucinations I have experienced did not necessarily appear to have relation to me. They were generally events of which I was only a mystified observer. I cannot find or recollect any portion of them —barring the first appearance of a comforter who spoke flatteringly to me in 1926—which bore upon my situation directly, though there was some indirect bearing upon me. In the retrospection upon delusion, for instance, I can pick out the self-serving character of much of the false schemes accepted of this element, except as they might be eagerly accepted as "signs and portents" of an extraordinary reversal of ordinary physical appearances. And there was almost an equal distortion of outlook, to that disclosed in the previous attacks. The conscious mind, except for brief periods, was presiding over the personality, though it had lost contact with reality . . . [but it] undertook the job of constructing delusional theories and all of its abilities were turned into a moronic rationalization endeavor. (Graves, 1942, pp. 668–669)

The successive manic and depressive periods did greatly interfere with Graves' career and with his personal life. He was married and divorced several times. The positions he held became progressively less satisfactory to him, particularly because his promotions in newspaper work were not those to which he felt he was entitled. He did recognize that the repetition of the episodes of derangement did take a toll on his general level of capacity. He wrote about this loss as follows.

There was definite and practically unregained loss from the second hospitalization. The third hospitalization was an accentuation of this. . . . The fourth hospitalization caused no additional loss; there wasn't anything in my stock of character or material assets to be dissipated. Now I find that the workable talent has been entirely destroyed, the initiative and interest characteristics particularly being affected, while the willingness to exert disappears under the crashing recognition of the uselessness of the attempt. Behind the surface of the mental structure is a weakening of will, of grip, and of nerve which is rather astonishing in my own view. (Graves, 1942, p. 690).

The loss which mental patients experience is rarely evaluated as clearly as Graves has related his own experiences. If the person has only one episode and if the onset, course, and recovery were sharply set off from the normal stream of the person's ordinary existence, then the recovery may be complete with but little "scarring" of the total personality.

In Chapter 3 I mentioned the letter written by a young female patient in which she informed her parents of her return to a normal state of consciousness, a circumstance that determined the regaining of her sanity. As will be recalled, she summarized the first six months of asylum life by saying, "I remained deprived entirely of reason, and nearly deaf and blind at times, and subject to the greatest agony of body and mind." After giving further details of her subsequent suffering, she continued as follows.

I will now give you a brief account of my first returning consciousness. The Matron presented me with [the material for] a new dress on condition that I would help make it. I regarded this as the price given me to betray Christ, and refused to accept it on any condition whatever, but she and others insisted upon my taking it. I at length yielded to their importunity and accepted it, but not without great suffering of mind.

After I had taken it, it seemed to me a dreadful burden imposed on me, I would lay it down, and run from it as from a snake, and at other times take it up and run after the attendants, and beg them to release me from it, though I did not speak, my tongue seemed palsied, and I could express my wishes only by signs. I laid down the cloth, and went out with one of the attendants to take a walk, and when I returned to the house, I tore off the breadths one by one. It seemed at first like severing the soul from the body. The struggle was great. But it was the beginning of returning reason. I went to bed that night feeling better, and next morning was a reasonable being. (Anon., 1846–1847, p. 343)

She went on to say that she had now been well for two weeks, felt no more pain, and was sure that she was regaining her health.

Since only this one letter was published, one can not know whether or not the recovery was complete and final.

A description of the experience of a manic episode, as related by a charge nurse, was given in Chapter 3. Her account of her period of recovery is as follows.

The first symptom of recovery was a gradually increasing power to direct my thoughts into desired channels. I discovered that what seemed to be facts were in many cases delusions. Suddenly one day a feeling of self-control returned. The rapidity of thought seemed greatly lessened, and I was once more able to concentrate my mind on one subject for more than a few minutes at a time. Then came the feeling that I was well and must go home. Previous to this I realized my abnormal mental condition, and had no desire to see or be seen by my friends. Now I was seized with an eager longing to see my relatives and friends. It was like coming back from the dead. I overcame my restlessness by cleaning, scrubbing, mending and writing. My brain seemed unusually active and clear. I wrote for hours at a time; essays, poems, aphorisms, etc., flowed from my pen with great rapidity. I again began to take an interest in my personal appearance, and gradually returned to my normal mental state. (Reid, 1910, pp. 617–618)

She remarks that she gradually gained the feeling of being able to control and direct her thoughts. For a time she remained overproductive, but slowly the press-of-activity lessened until she found herself normal again.

Another individual, who for several years had heard voices of demons talking to him clearly and distinctly, recounted the fashion in which they gradually faded out of his experience. The voices had been so demanding that he had had to withdraw from his profession but he was never thought to be insane, either by himself or by his associates.

I could plainly distinguish about seven voices; two of them struck me as the voices of females; one of these sometimes spoke in over-soothing, complaisant accents to me, but these were generally used only to turn me to ridicule afterwards. The seven voices remained with me many months, when three left me, and four continued to torment me for nearly a couple of years; and since then I have only had two, a male and a female, who have gradually less and less annoyed me for the past year. (Anon., 1849a, p. 466)

Note that he said that the hearing of seven demoniacal voices slowly dropped out of his experiences; first, three ceased, and then two, leaving a final pair which were gradually fading at the time of his report. It is also noteworthy that he continued to believe in the reality of his demoniacal possession even though no longer concerned by the specific accusations the voices had flung at him.

Some patients recover rapidly, even suddenly, for no apparent reason. The change, like that of the lucid interval, may or may not be noticed at the time, either by the doctor or other observers. But the patient is quite certain of the event. Such was the experience of the journalist quoted earlier in this chapter, who wrote as follows.

On Monday afternoon . . . when I had just finished tea . . . quite suddenly I felt a change take place in my head.

The noise going on ceaselessly in my head—voices and sounds—had, until that moment, resembled exactly the rushing, roaring, sound one hears in one's head when seated in an express train speeding through a tunnel.

The sensation I experienced at the moment of which I write resembled exactly the emerging, in the express train, from the tunnel. . . . I said to the nurse—"Oh, nurse, my head does feel so much better!" She said, "Does it? I am so glad!" But I believe she did not think my remark of sufficient importance to note or report to the doctor. From that date I was sane. (Anon., 1932a, pp. 240–241)

This patient had been acutely ill and out of contact with her environment for several weeks. Her delusions had started abruptly and the process ended with equal abruptness. She retained some memory of several lucid intervals, but as she said, the entire psychotic episode seemed to her similar to a long and complicated nightmare.

Maude Harrison, also a journalist, suffered for several months from a psychosis from which she gradually recovered, although her autobiography, *Spinners Lake,* indicates that many minor symptoms and an exaggerated emotional sensitivity still persisted after recovery. During the convalescent period she was visited by a woman friend who worked for a rival newspaper company. The friend made several common-sense remarks concerning the delusions the patient still cherished. For example, one of the patient's notions was that the facts of her early life and present mental illness had been regularly published on the front pages of the daily press. Her friend pointed out how absurd this idea was, when the news of world affairs was always pushing individual items out of the limelight. Somehow, this simple statement shook the patient's convictions so that she began to laugh at her own foolishness. After the friend had left, she went to her room and started to muse, talking to herself.

I went on shaking, and talking incoherently for a few minutes and then sank back suddenly in my chair, steeped through and through in artificial peace. . . . Was I to be ill like this forever? No. . . . Still trembling, I rushed out into the gallery and asked to be allowed out into the grounds again . . . Out in the air I feel better. . . . I must, must, must be alone.

Very much as if I held the reins of a frightened horse I force my mind to take its last hurdles . . . my jigsaw became clear . . . my mind driven by my will. It is breathless, that leap, but we come down safe on the other side. There were no voices.

Hadn't the beloved Under Matron and the unbeloved (but still deserving of love and gratitude) Doctor said that scores of times? There were no voices. . . . I have stopped shaking. I am very, very still now.

Laughter, a score called from the tennis court. . . . Scent of the flowers deepening with the approach of evening . . . the sun will set, and I shall know at last that it is the real sun setting to the glory of God, setting to bring us the brief midnight dusk of summer, with its solace and renewal. I am sane. [Later:] You must have felt as if you were waking from a bad dream, [said] some of my friends to me in due course. . . . People always think that insanity feels like a dream, like dark clouds.

Of course it doesn't. If it did, it would not be insanity. Insanity, believe me, feels like the truth. It has a horrid concrete reality. Real life becomes the dream. I do feel as if a stone has been rolled away. Sanity is a coming of life, a resurrection. I am born again. (Harrison, 1941, pp. 159–161)

The author of these striking words went on to say that it was as if an angel had come and put the devils to rout. She said that her recovery began with faith; faith in her friends, in the nurses and the doctors; in the truth of their statements; faith that there were no voices; that she had not been wicked; that she would get a second chance to prove she could be sane again. According to her, her faith grew until it exploded into knowledge and overcame the deluded convictions which had been a central feature of her insanity.

Note her statement that insanity never felt to her like a dream, rather, *insanity felt like truth.* What she has said, in essence, is that her insane experience carried with it a conviction and inner certainty which she had never felt as vague or dreamlike.

Another autobiographical description of recovery, in *Memoir of the Early Life of William Cowper, Esq.*, relates how faith affected melancholia. Cowper, a well-known English poet, suffered for several months from a severe melancholia. He recovered slowly and, although still feeling filled with despair, could at least take part in a conversation. On one occasion during his convalescence when his brother asked him how he found himself, Cowper answered "As much better as despair can make me." His brother insisted strongly that this despair was but a delusion. He was so vehement in his assertion that Cowper could not help paying some attention, and finally bursting into tears he said, "If it be a delusion, I am the happiest of beings." With that, he later said that a ray of hope shot into his mind but, "he was afraid to indulge." Something seemed to whisper to him, "Still there is mercy." After his brother left, this change in mood seemed to gain ground, though in a fluctuating fashion. He slept well that night and described his experiences the next morning as follows.

Having risen with somewhat of a more cheerful feeling, I repaired to my room, where breakfast waited for me. While I sat at table, I found the cloud of horror, which had so long hung over me, was every moment passing away; and every moment came fraught with hope. I was continually more and more persuaded, that I was not utterly doomed to destruction. The way of salvation was still, however, hid from my eyes; nor did I see it at all clearer than before my illness. I only thought, that if it pleased God to spare me, I would lead a better life. . . . [so that I might] shake off my fetters, and afford me a clear opening [to] the free mercy of God. (Cowper, 1816, pp. 76–77)

The rapid realization of being once again sane, the lifting of the cloud which Cowper described may be contrasted with descriptions of more gradual recovery, where the patient finds it difficut to say just when he became certain that psychopathology had ended. A description of this sort was written by Hackett.

I was different, but there was no definite point where things had changed. It was just the process of getting better. I said that to [the doctor]. "It was just that I was sick then, and now I'm better though the doctors aren't convinced yet. At least I know myself a lot better, and your values change in here. . . ."

[What do you feel made you well?] "A lot of things, Doctor, my wife stayed with me through all the trouble, other patients helped me too, and the doctors have. I guess a lot of factors merged and worked to save me. I know the signs of going off. I know what it feels like to be sick and I know what to do if it starts again. I don't think the delusions can ever get possession of my mind again." (Hackett, 1952, pp. 294; 305)

This conversation with the doctor took place some time after Hackett had first experienced the lucid interval I quoted earlier in this chapter. He came to realize what a burden his illness had placed on his wife and how little he had been able to do to ease her fears or to assist in caring for their children. The voices no longer bothered him and he felt that he was able to control his periods of senseless anger and fear. He wanted to make the best impression on the doctors that he could so that he might be released from the hospital. Whether he had completely recovered he did not know, but he did think that he had regained self-control.

The patient whose first lucid interval took place when he became aware of his confinement in a small locked room, the description of which I have already cited, gave the following account of his recovery.

The quality of the food was poor, it was badly cooked, the chances of quiet for rest either by day or night were very small. The weather had changed and become wet and cold, yet I improved mentally and emotionally. This could certainly not have been due to the treatment or rather the lack of it— but simply that the illness—whatever it was—had run its course. I even gained the false reputation for being "happy" because I found it quite easy to keep the nurses amused, when they were with me. The knowledge that the date was fixed for my departure was the only relieving factor at this time. (Anon., 1931, p. 358)

Evidently, this patient's disturbance had had a sudden, acute onset and he had been certified as insane and removed to a mental hospital without retaining any memory of the events involved at the time of onset. He began having lucid intervals and periods of lesser mental confusion. Then, as he saw it, he began to recover without the assistance of any of the circumstances that are usually thought to help in regaining one's mental equilibrium.

In his *Narratives* Perceval described the events and experiences that, he believed, led to his recovery. As we have seen, he told how he had labored under the delusion of being under the controlling influence of spirits or voices that attempted to, and did, direct his mind and behavior. These spirits commanded him to act in ways that had endangered his personal safety. They prophesied the future. They accused him of many crimes. He usually attempted to obey these voices, but said that he had often been dubious as to the wisdom and truthfulness of the directions and orders he had followed.

My recovery was very gradual, but its periods remarkable. Three times my spirits prophesied to me, that a great change would take place in my situation. I expected a marvel, but the change took place in me, by natural causes, altering my apparent relationship to the persons around me. I had been continually haunted by the idea, that the sufferings I saw or fancied others enduring, were endured for me, and that it was my duty to try to partake in them or to alleviate them . . . for my neglect of which they were punished in my stead. . . . But after one of the prophecies . . . I began to hear words added to the message. . . . Then I knew that I had been deceived; and my mind received quiet. I was relieved from the oppression that I was continually causing the misery of others by my misdemeanours, and from the harass of being always called upon to perform some hazardous duty in order to relieve them. . . . I joked inwardly at the absurdity of my delusions. By this a great alteration took place in my mind. Objects began to stand around me in a new light. I began to be less ready to give up the dictates of common sense, to the injunctions of invisible agents. . . . I had been so long deceived by my spirits that now I did not believe them when they spoke truth. . . . My delusions being thus very much abolished, I soon after got liberty of limb during the day-time. (Perceval, 1838, pp. 211–212)

Actually, Perceval continued to be influenced by delusional ideas for several months longer, but did not blindly obey the commands as he originally had. His final recovery was an extremely slow process. Indeed, eight years after the acute phase of his illness, his behavior and thinking still continued to be motivated by a few delusional ideas, all of which caused him many difficulties with his family and former friends.

The descriptions of the inner experience of recovery which have been given thus far are those of "spontaneous" recovery. Other than physical care and restraint, no particular medical treatment or psychotherapy had been utilized, or if they had, the patients whose accounts I have given in this section were not aware of the fact.

Recovery Following Specific Therapy

Since the mid-1930's several specific procedures have been developed that have been used in the treatment of psychiatric patients suffering from practically every variety of psychopathology. As a group these methods are known as *shock therapies*. From the standpoint of medical science all the shock methods are irrational, in that there is no consensus on the relation of the treatment to either the cause or the recovery from the illness. There can be no doubt that these "shock" methods have brought about relief from "psychic pain" and recovery from psychopathological symptoms in a fair proportion of patients. The descriptions of the experiences of spontaneous recovery that have been given thus far in the chapter may briefly be compared to the experiences of recovery reported by persons who have benefited from the various forms of shock therapy.

INSULIN COMA (IC)

The first variety of shock therapy developed was insulin coma therapy (IC). The theory of Sakel, the inventor of the method, was that overdoses of insulin would exhaust the sugar held in the brain tissue and with sugar withdrawal there would be a depletion of the toxic wastes also held in the brain. He theorized that accumulated toxic wastes were responsible for the malfunctioning of the brain, and that their existence was the direct basis of insanity.

Repeated injections of insulin (usually every other day) in doses of sufficient amount to bring about loss of consciousness (coma) have been used as a therapeutic procedure with very large numbers of mental patients since the introduction of Sakel's method. There is no agreement among investigators as to the rationale of the method, but there can be no doubt that many recoveries from psychopathological states have indeed followed IC treatment.

The following account was given by an anonymous recovered mental patient who said that she had been extremely hostile and suspicious during her derangement. She also said that when the IC treatments were started she was very resentful and frightened. As far as her physical condition was concerned, she slowly improved, yet remained mentally confused.

That day when I woke up [from insulin coma], there was no sleepy fluttering of the eyelids, no yawning or stretching to pull myself awake. I just came alive with all cylinders in perfect working order. I went down for the last insulin injection, and it was just as horrible as it had always been. When it was over, I came upstairs with my nurse, feeling as though I had had three glasses of champagne. After a bath and clothes, we went out to walk. The world never looked so beautiful. I couldn't breathe enough of the air or look enough at the sky. We walked and walked with the cool wind whipping my hair about my face. It was like sailing on a September day when the blue water is full of sun glint. We sat in one of the arbors while I smoked a cigarette, and I talked and talked, making up for lost time. It seemed so strange to see cars on the road beyond the fence. The world going on about its business as usual. I felt well, I liked what I saw, and I was happy. (Anon., 1940, p. 813)

The recovery was evidently so complete that her recollection of the unpleasantness of the treatments evaporated together with her delusions and despair. In fact she concluded this account, which she read to the medical staff meeting at the hospital where she had been treated, with this sentence, "Insulin, and I say hooray."

Sullivan's patient, who had experienced several periods of depression and of elation, wrote the following unsolicited account of his recovery as a result of insulin treatment.

I knew at the time I was sent to the insulin ward that I was well on the way into another depression. I also knew that my periods of depression varied in intensity, and I was afraid that conditions in the ward would intensify this depression. But at no time during my three weeks and three days on the ward did I suffer the depths of depression that I have known under ideal conditions at home. During the first three days and nights I had no sleep (sleeplessness always accompanies my periods of depression and of elation). I was afraid that I was in for another week or two of sleeplessness, but on the fourth day I was "shocked" slightly, and that night I slept for six hours. . . . In my second week of insulin treatment I began to feel so well that I feared a period of playing the fool [as he did when elated]. . . . The third week was a re-affirmation of my peacefulness and steadiness. . . . My amazement at the effects of insulin treatment is equaled only by my amazement at the equanimity of the physicians who bore my insults during the first week. My deepest gratitude is for the knowledge of the efficacy of insulin, because my fear of depression was almost as painful as the depressions themselves; that is, I can now cease to worry about them, for I shall unhesitatingly have the treatment again when or if my depressions recur. (Sullivan, 1948, p. 211)

The account of the onset of a prolonged depression, written by Lenore McCall, has been cited in Chapters 2 and 3. After having been hospitalized for a period of three years, she was treated with IC, which was, at the time she was a patient, still somewhat experimental. She hated these treatments, since they added physical discomfort to the horror of her melancholia. The account of her recovery (part of it written in the third person) is one which portrays vividly the release from bondage she experienced.

The woman awoke in her room in Ellicott and felt her body warm and comfortable, relaxed and refreshed. She stretched luxuriously, her feet touching the footboard, her arms over her head. She opened her eyes and, without hesitation, turned her head to the window across the room where the luminous glow of the sun penetrated the drawn shade. She rubbed her eyes. A lovely day, she thought, the sunlight looks warm.

I sat up suddenly, my heart pounding. I looked around the room and a sweep of wonder surged over me. God in heaven, I'm well. I'm myself. My mind is working. I'm glad to see the day; the sunlight is beautiful to me. I'm well. I've come back from the dead.

I sprang from the bed, thrust my feet into the slippers beside it and reached for my dressing gown. . . . I turned and looked around the room. I'm really seeing it for the first time. I went to bed last night, sicker than I thought I'd ever been and this morning I'm well. It's a miracle, I was wrong; I thought it could never happen and it has. I'm well. . . . I turned on the radiator and went quietly about my dressing. I swept the underwear on the straight chair into a bundle and put it in the laundry bag in the closet. Everything must be fresh today. I'm well, I'm well, my mind works. I know what I want to do. I can think, my brain clicks and responds. I'm well. I opened a bureau drawer and selected the nicest underwear I could find. I dressed with no hesitation or fumbling, as one does the things which are habitual. . . .

I was stripping my bed when Miss Kelly opened the door. The dark-haired nurse stood still and I saw amazement in her steely, blue eyes.

"I'm well, Miss Kelly, I'm well. I woke up half an hour ago and the moment I opened my eyes I knew I was well. Isn't it like a miracle?" (McCall, 1947, pp. 285–288)

This portion of her account does not dwell on the suffering she had experienced before, neither does it speculate on why the illness had occurred nor how it had suddenly changed. It somewhat resembles the experience of any person who has recovered from, let us say, a prolonged and painful headache. One does not try to remember what the pain felt like; one does not speculate why the headache happened. It is enough that it has vanished. Forget it! The world is wonderful again. This is, so to speak, the usual, normal reaction to recovery. Somehow, the person who has had the experience seems to hold a certain belief that the suffering should be magically put out of mind and forever forgotten.

ELECTRIC CONVULSIVE THERAPY (ECT)

The primary effect of the application of an appropriate alternating electrical current across the head for about a tenth of a second is to bring about an instantaneous unconsciousness, usually accompanied by muscular spasms similar to those which characterize an epileptic seizure. These seizures are followed by a gradual return of consciousness, as if the shocked patient were slowly awakening from a deep sleep. The repetition of the procedure (usually every other day) results, after three to ten treatments, in a partial, but transient, loss of memory. Many patients are fearful of these treatments. They fear the loss of consciousness and are often disturbed by the increasing memory losses during treatment. However, ECT is almost always effective in bringing about rapid recovery in depressions as well as recovery from many varieties of manic states. It is therapeutically less effective in other forms of mental illness.

Custance tells in his autobiography, *Wisdom, Madness and Folly*, how he suffered from repeated manic-depressive episodes, and commented introspectively on the effect of ECT treatment.

The Military Hospital gave me only two [ECT] convulsions. At the time I was in a state of acute mania, seeing continual illusions, imagining everybody around me to be resurrected historical personages and convinced that I was destined to start then and there a movement that would save the world. The two convulsions were sufficient to break up the whole related syndrome of vision and phantasy, and within a little more than two months I was discharged as cured. I had no recurrence for two years. . . .

Introspectively, ECT appears to shift my observing ego from one state of consciousness to another, or using another metaphor, to push one state of consciousness below the "threshold" of observation and replace it with another. In Hamburg this process was startingly distinct. As I awoke from the period of unconsciousness which follows the convulsion, I could actually feel the phenomena of elation being pushed away from my consciousness. It was apparently analogous to the process which takes place in the mind as one awakes from sleep. . . . Consciousness drives the Unconscious away. (Custance, 1952, pp. 250–251)

In general, Custance thought that the effect of the ECT was to break up both the feelings of elation and depression which had somehow dominated his conscious life. Some patients have said that this driving out of the overwhelming affect of depression or mania was apparent after very few treatments, while others have stated that the process was a more gradual one.

The patient whom I quoted earlier as suddenly imagining that people were talking about him wrote the following description of the effects of an ECT treatment and his slow return to consciousness after treatment. He also included several remarks concerning his final recovery.

Very deliberately, very slowly a black shade came up over my eyes. I woke up sometime later feeling completely refreshed, not tired or logy, or drugged with sleep, just ready for a big day. I started thinking what I would do today but I could think of nothing. I began looking around. I was in a large cream colored room with fifteen or twenty beds neatly made, and covered with white counterpanes. It looked like a hospital, but why should I be in a hospital? There were large windows along one wall. The room looked strangely familiar. I shut my eyes and tried to think. But nothing came.

[He continued, describing the mental processes through which he went in order to recall what the date was, where he was, how he had gotten there, and so on. He said that he went through this sort of mental reconstruction of the world after each treatment.]

Slowly I began to remember things. Some things I couldn't remember at all. But this didn't worry me. All things came in time. One day I realized that I was normal. I wasn't depressed, but I sure wasn't elated. (Alper, 1948, pp. 205–207)

Since this patient previously had undergone several cycles of mania and depression without receiving any form of shock therapy, he was not particularly astonished by the end of the depression, but he was somewhat surprised that the usual phase of elation did not follow. Usually, patients remark that the period of abnormality ends in much the same fashion as previous periods during which they had not received shock treatment, but that the duration of the episode ended by ECT is much shorter.

In the case of schizophrenic patients treated with ECT, only a fraction of the group responds to any extent, and a yet smaller number actually recover from the psychosis. Dearborn's *Time Out for Death* is an autobiographical account of her schizophrenic episode, which had been marked by religious delusions. She had developed a system of omnipotent delusional beliefs that had been unsuccessfully treated by intensive psychotherapy for two years before her physician decided to try ECT. She commented as follows on the decision her physician had made concerning this change of treatment.

There had been some debating about it, with arguments pro and con; for Dr. C. had noted in other places an indiscriminate use of electric shock, with the patient ignorant of its aim. Considering such a procedure imprudent, he made sure that I was carefully informed of the purpose, namely, to prove that there was a force greater than my delusion, to show me conclusively that I was not God. . . . My doctor had concluded that this method of strong dispatch would knock down the flimsy framework of my sham defense for I would inevitably see that I could not keep on being Jehovah and still lose consciousness. It is so absurdly simple to look back upon: Imagine an unconscious God! But I did not know its demolishing potency. If I had, I would not have reacted with such supercilious indifference to his announcement that the treatment was to be employed. Jehovah, of course, is exempt from all assault; and what is electricity to the Almighty? This was my attitude toward the announcement.

[Later:] I am rapidly gaining back my health. The shock treatments have ceased, but the word sets my heart beating like a threat of annihilation. Dr. C. is able to reach me: He has shown the mastery of reason, the marksmanship of science; he has bowled a strike with the trusty ball of practice, and down have fallen, in painless consequence, all the tenpins of my defiance. (Dearborn, 1950, pp. 99–100)

Whether the above interpretation of ECT is of any value to anyone except to this one patient is doubtful. But it was evidently a suggestion sufficiently potent for this woman to question the fixed ideas of the Jehovistic delusional system that had possessed her mind.

PSYCHOSURGERY

Another method of therapy, known as psychosurgery, consists in the surgical severing of nerve tracts leading to, or the removal of, portions of cortical tissue from the frontal lobes of the brain. Thousands of patients who have suffered from a wide variety of psychopathological complaints were subjected to this type of brain surgery during the period from 1940 to 1955. Generally speaking, about one third of the patients so treated were relieved of all, or some, of their psychic distress. Psychosurgery was used, for the most part, with chronic patients who had failed to respond to any other form of therapy. An account written by an anonymous patient of the experience of the operation and subsequent recovery was reported in this way.

What was the psychological effect of the operation? One or two well-meaning people have objected that leucotomy [brain operation] is unwarranted interference with the "soul!" It is *not*. One is obviously the same person after as before the operation. There is no black-magical change, no dramatic discovery of an entirely new personality. One's memories remain the same; one's intelligence is unimpaired, if not improved; one's basic feelings about life remain unaltered. The only thing which really changes—and this is a very gradual process—is the ability to alter the badly set pattern of one's life; there is more "drive," more resilience, more objectivity in regard to oneself and one's environment. The leucotomy operation itself is only the very beginning of one's cure. The actual improvement in a human life still remains for the individual himself to accomplish.

What have I myself experienced since the operation? In a remarkably short time I regained a sense of physical well-being, which I had almost completely forgotten. Psychologically, the prison doors are opening at long last; it is up to me to walk through them, so that in time I may complete my own cure. Already it is a truly wonderful release from bondage. For the first time in ten years I can really enjoy a cinema show; I am free to go about without excessive anxiety (even to places my divorced wife and I knew together); my mind is clearer and my intellect, if anything, improved thereby; and when necessary I can again stand up to people. (Anon, 1954, p. 1233)

This account is informative. The operation removed, so to speak, the psychic pain, the chronic, overwhelming, disabling fears and anxiety which had made the patient's life such a burden to him. How the mental symptoms were removed, or where the fears had gone, did not concern the patient. It was sufficient for him that his mind seemed clear once more.

PSYCHOTHERAPY

The original form of therapy employed with mental patients is now, and has been for centuries past, psychotherapy. By psychotherapy is meant the attempt to heal by words and persuasion. At the present time psychotherapy usually involves the therapist's encouragement to the patient to disclose in detail his own account of his life history, including the expression of his symptoms and complaints. Ideally the present-day therapist who has been trained in modern techniques of psychotherapy offers a minimum of guidance and comment, regardless of whatever the patient may say. It is generally held that the therapist should never utter a reproach. The basic idea is that self-revelation will bring insight to the patient, together with some appreciation of the role played by his unconscious motives, thoughts, and instincts in both past and present patterns of behavior. Optimally, the patient will come to realize the various motivations that had constituted the sources of his mental troubles.

The acquisition of insight and the awareness of unconscious motives on the part of persons who are suffering from neuroses, overwhelming anxiety, or obsessions and compulsions, often results in a relief from the more acute symptoms. In searching for firsthand accounts of insights-to-cure, one finds examples such as that published by Lucy Freeman, who described in the following incident how the gaining of insight produced recovery from ailments.

I lived through the experience once more, describing it to John [the therapist]. As I put it into words a strange thing happened. I started to sob and could not stop. I sobbed as though making up for all the tears I could not shed that day I felt abandoned. . . .

"I'm sorry," I apologized. "I didn't mean to cry." I scorned tears.

"Maybe it's time you cried," he said. "Maybe you have wanted to cry all these years and couldn't." . . .

As I stood up, I felt strangely light-headed. My hands flew to my nose. "Gosh!" I exclaimed, "I can breathe."

Then I said sharply, missing the peculiar pain of it, "Where's my sinus?"

"Perhaps it cleared up as your tears came out," he said quietly.

"I can't believe it," I marveled. "Look!" I breathed deeply through nostrils that had been clogged for several years, showing off like a baby taking first steps. I felt as if a thick gag had been torn from my mouth, heavy chains lifted from my ankles. (Freeman, 1951, pp. 45–46)

In this instance the patient had complained of mild phobias, compulsions, and obsessions, in addition to a variety of physical disabilities, the most persistent of which had been a nasal congestion. In telling her life history to the therapist, she told how she had once felt rejected and abandoned by her mother. This confession started her crying. The crying in turn brought, not greater nasal congestion, but a disappearance of the sinus condition. This relief she and her therapist attributed to the achievement of insight; that is, the realization and acceptance of the fact that she had never actually been rejected by her mother.

Just as spontaneous recovery leaves the patient with little knowledge of how he has regained his normal functioning, so is it true that neither IC, ECT, brain surgery, nor psychotherapy provide the sufferer with any clear explanation of the specific inner change beyond the fact that the mental distress has ended. The linkage, if any, intrinsic in these therapeutic cause-and-effect relationships has never been clearly demonstrated. While there is endless speculation regarding the events or circumstances that lead to mental disease, conjectures about recovery are few. Apparently, there is a general human tendency to be grateful for the fact of recovery and to avoid inquiry as to why the latter occurred.

DISCUSSION

In Chapter 2 I gave and discussed autobiographical descriptions of the way in which psychopathology begins. It was noted that each individual found himself, either suddenly or gradually, entering an unfamiliar world where he had a variety of unreal, painful, and immensely distressing experiences. As far as each individual was concerned, we have seen how he first thought his experiences were unique and how he had difficulty in acquiring the necessary vocabulary to describe the phenomena adequately. He did realize his mental confusion and bewilderment, but could not give it adequate verbal expression. Frequently, such patients spoke of a feeling that part of their mind (the EDITOR) was watching the rest of the self proceeding in an out-of-control fashion. Such patients could give no satisfactory account of what had happened or of their failure to control either their mind or behavior.

The present chapter has dealt in a general fashion with the experience of regaining sanity. Having inadvertently, or with a feeling of being forced, entered into the abnormal realm, some patients have experienced intervals during which the whole feeling of abnormality was lifted. During such intervals they felt sane and in complete self-control, only to have these lucid periods succeeded by relapse into a clouded, confused mental state. During periods of relapse even the EDITOR process was so overwhelmed that their minds somehow became part of a fantasia of uncontrollable unreality. Finally, we have observed that a large fraction of these disturbed individuals recovered their sanity. The return to their previous normal existence may occur either gradually or suddenly.

In most human thought processes there is a tendency to explain the course of events in terms of a causal temporal sequence, such as, "The whiskey made me so dizzy that I fell and broke my arm." If such a train of statements has commonly been reported by many persons, as having occurred under differing circumstances and at different times, then most people are inclined to say that this is a common-sense explanation, even though the connection between whiskey and dizziness remains unclear. Most attempts to understand psychopathological experience follow this sort of an explanatory pattern. A traditional explanation of melancholia has been, "He became convinced that he had sinned and hence lost all hope of forgiveness, which caused him to feel the tortures of despair"; if recovery occurred, then an acceptable explanation might be, "He sought forgiveness, and with the forgiveness, the hopeless despair left him." Occasionally, such a sequence seems to be a sufficient explanation. Unfortunately, many depressed patients are unable to find forgiveness, neither does their recovery always seem to be associated with a feeling of having been forgiven.

Every man is convinced that his own private mental life is self-evident, unquestionable, and fully real. If a person is overwhelmed by feelings of anxiety, fear, and depression; if his mind is filled with delusions and peculiar religious ideas; if he is overpowered by painful lethargy; if he hears voices and sees visions that no one else hears or sees; if any or all of these phenomena occur, it still remains true that his subjective experience cannot be questioned. It is what it is. He must believe his own experience in spite of his inability to control that experience. At some later date he may recall his past experience and then conclude that he had been irrational or that he had lost control of his mind.

In the totality of his mental life any person can, and does, find reassurance and confidence, so long as he is able to anchor his recollections to landmarks that seem subjectively to have the quality of an unquestionable objective reality. Hence, if some specific therapy has been employed—for example, IC—the therapy, having a basis as an objective event, provides a certain anchorage for the subjective changes that occur during recovery. In the quest for an anchorage even an authoritative statement by a doctor often furnishes a satisfactory reference point. But the scholar who is seeking better and more comprehensive explanations in terms of cause and effect for the subjective changes manifested from the beginning through the course and on to the time of recovery is forced to conclude that the statements of therapists furnish at best very flimsy evidence on which to base explanations.

It must be remembered that the occurrence of a cure is never in itself evidence of the fact that the circumstances leading to the cure were in any way responsible for the recovery. It is commonplace to hear a statement such as: "He was having peculiar experiences and feelings. He was told to follow certain advice so that he might gain self-control. He followed this advice. He recovered. This proves that the method which was used will cure this kind of disability." Over the centuries, generation after generation has found that it must be skeptical in accepting *post hoc, ergo propter hoc* evidence of "cures" of mental disorders. This skepticism has grown out of the realization that no particular method results in a durable cure any more frequently than would occur as the result of the passage of time and the operation of the simple laws of chance and probability.

There is at present no other way to understand the phenomena of subjective experiences than to consider what a person says and does. If a man states that loud, clear, distinct voices are speaking to him, but no one else hears them; or if he says that he is overwhelmed by unaccountable despair and hopelessness for which no outsider can conceive a probable reason; or if such a man says that his mind has returned, his false beliefs have gone, and he feels in command of himself again; then we may *speculate* about the nature, cause, and effects of the experience he has described. If we find, as we do, that such feelings have been described in very similar fashion by many persons, each of whom intimated that he thinks (or thought) that his experiences were unique, we cannot doubt that such experiences do occur and that they have, in all probability, common elements.

Those who have suffered from these experiences may differ in their "explanation" of the abnormal phenomena or offer no explanation at all. Those of us who have not had such experiences are entitled to theorize and speculate about the causes, courses, and recoveries from psychopathological experiences, but in all honesty, we should carefully label our remarks as theory and speculation, and should give as much credit as possible to the explanations advanced by those who did live through abnormal experiences.

This and the previous chapters have given a broad view of the personal experience of onset, course of, and recovery from, episodes of mental derangement. Most of the following chapters will deal with more specific phenomena of mental abnormality, particularly perceptual disturbances, hallucinations, and kindred phenomena.

> If this I did not evry moment see,
>   And if my Thoughts did stray
>   at any time, or idly play,
>   And fix on other Objects; yet
>   This Apprehension set
>   In me
>   secur'd my Felicity. (*Traherne*, 1910, p. 88)

CHAPTER **5**

Disturbed Perception

INTRODUCTION

A flash of light is seen; the flash is recognized as a signal. A noise is heard; one knows the noise to be that produced by a running stream of water. The experience of the flash or the noise is called a sensation. The mental process of recognition that follows sensation is called perception. In the realm of mental phenomena sensation is the simplest or ultimate element. Distorted or disturbed sensations are not necessarily psychopathological. Seeing flashes of light or feeling cutaneous pain may be unpleasant, but only when unusual *meanings, ideas,* or *memories* become attached to such sensations does the process become psychopathological.

Primary sensations combine with memories, ideas, images, feelings, volitions, and so forth when these give rise to the secondary mental processes that are called perceptions. Perceptions, then, arise out of the complex association of memories, prevailing feeling state, and store of images and ideas, as well as from all the existing primary sensory material reaching a person's mind at each successive moment in time.

Of course, the process of perception is never as simple as this scheme. This analysis of sensation and of the process of perception is the result of late nineteenth century experiments in introspective analysis of mental processes. This scheme of presentation of psychopathological events is still useful in dealing with the secondary material of normal mental life. As Traherne said, "This *Apprehension* set |In me| Secur'd my felicity"— that is, my organized knowledge provides my sanity.

The philosopher Santayana gave us some idea of the complicated nature of perception and its relation to psychopathology in his essay "The Suppressed Madness of Sane Men."

Perceptions fall into the brain rather as seeds into a furrowed field or even as sparks into a keg of powder. Each image breeds a hundred more, sometimes slowly and subterraneously, sometimes (when a passionate train is started) with a sudden burst of fancy. The mind, exercised by its own fertility and flooded by its inner lights, has infinite trouble to keep a true reckoning of its outward perceptions. It turns from the frigid problems of observation to its own visions; it forgets to watch the courses of what should be its "pilot stars." Indeed, were it not for the power of convention in which, by a sort of mutual cancellation of errors, the more practical and normal conceptions are enshrined, the imagination would carry men wholly away,—the best man first and the vulgar after them." (Santayana, 1920, p. 7)

The seeming simplicity usually attributed to the concept of perception is illusory. The incoming signals of primary sensory experience may or may not give rise to normal perceptions. The relevance of memory, meaning, and symbolism, which acts to maintain mental balance and sanity, is acquired as a part of childhood experience. The acquisition of the "pilot stars" of common sense is a slow uncertain process, not explicitly taught or recognized. Indeed, this process of self-development, which gives rise to the normal mind of man, has thus far defied any rational formulation that might serve as a basis for understanding what has been called the "mental hygiene" of early childhood.

Illusion

We may begin with one of the simpler problems that anyone may encounter in the realm of disordered perception. How can a person recognize a normal illusion from an experience that he should consider abnormal? Consider the following excerpt from an account written by a patient who awoke after a night of feverish delirium.

The cold grey dawn of a summer morning broke at last in upon my delirium, but its uncertain light at first gave greater scope to my disordered imagination, which converted the folds of the bedclothes into serpents and reptiles, and all sorts of loathsome creeping things, "hydras, gorgons, and chimeras dire." With this impression stamped on my brain, I started to my feet in horror, with my eyes riveted on the hideous sight; and there I stood transfixed, and unable to move for many minutes, in unutterable terror. At length, slowly reaching down my hand, as daylight increased, to touch one of the immovable monsters, I was mightily relieved to find nothing but the folds of the bedclothes, and that I myself was the only living thing in the room." (Anon., 1855, p. 10)

The man who wrote this passage had become acutely depressed and delirious, seemingly without good reason. During this delirium he made an unsuccessful suicidal attempt and was then taken to an asylum. When he regained consciousness in the asylum, he continued in a very agitated, confused state. In this profound agitation and in his state of semiconsciousness, the dimly comprehended sights and sounds persisted in his mind as a delirious nightmare. Any outsider can readily understand why this patient's perceptions of the disordered bed clothing gave rise to overwhelming horror and terror. The instantaneous correction of the illusory interpretation of his perceptual experience brought about by merely touching the bed clothing, argues for the conclusion that he was sufficiently intact mentally to control in part the perceptual disorders which were involved in his over-all derangement.

Experiences of illusory perceptions are as distressing to the sufferer as are those more complete experiences for which adequate mental orientation is difficult to establish. Usually the mental correction of an illusion brings respite from doubt or fear, but the very fact that one may become disturbed by the frequent occurrence of illusions is in itself recognized as a danger signal. The experiencer himself believes that such misinterpretations of perception would never happen were his mind functioning with normal efficiency.

Usually, if an individual is able to find some basis in fact that offers a sufficient explanation for an illusory experience, such as illness, drunkenness, fatigue, or exhaustion, then his illness may result in a division of the stream of thought, so that in part the experience seems true and real, while at the same time part of his mind recognizes that the experience may be an illusion. The EDITOR process seems to watch, comment, and attempt to correct the aberrant perception. Peterson published in 1889 an article entitled *Extracts from the Autobiography of a Paranoiac*. The patient described the development of his illusions since the time of his boyhood in the following way.

I have been troubled from my boyhood with a tendency of my brain to see things it ought not to see in what is placed before my eyes. This refractoriness does not extend to all kinds of monstrous visions, but is limited to the singling out of the lineaments of the human face in the outlines of objects seen. . . . When I used to be sick . . . I would lie in bed and gaze at the coarsely-daubed window shades in my bedroom, until I had made out every possible kind of a profile that could be distinguished.

The other of the two most serious abnormal peculiarities is the supplying of missing articulations to vocal sounds, heard but not understood distinctly, so as to give my mind the impression of certain words, at the same time that I knew I had not understood. Sometimes I have been really cheated this way, and only found it out by inquiring afterward. . . . If it were proclaimed aloud, far enough for me to allow the inflections but not the articulations to reach my ear with certainty: WE SEE WHERE LIES THE DREADFUL SECRET! My mind might involuntarily and instantaneously reshape it in such a way that I would understand: DECEIVE WHERE LIES WERE EVER SACRED! (Petersen, 1889, p. 213)

The experience of finding profiles in mottled visual fields or of supplying meaning to random noises is a common experience very evident in children, and one that may occur in adults in ordinary states of reverie or daydreaming. In these instances abnormality occurs when the figures that appear in an ambiguous visual or auditory field have meanings and certainties attributed to them that cannot voluntarily be resisted or corrected. As long as one realizes that these experiences are imaginary and can be voluntarily controlled, they are in no way considered as other than one of the phases of a sane mental life.

Disturbances in Quality or Intensity of Sensation

A wide variety of perceptual changes occurring during the acute phase of mental illness has been described by patients. These changes range all the way from complete anesthesias to marked hyperesthesias, in one or in any combination of sensory qualities. To these must be added paresthesias, or false sensations. Peters included in his autobiography, *The World Next Door*, a description of some of these sensory fluctuations that occurred to him during the early, more acute phase of his psychosis.

Whenever I took my eyes off them [the hospital guards], they disappeared. In fact, everything at which I did not direct my entire attention seemed not to exist. There was some curious consistency in the working of my eyes. Instead of being able to focus on one object and retain a visual awareness of being in a room, a visual consciousness of the number of objects and people in that room, all that existed was what was directly in my line of vision. My other senses were similarly affected in that I ceased to hear or smell that which I did not see in front of me, and I had also lost the power of moving my eyes independently of my head. In order to see anything, to look for anyone, it was necessary to move my entire head. Now, looking for the guards, the process was as always one that made me dizzy. I would turn my head and the objects in the room would sweep before me in a cluttered, unidentifiable mass. I had learned, instinctively, not to move my head quickly for if I had, I would have become ill from making the dizzying sweep. (Peters, 1949, p. 47)

The confusing features in these perceptual disturbances were the prepotency of vision and the disequilibration caused by head movements. Peters complained that he could only hear or smell that which was in his direct line of vision and when he attempted to move his head rapidly it made him dizzy. Experiences of this sort are often reported by patients suffering from febrile or toxic states which physicians usually say are of an organic nature. However, Peters' derangement was probably schizophrenic.

A somewhat similar perceptual disturbance involving partial visual and auditory anesthesia was described by Jane Hillyer in the following way.

I could feel the nurse's fingers, but she didn't seem there, herself. Beyond my reaction to her touch I was unable to project her into my consciousness. I could see her but it made little impression. Everything was like that. I was veiled. It was quiet and restful, but a little wearing after a time. I tried to brush something cobwebby from before me; it would not brush. Sounds came to my ears. They meant little besides just noise. I was unable to translate them into the milkman's cart, the doctor's machine, the ice cream freezer. They were just so many vibrations hitting my ear-drums. (Hillyer, 1926, p. 51)

These inabilities to render sensations into perceptions, which Miss Hillyer experienced, may have been partially due to a generalized inattention, but even when she voluntarily attempted to attend more closely, her sensory world continued veiled and hazy, with touch being the prepotent sensory modality still available to her. Absence of sensation or distortion of sensation that ordinarily gives rise to perception is so to speak, an abnormal experience. In comparison, other deranged patients have at times reported that certain sensory experiences may have had an exaggerated intensity. The social worker referred to in Chapter 2 spoke of the experience of changed visual intensity.

Occasionally . . . there was some distortion of vision and some degree of hallucination. On several occasions my eyes became markedly oversensitive to light. Ordinary colors appeared to be much too bright, and sunlight seemed dazzling in intensity. When this happened, ordinary reading was impossible, and print seemed excessively black. (Anon., 1955, p. 681)

Later in this chapter excerpts from patients' accounts will be given of occasions when various kinds of noise or music seemed deafening to the ear or when the body seemed too heavy to be moved. Instances of the experience of overintensity of the sensations of taste, smell, and pain have also been given, but as a rule such hyperesthesias become incorporated in a total delusional system and are therefore not reported as isolated abnormalities.

An illustration of cutaneous perceptual disorders as they were incorporated in a delusional system is provided by a passage from

Schreber's *Memoirs*. Schreber, the reader will recall, was thoroughly convinced that he had been selected by God as the sole living person who could serve, by means of nerve contacts, as an intermediary for communication between God and all other human souls, both living and dead. He said that since there was always much competition for these lines of contacts with God, many miracles affected his body.

> Miracles make my feet cold and my face hot. . . . From youth accustomed to enduring both heat and cold, these miracles troubled me little, except when miracles made my feet cold while lying in bed, as happened often. Conversely I myself have often been forced to seek heat and cold. . . . I frequently clung to the icy trees with my hands for many minutes during the winter or held balls of snow until my hands were almost paralyzed. For some time . . . I put my feet through the iron bars of the open window at night in order to expose them to the cold rain. As long as I did this the rays could not reach my head . . . and I felt therefore perfectly well apart from frozen feet. (Shreber, 1955, pp. 145–146)

Schreber explained these "miracles" by pointing out that the rays from the evil souls who were competing for his mind were more easily deflected toward the colder portions of his body. Thus, by keeping his hands or feet cold, the evil rays were directed downward, while the rays to and from God were directed to his head, which was either warm or hot. (He was very resentful when the doctor arranged for the installation of shutters so that he could no longer sleep with his feet outside the windows.)

It has long been recognized by physicians that schizophrenic patients are relatively insensitive to pain. These patients will suffer bodily injuries or will inflict injury—sometimes serious—to themselves, with no evidence of pain. Their statements likewise indicate that they experience little or no pain. For example, Jane Hillyer, who suffered a long scalp wound which had to be sutured, recorded the following episode in her autobiography.

> "Jane, you don't even give a twinge when I put in these stitches," she said as she skillfully sewed up the gash. "What does she think I am, a baby," I asked myself. To her I said, "It doesn't hurt." In fact I rather liked it. There was something clean and definite about that slight pain, so much more desirable than the dull confusion *inside* my head. (Hillyer, 1926, p. 95)

In this instance, there was mention of a definite but slight pain, which was, however, disregarded because of other and more unpleasant feelings inside her head. She noted elsewhere other incidents of injuries from which she suffered little or no pain.

The account of Peters is relevant to this point. He was assaultive and destructive during the first few weeks of his stay in a mental hospital, and in order to control his destructiveness his hands were restrained by handcuffs, which held his arms rather loosely. On one occasion, his request for a cigarette was gratified by an attendant who placed a cigarette between his lips. He described this incident as follows.

I managed to extract the cigarette from my lips and hold it between the thumb and index finger of my left hand. It seemed to me that since there was no way to get the handcuffs off, the only solution was to burn my hands off. I applied the burning end to the back of my right hand and held it there. I could smell the burning flesh and hair but I could not feel anything, so I pressed down harder. After some time, I lifted the cigarette and found that I had made almost no progress. I shifted the cigarette to my right hand and performed the same operation on my left. When I had burned a small hole in the back of each hand, I put the cigarette—hardly more than a butt now— back between my lips and surveyed my hands. I was struck by a sudden memory of the nails that had been driven through Christ's hands on the cross, and realized at once that it was the disbelief of this man in white that had forced him [the attendant], through his own fear, to put me in handcuffs. (Peters, 1949, p. 22)

He mentioned from time to time, later in his narrative, that his hands became infected and bled, that they required surgical dressings and care; but he said that he never experienced pain.

It is seldom clear in patients' accounts whether these disorders of sensation are due to distraction, confusion, and inattention, or to some actual blockage of normal sensory experience. It has often been reported that normal persons during a hypnotic trance may fail to respond to sensory stimulation, if the hypnotizer suggests that the subject is anesthetic to stimulation. For example, pin pricks or burning objects may be used on the finger tips of a well-hypnotized person after he has been told his hands will have no feeling, and will elicit no reaction. The anesthesias which psychiatric patients have described seem in a way similar to those which have been contrived during hypnosis, but the similarity in no way proves that the same physical or mental mechanisms are involved.

Disturbances and Distortions of Perception

Another variety of distortions or disturbances in perception may occur when one is inattentive, preoccupied, or distressed. These fleeting disturbances are usually rapidly corrected, since the flow of experience that follows does not accord with the first or original interpretation of the perceptual experience, so that the person is struck by the contradiction. For example, Arieti cites a patient who wrote as follows.

I see in the paper "Camera Fotoshop" and I read "Campo Formio," which is the name of a peace treaty. I see "Triumph" and I read "Truman." While walking on the street I saw a girl with a button on her blouse on which a word was written beginning with a large F. I immediately read it as "Frustration," but on coming closer, I saw it was "Fieldston," the name of a school. Again while in my uncle's office, I was writing the name "Davis and Mahigian" on a bale of oriental carpets. I immediately thought "David and Goliath," and I actually wrote David on the bale and was about to write more when I stopped myself. When I meet people who have a certain appearance and manner, a name will often flash into my mind and I will think of this name each time that I see the person subsequently. (Arieti, 1950, p. 290)

There is nothing particularly unusual in the content of this account, yet it is easy to understand why the persistence of similar occurrences led this young man into difficulties in holding any regular employment. The particular portion of his narrative I have quoted deals with his first recognition of mental confusion, a condition that continued to defy his attempts to exercise self-control over his everyday mental life. As might be expected, eventually it led to a psychotic episode.

A more complete account of the way in which such incorrect perceptions lead to further distortions, to delusions and hallucinations, was supplied at some length by Custance, when he described how these experiences occurred during one of his acute periods of melancholia.

A crumpled pillow is quite an ordinary everyday object, is it not? One looks at it and thinks no more about it? So is a washing-rag, or a towel tumbled on the floor, or the creases on the side of a bed. Yet they can suggest shapes of the utmost horror to the mind obsessed by fear. Gradually my eyes began to distinguish such shapes, until eventually, whichever way I turned, I could see nothing but devils waiting to torment me, devils which seemed infinitely more real than the material objects in which I saw them.

They had names, too. There was the god Baal, with a cruel mouth like a slit (a wrinkle in the side of a bed), waiting to devour me as a living sacrifice. There was Hecate, who used generally to appear in pillows, her shape was, I think, the most horrible of all. When I went out, I saw devils by the hundred in trees and bushes, and especially in cut wood, generally in serpent form. Even now, I can still see them on occasion; the trick of illusion by which they appeared remains with me to some extent; and now that I am depressed again I cannot help wondering if they will reawaken the sense of utter terror that they did when they first appeared. I thought I had exorcised them, but now I am not so sure.

With these visions surrounding me it is not strange that the material world should seem less and less real. I felt myself to be gradually descending alive into the pit by a sort of metamorphosis of my surroundings. At times the whole universe seemed to be dissolving about me; moving cracks and fissures would appear in the walls and floors. This, incidentally, is a phenomenon which I have often noticed in the opposite state of acute mania, though it has then, of course, a totally different underlying feeling-tone. . . .

There was a series of sporting prints round the walls of the ward dayroom. They were so placed that, if you sat in an armchair with your back to the large windows, and facing the prints, you could see, reflected in the picture-glass, the buildings . . . on the opposite side of the small lawn . . .

I used generally to sit concentrating on a novel—that was another good way of keeping the horrors at bay—with my back to the windows; there seemed to be fewer devils in the ward than there were outside, somehow. Little by little, over a period of about a month or six weeks probably, the reflection of No. 9 ward was distorted. The chimneys left the vertical plane and moved round to the horizontal, eventually to forty or fifty degrees below the horizontal, while the reflection of the building itself became correspondingly curved, until the whole vertical structure formed a sort of inverted U. This puzzled me greatly; I don't think I was horrified at first. What could it mean? My vision was otherwise quite normal; I could play badminton, billiards, and so on. But whenever I sat in one of those chairs and looked at the prints, I could see this strange phenomenon. . . .

Then, suddenly, the answer came. Bishop Berkeley was right; the whole universe of space and time, of my own senses, was really an illusion. Or it was so for me, at any rate. There I was, shut in my own private universe, as it were, with no contact with real people at all, only with phantasmagoria who could at any moment turn into devils. I and all around me were utterly unreal. There in the reflection lay proof positive. My soul was finally turned into nothingness—except unending pain. (Custance, 1952, pp. 72–73)

This account begins with a description in seemingly simple and understandable terms, but the interpretation Custance's disturbed mind placed on the ensuing distortions of perception became increasingly fantastic. There was not merely an addition of delusional elements but apparently a complete distortion of the visual field, which became more and more confusing. The chimneys he saw extending 40 to 50 degrees below horizontal, while the rest of the visual field remained normal; this is indeed a peculiar experience. To say, as Custance did, that all his experience was an illusion is but to name the phenomena without offering an explanation. That he could see well enough to play billiards in one setting, but experienced such great visual distortion under other conditions, points to the existence of selective factors operating in his visual world.

More disturbing for the patient, and more difficult for any outside observer to understand, are the experiences during which the nature of the perception changes markedly while the sufferer is actually looking, so that the external world seems to alter while it is being observed. For example, Perceval described how during the first few days of his derangement the spiritual voices had told him that a dinner had been ordered for him by his brother, who had asked that he be served an Irish stew. The voices said it was intended that he should eat the stew, but that if a fowl should be sent him to dinner, it would be a temptation he should reject.

After some time the door opened, and a servant came in with the dish, containing a boiled fowl, which appeared very large and plump; I looked for the Irish stew, but it did not appear; the fowl on being brought near appeared small and meagre, and again plump, and twice its former size. (Perceval, 1838, p. 81)

He was disappointed that no Irish stew had been provided and puzzled by the fact that the size of the fowl changed before his eyes. The spiritual voices then reassured him by saying there was only one dish, but that he saw it in two ways, both in heaven and on earth, so that he might choose whether to yield to temptation or not. He had not the will to refuse to eat, but continued perplexed by the changing appearance of the meal, not knowing whether it was heavenly or earthly.

The relationships that exist between both the quality and the intensity of perceptual experience may vary during a mental derangement, so that in place of seeing and hearing things in the surrounding world in their usual intensities, the images and sounds may alternate, while the intensity and clarity of the experience increases and decreases as though the focus and volume control of a television receiver were being randomly varied. Among those who have described this sort of experience, Peters told how certain aspects of his experiences varied during semirational intervals of his acute illness.

I awoke again, reverberating to the intermittently deafening noise of a radio blaring into my ears. My eyesight had undergone another transformation and seemed linked in some way to my hearing. As great waves of blaring music poured into me, my vision became steadily clearer only to fade almost to blindness as the music descended into near silence. As far as I was able to judge in moments of visual clarity, the sound came from behind a screen which surrounded part of the bed next to me, concealing all but the lower half of a body. The sound was so loud, or suddenly so soft, that it was impossible to identify exactly what it was but it seemed to me the playing and singing of various popular songs simultaneously, accompanied by continuous static. After some moments of listening, I contributed to the din in the room by beginning to scream at regular intervals: "Quiet! Quiet! Can't we please have some quiet?" . . . My screams did not precipitate any sudden quiet but only the appearance of several of my captors [the attendants]. (Peters, 1949, pp. 53–54)

The changing intensity of the experience added so to his mental confusion that he could no longer recall or be certain just where he was, who the attendants were, or what was real and what was only imaginary. When he did regain consciousness, if only partial, he was possessed by the idea that he must fight against great odds in order to maintain at least part of his sanity. In later attempts to recall, he seemed to remember that at times he could see and hear and at other times he could not.

In general, we may conclude that perception may be distorted and disturbed in almost any fashion. Everyday words are easily applied to perceptual experience, hence this aspect of mental abnormality has been well described by many persons. Probably the role of distorted perception has been overestimated at the expense of other varities of mental disturbance for which verbal expression is not so well organized.

Levitation

Many persons, both in health and illness, have reported dreams in which they had the experience of flying or floating freely through space. A commonly accepted explanation of this phenomenon is that during wakefulness most of the musculature of the body is in a state of partial tension, which is, at least unconsciously, perceived in the form of kinesthetic sensations. During sleep most of this tension is relaxed. The decrease in the level of intensity of kinesthetic sensations is perceived in some unusual fashion and the lowered level of sensory quality serves as a basis for the dreams of floating, flying, or lack of support.

The experience of relative weightlessness, or of the ability to float easily and freely through the air, has been frequently reported by mental patients. The following excerpts from Davidson are typical of many accounts of the sort.

I felt so light that I was certain I should have risen off the ground if I had not had hold of his [the attendant's] arm. I told him this, and said it was more than I could understand; and as I got lighter and lighter, I got quite frightened, and clutched hold of him, saying I had not the slightest idea where I was going to if I "went up." Instantly I felt as heavy as lead, and could hardly lift my feet off the ground; but as soon as I mentioned this to him, I became quite normal again. I had a strong suspicion that he was "willing" me to feel these sensations; indeed, I felt somewhat afraid, and went off by myself. . . .

[Of another occasion he reported the following.] I jumped out of my low study window into the garden. I heard the leaves suddenly rustle through a holly tree on my right hand, and I felt a gentle gust of cool air strike me. To my intense surprise, all the strength seemed to leave my body, and I fell, as if I were a lump of dirt, on my left shoulder. My face was pressed into the gravel so that I got some into my mouth, and I felt for a second exactly as if I had been a devil who had been thrown down and his neck trodden on by some angel. (Davidson, 1912, pp. 63; 151)

Davidson's disturbances in feeling his own body weight are but two of the many he recorded. The disturbance was in every instance incorporated in (or grew out of) his delusional system of thought that was prevailing at that particular time.

These kinesthetic disturbances are even more unreal and pervasive in some patients than they were for Davidson. For example, Rows' patient commented as follows.

The lightness you feel when you are crazy is a very real feeling. When I was at home I stood on the bed, nude; I seemed to be a half a yard only from the ceiling: I had not grown, but I felt I should not be surprised if I changed into a spirit and floated out through the window. At that time going out to walk I felt funny inside the clothes, and the clothes were dreadfully heavy. (Rows, 1914, p. 195)

Note that this patient said that the feeling of lightness was a particular feature of his insanity, that is, the floating was primary and the delusion was secondary. Another patient implied that this same feeling of freedom from the force of gravity gave rise to a total delusional scheme in the following fashion.

I tried to escape from the window, and should have precipitated myself boldly from any height, for I had no doubt whatever that I should fly direct to Jupiter, could I get into free air. An ethereal lightness seemed to pervade my whole frame, and the great stone edifice itself appeared to be sustained in mid-air. It was a long time after I began to recover and walked out before the earth seemed firm and resisting under my feet. (Anon., 1856a, p. 34)

Disturbance or Loss of Depth Perception

For the most part, our ability to perceive the third dimension of space depends primarily on the fact that we have two eyes and two ears. That there is a slight difference between the sensory intake of one eye and one ear in comparison to the other eye or ear gives rise to tridimensional or stereoscopic vision and stereophonic hearing. A perceptual oddity mentioned by some patients is that the ability to perceive three dimensions seems lost. To these patients the world seems as flat as the scenery of a stage setting; the everyday outer world seems as though it were all constructed out of flat cardboard. This phenomenon so impressed Hackett that he entitled his autobiographical book *The Cardboard Giants*. In a passage in the introduction to his book, this phenomenon is expressed in symbolic terms.

He finally turned to cardboard, and his mind was confused, and they put him away in an asylum they call a hospital, for to see such a sight would frighten other giants, not to mention millions and millions of little people.

He lies in a bed, and his arms are cardboard, and his whole body is cardboard, and doctors come to see what has made the giant fall. With him are many fallen giants, and they all wait to see if their strength will return, or if someone sets a match to them, or throws them away, or puts a straw hat on them and puts them in the fields, or locks them in a dusty cellar forever. (Hackett, 1952, p. vi)

The experience of the initial loss of the third dimension was very vividly told by Renee in the *Autobiography of a Schizophrenic Girl*. She said that before the actual onset of her first acute mental disturbance, which occurred when she was a young girl, she had been rather good in drawing and had no difficulty in correctly representing perspective (third dimension) in her drawings. She described her condition after recovering from her first attack as follows.

Just the same I was a good student. Drawing, sewing, and singing remained weak subjects. Concluding my efforts were in vain, I hardly tried to understand perspective, rhythm, or the placing of fabric; I had completely lost the sense of perspective. . . .

[She went on to tell how this flatness affected her everyday life, saying]: We were walking on a country road. . . . Around us the fields spread away, cut up by hedges or clumps of trees, the white road ran ahead of us, the sun shone in the blue sky and warmed our backs. But I saw a boundless plain, unlimited, the horizon infinite. The trees and hedges were of cardboard, placed here and there, like stage accessories, and the road, oh, the endless road, white, glittering under the sun's rays, glittering like a needle, above us the remorseless sun weighing down trees and houses under its electric rays. (Sechehaye, 1951, pp. 15; 17)

These portions from Renee's autobiography indicate that the loss of visual perspective was, as far as she was concerned, a fact and that there was a definite change from her original ability to depict perspective as shown in drawings which she had made before her illness began. Even though the loss seemed to be one of objective fact, it is noteworthy that she incorporated this disturbance, in a symbolic way, as part of her total disordered mental content and did not, herself, regard it as an isolated symptom.

Other patients have spoken of this disturbance in perceptual organization in a variety of ways. A few excerpts such as the following may provide a better comprehension.

I felt like a moving picture projected on the wall. I only existed because you [the therapist] wanted me to and I could only be what you wanted to see. I only felt real because of the reactions I could produce in you. (Hayward and Taylor, 1956, p. 222)

We were all painted ships upon a painted ocean. I was simply a figure on something more lifeless than canvas, a character in something more unreal than a dream. (Davidson, 1912, p. 249)

I had not reached the stage at which any credentials could pass people as being real. I said, "I must explain that I do not know if you are acting or not." . . .

His expression said, "You poor old thing." Then he winced. "For my own sake I wish I were acting," he said. He added, "I suppose you know the hospital is real?"

"No, I don't. It may be—cardboard, for all I know."
"But look at the birds, flying in and out of their nests; look at them now round about the tower, they're real." (Harrison, 1941, pp. 122–123)

I found the visual disturbances most unsettling. Everything looked flat, two-dimensional, and unreal. I often used to stare at clouds and fields and will them to come real again; and even now, cured and years afterwards, these feelings of visual unreality linger on. Other neurotics have declared that everything looks like a theatrical backdrop; it is an accurate description. After vainly trying to get back to normal seeing, and getting refracted without improvement, I noted similar changes in the other senses. (Lancet, Editors of, 1952, p. 84)

The way in which this "cardboard" or "stage" illusion has been described by mental patients makes it difficult to ascertain whether it is actually a disorder of visual perception, that is, a failure to synthesize the visual fields from the two eyes, or whether the reports are merely symbolical expressions of unusual experiences. Disturbances of this sort are not mentioned by many patients. No one seems to know how frequent the experience is. Whether the loss remains constant or waxes and wanes, whether normal depth perception is recovered if the mental illness remits, whether it is characteristic of certain types of disorder, and what the basis of such a loss might be, are all as yet unanswered questions.

Image as Seen in a Mirror

Various patients have mentioned the effect of seeing their image in a mirror. Sometimes the reflected image seems real and usual; in such instances its unchanged quality is reassuring. In other instances the changed countenance is taken as evidence of past suffering, while on occasion the image seems so extremely changed as to become unreal and frightening.

I saw my countenance and form in the glass fair and bright—but when I was likened to Judas, my face was dark; whether this arose from any internal operation of the mind, by which the visual organs were affected, or, from my face being accidentally in the shade without my observing it, I do not know; the first is most probable; because afterwards I saw the countenances of others thus change from light to dark when in the same position relative to me and the light; but they appeared more black, and I was then more weak. I have seen large pier-glasses in England and in France which make the reflections from them appear black instead of fair—they who have looked into them, and noticed the fact, will understand in some sort the effect of my experience. (Perceval, 1840, pp. 262–263)

This excerpt is from the extended edition of Perceval's *Narratives*. In Chapter 4, I cited another excerpt from Perceval, who seeing his image in a mirror, became lucid for a moment and exclaimed, "*Ichabod.*" Perceval, like many other patients, made occasional use of a mirror to test his sanity: that is, his experiences of reality or unreality.

Davidson, in his *Remembrances,* also recounts several incidents involving a mirror. The following is an instance when the image reflected back seemed to change, as it did for Perceval in the excerpt cited above.

Afterwards, I got tired of walking, and stopped beside the mantel-piece, on which there was an old clock and a mirror. Some days before, I had shaved off my moustache by way of smartening up my appearance; but I now noticed, for the first time, that this had a reverse effect, and made me look like a somewhat melancholy, unstable, very second-rate sort of priest or parson; and I wondered what I would have looked like if I never had been guilty of any sin.

The first thing I then became aware of was that my appearance in the glass was changing; then, to my astonishment, the appearance became somewhat similar to what I had seen happen before to others in a few cases: and I hope I may appear like that some day. It was myself, but marvellously transformed; and the words, "When I awake up after Thy likeness, I shall be satisfied with it," came into my mind, though I never remember knowing them before. (Davidson, 1912, p. 189)

Davidson was not of an investigative turn of mind, as was Perceval. He was quite willing to accept mystical or supernatural explanations in order to understand his experiences. Both Perceval and Davidson were fundamentally convinced of the religious nature of their psychotic experience, but Perceval, whenever possible, sought a "natural" explanation.

Another account of a reaction to seeing oneself in a mirror, at the beginning of a mental break, when the reflected image verifies the inner struggle of the sufferer, was related by Miss Dearborn as follows.

The night before the break, I suffered endless hours of insomnia, undergoing an indescribable mental struggle . . . As early morning dawned, I rose and went over to the dresser, where I looked into the mirror at a strange, drawn, haunted face. The eyes were deep and staring . . . not wild, but seemingly determined, fraught with some inexplicable flash triumph. Time seemed to stop altogether; the atmosphere was breathless, suspended, and dead quiet. The sensation of being in another world was overpowering, terrifying. I stood stockstill; I paced the floor; time still held its breath. (Dearborn, 1950, pp. 90–91)

For this patient, seeing her image actually seemed to crystallize the realization of her mental disturbance. Until she saw herself, she could still hold to the lingering doubt that her troubles might be imaginary, but the reflection of her face confirmed her worst fears and brought home to her the final realization of her insanity.

In contrast to this type of realization is the reassuring one, when the acute disturbance seems to have ended or become less severe, of seeing oneself in a mirror and recognizing the image as real. For example, Peters wrote as follows.

Above the sink was a mirror and I stared into it, looking at the not-quite-clear wavy image. It must be me. I touched my hand to my cheek and felt the heavy growth of beard. Then I touched the glass with my hand it was immediately reflected. No doubt about it, that was me. The reflection seemed incredibly thin. It was as if I had never seen myself before. (Peters, 1949, pp. 93–94)

At this instant Peters' mirror-image did reassure him that he was himself once more and not Jesus Christ as he had thought during the preceding weeks.

A man who is alleged to have experienced an amnesia of thirteen years' duration, during which time he had wandered about the United States under another name, reverted one morning to his original personality and regained his memory.

When I went into the bathroom and saw myself in the mirror, I knew there was something damn wrong. It wasn't me at all. I had lost weight, lost hair, and my face had many more lines in it than I had ever noticed before. I really didn't know whether the person in the mirror was me or somebody else. Just about that time someone came up to me and asked, "How are you feeling this morning, John?" I turned around and said, "What in hell are you calling me John for?" "You're not stuttering this morning," he said. I told him I never stuttered in all my life. He asked me if I knew where I was and I had to admit that I did not. (Weickhardt and Langenstrass, 1947, p. 245)

One final example of the critical juncture determined by the sight of one's mirror-image, which occurred on the morning of recovery from a four-year period of melancholia, was given by Lenore McCall, whose account of the beginning and the end of her four years of melancholia has been cited in previous chapters.

I caught sight of myself in the mirror . . . "Yes, it's you Anne Fowler. It's you. I certainly need some grooming, but I'm myself, and that's all that matters." (McCall, 1947, p. 287)

The sight of one's image in a mirror is often very serviceable as a reality-testing device.* One's own mirror-image is a most familiar perception. If it seems not too different from the way it has usually been seen, it may represent an objective test or reference point for the evaluation of one's normality and rationality. If, as one watches, the image seems distorted or changing, it provides direct and visible evidence that something is really wrong. More than most ordinary perceptions, the mirror self-image furnishes a satisfactory basis for the reassurance or questioning of one's own normality or possible abnormality.

---

* *Reality testing* refers to a fundamental intellectual (cognitive) process that results in the evaluation and judgment of the outside world.

Reality Testing

The way in which a person will repeatedly attempt to test his own reality and that of the world around him, while suffering from severely distorted perception, may be illustrated by an account written by Heveroch's patient.

Following the blood rushing to my head, I felt a roaring in my ears and my mind darkened. I held a newspaper in my hand but did not understand what was written in it. After I had risen, I reeled, and everything turned about me in a circle. Light was flickering before my eyes. I looked into the mirror, but my face was not distorted. I believed myself to have been poisoned, and therefore quickly wrote my observations on a piece of paper. Besides, I resisted calling anyone for help, because it appeared to me that there was nothing to be done. It appeared to me as if something was trying to isolate me from the outer world; at the same time a softened atmosphere formed itself about me, although I knew quite well that it was broad daylight. I also felt this dampening of the atmosphere in the sensations of the skin; a sort of isolating layer separated me from the outer world and it appeared to me as if I had been transported from this world into an infinite distance and, therefore, I said repeatedly: "I am in the far, far distance." Nevertheless, I could see that I was not far away. I was able to remember exactly what had happened; but between the moment that preceded the attack and the moment that followed it, there was an unmeasurable interval of time and a distance similar to that of the earth from the sun. . . .

Later, people and objects diminished in size and receded from me into an infinite and boundless distance. I looked about me with horror, the world receded everywhere. It took an enormous effort to make me conscious of the fact that I am really in my street, that I am walking, that I am actually speaking to the coachman. I was surprised that the coachman understood me because my voice seemed to be coming from a remote distance and was unlike my own voice. I stamped on the floor with my feet and thus convinced myself about its solidity, a solidity which only seemed to be so, because the weight of my body had almost completely disappeared. I felt fatigue, yet I felt that I had no physical weight. Objects appeared to be far away and flat. If I spoke to anyone, the person in question looked, to me, like a cutout picture, without relief. (Heveroch, 1913, pp. 430–431)

The process of reality testing is commonplace, at least implicitly, in everyone's mental life. The immediate primary sensations that give rise to perception very often result in an experience not in line with what has gone before or what might reasonably be anticipated. If one's mind has been somewhat confused, or if one's emotional life is in a turmoil, there is more than the usual chance that perception will be distorted or disturbed. Hence, either at the onset of, or during recovery from, a period of mental disorder, it becomes necessary to verify as often as possible one's perception and stream of thought as they reflect the outer world. The description cited of the uncertainties of perception during the beginning of a period of derangement illustrates some aspects of the process of reality testing. This man could see but could not comprehend the printed content of the newspaper he held; he could recognize that there was nothing wrong with the image of his face in the mirror, yet it seemed distorted. The surrounding atmosphere was experienced as somehow soft and dim and yet it was broad daylight. He felt far away but his eyes told him that his feeling was incorrect. His body felt weightless and yet the sidewalk was solid. In brief, he had to test at every point the accuracy of his total primary sensory experience. Under such circumstances one can begin to comprehend how in fact the world does become more and more unreal as the psychosis develops.

As we have remarked, patients also resort to reality testing as a method of measuring, so to speak, the return of sanity. For example, the ex-patient whom we have already encountered in Chapter 4 when discussing transient periods of lucidity stated as follows.

On the table was a book—it was *Uncle Tom's Cabin*—which I opened in order to test my sanity. I had great difficulty in focussing, although the print did not strike me as bad—when I reached the centre of a line the two ends zigzagged up and down from it. However, I persevered and read a paragraph and was satisfied that I was sane enough to understand printed matter. I do not know whether I went back to bed of my own accord or was sent back. (Anon., 1931, p. 348)

In this instance, perceptions still seemed distorted, the lines of print zigzagged, but the patient concluded that he could comprehend the paragraph he read. Patients often find that the process of reality testing is best applied to events occurring in the objective world. Reality testing often fails to satisfy the patient when he tries to examine his emotions or volitional processes, since in such experiences there is no appropriate or well-anchored measure of cognitive reference.

Attempts to Determine the Basis of Disordered Perception

Several of the more skeptically-minded patients have expressed in writing their attempts to find some basis from which they might proceed to understand the illusions, hallucinations, and delusions they had experienced during their acute psychotic phases. Perceval, whose *Narratives* (1838 and 1840) have already been cited several times, gave instances of his attempts to correct or explain his disturbed perceptual experiences as objectively as possible. More than in any other autobiographical account I have discovered, he recounted the procedures he utilized in trying to find some objective basis for his supernatural experiences. In view of their ingenuity, certain of his "experiments" are worth citing in detail. In order to control his agitation and assaultiveness, Perceval had been locked in a chair so that he could not move his arms or legs. He recalled that during these periods of restraint, he had rested his nose on the arm of the chair, in an attempt to suffocate himself.

For I recollect during my recovery at Dr. Fox's, I used to place myself in the different positions I had formerly occupied, in order to retrace my thoughts, and see if I could account for my feelings—on one of those occasions I sat down in a niche, into which I had been fastened, in the bow [window] at the end of the common room. I experienced then an extraordinary sensation of suffocation, *and I found it was produced by the position of every object and of every line in the room being oblique to my visual organs instead of square;* and I have no doubt this sensation caused the idea continually to haunt me when I was seated in that niche, where I passed whole days pressing my nostrils to a wooden ledge, that served to support the arms, as in an arm-chair.

Moreover I have remarked, that when my mind is most disturbed, I breathe at that time violently and rapidly, and with difficulty through the nostrils, and I have observed in the glass, when I have been exasperated, my nostrils compressed above and dilated below, and quivering rapidly with the violence of my breathings . . . The spirits also which I conceived to speak to me, used to direct me to control my breath, and "to breathe gently up one nostril down another." I have often found too, that when I am depressed or agitated by any passion, a deep-drawn breath will change the whole complexion of my thought and the tenor of my desires.

I am afraid that these details will appear tedious and frivolous; but on a subject, on which medical men are evidently so ignorant, and, usually, so thoughtless—and nearly all others are desperate, because they deem it beyond their comprehension, I hope I may be excused in entering upon these minute particulars, though they are but lucubrations on the operations of a deranged understanding—still that *was* a deranged *understanding*. . . .

I observed that the cause of that delusion, whereby the stature of persons appeared to change, consisted in my comparing them in the agitation of my spirits, and in that weak state of health, solely with the objects around them, or in the distance, in the same way as I have often found when attempting to draw—I have made all the objects in the middle distance in fair proportion one with the other, but much too large to sort with the size I was compelled to give to the objects in the foreground, on account of the dimensions of my paper. I will not, however, be too positive of the cause being rightly stated, though I think it was so; but this I know. . . . that this delusion arose from a defective use of the visual organs. This weakness of sight giving also a kind of unsubstantiality to persons I saw—for their forms seemed to dilate and contract. . . .

About the same time, moreover, I discovered the source of this kind of delusions—or rather the means by which they are presented to the spirit. One day I entered a dark closet in which there was opposite the door a small opening to give light, and in it two or three upright bars. I gazed a short time unconsciously at this, and turning to the left, I saw to my astonishment a window or opening in the dark wall which I had never observed before. Recovering from my surprise I found that what I saw was not real—but visionary, and then reflecting, I found that the image formed on the retina of the eye, by the light from the opening on which I had gazed upon entering this dark chamber, appeared by an ordinary law of nature, thrown out upon the wall which was in shadow, to which I afterwards turned. In the same way as if any person gazes on the sun—he will see several green and blue suns floating in the air around him. . . .

I have said that these visions are presented to the mind through the retina of the eye or otherwise, because . . . the eye is merely an organ for communicating impressions from without to the spirit. Often when observing objects around me in the room, I have at the same time seen miniatures of friends, or other small pictures, as it were, in my loins or other parts of my body; and any person of a lively imagination, if he chooses, may fancy horses, churches, houses, or children running with their hoops, behind him, whilst he is looking to the front. For these reasons I do not think the retina of the eye the necessary instrument for the perception of visions. . . .

These phantasms are not always produced, merely by *internal* lines and shades artfully disposed together, neither are dreams. I recollect one morning awakening with a shout . . . after dreaming that I was in an Irish village, with a lady and a friend, and that an Irish peasant pointed a musket at me, close before me. I found that I had been sleeping with my eyes partially open, and that part of the window, through which the sun shone upon me, had formed in my dream the muzzle of the musket. Thus, also, the ciphers which I have seen and copied on paper when writing, are, I conceive, partly caused by the internal arrangement of light and shade in the eye, partly by that of the lines and light and shade on the paper being combined with the other. If this is not the case with the writing, at least it is with sketches and figures, which I often see on the paper, but now imperfectly; and which, I recollect, even many years before I was ill, often tempted me to use the pencil. Now of this phenomena all people of any imagination are, I suspect, more or less conscious; for it is the same thing, when we look into the fire, and see our friends' faces, or picture to ourselves other forms in the glowing and ever-changing cinders, or trace out forms in the veins of a marble chimney; only I must distinguish between the mere notice of certain lines that are *like* a man or *like* a face, or *like* a horse, or *like* a tower, and that pleasing apprehension of the very figure itself, caused by an internal operation of the mind, combined with the lines which are without. . . .

I observed also, during the slow progress of my recovery . . . that He who rules the imagination has the power, not only to produce written or printed words, and to throw them out upon *blank* paper; but to cover written or printed words or letters with other words or letters that are not there. This is also the case with larger objects—but not so usual. It takes place (I will not say *always*), when in reading, persons put one word for another, and it generally happens in little words that will derange the whole sense of a sentence; such as *no*, for *yes; from*, for *to; unlike*, for *like;* or in words similar, *humor*, for *honour; quack*, for *quick;* and *sample*, for *simple*. When persons make these blunders in reading, they immediately correct themselves and say, "Oh! I have made a mistake"; but generally speaking, I am persuaded, they make no mistake, but read the word which they saw—but being in good health, the operation of the mind, of the muscles, or of the pulses, which cleared the eye of the film, on which the Almighty produced the false word, which at the same time He threw out apparently upon the paper—was so rapid that it was not perceived; but my pulses, and my circulation, and the operations of my mind being unusually slow, through disease and oppression, I saw and discovered the sleight that was played upon me. A trick which, until I became stronger in health, made me doubt that the objects round me were REAL; so that I threw myself against doors and walls, expecting to find that they were not there. (Perceval, 1840, pp. 278–279; 296; 327; 328; 333–336)

It is evident that Perceval was innocent of any technical knowledge concerning the phenomena and mechanisms of vision and had no adequate technical vocabulary; even so, his report does indicate that he was very shrewd and observant. As he said, he actually put himself in the same place and posture in which he had spent many weeks of physical restraint, and found that the physical posture and the distortions of the visual field reinstated the sensations of suffocation. Perceval discovered for himself the phenomena of visual afterimages, which he thought were the basis for certain of his delusions. He noted that his drawings had shown a distorted perspective although he did not speak of them as indicating a loss of perspective. He speculated on the way in which mottled or visually disorganized surfaces might serve as a basis for either hallucinations or delusions. Also, he remarked how similar words which he frequently misread or misheard gave rise to distorted meanings and these distortions were, according to him, *no mistake* but tricks the Almighty played on his mind, weakened as it was by his illness. These verbal mistakes and substitutions are similar to the material cited and elaborated by Freud in *The Psychopathology of Everyday Life* published in 1904. Perceval, while he found and offered a basis for part of his delusions and hallucinations, continued to insist that the essential content of his experiences had been supplied by the Divine inspiration acting upon him.

Boisen gave an example from his own experience, in which the correction of an illusion furnished, in his opinion, the turning point that led to his recovery from an acute mental illness.

The idea which had first bowled me over was, as I have said, that of a coming world catastrophe. . . . I was therefore much impressed one night, as I lay awake out on the sleeping-porch, by the observation that the moon was centered in a cross of light. I took this as confirmation of my worst fears. . . . In order to be sure I called an attendant and inquired if he also saw the cross. He said that he did. I was greatly impressed and agitated. But some days later in the early watches of the morning as I lay awake looking at the moon, speculating about the terrible danger which that cross betokened, I made a discovery. Whenever I looked at the moon from a certain spot the cross did not appear. I immediately investigated and found that from that particular spot I was looking at the moon through a hole in the wire screening! With this discovery the edifice I had reared upon the basis of the original premise began to fall. And only a few days later I was well again. (Boisen, 1936, p. 4)

Whether this rectification of an illusion, this testing of reality, actually was the starting point of recovery, or whether it was no more than an associated incident, cannot be determined, but it is certainly in accord with similar reports made by other sufferers who have recounted how the appropriate correction of perceptions was at least associated with, even if it did not lead directly to, recovery.

DISCUSSION

That perception is both a simple and at the same time a very complicated mental process is evident. During most of one's normal waking life the relationships, meanings, and memories are added directly, immediately, and usually correctly to the primary sensory material of consciousness. When misinterpretations do occur in the normal mind, they are corrected with but little confusion or disturbance. If one wishes to subscribe to an instinct theory of the operation of consciousness, then most of the filling-in aspects of perception are instinctive and only in difficult situations does conscious thought ever enter into the process.

In earlier chapters I have stressed the point that a very important consideration which may act to convince a person that he is losing his mind is the realization that he has lost his ability to effectively exercise self-control over his thoughts and behavior. Almost as disturbing, although by no means as convincing as the loss of self-control, is the recognition of distortions of perception. If while watching, one sees one's image change in a mirror, or if one sees live reptiles on one's bed, which suddenly change to wrinkles in the bedclothing, an individual is very apt to call his sanity into direct question. Such experiences seem neither normal nor natural. If a person cannot believe his own perceptual experience, he cannot avoid regarding it as direct evidence of some underlying disturbance.

The concept of reality testing is of value in that it enables the observer to understand some of the problems which mental patients must face. Most of these patients have found that they cannot trust their own sensory experiences as they were normally accustomed to do before the beginning of their illness. It is necessary for such patients to test and retest their sensory experience before they can discern whether their previous perceptions corresponded to reality or not. For example, recall that Perceval said he had often walked directly into a wall, having seen a door which did not exist.

The descriptions of the sensory and perceptual distortions cited in this chapter are merely samples of the wide variety of strange psychological processes that plague the mentally disturbed patient. I can see little reason to believe that distortions of perception are the primary events in mental illness. It is well known that there are a variety of drugs which will act to produce perceptual distortions. As long as the drug does not produce intense feelings of fear, anger, or unreality, the drugged person may calmly observe and even enjoy the visual display or kinesthetic changes, without ever thinking of the possibility that he might be insane.

The perceptual world of experience is the most real aspect of a person's life. This probably grows out of the fact that the human mind invented the system of verbal signs and symbols of language that serves to hold the disparate sensory elements in a semiorganized fashion, which is regularly recognized and comprehended by any individual and among individuals. Language constitutes a flexible reference system and makes possible the interpersonal communication of perceptual events. Affective and volitional experiences, on the other hand, have little or no basis in language, and the language designations of these phases of experience are vague and remote. One may say to oneself, "This feeling is fear," but it is almost impossible to be certain when someone else says, "I am afraid," that his feeling is similar to the personal experience I call fear. In other words distorted perception plays a major role in psychopathology, mainly because discriminable parts of the process can be recounted in universally recognizable terms.

Much of the experimental investigation with word association tests during the past century indicates that psychiatric patients do make unusual associations, the peculiar associative processes being shown most clearly in the way in which such persons link meanings to primary experiences. Not only are the associations unusual, but often neither the patient nor those about him can supply a rational basis for them.

Loosened associative mental bonds permit the formation of delusions. The loose bonds result in a succession of misinterpretations of primary sensory material. The ordinary methods of reality testing do not correct the unusual meanings. In order that the hodgepodge of irrational experiences may find some sort of internal organization, a delusional system is conceived. The delusions generally contain a large element of magical and mystical, or at least illogical, thought. If part of these unusual perceptions seems to have no possible rational associative basis that can be quickly provided by normal reality-testing processes, reverie and magical thinking are usually introjected. Strange visions, odors, tastes, and tactile sensations often occur and tend to persist in the patient's experience. The outsider is inclined to say that all these are simply imaginary. And imagination it may be, but why does it occur in the rather stylized and systematic pattern content that it does?

This point has been somewhat clarified by considering the descriptions given above of a person's perception of his image in the mirror. One's image may have been seen to change as one watched; or one's image may have reflected the harried and disturbed mental experience, thus confirming the feeling of possible illusions; or one's image looked as it should, and so provided the gateway for, or at least coincided with, a lucid interval or the return to normalcy; one's image indicated certain facial changes, so that a lost period of time must have gone by; or one's image seemed to reflect the return of one's sanity. But if one sees one's face change as one scrutinizes its reflection, without experiencing any of the secondary sensory cues that would have been sufficient to explain the change, then it seems to be easier to accept some magical or delusional explanation than to seek a more rational explanation.

Attempts to rectify illusions, visions, and voices are all evidence of the way in which a mind may proceed in an attempt to regain self-understanding or sanity. It is possible to convince oneself that the voices or visions may have been illusions, misinterpretations of breathing sounds, or visual afterimages, but the belief in the outside determination of the content of the experience can only rarely be corrected—the belief is at the time accepted as some supernatural truth and later such explanations have to be ignored or deliberately obliterated from the person's remembrances.

CHAPTER 6

Hallucinations

INTRODUCTION

In the foregoing chapter I discussed various disorders of perception. Illusions and delusions result from comparatively simple misinterpretations of sensory material. The patient who thought that his bed was full of snakes, but quickly changed his perceptual organization after touching the folds in the sheets, had experienced and corrected an illusion. If such a patient were to report that there are several coiled snakes on the floor of a bare and vacant room (where others could see nothing except the uniformly illuminated surfaces of the floor), and if the patient were to persist in his conviction after others have looked and seen nothing, then such a false perception (for which no sensory basis can be found) is spoken of as an hallucination.

Hallucinations are disorders of perceptual experience in which ideas and the images associated with them become so vivid that the experiencer insists on the truth of his experience despite sensory evidence to the contrary and despite anyone's remonstrances to the effect that his sensory experiences are false.

Although hallucinatory experiences are most common among persons suffering from mental illness, such experiences do occur also during a variety of other conditions. For example, hallucinations are regarded as symptoms in several types of physical illnesses, particularly those that are accompanied by high fever; the experience is likewise not uncommon during the growth and development of a brain tumor; hallucinations may occur after prolonged loss of sleep or in cases of fatigue associated with great exhaustion; hallucinations may also be induced by the absorption of certain drugs, such as mescal, hashish, or alcohol. On occasion, auditory, visual, and tactile hallucinations may apparently occur during some period of time in the life of certain persons who have had no obvious mental abnormalities. An old extrasensory-perception questionnaire, based on replies from 17,000 supposedly normal persons who were asked whether they had ever experienced an hallucination, reported, men, 7.8 percent, and, women, 12 percent. Of these experiences 8.4 percent were supposedly visual, 3.3 percent were auditory, and 1 percent were tactile (Sidgwick, 1894, pp. 39–41). There is some question whether the subjects knew exactly what an hallucination is.

Hallucinatory experiences are undeniable phenomena in the inner life of a person when they occur and are, of course, essentially unknowable to anyone except the person who has experienced them. Even though about one person out of ten may claim to have had at least one hallucinatory experience, such events are so uncommon subjectively, that they generally astonish the experiencer on the first occasion, unless he has had hallucinations from childhood and is rather deficient mentally. If the hallucinations continue, the astonishment usually changes to fearful apprehension. The apprehension appears to be terrifying since the hearing of voices and the seeing of visions are traditionally associated with the loss of mind. A large percentage of (but not all) mental patients experience hallucinations. They may be experienced by mental patients assigned to almost every diagnostic category, although most of the recorded descriptions have been given by psychotics. Auditory hallucinations (usually the hearing of voices) are a leading symptom in the schizophrenic forms of psychosis, whereas visual hallucinations are among the more ordinary complaints offered by those who suffer from toxic and alcoholic psychoses. Hallucinations may involve any single sensory modality or any combination of modalities. Their intensity may vary from barely perceptible to overwhelmingly intense. Their organization may vary from simple clicks heard or flashes seen, to a completely organized perception of the entire experiential world.

Several thousand books and articles have been published dealing with the topic of hallucination. Since these phenomena are subjective individual accounts must be considered on their own merits. The only understanding and conclusions that any outside observer may gain with respect to the nature of hallucinatory experience derive from the various elements that are found to be shared among the reports made by thousands of individuals who have described the phenomena involved. Each patient so afflicted believes that he is probably the first human being who has ever had such experiences, but there are many elements in common in the descriptions offered by different persons. Indeed, the frequent concordance of the accounts convinces one that there are some nearly identical congeries of experiences which tend to occur in a variety of patients. It is almost impossible to overestimate the disturbing role that hallucinatory experience may play in the inner life of certain sufferers.

Analysis of Hallucinatory Experience

The difference between the subjective experiences of delirium and of hallucination is not obvious. Usually the term *delirium* is used to characterize the mental experiences that accompany a state of fever. The physician Dumont made the following generalization in describing a delirium which he experienced.

In fever you are subject to a host of errors with respect to persons and things; you are no longer conscious of time; you exaggerate distances; you undergo automatically the spectacle of an internal phantasmagoria, which in a vague way tires you, obsesses you or relaxes you; in a word, *it is a delirium.* In this intellectual confusion, there is nothing for the self, neither aberration nor disorder; only, we see very clearly thoughts which are strange to us which we do not recognize as ours, and which introduce themselves from without, multiply and swarm around with the greatest rapidity. (Dumont, 1865, pp. 14–15)

These abnormalities, which are characteristic of a delirium, are usually recognized by the patient as unreal and related to the general illness from which he is suffering at the time. Hallucinations, on the other hand, may or may not be considered unreal by the person having the experience. Persons who have experienced hallucinations for prolonged periods of time are often too confused in their thoughts to present their experiences in any organized fashion. More than twenty years ago the pseudonymous Jonathan Lang, who had suffered from schizophrenia and been a patient in a mental hospital for more than eight years, wrote and published two articles entitled *The Other Side of Hallucinations* (Lang, 1938, 1939a). These are remarkable documents. He presented here an account of his hallucinatory experience in an organized and systematic fashion, also giving evidence of considerable insight and self-understanding. Since Lang's formulation is so comprehensible and one of the most detailed on the subject, we will, for the most part, follow its outline in this chapter. In introducing the articles he wrote as follows.

Because of the subjective factors present in the experience of hallucinations, the patient obviously finds difficulty in considering them objectively and in reporting them with any degree of objectivity. Yet the report of the psychotic patient provides the basic data concerning hallucinatory phenomena.

As a schizophrenic who, though he has experienced various types of hallucinations over a period of more than eight years, has still retained a certain amount of intelligence, and who has some knowledge of general psychiatric literature, the writer feels that an account of the phenomena which he has experienced might be of some value. While he makes no pretense of having completely eliminated subjective factors, he has attempted to be as objective as the circumstances would permit. (Lang, 1938, p. 1089)

VISUAL HALLUCINATIONS

SIMPLE STATIONARY   There are more records, from a wider segment of the general population, of the experience of visions than of any other sensory modality but one gains the impression that auditory hallucinations are commoner. Possibly auditory hallucinations occur in persons less inclined to write about them. In older literature one can find innumerable accounts of persons who claimed to have witnessed apparitions such as ghosts, spirits, and the like. Sometimes these were said to be stationary, sometimes moving. Usually, the vision was organized and meaningful, although it may have been kaleidoscopic. An account may be cited here of a simple vision published by Ferriar in 1813 in his *An Essay towards a Theory of Apparitions.*

I had, in . . . 1791, the . . . experience [of] several extremely unpleasant circumstances, which were followed . . . by a most violent altercation. My wife . . . came into my apartment in the morning in order to console me, but I was too much agitated . . . to be capable of attending to [her], on a sudden I perceived, at about the distance of ten steps, a form like that of a deceased person, I pointed at it, asking my wife if she did not see it? It was but natural that she should not see any thing, my question therefore alarmed her very much, and she sent immediately for a physician. The phantasm continued about eight minutes. I grew at length more calm, and being extremely exhausted, fell into a restless sleep. . . . At four in the afternoon, the form which I had seen in the morning reappeared. I was by myself when this happened, and being rather uneasy at the incident, went to my wife's apartment, but there . . . at intervals [it] disappeared and always presented itself in a standing posture. (Ferriar, 1813, pp. 45–46)

Ferriar continued to see, at intervals, not only one figure, but an increasing number of persons. Then these visionary people started to make remarks about him, speaking in a derogatory fashion. After two months of these experiences, he was bled by a surgeon, during which treatment the phantasms faded out and finally dissolved in the air. He later said he had been sick but not insane during this episode.

During the latter part of the eighteenth century, Joanna Southcott, a simple English woman, began having experiences of visions and "communications" that she considered revelations of the Divine; these revelations eventually formed the basis of a religious faith and organization that she founded. As a sample of one of her visions she recounted the following.

> I omitted to mention . . . that, at the end of 1794, I had a strange vision —As soon as I had laid down in my bed, a light came over the room. I looked at the window; but saw no light proceed from thence. I looked at the door, to see if any one was entering with a candle; but no person was there. The room now appeared to me to be full of lighted candles, hanging, in candlesticks, on lines crossing the room. Being astonished and frightened, I covered my head with the bed-clothes, and then saw a spacious room, with a chandelier of many branches, and lighted lamps sparkling with great lustre. In the midst of the room stood a large table, with large lighted candles thereon; so that the light equalled the noon-day. (Southcott, 1801, p. 17)

In this description there is no mention of movement, or of human figures. Rather, there is a report of a great increase in the level of illumination experienced both when the person's head was under the bedclothing and when she was alone in a darkened room. When her head was covered, thus excluding all competing visual material, then she thought she was in a lighted room with lighted chandeliers. The "communications" she experienced came not through the hearing of voices but by direct knowledge that she felt God bestowed on her mind.

Lang discussed in the following way the simple and more frequent visual hallucinations he experienced.

> At an early stage, the appearance of colored flashes of light was common. These took the form either of distant streaks or of near-by round glowing patches about a foot in diameter. Another type which took place five or six times, was the appearance of words or symbols on blank surfaces. Closely connected with this was the occasional substitution of hallucinatory matter for the actual printed matter in books which I have been reading. On these occasions, the passage which I have been seeing has dissolved while I have been looking at it and another and sometimes wholly different passage has appeared in its place. In passing, mention may be made that the inhibitory or anesthetic factor must have been involved in this form of hallucination since at one time or another the actual stimulus must have been blocked. Still a further form of visual hallucinations that happened on two occasions was the appearance on a wall of the pictures of young women as though projected from a projection machine. These pictures were of women whom to the best of my knowledge I had never met. (Lang, 1938, p. 1093)

MOVING FIGURES Visions that involve moving, living figures are more frequently reported than are the simple stationary visual hallucinations. Often the moving figures occur after the simple stationary figures have first been experienced, as was related in the cited incident published by Ferriar.

Another example may be cited from the account written by a literary man, who had gradually acquired the habit of drinking large quantities of whiskey daily. Fearing he might acquire some mental disorder and in order to break this habit, he finally placed himself under the medical care of Dr. Dawson. His treatment consisted in the withdrawal from almost all alcohol, together with a daily injection of a small dose of atropin. After two days he began to have visual hallucinations. The patient was aware of the unreality of these experiences but was unable either to stop or to alter their course.

The first I saw of them was the brown man. He was leaning over my bed at arm's length; I could easily have touched him. He was a tall, dark man with brown eyes and beard, and he looked very grave. I was wide awake and took in every detail of his dress and expression, though it was night and the room was dark. His appearance surprised me very slightly, for I had noticed him walking about close by in the grounds outside my window, which was on the ground floor. I thought he had mistaken his bed-room, and said so. I had no suspicion that he was any other than the man I had seen walking in the afternoon. I fancied that he explained that he had come to see how I was getting on, and then he slowly backed towards the door and left the room. I noticed that he did not seem to open the door but simply went through it. Then for the first time it flashed upon me that he might not be a real man, and I remember that I was not exactly frightened but felt a little uncomfortable. I was not perfectly sure about the closed door; I might have been mistaken. I remained absolutely awake and alert. I did not light my candle. I was wondering if the brown man would reappear or come back. . . . The pale girl completely set at rest all doubts. She appeared soon after the brown man had left, but she did not come in at the door, but suddenly stood at the foot of my bed. (Dawson, 1909, p. 713)

He continued his account by relating that various other persons came to visit him, all of whom he considered to be unreal. The following day, he said, while walking in the garden, he saw a horse and cart, a dog, and a group of people, none of which was real. He then went indoors and there observed that all his windows seemed filled with people who silently watched his every move. During the next several days apparitions of this sort continued to plague him until they finally vanished. It is worth noting that many of these apparitions appeared only while he was in bed in a dark room. He saw them with astonishment but without apprehension. He somehow knew that the figures were unreal, so that, he said, the experience did not actually frighten him.

Davidson, from whose *Remembrances* I have quoted previously, experienced a wide variety of hallucinations. He told of one occasion, during the recovery from his second psychotic attack, when, having turned off the light and gone to bed, he saw a small, bright ball of fire that came slowly down through the transom, hung for a few seconds in mid-air, and then went out. This was followed by a wonderful and immense solid ball of fire that remained suspended in the room for some time and then also disappeared. He thought these visions meant that God had tried to convey a message to him. Wishing to be certain of the experience, he got up and opened the door to see whether the electric lights in the corridor might have changed and thus have given rise to the vision. He saw that the hall lights were of a different color and much less intense than the fire balls had been. He returned to bed, closed his eyes and attempted to sleep but was overcome by a pleasant swimming sensation. He describes his experiences after he had opened his eyes in the dark.

I first saw thick clouds of a dark purple colour roll past, as if driven by a strong wind from my right hand to my left; while from my left, rays of bright golden light came down through the clouds, lighting up most wonderfully their inner linings. Then from my right hand there appeared, in amongst the clouds, the figure of a young man. He was standing, reading a book that was in front of him on the back of a living lectern, in the shape of a large and powerful bird, like an eagle, except that its plumage was black or dark brown and white, and its bill, though thick and powerful, was not curved, but straight, and of a golden colour. The young man was dressed in a long purple robe, which was fastened high and close round the neck, and similar in colour to the clouds. He was standing turned somewhat away from me; and I noticed that he was very dark and sallow, and his features clearly cut and straight. I was most impressed by the fact that he was either very bald or had the tonsure of a monk, and that what hair he had was short and very black. (Davidson, 1912, p. 241)

This vision became brighter and brighter so that he turned his head and closed his eyes, at which instant the vision disappeared. He wrote, "It was not an hallucination nor yet a reality, and it had not been caused accidentally." For a time he thought that this had been a vision of either St. Paul or St. Patrick; later he thought it had been the devil. He never once considered the possibility that the experience was other than some sort of supernatural revelation. Throughout both of his psychotic episodes Davidson saw many visions, which he always considered to be either divine or demoniac revelations.

In contrast to Davidson, Lang seldom had visual hallucinations of moving figures.

In its pure form, unassociated with other types of hallucinations, it has come within my knowledge only once. . . . it consisted of the apparition of a woman dressed in a white dress which seemed to be gliding down the street ahead of me one night before disappearing into the thin air. The figure was definitely outlined. It was opaque: in other words, it must have included an anesthetic factor since having no real existence, it should not have blocked light radiations which nevertheless were blocked. The figure moved without any sound, though the night was quiet, and though it appeared within the zone where sound should have been heard. (Lang, 1938, p. 1093)

Most hallucinatory experience is so exactly like ordinary everyday sensory life that the experiencer first considers the event to be real though somewhat unusual and startling. Frequently, only later events supply meanings to the experience, thereby giving some clues to its possible unreality.

LILLIPUTIAN FIGURES There are several oddities, which have been reported by various persons, that are worth singling out. Among these are the so-called lilliputian figures, of which the following passage, told by Leroy's patient, is an example.

The evening of the day that I became ill, I was astounded and amused to see appear, on a kind of ledge going the round of the room formed by beams situated at some distance from the ceiling, about a hundred little men and women about six inches in height. They wore yellow, red or blue trousers and skirts. The men had a kind of fez and the women wore bonnets. Certain of them were mounted on small bay colored horses proportionate in size. All this little world in miniature walked, stopped, gesticulated, turned round and appeared to be speaking without my hearing any sound. These personages gradually disappeared and departed in columns at the end of half an hour. (Leroy, 1922, p. 326)

Lilliputian figures are usually experienced as silent. They commonly occur in the experience of patients who are suffering (or have recently suffered) from either a toxic psychosis or alcoholic hallucinosis, and have been reported by normal persons in isolation. Usually, the experiencer realizes that the lilliputian figures cannot be real, which fact in itself justifies their appearance as a disconcerting experience.

The following account of hallucinatory lilliputian figures, written by a seemingly normal man to Professor Conklin, is more detailed than most records of the sort.

When I sit down or lie down, day or night, and close my eyes, I seem to be in a different realm, though still awake, and can open my eyes at will. As I close them the vista and perspective broadens and opens out, mountains, sometimes, appear on the distant horizon, hills and valleys come and go, trees with the most delicate green leafage imaginable appear gently shimmering in the shadowy glow, and then passing to and fro, in this mysterious land the [small] forms in human shape that I call spirits begin to make their appearance. . . . They are all happy as they pass in review before my vision, and smile sweetly as they look my way. They converse by thought transference instantly expressed in a most silent manner from mind to mind. . . . Mere volition or motion in these forms show what they are. . . . I have seen [minute] elephants and cattle, horses and mules, lions and tigers, wandering around the pastures and jungles of my vision. . . . I control these subjects to a certain extent, but I never take any advice from them nor do I give any. I have tried to draw them out on subjects of astronomy, art, literature, and inventions but to no purpose. They have shown me crude inventions of their own which would be utterly useless, but they are all very simple minded. I have seen them in vast throngs passing me by, to where, the Lord only knows. The bluest of blue eyes with the sweetest little oval faces have come out of the great somewhere, and within six inches of my face have looked me over with infinite sweetness and then slowly vanished. (Conklin, 1925, pp. 133–134)

The author of this report was so thoroughly convinced of the reality of these experiences that he attempted to photograph them. The prints he submitted showed a textured background on which, by using a certain amount of imagination, one could discern fragments of isolated faces, portions of a human body, and so on.

AUDITORY HALLUCINATIONS

SIMPLE The onset of Schreber's psychosis furnishes an excellent sample of this kind of abnormal phenomena.

The first really bad, that is to say almost sleepless nights, occurred in the last days of October . . . It was then that an extraordinary event occurred. During several nights when I could not get to sleep, a recurrent crackling noise in the wall of our bedroom became noticeable at shorter or longer intervals; time and again it woke me as I was about to go to sleep. Naturally we thought of a mouse although it was very extraordinary that a mouse should have found its way to the first floor of such a solidly built house. But having heard similar noises innumerable times since then, and still hearing them around me every day in daytime and at night, I have come to recognize them as undoubted divine miracles—they are called "interferences" by the voices talking to me. (Schreber, 1955, p. 64)

These sounds, resembling the noisy background of poor radio reception, have been mentioned by many patients. They may be disturbing but usually do not convey any particular meaning to the listener.

WITH INANIMATE REFERENCE Lang gave the following example of this variety of hallucination.

A closely allied type of hallucination . . . was the appearance of words synchronized with environmental sounds. The words were definitely formed and sometimes even were grouped to form short sentences, though the repetition of a single word was commoner. They seemed to originate from the locus of the sound with which they were associated. They were synchronized with the sound, *i.e.*, the words changed in volume with changes in the volume of the sound. (Lang, 1938, pp. 1089–1090)

Phenomena which have inanimate reference as the above are often confused with illusions, in that voices or meaningful sounds are attached to, or formed out of, all the random noises that take place around every hearing person throughout his lifetime. In a few instances such auditory experiences have been said to be associated with the neuropathological changes that occur during the development of brain tumors.

A journalist, Karinthy, wrote the following account of this particular psychological symptom, which was the first he experienced and which occurred during the development of a brain tumor.

And at that very moment the trains started. Punctually to the minute, at ten past seven, I heard the first one. I looked up in surprise to see what was happening. There was a distinct rumbling noise, followed by a slow, increasing reverberation, as when the wheels of an engine begin their unhurried movement, then work up a louder and louder roar as the train glides past us, only to fade gradually into silence. . . . Only a minute had gone by when the next train started, to precisely the same rhythm—rumbling, reverberating and fading away.

I raised my head irritably towards the neighbouring street. What were they playing at? Trains running outside, or was it an experiment with some new means of locomotion? . . . A few cars passed, but no other traffic. Three times I raised my head, and it was only when the fourth train started that I realized I was suffering from an hallucination. (Karinthy, 1939, pp. 12–13)

Karinthy reported no other forms of hallucinatory experience, although he did have a rapidly growing brain tumor which led to an increasing dimness of vision, but which never gave rise to any form of visual hallucinations.

WITH HUMAN REFERENCE   According to Lang's system of classification, the third variety of auditory hallucination is the following.

This phenomenon can perhaps best be depicted by a description of the first time I experienced it. I was one of four men at a bridge table. On one of the deals, my partner bid three clubs. I looked at my hand: I had only one small club. Though my hand was weak, I had to bid to take him out. My bid won. When my partner laid down his cards, he showed only two small clubs in his hand. I immediately questioned why he had bid three clubs. He denied having made such a bid. The other two men at the table supported him. There was no opportunity and no reason for the three of them to have been framing me. In actuality, he had not made a bid of three clubs despite the fact that I had distinctly heard him do so. Not only had the hallucination included a spatial component synchronized with man's position, but it had also duplicated exactly the vocal tones of the man. Furthermore, the man had actually declared a different bid at the time I had heard him bidding three clubs. This bid I had not heard. Somewhere along the line of my nervous system the words which he had actually spoken were blocked and the hallucinatory words substituted. . . .

Hallucinations with human reference are, at the time of their occurrence, impossible to tell from the actual speech of the person who seems to be making them. Sometimes the lack of relationship of the hallucinatory remark to the other conversation of the person, provides a clue to some form of deviation, but, otherwise, the person who experiences an hallucination of this type, receives no indication of its non-normal origin in the experience itself. Only a subsequent check with the person who seems to have made the remark, can provide a check as to the actuality of the occurrence. In some cases, this subsequent check even is of little value, for to the person experiencing it, the hallucination is actual experience over-weighing the subsequent testimony of the person who seems to have made it, since to the hallucinated person, the testimony may be a lie which the seeming originator of the hallucination may be making to conceal his former act. (Lang, 1938, p. 1090)

The hearing of unreal voices is, as Lang points out, a very confusing experience in the mental life of any person. In part, a patient can realize that there is something which may be unreal in his experiential world, but more usually there is such a mixture of real and unreal that everything seems real, and since the hallucinatory voices do occupy such a large portion of his conscious waking life, they are most apt to override any corrections he might otherwise make.

Schreber discussed his voices as follows.

The "voices" manifest themselves in me as nervous impulses, and always have the character of *soft lisping noises* sounding like distinct human words . . . Predominant is their absolute nonsense as the phrases are stylistically incomplete, and the many terms of abuse which aim at provoking me; that is to say to make me break the silence necessary for sleep. . . .

For about almost seven years—except during sleep—*I have never had a single moment in which I did not hear voices.* They accompany me to every place and at all times; they continue to sound even when I am in conversation with other people, they persist undeterred even when I concentrate on other things, for instance read a book or a newspaper, play the piano, etc.; only when I am talking aloud to other people or to myself are they of course drowned by the stronger sound of the spoken word and therefore inaudible to me. But the well-known phrases recommence at once, sometimes in the middle of a sentence, which tells me that the conversation had continued during the interval, that is to say that those nervous stimuli or vibrations responsible for the weaker sounds of the voices continue even while I talk aloud. (Schreber, 1955, pp. 224–225)

It is worth noting that the voices spoke and were heard during *all* of Schreber's waking life. Only when submerged by some greater sound volume were they displaced from the primacy of his hearing world. He did not question his experiences with the voices nor the meanings they communicated to him.

Perceval, like Schreber, continued to hear voices throughout most of the acute phase of his mental illness. He wrote of them as follows.

The voices . . . were mostly heard in my head, though I often heard them in the air, or in different parts of the room. Every voice was different, and each beautiful, and, generally, speaking or singing in a different tone and measure, and resembling those of relations or friends. There appeared to be many in my head, I should say upwards of fourteen. I divide them, as they styled themselves, or one another, into voices of contrition and voices of joy and honour. Those of contrition were, I think all without any exception, on the left temple and forehead; those of joy and honour on the right temple and forehead; but on each side of the head, as it were over the middle of the eyebrow, two spirits seemed always to sing or speak to a measure more quick and more flaunty than the others—that on the left was, I think, called the spirit of my eldest sister—that on the right was the spirit of Herminet Herbert. I understood the use of these spirits, which were spirits of humor and politeness, to be necessary to a holy turn of thought, and that the world did not like the use, or understand the use of them. My thoughts flowed regularly from left to right, guided by these voices and their suggestions; and if I turned them from right to left, I was told that I was playing the hypocrite. I think it right to mention this because it was always so; and though it may appear fanciful, there may, nevertheless, lie hid some truth in it connected with the nervous system which I cannot venture to explain. Amongst the names given to the spirits were those of Contrition, those of Joy, of Gladness, of Joviality, of Mirth, Martha (by which I understood overanxiety), and Mockery, of Honesty, or Sincerity, and, amongst others, "a spirit of honorable anxiety to do my duty to the best of my own satisfaction," which I was told was the spirit of my sisters —the use of such a phrase is evidently humorous, or ironical, or satirical. (Perceval, 1840, pp. 297–298)

The citations which have been given from Schreber and Perceval point out the fact that the experiencer regarded the voices as supernatural, of divine or demoniacal origin. Although such voices are usually said by patients to be supernatural, some patients have reported that they heard voices which made no claim to divinity. This is found in the following incident, which was reported in *The Maniac* as having happened at the onset of an acute psychosis.

I did not read in bed, but blew out the candle immediately. My head had scarcely touched the pillow when a man's voice—a very pleasant baritone voice—proceeding apparently from the large armchair by the fireplace, asked clearly and aloud—"Are you awake?"

I raised myself on my left elbow, and facing the direction whence the voice came, and feeling suddenly no longer tired, but brisk and most alert, I answered—"Yes, wide awake. Who are you?"

(I have never in my life heard any "voices," and should have been extremely startled at hearing one then had I been in my right senses. As it was, I was no more startled than one is startled by dreams, when the most astonishing and unlikely things seem quite natural and ordinary.)

The "voice" ignored my question and went on—"Are you not the author of [*Beyond the Occult*]?" . . . "Yes!" I exclaimed in surprise. "But how can you possibly know of it? It was never published." . . . "If you know so much about the creation of that work, you must be the artist? You must be . . . Ray Hall?"

The voice did not deny this indictment, and throughout the entire remainder of my attack of madness I was fully convinced that this man's voice continually holding converse with me was the voice of that artist. (Anon., 1932a, pp. 7; 9)

It is significant that the woman who wrote this account pointed out that she should have been startled at the hearing of a voice, but was not; indeed, she took the incident for granted. She also noted that the voice never actually admitted to its being that of Ray Hall; neither did it deny it. This attribution of a definite name to a voice or vision (without any direct confirmation) has been noted by many patients, as forming part of the total hallucinatory experience.

Since the experience of hearing voices is so commonly reported by mental patients, one could easily continue citing one example after another. However, since the most commonly reported, if not the most commonly experienced, hallucinations are those that combine the various sensory modalities, particularly vision and audition, I will proceed to detail these.

COMBINED VISUAL AND AUDITORY HALLUCINATIONS

SYNCHRONIZED   As a first example of this concurrent experience the following reminiscence, written by an anonymous patient, may be cited.

The instant my eyes closed, as they did frequently and almost involuntarily, vast apartments would open before me—halls, corridors, and gorgeous suites of rooms—at first all empty, but in a moment they would be filled with multitudes of people of all ages, sexes, costumes, nations, and tongues. I could hear them thronging on the stairways before they appeared, and see them take their places in vast masses and serried columns. Not only did they all talk incessantly, but every one of the countless multitudes gazed fixedly upon me. Many pointed at me with their fingers and canes, and ogled me through their opera-glasses. This ordeal would become intolerable, and, on opening my eyes and turning over in the bed, the vision would vanish. . . . Of all the countless spectres of that night I recognized but one. His was a stalwart figure, towering a head and shoulders above all the rest . . . I need scarcely add that this was Gen. Winfield Scott. (Anon., 1857, p. 160)

The gentleman who wrote this account suffered from a psychotic episode that was probably complicated by acute alcoholism. The spectacle described above seemed somewhat unreal to him when it began, but during the days that followed the disturbance developed into actual madness.

Lang listed several examples of these audiovisual hallucinations with rather more considered and detailed analytic considerations than are offered by most patients.

I have twice experienced this intricate [audiovisual] phenomenon. Its first occurrence was during the third month of the psychosis, and may be labeled "the hallucination of the young lady." I was walking down the street on a bright sunny morning. The door of a house about 15 yards in front of me opened, and a young lady stepped out and started walking down the sidewalk in front of me. I recognized her as a woman whom I had previously seen coming out of the same house, but otherwise I did not know her. Every aspect of her appearance was exactly lifelike; her figure was perfectly three dimensional; it was opaque. And every time that her heels struck the sidewalk I distinctly heard the click of their contact with the sidewalk. After the figure had kept ahead of me for about two blocks, I happened to look down; when I glanced up again, the figure had vanished. It had been passing a vacant lot, and there was no house for it to have gone into.

The second time that it took place, was some three years later. This second appearance involved the seeming seeing of a phantom street car. At dusk one evening, I was walking down a street which cut across a street car line about a block above the south end of the street car line. When I was about half a block above the street car line, a street car passed heading toward the end of the line. The car had every appearance of an actual car. Its shape was three dimensional; it was opaque, except for its windows; it had passengers and crew; its trolley sent sparks flying from the trolley wire. In addition, I distinctly heard the rumble of its wheels as it swept past. Yet when I reached the street on which the car ran, and looked toward the end of the line where the car should have been standing, there was no car to be seen. Actually no car had passed. Two factors common to both occurrences may be noted. Firstly, as long as the hallucinations continued, they were indistinguishable from other factors of the normal external configuration with which they were perfectly integrated; it was only in the manner of their disappearance that they evidenced their non-normal origin. Secondly, they included the occurrence of a marked involvement of the anesthetic factor. In order for the hallucinations to have had opaqueness, a moving swathe of actual light radiations must have been blocked. (Lang, 1938, pp. 1093–1094)

In no one of the audiovisual hallucinations cited thus far were the phenomena of particular significance or meaning to the patient. However, the more usual phenomena of this sort do convey a mystical or religious meaning that is easily incorporated into the patient's delusional system. For example, Davidson related several instances of complicated audiovisual hallucinations that were fitted into his total delusional system. He had, during his first psychosis, believed that his hospital attendant, named J——, was really Jesus Christ. One day, while walking around the hospital grounds, the following incident occurred.

I became aware of something remarkable happening in the air only a very short distance in front of me. It seemed to me that there had been some big air waves, and then through them the well-known form of J—— appeared, facing me, and coming towards me. I thought for a second that he had been rendered invisible by ordinary heat waves that had happened to be between us, and that he had just walked through them. As soon as I thought this, he seemed to disappear for a second; once again he became clearly visible, firm, and solid, all but his feet, which seemed lost in vibrating air; an instant afterwards they became visible, and I heard the gravel crunch under his tread as he took four of five paces up to me. The whole thing was almost as quick as thought and only a matter of a few seconds, but for a moment I was astonished, and thought that indeed I was standing in the presence of the God of Israel. I was not in the least frightened; indeed, I was very much relieved; and if an angel with lightning-like countenance and glistening wings had appeared, I would have been delighted. (Davidson, 1912, p. 61)

Incidents of this sort occurred many times during Davidson's illness. The experiences, as related, seemed to him to have the features of an externally based perception, plus elements that were added to the whole by his religious delusion.

Schreber, whose delusional thinking was more mystical and disorganized than was Davidson's, wrote as follows about the visually perceptible apparatus involved in the production of auditory hallucinations.

Visual stimuli (visual hallucinations) are in my case almost as *persistent as auditory stimuli* (voices, auditory hallucinations). With my mind's eye I *see* the rays which are both the carriers of the voices and of the poison of corpses to be unloaded on my body, as long drawn out filaments approaching my head from some vast distant spot on the horizon. I can see them *only* with my mind's eye when my eyes are closed by miracles or when I close them voluntarily, that is to say they are then reflected on my inner nervous system as long filaments stretching towards my head. I see the same phenomena with my *bodily* eye when I keep my eyes open: I see these filments, as it were, from one or more far distant spots beyond the horizon stretching sometimes towards my head, sometimes withdrawing from it. (Schreber, 1955, p. 227)

Schreber's belief was, as we mentioned before, that he was in constant "nerve contact" with God and all other souls of the Universe. These rays or filaments were the lines of communication over which voices and poisons were carried to and from God through Schreber's brain.

DIVINE AND DEMONIACAL HALLUCINATIONS There are many records of persons, otherwise sane, who have described divine and demoniacal supernatural experiences. Often it will be found that such incidents have been recorded by mystics, saints, and other religiously inclined persons. It is difficult to distinguish clearly between accounts written by religious persons and those provided by persons who had never given particular attention to any religious belief or practice.

Swedenborg, one of the world's greatest physical scientists, began during his fifth decade of life to experience mystical revelations. He was never considered to be insane, either by his contemporaries or by himself. A few citations from the account of his mystical experience are as follows.

Certain spirits appeared over my head, and thence were heard voices like thunder, for the thunder of their voices exactly resembled the sound of thunder from the clouds after lightning; I at first conjectured that it was owing to a great multitude of spirits, who had the art of uttering voices attended with so loud a noise. The more simple spirits, who were with me, smiled on the occasion, at which I was much surprised; but the cause of their smiling was presently discovered to be this, that the spirits who thundered were not many, but few, and were also as little as children. (Swedenborg, 1839, p. 73)

Then other spirits withdrew. At the right, above, were those who spoke with me; they did not allow . . . them to operate, and so long did good spirits talk with me, and these infused (their persuasions), till I was almost worn out with hearing good spirits speak . . . The good spirits were continually saying that (these evil spirits) are allowed to operate into the right part of the head, not into the left, and from the right part of the head into the left side of the thorax; (but) by no means into the left of the head, (for if) so, they said that I would be destroyed. (Swedenborg, 1883, p. 34)

The speech of angelic spirits was perceived, but not heard or understood; it was only perceived by the sense of sight under the form of a shining vibration. They spake for some time among themselves, and it was said to me that this was the speech of angelic spirits. (Swedenborg, 1883, p. 327)

Experiences and revelations of this sort started, as we said, in the latter half of Swedenborg's life. For thirty years or more he occupied himself with the recording and publishing of his divine revelations, which he organized into a systematic theology.

I continue by giving brief citations from Perceval and from Schreber, which may be both contrasted and compared to the above extracts from Swedenborg's *Spiritual Diary.*

During this year, also, I heard very beautiful voices, singing to me in the most touching manner—and on one occasion I heard the sounds of the cattle lowing and of other beasts in the fields, convey articulate sentences to me, as it is written of Balaam. On another I was threatened terribly by the thunder from heaven—in short, nearly all sounds I heard were clothed with articulation. (Perceval, 1840, p. 264)

All these souls spoke to me as "voices" more or less at the same time without one knowing of the presence of the others. Everyone who realizes that all this is not just the morbid offspring of my fantasy, will be able to appreciate the unholy turmoil they caused in my head. It is true that the souls had . . . their own thoughts and were therefore able to give information of the highest interest to me; they were also able to answer questions, whereas for a long time now the talk of the voices has consisted only of a terrible, monotonous repetition of ever recurring phrases . . .

I believe I may say that at that time and at that time *only,* I saw God's omnipotence in its complete purity. . . . The radiant picture of his rays became visible to my inner eye, while I was lying in bed not sleeping but awake—that is to say he was reflected on my inner nervous system. Simultaneously I heard his voice; but it was not a soft whisper—as the talk of the voices always was before and after that time—it resounded in a mighty bass as if directly in front of my bedroom windows. (Schreber, 1955, pp. 72; 124)

The accounts of Swedenborg, Perceval, and Schreber describe the voices and visions of spirits, souls, or angels who sang beautifully and gave divine inspiration and knowledge, all of which was considered by each experiencer as directly related to God and to His high regard for the individual in question.

In contrast, as far as content is concerned, are the experiences of demoniacal hallucinations. For example, I cited in Chapters 2 and 4 from the letters of an otherwise normal Englishman who, in two different publications, related his sufferings, which he attributed to his being possessed by evil spirits. These accounts he handed to the editor of the *Journal of Psychological Medicine*. In the following I cite some further details he included in these letters.

Whilst taking a quiet walk one evening, far from the busy hum of men, about five years since, I heard the sound of voices near me, speaking of me. I looked in every direction, but could not discover any one; I got over some banks, thinking that, probably, the persons might have been concealed from view by them; but no human creatures were there. I walked away from the spot, still the voices pursued me. I mixed with the thickest of the throng in the metropolis; the voices still continued to haunt me, and the words then uttered were—"Who is he?—do you know who he is?" The response was—"He is Satan's own." These words seemed continuously to proceed from the persons I passed. I crossed and recrossed the bridges; still the same voices followed me. (Anon, 1849a, p. 463)

[His suffering continued, and in his second letter he wrote]: Whilst at home I was incessantly tormented by the evil spirits by day—the idea can be but inadequately conceived, of seven persons continually talking to each other, or to me, or of me, on all kinds of subjects, making observations, satiric or pleasing, on what I thought, or did, or said, or intended; carrying my attention from the subject on which I might have been engaged, into other extraneous channels, thereby preventing my reading or writing, thinking, acting, or speaking, without confusion or forgetfulness; incapacitating me for the exercise of my profession, which I had increased to a very large extent, and which I have, chiefly on this account been obliged to relinquish; and by night causing me, by the most horrible proposals, threats, and artifices, to keep awake for five or six, or more hours, every night, in the most dreadful state of agony that it is possible for the human mind to portray. . . .

I have always enjoyed the entire possession of my senses; I have never seen any of the spirits; I did not believe in them until this visitation,—but voices occurring in this manner cannot be those of the human race. I can readily imagine the recurrence of the brain to vocal or instrumental music contrary to one's own wishes,—this would be a species of reverberation of the sound of that which one had previously heard; again, the recurrence of a murderer to the scene of his guilty catastrophe, is attributable to his thoughts constantly dwelling on the subject of his crime; but voices speaking distinctly to one on topics unthought of at the time, using expressions to which one has been unaccustomed, pointing out what one has wholly forgotten or omitted, or done or thought wrongly or amiss, cannot be caused by reverberation of sound or recollection of ideas. They are not the reiteration of sounds, the refraction on the mind of bye-gone objects; here the brain, it must be borne in memory, is not approached through any other but *one* sense, and that is the faculty of hearing. Whence can sounds, then, so dissimilar, so dissonant, to one's innate nature originate? (Anon., 1850c, pp. 266; 267–268)

This man recognized the social difficulties in which he placed himself by describing to the world at large the feelings and experiences that others would call hallucinations. Yet he felt compelled to do so, since long reflection had convinced him that there was no other way to account for the voices but to believe that they emanated from Satan, and this belief he felt driven to proclaim. He concluded that the Devil was roaming about like a roaring lion seeking souls he might devour. His account, he hoped, might convince others to turn their thoughts to the seeking of divine salvation. Other than the fact that the voices announced to him that he was "Satan's own," his account gave little reason for the assumption of his being possessed by the Devil. The inner distinction which any individual may have made as to whether the audiovisual hallucinations were good or evil seems to depend on some personal judgment or conviction that is rarely stated in a clear fashion.

A somewhat similar account was recorded in a letter sent by a patient to a physician (Dr. Mayer) who saw him in consultation. The patient's original complaint had been sleeplessness, but after the medical consultation he wrote the following letter to the doctor.

One evening it began to talk to me, telling me some funny stories, and it kept that up for a week, when one Saturday evening it hypnotized me as I sat in my chair, and I went to bed that night and was in bed until Monday, hypnotized, I suppose, for I was seeing pictures of all kinds all the time until I got up to go to work Monday morning. He has been talking to me ever since. He says he is the devil from hell and he is going to take me to hell as soon as he gets ready. He makes me speak words as if he has my tongue in his control when he is talking to me; but if I talk to any person, I have control. He makes me smell different things and he will tell me about it at the same time. It feels as if there is a flea or bug on my eye, nose, or throat, or any place, and he will say to me, "Brush that bug off." He bothers my eyes, so that I cannot see right at times, and he bothers my stomach at night, saying, "I'll fix your stomach for you so you cannot eat." Three weeks ago, he shook my brain like you would a handkerchief, saying to me, "See what I am doing to you, I'll fix this block of yours." He talks to me all day and night, waking me at night to tell me what he made me dream. He makes my head hurt in the back and it feels hot, and he says it will be worse later on with me. (Mayer, 1911, pp. 265–266)

Six months later, after a short period of psychotherapeutic treatment, he again wrote the doctor saying that the voice was now almost always quiet and only occasionally did he hear softly spoken fragments of sentences. It was not stated that this patient was, himself, ever convinced of the true demoniacal nature of his experiences nor was it recorded whether or not he was religiously inclined.

Macalpine and Hunter translated and published under the title, *Schizophrenia, 1677*, the manuscript* account of a demoniacal possession by a humble painter. This painter had written and illustrated the original manuscript for the monks of a Holy Order, who had treated him by exorcising the Devil to whom he said he had sold his soul. Part of this account runs as follows.

In the evening I went to my bedroom to say my prayers there and after I had said them there was a clap of thunder and a bright flame came down on me so that I again fell into a swoon.
Thereupon my sister came and with her a gentleman who called me by my name, and with that I came to myself. Then it seemed to me as if I were lying in nothing but fire and stench, and could not stand on my feet. I rolled out of my chamber into the room, and rolled around the room until the blood gushed out of my mouth and nose. Then my sister did not know what to do with me; so she sent for the priests. After they had come the stench and heat disappeared. As I could not yet stand on my feet I was lifted on a chair. A quarter of an hour after the priests had left me again, something came to my side and spoke to me; this suffering is given to you because you have such worthless and idle thoughts. . . . On the 26th day of December and on 30th December, two evil spirits tortured me with ropes, which I felt on my limbs for two days afterwards. (Macalpine and Hunter, 1956, p. 80)

These paragraphs detail a short sample of his description of his struggle with the Devil. He recounted that nine years earlier, being in a depressed mood, he had made a pact with the Devil. The period of the pact had expired and he was now being tortured by the Devil to whom he had promised his soul. With the manuscript he left eight paintings depicting the various forms in which the Devil had appeared to him.

Many descriptions of audiovisual hallucinations of religious and mystical events are available in the published literature. They range from well-organized evidence of divine revelation to fantastic and unbelievably tangled tales of the belief or conviction that the experience had conveyed to the mind of the individual. In Chapter 8 on *Delusion* I will return to and consider in more detail the problems raised by the

---

* In 1923 Freud published a paper entitled *A Neurosis of Demoniacal Possession in the Seventeenth Century*, based on his reading and analysis of this manuscript.

conviction of supernatural truth that hallucinations elicit in the mind of a mental patient.

SILENT VOICES AND THOUGHTS-OUT-LOUD

Many patients have described the experience of hearing their inner thoughts whispered or spoken aloud by some outside agent. Sometimes these thoughts are "stolen" from them and directly spoken or they may be distorted while being expressed. At other times certain thoughts may be involuntarily impressed on their mind and then compulsively uttered. Some patients have called these phenomena *silent voices* or the *voice of conscience*. Such experiences of double thought, heard both from the inside and from the outside, are described as having no auditory component. The experiencer knows and realizes the meaning and the content of the silent voices but never "hears" them.

Very appropriately, Lang called these silent voices *thoughts-out-loud* and discussed them as follows.

Because of certain points of similarity with auditory hallucinations, I myself . . . related the phenomena of thoughts-out-loud to auditory hallucinatory phenomena. Recently, consideration of an accompanying minimal tonus of the vocal muscles and of the ease with which the thoughts-out-loud slide over into automatic speech, has led me to the view that the phenomenon is in part rather to be classed as a "minimal compulsion."

Regardless of its classification, thoughts-out-loud has formed one of the two major factors of my psychotic symptomatology. First appearing during the latter part of the first month of the psychosis, it has continued throughout the eight years. In its original state, occurring only for short periods of only a few minutes in length, the duration of its occurrence spread rapidly. By the end of the second month of the psychosis, it spanned practically all the time that I was awake. Since that time, it has continued to maintain this extended duration. . . .

The factor of the verbal productions of the thoughts-out-loud is of the greatest importance. It may be said practically to absorb the function of verbal productions of the individual. Except in actual social conversation with another person, verbal expression of the thoughts of the ego appears only in the thoughts-out-loud. The ego does not have a direct access to words. Besides the expression of the ego's thoughts, the verbal productions of the thoughts-out-loud present ideas foreign to the ego.

These two differing phases of the verbal productions of the thoughts-out-loud, have in general their own forms of expression. In respect to the phrasing of the ego's thoughts, two styles of constructions take place the most frequently. . . . When the ego has an overt orientation, as in reading or writing, or in observation of the environment, the verbal productions of the thoughts-out-loud take the form of a running presentation of verbals suited to the activity holding the interest of the ego, adding an occasional side remark addressed to the ego. For example, if the individual is reading, the thoughts-out-loud reproduce the words of the book the individual is reading, sometimes making a comment on a passage. When the orientation of the ego is more strictly introvert, as for example in reflection, the verbal productions often take the form of an imaginary conversation between the individual and some person with whom the individual is acquainted.

In connection with the expression of foreign ideas, the verbal production of the thoughts-out-loud usually takes the form of monologues attempting to persuade the ego to adopt a belief in the authority of the agent behind the · thoughts-out-loud, and to accept a Messianic fixation. Attached to these monologues are expressions of the thoughts of the ego concerning the arguments. Another variant is the presentation of arguments seeking to persuade the individual to specific acts. . . .

The two phases of the thoughts-out-loud,—the presentation of the thoughts of the ego and the presentation of foreign ideas,—are not hard and fast categories. Elements of one are often mixed with elements of the other. Transitions between the two phases occur several times during the day. Commonly these transitions are made easily, the thoughts-out-loud tending to provide verbalization of the thought trends of the ego whenever the ego develops a strong orientation. However, sometimes the thoughts-out-loud continued to present foreign ideas despite the fact that the ego is trying to engage in activities which demand words. Such a situation naturally involves conflict, and sometimes leads to the outbreak of hysterical rages. (Lang, 1938, pp. 1091–1092)

Other patients have given different names to these hallucinations of silent thought. For example, Schreber called the phenomena "nerve language" and described them as follows.

Apart from normal human language there is also a kind of *nerve-language* of which, as a rule, the healthy human being is not aware. In my opinion this is best understood when one thinks of the processes by which a person tries to imprint certain words in his memory in a definite order, as for instance a child learning a poem by heart which he is going to recite at school, or a priest a sermon he is going to deliver in Church. The words are *repeated silently* (as in a *silent prayer* to which the congregation is called from the pulpit), that is to say a human being causes his nerves to vibrate in the way which corresponds to the use of the words concerned, but the real organs of speech (lips, tongue, teeth, etc.) are either not set in motion at all or only coincidentally. (Schreber, 1955, p. 69)

Joanna Southcott, the religious leader, designated these experiences as her "communications."

I have heard my name called in an audible voice, but my "communications" are not given thus; but the words come as distinct to my hearing as though they were spoken audibly. No one can understand how a Visitation comes, how it speaks within, yet is distinctly heard with the outward ear, by those who have experienced it. (Balleine, 1956, p. 13)

The names given to these phenomena by different patients are legion. Hallucinations seem to each experiencer to embody a unique and unnamed phenomenon which he attempts to describe and to name to the best of his ability. The descriptions have so many elements in common that one may safely conclude that they constitute a common class of experience. Lang's discussion of the effects of thoughts-out-loud on the rest of his mental life may be taken as typical of the effect of such experiences on most of the patients who have had them.

MENTAL CONFUSION ARISING FROM THE VOICES

The continual experiencing of voices and thoughts-out-loud is at first disconcerting. As it persists day after day into year after year, the patient starts to realize that the voices tend to speak in metaphors, similes, and fragmentary sentences which only serve to add to his mental confusion, making clarity of thought increasingly difficult. Several observations made by Schreber may help to clarify this point.

Thus for years I have heard daily in hundredfold repetition incoherent words spoken into my nerves without any context, such as "Why not?" "Why, if", "Why, because I", "Be it", "With respect to him" . . . [together with] certain fragments of sentences which were earlier on expressed completely; as for instance 1) "Now I shall", 2) "You were to", 3) "I shall", 4) "It will be" . . . The original meaning of these incomplete phrases . . . ought to have been: 1) Now I shall resign myself to being stupid; 2) You were to be represented as denying God . . . 3) I shall have to think about that first; 4) It will be done now, the joint of pork. . . .

Throwing into my nerves unconnected conjunctions expressing causal or other relations ("Why only", "Why because", "Why because I" . . . etc.) forced me to ponder many things . . . It is often not at all easy, particularly in the case of sensations and feelings, to account for reasons ("But why") satisfactorily . . . Nevertheless this question is stimulated in me by the voices and moves me to think; but as I said before continual thinking is too wearying . . . Finally a very ordinary event to illustrate the above: I meet a person I know by the name of Schneider. Seeing him the thought automatically arises "This man's name is Schneider" or "This is Mr. Schneider". With it "But why" or "Why because" also resounds in my nerves. In ordinary human contact the answer would probably be: "Why! What a silly question, the man's name is simply Schneider". But my nerves were unable or almost unable to behave like this. Their peace is disturbed once the question is put . . . My nerves perhaps answer first: Well, the man's name is Schneider because his father was also called Schneider. But this trivial answer does not really pacify my nerves. Thus an extremely simple observation under the pressure of compulsive thinking becomes the starting point of a very considerable mental task, usually not without bearing fruit. (Schreber, 1955, pp. 172–173; 178–180)

Perceval described the mental confusion which he experienced when he attempted to comprehend the specific meanings of the words used by the voices and which he had comprehended as divine commands.

Now the voices I used to hear during my illness . . . told me that the state of mental perfection they required me to attain to, was dependent upon the proper command of my heart and my head, and if I recollect rightly, of my conscience, which I was made to suppose dwelt in my bosom. I was repeatedly desired to "keep my head and heart together," not to let "my head go wandering from my heart,"—"if I kept my head and heart together," I should do well; but that this third power, which, if I am not wrong, was conscience, ought to regulate both, if I would be perfectly happy. I understood very little of what I heard at the time. But now I conceive that the voices when they told me to keep my head and heart together, meant me to think on what I was in need of, or desired; of those subjects or objects my heart and health dictated to me, since the head may be occupied on subjects which are repulsive to the heart, or out of time, and out of place, and out of character. (Perceval, 1840, p. 275)

The various forms of auditory hallucinations, since they were experienced more or less continuously by these patients, interfered with what they considered to be their usual and normal ability to think and observe. The noise made by the voices fatigued them mentally and made sleep difficult. The questions which the voices posed, the incomplete phrases, the stupidity of compulsive thoughts, and the threats to their welfare which the voices uttered, all acted to disturb them and to create "unholy turmoils" in their minds. The inner voices *compelled* their thoughts to turn in certain directions and to dwell on certain topics. Freedom of thought was continually interfered with and mental relaxation became impossible. Visual as well as auditory hallucinations made vague and uncertain much of their ordinary perception of the surrounding world. The usual flow of perceptions became doubtful, while ordinary everyday experiences seemed strangely altered. The clothing that persons around them were wearing or the food served on their plate might suddenly change and shift in appearance under their very eyes. Indeed, it is remarkable that some of these patients could have kept such notes, formulated their beliefs, and presented their autobiographies as well as they did.

HALLUCINATORY PAIN

Pain, whether real or hallucinatory, is a very common complaint during the course of a psychopathological experience. In Chapter 14 we will devote ourselves more extensively to the topic of *Pain;* at present I will present pain as it is related to hallucinatory experience. Again I will follow the organizational scheme devised by Lang.

With the exception of the thoughts-out-loud, hallucinatory pains have been experienced more than any other type of hallucinations. During the past eight years, not a single day has passed which has not been marked by at least a few samples. They have constituted the most malignant factor of the psychosis, and they have provided the factor which has proved the leading obstacle to attempts to cope with the psychosis.

To the person who experiences hallucinatory pains, the pains feel identical with actual pains. There is no difference between the sensation of hallucinatory and the sensation of actual pain. The person who experiences it can distinguish it only by its lack of normal cause and its interrelations with other hallucinatory phenomena. The person who feels it undergoes real suffering. The fact that the cause of the pain is obscure and abnormal does not reduce the actuality of the suffering. . . .

To give some specific data concerning hallucinatory pains that I have experienced, it may be stated that they have varied considerably in intensity, in duration, and in locus. In intensity, they have ranged from slight irritation to agonies. In duration, they have ranged from a fraction of a second up to 10 minutes or so. In locus, they have ranged over all parts of the body. In type, they have included smarting, burning and aching.

There has been a tendency for high intensity, short duration and repeated occurrence in the same organ to adhere together on the one side, and low intensity, longer duration and frequent shifts of location on the other. Until within the past year, the pains of high intensity and short durations were felt almost exclusively in the penis. During the past year the locus of this type shifted to the soles of the feet. The pains of lower intensity and longer duration change their location frequently, sometimes appearing in five or six locations in the space of an hour. The pains of higher intensity have tended to occur in a series of spasms, each spasm about a second in duration with an interval of from a second to four or five minutes between spasms. The pains of lesser duration sometimes last 10 to 15 minutes continuously. In connection with the latter type, it has usually been possible to produce a temporary cessation by rubbing the part of the body in which the pain is felt, or by moving the part violently. . . .

From the very start, there has been an intricate interrelationship between the hallucinatory pains and the thoughts-out-loud. The hallucinatory pains first appeared at a time when the ego was developing a doubt of the claim of divine authority made by the thoughts-out-loud, and their occurrence was explained by the thoughts-out-loud as a penalty for the doubt. On several occasions since, pains have occurred following threat by the thoughts-out-loud that they would take place if commands made by it were not obeyed. The thoughts-out-loud takes cognizance of the pains, speaking about them and trying to explain and to justify them. During a four-month period two years ago, long involved arguments attempting to justify the pain, formed the major factor of the foreign aspect of the thoughts-out-loud. On a few occasions, the thoughts-out-loud have correctly anticipated moves of the pain from one locus to another, the anticipation having been made immediately preceding the shift. On other occasions, however, the forecasted shifts have either not been made at all, or have been to some locus other than that predicted by the thoughts-out--loud. Sometimes the thoughts-out-loud have briefly anticipated the start of a series of spasms of pain. Commonly, though, the pains start without any immediate warning. (Lang, 1938, pp. 1094–1096)

Almost every autobiographical account of a mental illness devotes some space to the description of the pains and agonies experienced by its author. As Lang so aptly pointed out, there is no difference between hallucinatory psychotic pain and actual physical pain except for the absence of an adequate stimulus. Subjectively, then, the two are equally unpleasant to the organism. If one can see the noxious pin, the knife, the flame, and at the same instant experience the pain produced by its contact, then we speak of it as actual and objective pain. But when there is no objective stimulus for the response, and the latter is erroneously attributed to the action of some absent agent, the experience is said to be imaginary or hallucinatory; for the experiencer, however, there is not the slightest qualitative difference. No observer should ever draw the conclusion that the pain experienced by a neurotic or psychotic patient, although imaginary, is not distressing. It becomes all the more unbearable in fact, because the sufferer knows or has been told that the pain has no basis in fact and that outsiders are convinced that his suffering is not real.

HALLUCINATIONS OF TASTE AND SMELL

Hallucinatory experiences of taste and smell are not uncommonly reported. Almost without exception they are of an unpleasant nature. The odors are those of carrion, rottenness, gas, chemicals, and so forth. Sometimes the phrase *sickly sweet smell* is used, or *pervasive odor of violets,* but *no* report has been found where either the smell or the taste was said to be really pleasant. Hallucinatory tastes are generally described as being elicited by body odors, spoiled food, poisoned drinks, foods unfit to eat, and so on, and are likewise never said to be pleasant. Usually hallucinations of taste and odor occur in close association, as in the following description written by an anonymous female patient.

I did not observe the tallow flow from that candle, but from a hole in the wall, whence it was discharged in an enormous quantity, resembling a furious torrent which has burst through its banks, so that I screamed aloud, and pretended that they were going to suffocate me. The incident made me suspect that they had the intention to poison the atmosphere, and ever from that moment I constantly experienced a disagreeable though sweet smell. All the viands offered to me had that taste. I thought that the meat they brought was human flesh, and insisted on the idea that they desired to poison me. (Anon., 1850b, pp. 395–396)

This incident illustrates the manner in which hallucinations of smell and taste may blend in with the entire delusional content of the moment. Davidson included in his *Remembrances* a mention of how this sort of hallucinatory experience was derived from actual objects in his environment and how it affected him.

I also suffered terribly from thirst; but the water had a horrible, sickly, sweet taste, and though it was as clear as ever in appearance, it tasted oily, and smelt as if it had come from some dark, damp cellar full of putrifying corpses that had died of loathsome diseases. It was worse, far worse, than one might imagine water to be that had a large amount of phosphine bubbled through it, for there was the unmistakable and awful sense of human corruption having defiled it. (Davidson, 1912, p. 207)

This particular experience originated during the acute phase of Davidson's second psychotic episode. He claimed that a sulphurous odor hung about him all the time. Also, when he attempted to smoke, the tobacco smelled and tasted like smoke from rotten feathers so that he was glad to give up smoking, a habit which had formerly given him great pleasure.

Lang commented on this sort of hallucination as follows.

On a few occasions, I have experienced olfactory hallucination. These have consisted of the seeming smelling of an odor as though originating from a source just outside the nose. Sometimes this odor has had a symbolical relationship with the thoughts-out-loud, as for instance, the appearance of an odor of sulphur in connection with a threat of damnation to hell by the thoughts-out-loud. (Lang, 1938, p. 1096)

Each of the descriptions cited makes the same point, namely, that extremely unpleasant odors and tastes do occur and usually as part of a larger delusional system. Even in the case of the simpler hallucinations which sometimes occur during melancholic states, the patient complains of having an ever-present unnatural body odor, often saying that the odor is due to the fact that "my brain is rotting away."

KINESTHETIC AND PROPRIOCEPTIVE HALLUCINATIONS

Lang described his unusual experiences related to these sense modalities as follows.

On one occasion, I experienced a very interesting example of a kinesthetic hallucination. I had gone down to a beach to attempt suicide by drowning. I poised on the edge of the pier. Then I tensed and jumped off. I felt myself falling through the air. I looked down to see how close I was getting to the water. I found that in actuality I had never jumped and was still standing stolidly upon the pier. I gave up for that night and went home.
. . .
The only other hallucination which has taken place with any frequency is that of proprioceptive pressure . . . It occurs generally in one of two states: (1) static, or (2) vibratory. In the static phase, it usually consists of feeling of pressure upon the back of the upper part of the head. The vibratory phase appears as a wave passing between two poles: commonly, one is at the back of the upper part of the head, the other, near the mouth. The waves seem to vibrate rhythmically from one pole to the other. For what it may be worth, I

might say that on three occasions, while I have experienced the pressure vibrations, I have felt my pulse, and I have seemed to notice a correlation between the pace of the pulse and the rhythm of the pressure. (Lang, 1938, p. 1096)

Further examples of such abnormal body sensations have been cited earlier in other connections. This general topic will be included at various places in subsequent chapters. Hallucinatory experiences of this sort are usually imbedded in disordered perception or in delusional belief.

HALLUCINATIONS OF TOUCH

In connection with the descriptions of various other sorts of hallucinatory experiences, I have given examples of hallucinatory pain, heat, cold, skin movement, and pressure. An example of hallucination of touch per se was recorded by Freeman. He was at the time treating a young woman who was almost completely blind and who had read and written braille code for many years. She came to him for treatment because she felt that her behavior and experiences were becoming bizarre. She said she was having auditory hallucinations and that the voices were unfairly accusing her in a very derogatory fashion. During the mental examination, the doctor left the patient alone for about a half hour in a soundproof room from which sound recordings were made. No articulate sounds were recorded during this period of solitude. The doctor (F) then entered the room and started questioning her (B):

F.: Tell me what was coming through. . . .
B.: The very second you came in the word "defense plant" came in my mind.
F.: Did that come as an actual thing you could hear? . . .
B.: You know, it seems to come from within my head and the lettering in braille lettering. It doesn't come out in handwriting or print. It seems to come out in braille lettering, like in front of my forehead, in front of my eyes. I see the words "defense plant" as I think of it.
F.: That's an amusing thing.
B.: It really is. It's in letters, but it's in braille. It has been like that since I have been home at various times, you know. It comes out in braille code.
F.: Were your eyes open at that time?
B.: Yes; they've been open the entire time. What I actually thought in my mind would sort of flow out of my mind and seem to focus in front of it. And it comes out in braille writing. At the same time I think of it—both together. (Freeman and Williams, 1953, pp. 630–631)

It is interesting that this woman seemed to experience the same delusional content in three sensory modalities. She heard herself spoken of as "a blind bitch," "a defense plant whore," and so on; she sometimes saw these phrases in braille print; and sometimes felt them as though she were "reading" braille code by touch.

Hallucinations can and do occur in every sense modality and in any combination of them. Usually there is no direct cue by which the experiencer can instantly differentiate between normal or ordinary perceptions and hallucinatory experience. Certainly hallucinatory experiences constitute one of the major difficulties in adjustment to everyday life for many mental patients.

The Self and Hallucinations

As we have seen in the foregoing pages, many disturbed individuals have described hallucinatory experience, and some of them have commented on the interactions that exist between the process of hallucinatory experience and their total personality or *self*. Lang's presentation of such complex relationships and their subjective effects is particularly interesting.

If there is anything that I can say with certainty concerning the problem of hallucinations, it is that hallucinations are not the product of the activity of the conscious self, of the experiencing individual. The conscious self acts merely as a spectator. It does not anticipate; it does not initiate; it does not control the hallucinations. To the conscious self, hallucinations come as phenomena which it experiences. They reach it as already organized configurations. They are, to the self, phenomena which arise outside its range.

Further, a series of more than 50 experiments which I have carried out, each time with negative results, have convinced me that the conscious self *cannot* produce hallucinations (using the term in the specific sense of a spontaneous false stimulation of the sensory nervous system). While I have been able to produce vague affects and vague eidetic images, I have never been able to produce a stimulation of the exteroceptive nervous system identical with that arising from normal external stimuli such as has occurred in the hallucinations which I have experienced.

Hence hallucinations are, to the conscious self, experienced phenomena over which it possesses no control. At the time of their incidence, the self cannot distinguish them from normal sensory stimuli except through the presence of clues in the surrounding situation which indicates such separate identity. They reach it as already organized sensory configurations. The self not only has no part in their organization, but also has no awareness of any factor in the organism to which it belongs which participates in the formation of hallucinations. Consequently it views them as the product of some external factor. When the surrounding situation does not contraindicate, the self assumes that the hallucination signifies the actual external presence of the experienced phenomena. It accepts the hallucination as the experiencing of normal external stimuli. When the surrounding situation indicates that the phenomena does not have normal external existence, the self still cannot accept the hallucination as the product of its own organism. It tends to the belief that the phenomenon is the result of the influencing of its organism by some external agent.

In complex cases, such as my own, the further conviction develops that the separate incidences of hallucinations and allied phenomena are not the products of separate agents, but rather the repeated manifestation of a single agent. . . . In my own experience, factors of continuity and temporal contiguity and of relevancy, have impelled me to this view. The approximate continuity of the thoughts-out-loud spanning nearly the whole period of wakefulness, day after day, points in this direction. The reference of the thoughts-out-loud to hallucinations which have taken place in the past and their anticipation of hallucinations and other events which subsequently occur, also tend to increase the impression. And their adherence to a central theme—the attempt to produce a messianic fixation—also helps convince me of the continuity of the agent behind the hallucinations. The reference of the thoughts-out-loud to other hallucinations in close temporal sequence—either shortly before or immediately after—supplies temporal contiguity. The accuracy with which the thoughts-out-loud often predict hallucination provides relevancy. The manner in which the thoughts-out-loud have accurately described shifts in the locus of hallucinatory pain, the way in which they have described hallucinations as they are taking place, and the occasions (not very frequent) when the thoughts-out-loud have accurately predicted the nature of hallucinations which have subsequently occurred, lend strength to the impression of an association and relevancy between the thoughts-out-loud and other hallucinations. The interlocking of these factors of continuity, temporal contiguity and of relevancy has forced the conviction of a central controlling agent behind the hallucinations and the thoughts-out-loud.

To sum up, the self of the experiencing individual has very little choice in the concept which it forms concerning hallucinations: the data of the experience determine the self's belief. The self cannot deny having experienced an intricate phenomenon. It knows that it itself did not produce the hallucination, and it believes that they do not arise from the activity of some other factor of its own organism. The self is forced to the conviction that hallucinations are the product of some external agent acting upon the individual's organism.

From my nine years of direct experience, I am inclined to the view that this subjective attitude rests upon an objective foundation. While I realize that difficulties exist, I believe that it is possible for me to isolate some approximately objective factors which support such a conclusion.

In the first place, hallucinations first appeared in the history of my case without antecedents. They appeared spontaneously and without warning. The original incidence—an auditory hallucination of a voice claiming to be that of God—came without preceding connections. While my general condition at the time was depressed, due to a hard year at college, it did not contain any factor of a seeking of divine aid. In fact my attitude toward the existence of a God who made direct contact with man, was one of skepticism. The hallucination had no basis in the patterns of my conscious thought. The hallucinations did not commence as the end product of a serial change of single factors; they started as the spontaneous appearance of an already organized configuration.

Except in so far as one form of hallucination has been anticipated by other hallucinations, this absence of antecedents has held true throughout my experience. . . .

Secondly, the experiential nature of hallucinations to the self has its objective as well as subjective value. The occurrence of the hallucinations in the central conscious (intrapsychic) field as already organized configurations, indicates their origin on the afferent side of that field. The lack of knowledge of the self concerning the hallucinations previous to their incidence, precludes the possibility that the hallucinations arise from conscious or post-conscious processes. As the central awareness—volitional factor of the conscious field, the self would necessarily possess knowledge of activity in the conscious field.

Thirdly, the inability of the self to produce hallucinations experimentally has its objective as well as subjective implications. It rests upon an experimental basis which the reader can test for himself. This experimental inability precludes the possibility that the hallucinations arise from self-initiated processes. . . .

Fourthly, the intricate pre-existing organization which hallucinations possess before reaching the central conscious field, objectively suggests the existence of some organizing factor. Before reaching the conscious field, an hallucination already demands (1) the selection of a specific sensory pattern with sometimes the synchronization of processes of more than one sensory system, (2) the addition of specific locational factors, and (3) sometimes the provision of an anesthesia for factors actually existing in the external configuration which are incompatible to the hallucinatory pattern. It is difficult to understand how such a complex organization arises except through the operation of some form of organizing factor.

Fifthly, the innervation of some factor of the afferent side of the nervous system possessing the ability of providing external locational factors, indicates the activation of the exteroceptive nervous system. The external locational factors do not arise in the central field as the product of faulty judgment or reference by the self. They are definitely integrated into the hallucinatory pattern when it reaches the central conscious field. Such incidence of external locational factors requires the overcoming of a basic safeguard of the psychophysiological mechanism of the human organism—the afferent-to-efferent principle of neural conduction, without which no distinction would exist between sensation and imagination. It is upon this distinction that adjustment to the environment depends. In overcoming this safeguard, the hallucinatory process involves the defeat of one of the major protections of the psychophysiological mechanism. It necessitates the operation of some special factor possessing the power to overcome this special resistance.

Sixthly, the hallucinatory process in so far as it involves the innervation of a part of the sensory nervous system of the human psychophysiological mechanism is not a mystic nothing-something. It must function as an energy discharge stimulating the nervous system. (Lang, 1939a, pp. 423–426)

The lengthy citation from Lang has an undoubted sincerity and an attempt at objectivity that makes it all the more impressive. Although later in his essay, Lang finally appealed to a theory of "psychic infection," his effort to achieve self-understanding is one of the most rational I have found.

In Chapter 5 on "Disturbed Perception" I quoted at some length from Perceval's *Narratives* concerning his attempts to find, insofar as possible, an objective basis for at least part of his hallucinatory and deluded experiences. I may cite Perceval's remarks further, in order to offer something of a contrast to the aforegoing discussion of Lang.

When I came to this house, I did not know that I was insane. And my insanity appears to me to have differed in one respect from that of many other patients; that I was not actuated by *impression* or feeling, but misled by audible inspiration, or *visible*, rather than sensible guidance of my limbs. To the voices I heard, and to these guidances, I surrendered up my judgment, or what remained to me of judgment, fearing that I should be disobeying the word of God, if I did not do so . . . I was told [by the voices] that they knew I was commanded . . . to prove my faith and courage . . . till they were satisfied of my sincerity. . . . I never spoke, hardly acted, and hardly thought, but by inspiration or guidance [from the voices]. (Perceval, 1838, pp. 91–92)

During the progress of my recovery there I kept watching minutely all my experiences, and my conduct, and that of other patients, comparing their cases with my own, and drawing such conclusions as in those painful circumstances I was able: I did this also with the desire of being able to remove the delusions of others. If any one knew how painful the task of self-examination and of self-control was, to which I devoted myself at that time, every minute without respite, except when I was asleep, in order that I might behave becomingly; they would understand how cruel I felt it afterwards, when I required my liberty for the further pursuit of health and of strength of mind, to have it denied to me for fear of my doing any person any bodily harm.

Keeping my mind continually intent upon unravelling and understanding the mysterious influence I was under, I one day saw an old gentleman who had been in China pluck a privet-leaf, and declare that it was tea; the same used to smear his face with the red clay, calling it paint. I thought immediately thus —the spirit speaks poetically, but the man understands it literally. Thus you will hear one lunatic declare that he is made of iron, and that nothing can break him; another, that he is a china vessel, and that he runs in danger of being destroyed every minute. The meaning of the spirit is, that this man is strong as iron, the other frail as an earthern vessel; but the lunatic takes the literal sense, and his imagination not being under his own control, he in a manner feels it . . .

Now all or nearly all the phenomena which I have narrated, strange as they may appear, are to some degree or other familiar to all men—and such, as I can in a certain degree recollect in myself during the whole course of my life. For instance, this power of a spirit to control the utterance is daily experienced, though not remarked, in what we call a slip of the tongue; where one word is put for another, and one letter transposed with another, and as the mind by a positive law always thinks on contraries at the same time, it almost invariably happens that the word made use of by mistake is the contrary to that intended. The universal for the particular—the affirmative for the negative, and the like. (By the same law, voluptuousness and cruelty have been so often united in one person.) The degree of error is not the same, but the phenomenon is the same—the organs of speech are made use of without the volition or rather intention of the person speaking. This is remarkable, because it would prove the residence in the temple of the body, of two distinct powers, or agents, or wills. (Perceval, 1840, pp. 273–274; 303)

The contrast between Lang's formulations and those of Perceval is interesting. Perceval maintained that he had lost his judgment because he had obeyed the visible and audible spirits and furthermore that he had completely lost his doubts as to the actuality of the spirits and their divine mission. Lang's voices were organized and externalized and, although they likewise offered divine guidance, he seems to have retained a degree of skepticism as to their messages and commands. Many patients, including both Lang and Perceval, noted that the voices were inconsistent in their commands and often made mistakes in the directions they conveyed. Lang questioned the essential wisdom of the voices, while Perceval blamed himself for his own failure in correctly carrying out the directions given by the spirits. We mentioned earlier that Perceval anticipated some of Freud's ideas, particularly those expressed in the *Psychopathology of Everyday Life*. The citation above repeats some of these anticipations to psychoanalytic theory and adds another of Freud's concepts, namely, that of the Unconscious. Note also Lang's concept of two distinct powers, agents, or wills in one single body, and compare these to Freud's concepts of the Ego and the Id.

Schreber, like Lang and Perceval, heard continuously recurring voices. In drawing up his plea to be released from the hospital, he considered the statements of the psychiatrist Kraepelin regarding hallucinations and their effects on the mind of the patient. Part of his argument to the court becomes relevant at this point.

Kraepelin's remark . . . that those cases in which "the voices heard" have a supernatural character "are not infrequently accompanied by visual hallucinations" is very valuable for my own ideas. I think it probable that in a considerable number of these cases it was a matter of real visions of the kind which I also have experienced, that is dream-images produced by rays, and which for that reason are very much more distinct than what is seen in ordinary dreams. . . . On the other hand the total content of the present work will hardly show anything *in my case* which justifies speaking of "the inability of the patient to use earlier experiences to correct thoroughly and accurately his new ideas". . . . or of "faulty judgment", which Kraepelin . . . says "invariably accompanies delusions." I trust I have proved that I am not only not "controlled by fixed and previously formed ideas", but that I also possess in full measure the "capacity to evaluate critically the content of consciousness with the help of judgment and deduction." . . . He who in Kraepelin's sense . . . understands "sound experience" simply as the denial of everything supernatural, would in my opinion lay himself open to the reproach of allowing himself to be led only by the shallow "rationalistic ideas" of the period of enlightenment of the 18th century, which after all are mostly considered to have been superseded, particularly by theologians and philosophers, and also in science. . . .

I can of course only speak with certainty of myself when I maintain that an external cause for these sensations exists; however, it is suggestive that there have been or are similar cases. In other words, those sensory impressions which are supposed to be solely subjective (illusions, hallucinations, or as the laity call them, sheer figments of imagination) may in other cases also have some objective basis, even if incomparably less than in my own case; that is to say they are brought about by supernatural factors. . . .

Human beings who are fortunate enough to enjoy healthy nerves cannot (as a rule anyway) have "illusions", "hallucinations", "visions", or whatever expression one wants to use for these phenomena; it would therefore certainly be desirable if all human beings remained free from such experiences; they would then subjectively feel very much better. But this does not imply that the events resulting from a diseased nervous system are altogether unfounded in objective reality or have to be regarded as nervous excitations lacking all external cause. I can therefore not share Kraepelin's astonishment which he expresses repeatedly . . . that the "voices", etc., seem to have a far greater power of conviction for hallucinated patients than "anything said by those around them." A person with sound nerves is, so to speak, *mentally* blind compared with him who receives supernatural impressions by virtue of his diseased nerves; he is therefore as little likely to persuade the visionary of the unreality of his visions as a person who can see will be persuaded by a really blind person that there are no colors, that blue is not blue, red not red, etc. (Schreber, 1955, pp. 89–90; 223–224)

Two points were brought out by Schreber which are particularly relevant. First, his flat rejection of Kraepelin's idea that faulty judgment *invariably* accompanies delusions and hallucinations. Schreber maintained that if an observer who has never experienced hallucinations will accept the report of patients who have had this experience, then the observer must agree that some measure of correct judgment does remain with the patient. Second Schreber argued that it is odd, but understandable, that the patient should be convinced of the inner reality of his hallucinatory experience. If the outside observer denies the patient's hallucinatory experience he casts doubt on much if not all of the remainder of the patient's experiences, since an outsider can have no firm basis for asserting which part of another person's life is real and which imaginary. Schreber reversed the usual argument by pointing out that it is easy to believe that a sane person endowed with "sound nerves" would be mentally blind when he tries to comprehend the visions of a hallucinated patient.

DISCUSSION

I have said that hallucinations are false perceptions. By *perception* we understand the apprehension of the phenomena of both the inner and the outer world. Perception is constituted by the sensory qualities of experience to which the mind adds ideas, memories, and imagination so as to transform the whole into a state that we call common sense. The total course of the process of perception gives rise to those qualities which are called real, actual, and natural. By this is meant that the knowledge gained through the process of perception can easily be compared to the knowledge which other persons may have, and that in general there is close agreement between the verbal expressions used to describe private experience and those that describe the corresponding percepts of others. The phenomena of perception are said to be real when there is general agreement; they become unreal when an individual's perceptual experience does not coincide with that of others. And, more particularly, when the perception is not in accord with one's own past experience (without good and sufficient reason) the resultant experience is considered to be possibly unreal. Normal perception has the attributes of actuality and verity, whereas false perception is generally lacking in a sense of reality. Hallucinations, for example, often suggest a quality of being unnatural or supernatural.

In the case of hallucinations—false perceptions—any one, but not necessarily all, of the qualities I have enumerated is false. I have given excerpts from reports where it seemed that the person was satisfied that certain sensory events had been correctly organized without the quality of reality being present—for example, the vision of many persons staring through the windows while the patient remained internally satisfied that the experience was unreal, hence recognizing it as hallucinatory. In contrast, the sensory impressions may be faulty, such as the feet and legs of the imaginary creatures being invisible, and yet the experiencer may remain certain of the supernatural nature of his experience.

Hallucination is the term generally applied by the observer to such abnormal inner experiences when they are related by a second person. The person who is having, or has had, the experience may or may not consider that his experience has been hallucinatory. The patient may or may not agree that the experience was really natural or supernatural, and he may or may not be convinced of the verity of his experience. The observer who says that another person is having, or has had, hallucinations uses the designation when the individual in question reports hearing voices, or smelling odors, having visions, and so forth, which no one else hears, smells, or sees, and for which no definite physical evidence can be found that might have provided an adequate stimulus for the perceptual experience described.

There are no independent or outside criteria that will serve a hallucinating person to evaluate such outside judgments. Whether the experience is considered real or unreal does not depend on the senses involved; neither does it depend on the intensity of the experience nor on the apparent points of reference that would ordinarily be used to judge the reality or unreality of a particular experience. As far as can be determined from the many acounts of hallucinatory experience, each individual has an immediate certainty of either the reality or unreality of his experience. Furthermore, in either case, this feeling of certainty is beyond all logical argument or authoritative statements on the part of outsiders.

The next consideration follows, in a way, from this curious nature of the patient's certainly regarding the reality or unreality of his abnormal experience; that is, the inner conviction which hallucinations seem to bear to most experiencers. Delusion means a systematized belief held by false premises. Persistent hallucinations may in large part furnish the basis for delusions. The patient's conviction of the truth of his delusional system, which he maintains in the face of any and all contradictory evidence, constitutes a major characteristic of insanity. Most patients claim that some important portion of their hallucinatory voices and visions are *supernatural;* that is, that their hallucinations are the manifestation of forces above and beyond man's normal scope of perception and action. Even when an outsider points out the factual objective evidence which would tend to show that the patient's network of beliefs is obviously *false,* the supernatural voices heard by the latter will continue to maintain the delusion and reinforce the patient's conviction in his deluded beliefs. Some patients, on regaining their sanity, find not only that their delusions have vanished (see pages 114–115) but also the basic convictions which originated and supported them. Other patients, however, as for example Davidson and Perceval, maintained the same beliefs in their delusional religious experiences long after having recovered from their illnesses.

Several other oddities about hallucinatory experience have become evident in our survey of the autobiographical material at my disposal. In terms of quality, all hallucinatory experiences, except states of religious ecstasy, are subjectively unpleasant, usually grossly so. In terms of content, I have found no account of a vision involving gigantic figures; apparitions are either normal or diminutive in size. With respect to auditory hallucinations, voices are usually heard as being soft and whispering, although a few patients have said that they have heard the voice of God speaking with a deafening thunder. Many patients complain of the compulsive nature of the voices, that is, the voices nag and threaten continuously in a fashion which is most unpleasant and intolerable, even in a world where everything seems to them already unpleasant and painful. Lastly, many, indeed most, persons who have had auditory hallucinations are of the conviction that the voices are all related to some outside *central* controlling agency which can take charge of their minds and does indeed do so much too often. The external controlling agent not only is able to direct mental experience in a positive fashion but can at the same time block out all evidence contrary to its existence and power. For example, Lang's incident of hearing himself making a wrong bid in a bridge game and carrying it out was a hallucination that blocked out the hearing of the real bid as well as having substituted for it a false bid. Most patients insist that the outside control can organize and impose a completely false experience while simultaneously blocking out what should be a real and factual experience.

Some mental patients deny ever having had a hallucinatory experience. In these cases, the usual complaints consist of physical illness, weakness, inability to think, and prolonged lapses of consciousness. Their later reports usually emphasize a dreamlike quality of their remembrance of the psychotic period. If they have been associated with other mental patients during their illness or are at all familiar with general psychopathology, they usually realize the implications of, and resent, the question which is often asked of them, "Do you or did you ever hear voices?" They constantly insist that while other patients may speak of having had such experiences, they themselves have never hallucinated. Such supposedly nonhallucinating patients may nevertheless have delusions, feelings of unreality, and periods of mental confusion. Their behavior and conversation may closely resemble those of other mental patients, but they never mention voices or visions. Hallucinatory experience seems to be an all-or-nothing affair. Either it has been experienced or it has not, and there is no uncertainty in the mind of each individual on the question.

I have followed, for the most part, the systematic organization of hallucinatory experience formulated by Lang. I may conclude this discussion with Lang's own summary and suggested theory.

The problem of hallucinations looms as an important one for the understanding of the nature of psychopathological conditions. From the viewpoint of actual experience, hallucinations form the epicenter from which the psychosis spreads. The clarification of the hallucinatory process will lead far toward the understanding of psychopathology. . . .

The complexity of the patterns of the hallucinations suggests the existence of some form of organizing factor. Already existing knowledge as to the physico-chemical nature of the nervous system implies that this factor must at least operate as a physico-chemical agent—say some form of energy system. Difficulties in locating and isolating such a factor within the human organism suggest the possibility of the entrance of an external agent. The question is raised as to whether the prevalent theory of spontaneous generation of psychopathological phenomena may not be retarding the clarification of the actuality behind hallucinations. The possibility that hallucinations may be produced by the intrusion of some psychic infective agent is one that requires attention. (Lang, 1939, p. 429)

Thought! Surely Thoughts *are tru;*
They pleas as much as Things *can do:*
 Nay Things *are dead,*
And in themselves are severed
From Souls; nor can they fill the Head
Without our Thoughts. Thoughts are the Reall things
From whence all Joy, from whence all Sorrow spring.
(*Traherne*, 1910, p. 116)

CHAPTER 7

Disorders of Thought
and Speech

INTRODUCTION

The more usual and obvious outward evidences of
psychopathological states are the peculiarities of
speech and thought of the patient. The speech and
conversation of a deranged patient often seems confused, nonsensical, illogical, disconnected, and unintelligible. Frequently his gestures and facial expressions
do not seem to correspond to what is being said.
During the past century numerous books and articles
have been published dealing with the language and
thought processes of psychotic persons giving examples
of abnormal speech, together with speculations concerning the motivation, significance, symbolism, and
associations that might have given rise to such productions. The account the patient himself may give of
his behavior, then or later, often bears little relation
to the speculations advanced by others. The patient
may completely reject such explanations or he may
agree with them by saying, or intimating, that the explanations offered may conceivably be true since he
has little memory and still less idea of the basis for
what he said or thought at some past time.

To follow my main scheme, I will limit myself in the present chapter, for the most part, to the presentation and description of thought and speech disturbances that have been written by mental patients, including such explanations or justifications as may have been advanced by each individual patient in his attempt to account for the phenomena in question. In previous chapters I have made as little use as possible of classifications based on psychiatric diagnostic categories, because the topics with which I was dealing were not particularly related to one or another diagnosis. Since disorders of thought form an important part of the basis on which modern diagnostic systems are built, however, psychiatric classifications must necessarily enter into consideration in the present chapter. Four of the major groupings of thought disorder are those that are typical of mania, depression, dementia, and schizophrenia.

Thought Disturbances in Mania

In a subsequent chapter on "Mania" I will present in detail examples of the press-of-activity, loosening of inhibiting restraints, distractibility, and lack of a clear goal, that are all characteristic of the manic process. In the present chapter I will limit myself to showing briefly how symptoms such as these are related to the confusion that is manifest in the patient's thinking.

In 1848 Dr. Brigham, the editor of the *American Journal of Insanity*, published the following letter written by a disturbed patient, which he cited as a very good example of the complete incoherence evident in the expression of many mental patients.

MY DEAR SISTER: As the cedars of Lebanon have been walking through Edgeworth forest so long, you must have concluded that I have returned to the upper-world, but I am still in purgatory for James K. Polk's sins, which, if they do not end in smoke, surely have as good a chance of beginning that way as the ideas began to shoot, for if T. had not left his trunk on the cart at the Depot, our shades would have been a deuced sight nearer to Land's End than Dr. Johnson said they would by the time the Yankees rebelled . . .

Do you know what this same long, taper roller is? well pop it off, if by their works ye shall know them. Pollock has as good a right to be a D.D. as that doctor we read of in Blackwood that sought so long for spoons and found them not because they were all lead until they were new burnished in Hollyrood palace very near the place where Polk traced his pedigree, a little too near the loins of William the Conqueror, for the pleasures of memory or sense either, for Thompson, Bryant, Africaner, Ainsworth, or anybody else. . . . No indeed for he silvered my head nicely, so as to make it shine afar off. But the end of these things is not yet—consult S. I should like to see H. Honor to whom honor is due—tribute to whom tribute—Give the Devil his due. (Anon., 1858, pp. 490–491)

This letter was written after the patient had been in an asylum for about three months in a state of acute manic excitement. After nine months in the hospital he recovered, returned home, and resumed his college studies. Subsequently, this young man entered medical school, graduated, and, during his residency in a large hospital, died of remittent fever. His father, after his death, found the following entry in his son's diary, which he sent to Dr. Brigham.

Yesterday I found in the "American Journal of Insanity," April, 1848, a copy of my letter written to Helen about six weeks before I left Utica. It is the most absurd medley of nonsense, but it recalled to my mind ideas of no little interest.

My memory during the whole period of my violent illness was preternaturally active, calling up scenes and recollections of very early childhood; the toys and various utensils then about me, the little adventures and queer speeches which will cling to one's memory, while more important matters escape—these, and almost everything which, in a varied and not limited series of reading—names, scenes, historical and personal incidents, fact or fiction, phrases of other languages, passages of poetry and of the Bible—all these, by the merest similitude of sound, of name, or any other near or remote principle of association were grouped in my mind, and would flit across its vision with inconceivable rapidity.

Often, I remember, have I lain on my sleepless bed, and strung one group of words together, as they thus occurred to me, and, catching at some slight analogy in the last, would run off into another distinct series; and thus, till the tongue fairly wearied, and the lips refused to move, have arranged the affairs and settled the disputes of generations past, present, and yet to be; of princes and potentates, of injured queens, and defrauded heirs apparent—rummaging the legends of the Tower, and all the dark, romantic lore of Scottish feudal life; righting the wrong in every department or age of human existence, quarrelling most irreverently and partly with many characters which good people deem sacred, and elevating in my own imagination many of those luckless but interesting heroes who, with many dazzling and redeeming qualities, had yet the misfortune to be wicked.

Here came out in full my sneaking liking for Saul and Pontius Pilate (a very clever fellow, by the way, who occasionally appeared in the hall, and had an unfortunate squint), Henry VIII., Herod (whose valiant slaughter of Judea's infant-ry always inspired my young mind with a dread feeling of admiration), and Nebuchadnezzar. All these were living, breathing personages to me—for death seemed but a voluntary step, and a slight one—and with *these* I communed in the night-watches. I thought I heard them answer me, and I spoke as in reply—sometimes sadly, remembering some sorrowful scene gone by, with which I intimately connected them; sometimes in irrepressible glee; and again in anger—the mood varying with the turn of a word. Sometimes I would fall upon what, to me, was a sublime thought, and remembering Napoleon's saying, was pretty certain to change to a ludicrous interpretation, or some other such turn.

Something of these fitful changes I recognise in this letter. It represents, tolerably well, the state of my mind—*very* well, for it is almost a transcript of what I would have said, if speaking to my sister. I well remember the day when the sheet of paper was brought me, upon which I wrote this, in a scrawl of a hand, for I dashed impetuously along and what a sane person would say was an ill-spelled letter. . . .

Shortly after I got a [letter] from *her* which most grievously distressed me. From it, I first realized that I was under restraint, and in an *Insane Asylum*. I held my head between my hands, and pressed it against the wall; every pulse came bounding with double force and rapidity; it seemed as if I *should* go mad then, and for ever. . . . Then the scenes with which many of my delusions were connected, were changed. . . . *I was changing.*

When Dr. Brigham passed through, I *begged* him to take me from this place . . . [Later] it was not without a voluntary effort, and *that* a painful one, that I tore myself from a glorious world of my own creating, and a throne of my own construction, to take my place in a real and very commonplace lower planet, full of ordinary and intractable characters. . . . And, as I descended from my throne, reason resumed hers. (Anon., 1858, pp. 491–493)

The original letter was incoherent, yet the diary comment written after his return to health still illustrates quite clearly the press-of-thought, the shift from one train of thought to the next, as well as the florid style of expression that is usually found in the productions of hypomanic individuals. When this young man was in a state of acute excitement, his thoughts ran at such a speed that the written production consisted largely of essentially disconnected phrases. Many were merely fragments of thought processes expressed so rapidly that the connections between the fragments were often missing or not apparent. The diary entry does not do very much to enlighten the reader as to the actual content of the letter. It does, however, give the reader some idea of the stream of thought of a manic patient and of his later attitude toward the content and quality of his thought process at the time of the acute excitement. It is quite possible that he had little or no exact memory of the actual ideas which went into the composition of the incoherent letter. During acute mania, thoughts flow so rapidly that the patient cannot hold purposive ideas in mind and therefore neither the patient himself nor his listeners can grasp the aim or goal toward which the manic had originally directed his thoughts and speech.

Thought Disturbances in Depression

During melancholia the prevailing mood of the sufferer is one elicited by a haunting sense of guilt; his conscience gives him no rest; he worries continually about his past sins and failures; he feels shut into himself and isolated from any contact with people and the world about him. During depression the patient's mind moves slowly and with difficulty. His thinking is painful and most of the time it seems practically impossible to think at all. The only idea in the melancholic's mind is that of personal hopelessness. All attempts to direct his thoughts in a purposive fashion seem fruitless because of his hopeless state.

The Rev. William Walford, who suffered from melancholia for more than forty years, described his depression at length in his *Autobiography* (1851). The following excerpt is relevant to his difficulties in concentration.

> Amidst these bitter agonies, I was annoyed more than can be imagined by a cause which seems trivial, but was far otherwise. Very often persons, places, and things, would occur to me, the names and particular appearances of which I was unable to recall without long endeavour of a most wearisome kind. I could not remember the name of some one, nor present to my fancy the faces or forms of various persons or things with which I had been familiar; nor could I banish them from my thoughts, but was constrained to use every method I could devise to bring to my remembrance what I was forced to pursue, until I alighted on the name or object that was suggested to me. Days together was I employed in this fruitless pursuit, without being able to discover what I wanted. Often when found, it would suggest to me something else of the same kind, with similar disquietude, till I felt that the labours of Sisyphus were less fatiguing and useless than those from which I could not escape. (Walford, 1851, pp. 188–189)

Considering that Walford suffered from melancholia for the greater part of his adult life, the fact that he could report this well about his deranged mental processes, during a period of remission, is remarkable.

In Chapter 2 I illustrated the onset of a depression by quoting a passage written by Lenore McCall. At this point, a section from the description of the beginning of her illness in which she spoke of her thinking difficulties may be cited.

> I was conscious towards the end of the summer that my thinking, my mental activity, very easily became disconnected like wires of an electrical apparatus. . . . This sort of thing, in one guise or another, happened repeatedly, as though it were an ever-increasing breach between my will and my brain. I also became distinctly and painfully aware that I could not concentrate upon anything in the way of reading nor could I retain what little I had recently read. . . . Gradually that barrier became like a thing of stone or wood in my mind and although it was intangible it was the most real thing in my life. I could see people through that invisible wall, I could speak to them and they to me, but the mental and spiritual I, the essence of me, could not reach them and this was a part of the horror which was enfolding me as I slipped into that dark and unknown world. (McCall, 1947, pp. 5–6)

In both mania and depression the associative bonds between words and ideas are weakened; in mania it is expressed as a flight-of-ideas, in depression it is shown by a weakening and breaking of ordinary connections. In mania the flight-of-ideas prevents any concentrated thought, even concentration which is no greater than that demanded by reading a newspaper. In depression mental concentration is likewise practically impossible because of the patient's low energy level ("I'm always tired") and the constant intrusion of feelings of hopelessness. As is suggested by the two citations given above, the depressed individual is not only sluggish in his present mental functioning, but becomes increasingly blocked with respect to his recall of past thoughts and ideas.

Thought Processes in Dementia

The term *dementia* is used in various connections when referring to psychopathological experience, but on the whole it implies an irretrievable loss of mind. Hence, very little autobiographical material relevant to true dementia can be found. However, the production of an elderly man, a mental hospital patient, treated by Dr. Gesell, who had kept a diary-like journal for several years in which he had written articles and comments, has been published and may be useful to illustrate the simple poverty of creative thought. Toward the end of his life, the contents of this diary had deteriorated into aphorisms, or truisms, at times clear and at others garbled. The following examples have been taken from the last volume of his journal.

God, Nature, my Saviour, Angels, Reason, Common-sense, and the Holy Bible inspire me.
Superstition makes men fear.
Why has a man a right to make law more unjust than God's law?
Faith without works avails nothing.
The mystery of life is solved: Harmony, Holy Bible, Nature, Reason.
"Look up" elevates. "Lie down" rests. "Bow down" degrades.
A man must obey Nature's laws in order to be happy.
God has winked at man's ignorance too long already. Awake thou that sleepest and Christ will give thee light.
I will fight until death in defense of God's Holy Bible.
I am will. Fight for God and Humanity forever.
Friends reproach me. I care not. God is with me.
In the name of God and Reason teach what Christ taught. (Gesell, 1905, p. 522)

Letters, diaries, and conversations of demented individuals are usually found to show striking poverty of thought together with a dearth of ideas, fabrication of memory, and circumstantiality of associations. The portions of the diary just cited give some evidence of these points.

Disorders of Thinking in Schizophrenia

Thought distortions and pecularities of speech are outstanding symptoms in schizophrenia. Lack of apparent logic (irrationality) and confusion of ideas are most evident to the outsider when the schizophrenic patient tries to communicate with other patients. At the time, the patient himself does not very often recognize the lack of logic or the confusion in his thinking. On later recall, however, he may remember the circumstances of his illness and furnish some account of the thought processes which gave rise to his seemingly irrational reports.

ILLOGICAL THINKING

MISUNDERSTANDING BY OTHERS Sometimes a patient may have regarded his thinking as being natural or normal, and insists later that others simply failed to understand what he said because they did not know, or simply ignored, what it was he was trying to express at the time. For example, "Ex-Patient," whom we have already encountered, wrote as follows.

My history shows that I was capable of making deductions from several different premises, or systems of ideas, and acting upon them. Presumably, these contradictory systems were held simultaneously. All that I can state with certainty is that during a definite period I was conscious of certain fears, phantasies and isolated or distorted details of reality, and I suppose that these motivated my behavior. I do not know how I switched from one system to another. One constant line is seen in the fact that for a whole month, inside my cell, I never saw (*i.e.* was conscious of) a single member of the staff. That however only shows a constant line of reaction as far as receiving impressions from other human beings goes—I received none. . . . My utterances during this time ought to be some indication of the ideas I was holding. Unfortunately of this I can give very little evidence, partly because the staff paid no attention to what a patient said, unless it was "funny" or constantly reiterated, and partly because they appeared to believe that it was bad for the patient to know anything about himself. But I did discover from a nurse that I used to complain to the doctor about my head having gone "wrong" and ask him to put it "right." (Anon., 1931, pp. 359–360)

This same point was stressed in a different way by Clifford Beers in his book *A Mind That Found Itself.*

Most sane people think that no insane person can reason logically. But this is not so. Upon unreasonable premises I made most reasonable deductions, and that at the time when my mind was in its most disturbed condition. Had the papers which I read on the day which I supposed to be February 1st borne a January date, I might not then, for so long a time, have believed in a special edition. Probably I should have inferred that the regular editions had been held back. But the papers I had were dated about two weeks *ahead.*

Now if a sane person in February 1st receive a newspaper dated February 14th, he will be fully justified in thinking something wrong, either with the paper or with himself. But the shifted calendar which had planted itself in my mind meant as much to me as the true calendar does to any sane business man. During the seven hundred and ninety-eight days of depression I drew countless incorrect deductions. But such as they were they were deductions, and the mental process was not other than that which takes place in a well-ordered mind. (Beers, 1908, p. 54)

Although this argument may seem to be somewhat peculiar, the point made by Beers that the psychotic can reason and deduce correctly is well taken. As Beers points out, the train of thinking itself was often correct, but the premises on which the thought process was based were faulty or incorrect and, as his basic premises were delusional, his deductions were more involved than necessary.

IDEOLOGICAL CONCEPT FORMATION   Lang held that his thinking difficulties grew out of the ideological content (premises) which he had conceived from the messages the voices (hallucinations) conveyed to him. He pointed out that the ideas foisted on his mind by the invading voices and thoughts-out-loud caused him to conceive of an outside central-symbolic mechanism that dominated his waking life. The common factor in his experience was, he said, the claim made by the hallucinations that there was a divine authority for the voices and for the ideas which they revealed. He continued as follows.

Certain aspects of the present hallucinoid ideological organization are more rational and more objective than some of the ideas held by normal individuals. . . .

To counteract the ideological and affective pressure exerted by the hallucinating agent, the self had to construct an ideological system which would serve as a basis for the mobilization of emotional forces against the hallucinating agent. Hence the primary construct of the stratum was that the hallucinating agent was some form of personalized external factor which was unfriendly toward the writer. It denied the hallucinating agent any authority over the writer. Facing persistent attempts of the hallucinating agent to control his conduct by promises of reward in heaven or threats of punishment in hell, the writer established the self-defense concept that neither heaven nor hell actually existed. . . .

In respect to concept formation by ideocentric schizophrenes, the distinction between the sensorimotor and the ideological levels should again be made. On the sensorimotor level, the schizophrene often handicapped by inefficient sensory discrimination and poor neuro-muscular coordination may find difficulty in discerning sensory cues needed for building blocks into an assigned design. Here the schizophrene may lack the sensorimotor ability to apprehend the common characteristic which he is supposed to select. Hence . . . one may report that the schizophrene lacks the ability of abstracting from sensory objects common characteristics which would permit their being grouped into a common category. To carry one's conclusion beyond this point and to expand it into a statement concerning the general mental attitude of the schizophrene, however, is a procedure which is open to question.

On the ideological level, the ideocentric schizophrene uses abstractions. He defines his ideological terms in general principles drawn from the consideration of a large number of phenomena. One of the chief quests of his thought is the search for abstractions. Since the ideological level is the most highly developed level in the ideocentric schizophrene, failure to study concept formation on this level leads to distortions concerning the intellectual capacity of the schizophrene. (Lang, 1940, pp. 391–393)

Lang's essential point is that it is easy for outsiders to misunderstand the thinking of a schizophrenic patient. He held that the patient is beset with hallucinatory and delusional experiences while at the same time his reactions are slow and his sensory intake is somewhat confused and partially nondiscriminative. Hence, his ability to think abstractly or to generalize correctly may seem to others to be either completely lost or greatly reduced. But in fact, the patient is performing remarkably well in view of the circumstances and handicaps which afflict him.

CONFUSION

ATTRIBUTED TO INNER MENTAL LIFE Very frequently, the mind of the patient will be so filled with hallucinatory voices that any attempt he may make to answer questions made by outside observers is interfered with. Hence, his replies become garbled, as though he were attempting to answer several questions at the same time, rather than one. For example, on of Milici's patients wrote as follows.

Voices are constant from day to day, very continuous. They seem to have no end and it is well nigh impossible to avoid them. They are clear and distinct and very, very well understood. I try not to pay attention to voices, yet without paying attention know what is said. They come from without, from persons close to me who yet appear unconcerned, or even from persons out of sight, from a distance, from people I am thinking about, seeking knowledge or giving answers to my questions. I hear too continuous voices inwardly, so rapid at times I can't remember all that's said. Voices upset my equilibrium altogether. They are rarely good and can't be changed. They have no regard for anyone or anything. (Milici, 1937, p. 55)

The behavior of this patient had been noted in his case record as "a poor worker in the laundry, preoccupied, silly, very evasive, rambling, incoherent and irrelevant." In view of what he expressed regarding the constant intrusion of the voices into his mental life, it seems natural that his behavior and thinking should have been preoccupied and incoherent.

A French army officer who had been hospitalized for more than three years wrote a letter protesting the fact that he was detained, stating that he was being unfairly treated. He related that a woman's voice was continuously speaking to him and explaining everything that was happening at the time in the entire world.

One is brokenhearted in seeing and in hearing every day so many victims tormented by torture which is illegally inflicted. She whispers to me constantly, she never ceases to tell me that by means of electro-magnetic fluid and by prodigious instruments of torture that she has, she kills every day all the people who die, she takes the mind away from those who lose it, she arranges the robberies that are committed, all the assassinations, all the rapes, all the adulteries, all the fires, all the shipwrecks, all the gas explosions in the coal mines, all the head-on train crashes, all the illnesses, without exception, of animals as well as of men, all the quarrels, etc.; finally, all the pains that afflict humanity. Nobody, she said, would think of pain if it were not for her suggestions and stimulation by the electro-magnetic fluid. If her mission were to stimulate for the good as it is to stimulate the bad, we would have a golden age much more perfect than any poet ever dreamt it. (Cullerre, 1886, p. 224)

Since the voice seemed quite real and the messages meaningful, this officer was at a loss to know for what reason he had been detained in an asylum and why the authorities had thus far failed to heed the important information with which he had been attempting to supply them. He did not for a moment consider that his mind was confused, although this fact seemed quite apparent to everyone else.

Perceval commented on the state of confused thinking which he himself underwent and gave a pertinent example of how the confusion affected his thinking.

Many of the things I have spoken, and many of the things I have heard and written, and done in the spirit, I have not understood for a long time after: and yet, when my understanding has perceived their meaning, they have often been quite simple. It seems to me, that in the effort to understand, made by a deranged mind, the faculties become stupefied and confused.

The following is another remarkable phenomenon, which I observed during my illness. When I was fastened down in my bed at Dr. Fox's, . . . the voices I heard gave me to understand that I was not to sleep—that as a spiritual body I did not need sleep, and that if I slept, I ran a risk of increasing the dreadful lethargy, which rendered me unable to resist any degrading or mean thought or feeling presented to me. . . . Weary at length, and unable to comprehend these commands, I sought to sleep, and recollecting what my mother had formerly told me of my father, that he used when he found himself unable to obtain rest, to keep continually counting to himself, I tried the same. But then the power of thinking numbers for myself was taken from me, and my mind or life lay in my body, like a being in a house unable to do any thing but listen to the sound of others talking around him, and voices like the voices of females or fairies—very beautiful—very small, and with a rapidity I cannot describe, began counting in me, and entirely without my control. First, one voice came and counted one, two, three, four, up to ten or twenty—then a second voice took up the word twenty, and kept repeating twenty—twenty—

twenty—whilst another after each twenty called one—two—three—four, and so on till they came to thirty—then another voice took up the word thirty, and continued crying thirty—thirty—thirty, whilst a voice called out after each thirty—one—two—three—four, and so on till they came to forty, and thus the voices within me proceeded, dividing the labour between them, and so quickly, that I could not possibly pronounce the numbers. (Perceval, 1840, pp. 304–305)

The last three citations all make the same point, that the persistent intrusive voices constantly interfere with the patient's ordinary mental processes and hence clarity of thought becomes impossible. The inner experience may be compared to any normal person's attempt to think in the midst of myriad conversations, which conversations are in some part related to the thought process one is making a voluntary effort to follow. Any effort to analyze the difficulty in deranged thought will be unsuccessful as long as the investigator remains unaware of the occurrence and content of the interfering voices. The patient's difficulty does not consist in peculiarity of the thought process but in the interference and intrusion of inner experiences.

DUE TO IMPERCEPTION By imperception is meant the faulty perception of the real world surrounding an individual. In normal mental life one may lose oneself in daydreams or fantasy. When one is lost in fantasy, many events pass without being registered as a part of our normal perceptual life, or similar sensory material passes without being recognized as such. Even that which was noticed becomes blended as part of the daydream process. Many patients have reported difficulties in thinking due to this dreamlike experience. Their thinking seemed to them to be at first fairly normal, and then somehow it seemed to change gradually into a semidream, much as one's normal thoughts may do as one goes slowly to sleep. For example, Kindwall's patient wrote as follows.

I tried to follow what the instructor was saying. I kept hearing her voice, caught phrases, separate bits of what she said, and found myself wondering why all this seemed difficult. As the work progressed, a change came. The ingredients of the cake began to have a special meaning. The process became a ritual. At certain stages the stirring must be counter-clockwise; at another time it was necessary to stand up and beat the batter toward the east; the egg whites must be folded in from left to right; for each thing that had to be done there were complicated reasons. I recognized that these were new, unfamiliar, and unexpected, but did not question them. They carried a finality that was effective. Each compelling impulse was accompanied by an equally compelling explanation. (Kindwall and Kinder, 1940, p. 530)

This transition was from semi-organized rational thinking to a fantasy in which a sort of ritualistic magic process seemed to be the organizing principle involved. Normal daydreaming often carries with it remnants of the magic and ritualistic thinking of childhood which is facilitated by imperception, but the psychotic imperception is more marked than that which may occur in the normal thought process of a child.

As one is going to sleep or becomes lost in daydreams, habitual skilled manipulative movements tend to become clumsy and fumbling. This motor clumsiness is yet another aspect of imperception and may in some cases form part of the psychotic disintegration. Renee in her *Autobiography of a Schizophrenic Girl* described such a difficulty.

In the gymnasium I didn't understand the commands, confusing left and right. As for the sewing lesson, it was impossible to understand the technique of placing patches or the mysteries of knitting a sock heel. Varied as these subjects were, they presented similar problems, so that more and more, despite my efforts, I lost the feeling of practical things. (Sechehaye, 1951, p. 10)

Renee had described in her journal, from which we have cited previously, how she was at first overwhelmed by fear and feelings of unreality. Her feelings, it will be recalled, were followed by difficulties in thinking and performance of habitual activity, which in turn, gradually changed to grossly delusional thought disturbances and catatonic-like behavior.

The way in which illusions may be mixed with correct perceptions in giving rise to imperception, and hence to mental confusion, is further illustrated by a discussion which Perceval undertook to explain why the letters he wrote would often seem confused and foolish.

The letters I wrote from Dr. Fox's asylum will serve as another example of what I mean. I may say that every syllable of these letters I saw by illusion on the paper before I wrote them; but many other sentences also appeared besides those which I chose; and often these sentences made light of or contradicted what went before—turning me to ridicule, and that ridicule goading me to anger and madness, and I had great labour and difficulty to collect myself to seize those that were at all consecutive—or not too violent—or not too impassioned. This was extremely painful. My readers will find in these letters a great deal of sense and forcible writing, mixed with a great deal of weakness and imbecility; thus the inspirations and guidances I have received have been often good and becoming, and therefore I conceive, in the sense in which the term is usually employed, divine; often they were defective, and much my judgment ought to have rejected, and probably would have rejected in calmer circumstances. (Perceval, 1840, pp. 270–271)

Many of these letters, which he included in the 1840 publication of his *Narratives*, exhibit a mixture of sense and nonsense, a rambling emotional production that lacks clarity as to both content and goal.

MIXTURE OF NATURAL AND SUPERNATURAL IDEAS Many peculiarities of thought stem from ideas and concepts of religious convictions, revelations and conversions that occur as part of the hallucinatory experience during an episode of abnormality. Very often the belief in the reality of the religious experience continues even after remission from the psychosis and the return of the person to normal society. These mystical experiences had been sufficiently vivid and had carried along with them the conviction of truth and reality to an extent which transcends any later conscious, rational correction.

Schreber, whose profound psychotic experience lasted for more than seven years, recorded the following incidents concerning an attempt he made to correct his troubled thinking during the course of his illness, without leading, however, to any considerable change.

I had a number of experiences which led me to a critical examination of my ideas . . . in consequence of which I arrived at a slightly different point of view.

In particular I remember three events which made me hesitate whether what until then I had considered true and correct was really so; firstly taking part in the Christmas festivities of the Director of the Asylum . . . secondly receiving a letter from my sister-in-law . . . addressed to me . . . thirdly a children's procession . . . which I saw from my window. . . . After these and similar events . . . I could no longer doubt that a real race of human beings in the same number and distribution as before did in fact exist. But this caused difficulties; how was I to combine this fact with my earlier impressions apparently pointing to the contrary. This difficulty remains even today, and I must confess that I am faced with an unsolved riddle, one which is probably insoluble for human beings.

I have no doubt whatever that my early ideas were not simply "delusions" and "hallucinations" because even now I still receive impressions daily and hourly which make it perfectly clear to me that, in Hamlet's words, *there is something rotten in the state of Denmark*—that is to say in the relationship between God and mankind. . . . I am quite sure that [the delusional] expressions and phrases . . . did not originate in my head, but were spoken into it from outside. This alone would make me assume that the ideas connected with them have some basis in reality corresponding to some historical events. Moreover in the course of the last six years I have unintermittently received impressions—and still receive them daily and hourly—which furnish me with incontestable proof that everything spoken and done by human beings near me is due to the effect of miracles and directly connected with the rays coming nearer and alternately striving to withdraw again. (Schreber, 1955, pp. 163–164)

It is apparent that one of Schreber's problems during the days of his slow recovery was that of reconciling the present or intermediate experience with other past and present experiences. What he did or said may have seemed mysterious and irrational to outsiders but it seemed relevant to him at the time, and probably continued to seem so even later despite his realization that "there is something rotten in the state of Denmark."

This mixture of real and unreal elements in the thought process is further illustrated by an incident of peculiar association described by Peters. He was, at the time, deluded, hallucinated, and agitated. He had been placed in restraint and was told to try to fall asleep.

I had no time to go to sleep. Instantly the board of judges appeared. I could not see them clearly and was unable to identify any of them since there were no features on any of the faces . . . hardly faces at all, just blank oval spaces, poised on shoulders. They were seated behind a raised wooden platform, peering over at me. How could they peer without eyes? Perhaps they had eyes but I could not see them? Of course, I didn't have my glasses. In any case, they were definitely peering. One of them pointed his finger at me, extending his arm directly towards my face. "Sun," he said in a loud, commanding voice.

Was this going to begin again? Dully I repeated after him: "Sun."

He jerked his arm at me. "Go on," he ordered.

I was tired but there was no resisting this command.

"Sun," I intoned. "From Sun to Son to Son of God. Son of God to Jesus Christ. From Christ to Christmas. Christmas to Mass. Mass to solid mass. Solid mass to earth. Earth to element. Element to four elements. Four elements to earth, air, water, fire, the four elements. Four elements to Universe. Universe to everything." (Peters, 1949, p. 61)

Strictly speaking, this is an example of a hallucinatory outside force that intruded and controlled the patient's thought processes. At the same time it illustrates a variety of disordered thinking in which the associations were the personal responses of the patient to outside commands, associations which were in themselves quite rational thinking although possibly incomprehensible to an outsider.

STOLEN THOUGHTS AND IMPOSED THOUGHTS Some patients attribute their thought disturbances to the fact that, while trying to think or to express themselves, their thoughts are "stolen" from their mind, and become distorted by some outside power. Thus, they hear themselves saying things that were not intended and are not representative of their own thoughts or intentions. Part of a patient's letter written to a state Governor illustrates this condition.

To the Governor of Minnesota:

In accordance with the right given us by the state law to appeal to your Excellency, I present my case in a few words that very poorly present the situation. To adequately represent would require a personal interview.

My difficulty is an outgo of my silent thought. It goes as it comes. I may think whatever I please, but whatever I do think goes as it comes. I suppose the constant irritation and annoyance they have kept up around me has affected the tension of nerve, so that unlike others who have the same phenomenal power, it goes as rapidly as my mind thinks. I have but to think a thought and it reaches other minds in sound without an effort on my part, and is sounded for a distance, I suppose, of two or three miles. If it goes farther it is renewed by some other man. How do I know? In the first place, men of sound judgment have told me that my views are correct. In the second place, I hear my silent thought sounded in steam, and wherever there is a noise it is liable to be echoed. A visitor gives me his name, and I sound it a mile away in the steam of some engine, done time and again. . . . I am constantly made the object of abusive language. Of course my silent thought is sometimes indignant and that reaching other minds keeps the ball rolling. (Flint, 1893, pp. 573–574)

Apparently this patient believed his thoughts were being taken and echoed abroad in, what was to him, a most disturbing manner. Since this kind of disturbance will frequently lead a patient to seek both assistance and possible confirmation of his difficulty, such complaints have often been published, and many examples of this sort may be found in the psychiatric literature. In spite of the fact that outsiders strongly insist that they never hear the spoken-aloud-thoughts, the patients usually find it impossible to accept the refutation because the voices are to them as real and distinct as any other auditory reality. Hence, they are apt to go further and invent rationalizations or delusions to explain why others fail to hear their hallucinatory voices.

Still another variety of thought disturbance experienced by some patients is their impression that thoughts from the outside, over which they have no control, are inflicted upon them to such an extent that their own thoughts become displaced, blocked, distorted, or completely changed. Such imposed thoughts utterly confuse and befuddle the patient and are apt to lead to inappropriate behavior. For example, a certain physician-in-charge of a mental hospital had difficulty understanding the remarks of one of his patients until the latter left the hospital without permission, leaving him a letter, part of which read as follows (material in brackets are insertions made by the physician, Dr. Channing).

On Saturday afternoon I thought you thought I ought to play croquet [I was thirty miles away], so I began, but could not go on, because it seemed as if you were definitely forbidding me to do so *by influencing my mind* [the nurses reported that she stopped playing croquet]. . . . I often see your thought as I go about, but if it is not in accord with what you have bidden me to do, it does not stop or confuse me. But this time it was different, and I *could* not go on. Please tell me if I did right to stop. . . . I was glad you and Dr. K. knew I would obey when I could. I was happier than I ever expected to be, because I could obey the highest influence, and the consciousness that came to me with the thought, "I shall be satisfied when I awake in Thy likeness." Last week I thought I was going in a direction you had forbidden, and later I was so overwhelmed with the thought I might harm you that I could not realize and be ready to obey. I have known many times that God spoke to me, or sent me help, and I tried to obey. (Channing, 1892, p. 201)

It is easy to comprehend the difficulties such a patient would experience since the orders she heard and attributed in part to the doctor
were often contradictory as well as confused with the voice of God.
Since the doctor was unaware of such directions uttered by the voices and
was ignorant of the fact that the patient was responding to what she
considered to be his own orders, his mystification is understandable.

A different sort of experiential imposition was described by Davidson in his *Remembrances*. This seemed to him to be more of a self-
imposed process, yet it was equally distressing as far as he was personally
concerned. He described the episode as follows.

Not long after this [period of doubting the divinity of his guardian-at-
tendant] . . . my mind began to form what might be called a cyclic prison for
itself. One morning, a certain picture from a certain seat started a sequence or
train of thought; when this was over, I changed my position, and another
picture gave me another train of thought; again I changed my seat, and the
view out of the window gave me yet a third. The train of thought was full of
self, and was self-centered and emotional. I was filled with pity for my own mis-
fortunes, without the slightest idea of blaming myself for them, or thinking
of anyone else at all. After dinner, as if compelled by clockwork machinery,
I occupied the same places in the same rotation. The same chain of thoughts
recurred, and almost forcibly clicked themselves through my brain. After
tea, the same thing happened. Again, the next day, the same identical
routine took place. I was not aware of it until just after the last item in part
one had been performed; and then, and only then, I became aware, to my
horror, that I had acted and thought in a cyclic manner; and yet I would
unconsciously proceed to go through the next item, only to become aware of
the fact when this was just over, and so on. I began to feel frightened, and
scarely knew what to do or think about it. After tea, at the end of the second
or third day, I found, with actual terror, that I had gone through two items.
I lay down on a sofa, closed my eyes, and tried to collect myself and overcome
the extraordinary impulse or mental whirlpool that seemed to be sucking me
round and round. I got up thinking I was all right, and walked out of the
room, across the passage into the other room, only to discover that I was actually walking to the chair by the window—the next place in the cyclic pro-
gramme. I stopped short, and with an effort rushed to a sofa, instead of to the
chair. I threw myself down and covered my face with my hands, in a desperate
endeavour to fight this terrible chain. It seemed as if this self-centered sequence of thought had in itself a fearful compelling power over my body to
force it to go to the correct place. I felt that the longer this went on the
stronger it would get, and I knew that it meant I should really go mad, and
perhaps die mad, tied by a cyclic chain of thought to a circular round of places.
I broke into a sweat with fear, and prayed a short but fervent prayer for relief
from certain appalling insanity and death. My eyes were tight shut, but I remember seeing a gentle flash of light and feeling a distinct click somewhere
inside my skull, and the chain was broken. I got up cool, collected, and normal

from that instant; and directly afterwards my guardian walked into the room to see how I was getting on. (Davidson, 1912, pp. 103–104)

In this example the self-imposed thought cycle was said by David-son to be akin to a ritual. He recognized the steps in the cycle but only by a determined effort of will was he able to break the spell. He resorted to prayer, as was his custom in many difficult situations; the prayer brought the feeling of a "click," which, he said, ended the imposition. It is interesting that he ended this account by mentioning that his guardian-attendant, whom he thought was Jesus Christ, came into his room pre-cisely at the moment the "chain was broken." This incident was but one of the many occurrences pertinent to the acute phase of Davidson's illness, one which puzzled him but was never really understood.

Similar phenomena of intrusion or stealing of thoughts produced a great deal of annoyance and discomfort in Perceval. He wrote about the disturbing subjective effects of the guiding voices in the following way.

The reason of this [feeling of uncertainty] was that many of the guid-ances I received proved themselves by their results to be true and reasonable, so that I could not doubt but that they were benevolent and divine; but often when I had submitted either to the directions of a voice, or to the motions of a spirit to a certain extent, I found myself left in the lurch, and unable to understand further what I was to do; and this in circumstances of great em-barrassment, likely to excite much laughter and astonishment in those with whom I had to do. For instance, I have been often desired to open my mouth, and to address persons in different manners, and I have begun without pre-meditation a very rational and consecutive speech . . . but in the midst of my sentence, the power has either left me, or words have been suggested contra-dictory of those that went before; and I have been deserted, gaping, speechless, or stuttering in great confusion. (Perceval, 1840, p. 269)

Experiences of this sort led him to remain mute much of the time, since he considered it better to say nothing than to appear confused, which is by no means an unusual reaction in such situations. Another point suggested by Perceval's comments is that the EDITOR process did continue to have some veto power over the remainder of his disorganized mind. His EDITOR process did recognize that such abnormal speech was deranged, hence enabling him to control the exhibition of his confusion by remaining mute.

ATTRIBUTED TO LOSS OF SELF-CONTROL Some patients attribute the confusion in their thinking to a failure of their volitional control, just as Perceval did in the excerpt cited. Others seek some different way of ex-plaining to themselves (or to others) the loss of their mental control. This loss is frequently attributed to sin, yielding to the Devil, and so forth. In essence, the patient is saying, "I don't know why I have been affected, but I no longer seem real to myself, since I can't control myself." For example, Bond's patient reported as follows.

Something has happened to bring my mind into the wrong way of thinking—The trouble is I didn't control myself when I could and now I can't. . . . It isn't sickness—it's wickedness—I've been thinking wrong and acting wrong. . . . I know that affects the mind—I am under a cloud—I blame nobody but myself. . . . Satan got hold of me. . . . I can't forgive them for bringing me here—It's all my fault being here—How I have been self-centered all my life. . . . The acute thing has quieted down and left me with this terrible belief—I think I must be insane—the possession of my soul and body by the devil—I can't grasp this thing of my being here—I have lost my identity. (Bond, 1917, p. 175)

This patient recognized the fact that she could no longer control her mental processes. Having no evident or factual basis to account for the misfunctioning of her mind she said the trouble was due not to sickness but to wickedness. At the same time her statement implies that the wickedness and self-accusation were an inadequate explanation and the confusion continued.

This confusion in thinking may express itself as a lack of responsibility or as an absence or inadequacy of the proper associative connections necessary for the process of thinking. This was phrased in the following way in the second case cited by Rows of a schizophrenic patient.

I suppose, as all responsibility has been taken away from me, I have grown irresponsible. I would really like to be serious, but it does seem to me that I shall do nothing henceforth but play. . . . [Later:] It is a loose thing to say; it would be more correct to say, I can't control it so that interest and concentration continue. That I have not control is because it looks as though I have not control because I vary so rapidly. My letters indicate that. When I write a letter I am centred on the phase I express at the time; then I express something else just after. I don't think it is a right condition; there should be some steadiness . . . I think it is stupid to fluctuate so, you can't depend on yourself. (Rows, 1914, p. 206)

DUE TO SELECTIVE LOSS OF MEMORY   Sometimes patients complain that they are confused because some portions of their memory have failed them. Davidson explained how some of his thoughts were stolen or blocked. After some meditation, he had come one day to the conclusion that there was no God and that all religion was a delusion. He sat down and proceeded to write a letter to his father about this new conclusion.

When I got to the end of the letter, a most extraordinary and unpleasant thing befell me—I could not remember my own name, either Christian or surname. I thought how absurd it was, and got an envelope to address to my father; but, for the life of me, I could not remember his name. To say I was surprised, or vexed, is not the word: I felt an absolute fool. I read the whole letter through, and it seemed fairly clear. I got up and walked about for some time, trying to think of my own name. I sat down and wrote on a sheet of paper every letter of the alphabet, to see if I could recover at least the initial letter. It was all quite useless, and I felt too ashamed to go and ask anyone. I took off my collar, and looked at my handkerchief, to see if my name was marked on them, but I could not find it . . . [He then went and asked his attendant what his name was, but was told to go back and think.] I went back and thought hard for some time, and then went down on my knees and prayed to God to restore this memory. That instant, my whole name came back. (Davidson, 1912, pp. 102–103)

Davidson then looked again at his collar and his handkerchief and was amazed to see his name clearly printed on each. In a sense, this incident partially depended on a form of negative hallucination, in that part of his confusion arose from his inability to recognize the clear laundry markings which were before his eyes. As in several other incidents that Davidson recorded about his psychosis, the act of prayer restored his clarity of mind.

PERPLEXITY IN THOUGHT   Often the confusion in thinking is such that the patient cannot truly account for his thoughts. He is, so to speak, perplexed and at a loss when trying to understand why and how his thought processes are operating. For example, in part of a verbatim account of her ideas of persecution, another of Milici's patients cast doubts on explanations that she had advanced a few hours earlier concerning her experiences.

As far as I know they used an oscillograph on me but I might be mistaken . . . Whether a dictaphone was actually in the apartment upstairs or not I don't know, I wasn't there . . . I did feel the effects of something. I couldn't say what it was, gas or not. I really heard the gas stove move but I could be mistaken . . . People across the street appeared to be signaling. It is possible I was wrong . . .There might not have been a scandal in the papers about me. The psychiatrists told me there was. But I didn't read the news . . . I was taking the psychiatrist's word for granted that he was a criminologist. That's so far as I know. I couldn't swear he was. (Milici, 1937, p. 665)

Doubt, perplexity, and confusion of this sort are usually transient. The patient cited above had been treated with insulin coma therapy and was nearly recovered from her paranoid disturbances. She had arrived at a point where she either had to continue in her delusion by accepting the reality of her unusual experiences or reject these altogether by suppressing or obliterating the ideas associated to them.

Another of Dr. Milici's patients (mentioned in this chapter) was urged by him to keep a day-to-day written record of his mental difficulties, his beliefs, and explanations. Toward the end of this record, shortly before leaving the hospital, the patient wrote as follows.

I was confused in mind, unable to do anything, in a puzzled, troubled, uneasy state. When thoughts like that came I was completely lost in them and believed them.

It is admittedly true, upon my own admission, that I have undoubtedly been exceedingly sick. My mind was in a state of the greatest confusion and unrest. Prudence was decidedly lacking in me. I was the one at fault, doctor, because I have been terribly wrong in my thoughts. I am heartily sorry for any offence I have given anyone. . . . In my mind there was a struggle, one, I could, the other, I couldn't. I have had the experience of being a person who had the burden of illness on my mind, yet I struggled along. (Milici, 1937, p. 72)

From this excerpt one gains the impression that the patient's memory of his confusion was that it had been in part experienced as a mental blocking or inertia. He remembered that he had been unable to force thought processes voluntarily. He had also coupled with this the feeling that could his intellectual will have been applied, a solution might have been found earlier.

These accounts of perplexed thoughts are often so confused that they become practically nonsensical. Grover published the account of one of two sisters who were hospitalized in the same institution and whose delusional systems seemed quite similar. They agreed with each other as to the nature of their delusions.

We were never born. My sister and I were made by a machine. She is not my sister, but she is nearer than a sister and we belong together by machine rules. We can not tell why. We were made by a machine. A lot of these things were taken out of my memory by a professor. We do not know how or why, but another professor did it but they are our friends. We call ourselves sisters to outsiders in order to avoid explanations. We are highly educated because it was the machine's wish. The machine is called the "invisible." We do not know how it works. We never hear voices; never saw visions. We have no sensations, no bad smells or tastes. We do not work for our living. We get it from the machine. We do not see the machine. Sometimes it changes to a person and then changes back again. Sometimes it becomes a light and we see the light sometimes. We hear it. It speaks like a person. The machine changes in time of trouble in order to give us information. We are always happy. We have seen in our life good natured singers, actors and dancers. We have both been worried about money. We could not pay our rent and were put out. (Grover, 1931, p. 309)

DISCUSSION

It is evident from the excerpts I have cited that there is no single organizational pattern which would bring the apparent difficulties and aberrations in thinking into any systematic scheme. Patients are faced with a diversity of handicapping problems insofar as clear thinking is concerned, and each attempts to compensate for this handicap in his own fashion. Some of the compensatory devices or rationalizations seem satisfactory to some patients, at least to the extent that the device seems to carry with it some degree of self-conviction, so providing the individual with at least part of his desire for a self-explanation. Some of these explanations, which may have appeared adequate to the patient at the time, are at a later time felt to be peculiar. Other patients realize that their minds are (or were) so confused, unclear, or cloudy that they disclaim all responsibility for their words or deeds. This denial is in itself interesting, since it indicates that their stream of conscious thought has been divided, so that a portion of it (the EDITOR process) remained clear enough to regard and recall the evident inability of the remainder of the mind to control or properly direct speech and action.

The incoherent productions of the manic patient are often understood by the individual after he has regained his sanity. The production is then usually interpreted as having been a condensation of many ideas only loosely connected with the normal associative links, which were themselves omitted or but vaguely expressed. In the press-of-activity at the time of the illness the patient either failed or neglected to express the usual connecting phrases that might have shown the specific way in which one idea led to the next.

For the depressed patient thinking is a slow and painful process. The patient finds difficulties in evoking names as well as other memory traces that would be otherwise readily at hand. His over-all thought processes seem to him to be incredibly retarded. He finds it sufficiently difficult simply to hold the elements of his thinking together. At the same time he is equally unable to dismiss from his mind ideas that he should be able either to recall or to forget voluntarily. The delays, the painful efforts, and the failures to provide answers to easy questions, all combine to give the observer an impression that the depressed patient is stupid, demented, or both.

Deranged persons are said to be truly demented when their speech and the content of their thoughts indicate that they can no longer carry through the kind of mental manipulations that at some previous time were rapid and easy everyday accomplishments. The thought products of the demented patient consist most frequently of fragments of old information in which the associative connections seem to be lost. New information is neither retained nor incorporated with traces of previous knowledge.

In mania, melancholia, and dementia, the more obvious effect of these disturbances on the thought processes is the weakening of the associative bonds that hold memories and ideas together. In mania, the bond is so weak that any sort of ideas may come together for brief periods only. In melancholia, the associative bonds are so adherent that very little flexibility of thought can be accomplished. In dementia, the associative linkage seems completely lost, so that fragments of memory or ideation come to the surface of consciousness with very little evidence of the continued existence of any real associative process that might serve to hold ideas together.

The thought and speech of the schizophrenic patient are usually mystifying to other people; in fact, it is precisely the speech of these patients that conveys the stereotype of insanity to the man on the street. Bleuler, the first to give this symptom-complex the name of schizophrenia, held that the fundamental symptoms consisted of disturbances in association and in affectivity, together with a tendency to resort to fantasy in thinking as opposed to the use of reality, the whole leading to a partial or total divorce of the mind from reality. Bleuler held that, of the thousands of associative threads of thought which guide normal thinking, there is in schizophrenia a haphazard interruption of single threads, of groups of threads and sometimes of large segments of associations, so that thinking becomes illogical, confused, and bizarre.

The autobiographical descriptions of schizophrenic thinking cited in this chapter can be grouped in two main categories, illogicality and confusion. The schizophrenic patient realizes these difficulties and is disturbed by them. The illogicality is the outcome of the patient's attempt to incorporate two or more systems of ideas into one single thought process. He is often partially aware that he has not been able to accomplish this condensation successfully and is thereby perplexed by his lack of success. Lang's self-analysis of this difficulty led him to attribute it to the defective integration of his ideation and the ongoing perception. This failure, he thought, was enhanced by a faulty capacity or inability to draw abstractions from total or concrete experiences.

Confusion in the thought process is realized and recognized by almost every schizophrenic patient. Perceval summarized this in the following way.

I conceive, therefore, that lunacy is also a state of confusion of understanding, by which the mind mistakes the commands of a spirit of humour, or of irony, or of drollery; that many minds are in this state; that, perhaps, this is the state of every human mind—that it certainly is the state of every mind in certain moods. (Perceval, 1840, p. 289)

Hackett spoke of this confusion in a more direct fashion.

So the voices of the past and their endless confusion joined the voices of the present and its endless confusion and to know which voice was of the present and which was of the past was hard to tell, only that the past confusion and the present confusion blended into a wave of confusion from which I could not escape. (Hackett, 1952, p. 93)

These characterizations of confused thinking are typical of many statements by other schizophrenic patients. Many patients have tried to attribute their mental confusion to a wide variety of reasons. I have classified and given descriptive examples of confusion attributed to events occurring in the individual's private mental life, as due to (1) imperception, (2) the mixing in thought of natural and supernatural experiences, (3) stolen and imposed thoughts, (4) loss of self-control, (5) selective loss of memory, and finally, (6) perplexity. These arbitrary groupings are the more frequent listings of the explanations given by patients, who do not really know why their thinking is confused. Only when it seems necessary for them to give an explanation to satisfy either themselves or someone else do they resort to these varieties of explanations.

The novelist Joyce Cary, in an essay in which he attempted to account for the formation of these explanations of the creative phenomena of inner life, wrote as follows.

For the gap between experience and thought, direct knowledge of the real and the reflective judgment, can be bridged in the subconscious, but only by the symbol which is highly fragile and very easily breaks down. We saw how allegory can break it, instantly dividing the reader into an emotional memory which is already losing significance, and a conceptual judgment which is coldly analysing and labelling a set of technical tricks.

We know how many people go about the world precisely in this condition—men who are on the one hand emotional without sense and on the other full of the most rigid opinions on every possible subject without regard either to fact or sensibility. (Cary, 1958, pp. 164–165)

CHAPTER 8

Delusion; Paranoia

INTRODUCTION

The immediate perceptual experience of any person,
as far as that individual is concerned, is real, true, and
beyond question. "I saw it with my own eyes; I heard
it with my own ears. How can anyone possibly question my experience?" On this point there can be no
debate. Others may insist that the perception was
illusory or hallucinatory and the person may finally
agree to the force of the arguments, yet at the time the
experience occurred it was subjectively real and true,
and beyond question. In the normal course of anyone's
mental life, each fraction of perceptual experience as
it occurs becomes incorporated into the framework of
memory and ideas of one's past life. Each bit is added
as a new item to the sum of one's conscious experience,
which sum constitutes the mind.

Every now and then some bit of private perceptual experience may seem somehow different or
peculiar. As successive experience follows this particular odd or exceptional perceptual element, the latter
may be corrected—that is, reconsidered, reinterpreted,
obliterated, or otherwise brought into the general

scheme of one's mental life. This relatively consistent scheme is influenced by childhood training; that is, by the period when the child is learning to evaluate the various facets of the world about him. At this time of life the broad explanations of parents, nurses, teachers, siblings, and other children combine to furnish a fundamental scheme of accepted explanations that is characteristic of the social group of which the child is a member. The "common sense" of any cultural group corresponds for the most part with the common interpretations and beliefs of a large proportion of the fluctuating number of persons composing the group. Common sense changes with time, with group composition and common experience. "Common sense" need not be based on reality or truth. For example, superstitions may be part of the common-sense system yet at the same time have no basis in reality.

Now suppose some element of experience (sensation, feeling, or idea) occurs that seems new, different, odd, or peculiar to the individual. To this one person, of course, it seems completely real and true despite its lying outside the scope of the experiencer's past mental life and foreign to his usual common-sense frame of reference. Further, suppose this same odd experience recurs or is for a while persistent, somehow defeating all attempts to incorporate it into any normal associative relationship through some process of self-control or voluntary effort. The experiencer recognizes that the peculiarity is outside his realm of common sense, but finds that he has somehow been overtaken by a process which increasingly or suddenly occupies both his intellectual and emotional life. This peculiarity need not extend to all his mental activities but tends to be attached to some set or class of ideas and feelings so that he cannot effectively eliminate the oddity from his mind. If such an intrusion or failure to eliminate occurs, then any portion of his associated memories and ideas is apt to become contaminated by this out-of-the-ordinary experience. The resultant system of ideas and feelings is to that one person unique, but undeniable. For example, a man may be reading a ghost story when suddenly he hears the creaking sound of a door opening that he knows to be closed and locked. The man thinks, "Only something evil could open that door and produce that sound." Then he feels a passing breeze and thinks, "An evil spirit passed by." He remarks to his wife about the evil spirit. She has not heard the sound or felt the breeze and tells him so, adding that it was only his imagination. But he did hear the sound and feel the breeze and is therefore alert for further experiences of this sort. Since his wife did not hear or feel these events, she is not alert. Should further odd events occur soon after in the man's life and acquire a magnified significance, he may be developing a delusional system. The man's delusion may either continue in a circumscribed fashion or expand until it governs most of his mental processes and behavior.

Delusions do not originate quite as simply as this example intimates. They have many additional peculiar characteristics. If a delusion becomes established it is obvious that it must carry with it a logic-proof conviction of its essential truth. No amount of argument or demonstration on the part of other persons can shake the inner certainty with which the false belief is held. Delusions seem to be maintained by the intellectual or cognitive functions of the mind, while in actuality they are maintained by emotional and volitional factors and are only superficially related to cognition. Lastly, delusional systems appear in a variety of forms and are associated with different psychopathological organizations. In some instances the delusions are secondary to some primary disorder, as in melancholia; in others the delusions are so intimately connected with pathological states that it is difficult to be certain which state is primary and which secondary. In pure paranoia the delusion is primary and the remainder of mental pathology is secondary to the central delusional concept.

Delusion Associated with Melancholia

After melancholia or depression has overwhelmed one's mental life the central feeling and essential pathology consist of a grey hopelessness, plus a dreary despair. The feeling of hopeless despair strengthens the half-born conviction that one's mind is breaking down, which in turn may become associated with the idea that the brain and other vital organs of the body are rotting. One may be convinced that one is slowly and with an evil odor dying, both physically and mentally. Lenore McCall told of her paranoid-like delusions during melancholia as follows.

It was during this year that the delusion or reference which I have already described became very pronounced. Everything which occurred around me I imagined was related to me. I would sit in a classroom and overhear a fragment of conversation and my sick mind would fasten upon a word or two that I thought referred to me. If a telephone rang in a classroom or in Ellicott I instantly surmised that the call concerned me. I was being transferred back to Group Three; I was being moved to another house; Henry was in the hospital and they were going to let him see me. If I heard the word "smell" I suffered tortures, knowing that it referred to the odor of corruption which, I was convinced, still clung to me. My hair had become coarse and dead, having something the appearance of dried seaweed and whenever I heard the word "hair" I knew that mine was being discussed. (McCall, 1947, pp. 262–263)

She was certain that other people were talking about her unfavorably, that she possessed an offensive body odor, and that her appearance was frightful. All these delusions grew out of the thoughts and circumstances surrounding her prolonged melancholia. In her case the feeling of hopelessness was primary and the delusions (misinterpretations of perceptual events) were secondary.

Delusion Associated with Euphoria

There are accounts of euphoric delusions (not associated with mystical experience) in which, as we have seen with certain melancholic delusions, the euphoria seems to be primary and the delusion secondary.

H. S. Sullivan published the account concerning a young soldier who had recently been drafted in the Army, where he developed an acute psychosis. When he recovered he wrote of its onset as follows.

The first delusion I recall occurred shortly after my arrival at Camp Meade. It seemed to me that I took a very enjoyable walk about the entire camp and was so exhilarated that it seemed to me that I was just touching the high spots and in actuality really flying over the surface. This dream or rather walking-dream occurred at sunset after the second or third evening of my arrival at the camp. I remember after walking or flying rapidly for a short time about the entire encampment, I came to the sun-warmed platform of a warehouse. This warm surface felt very enjoyable and nice to my touch, so I rested on its surface for a while and enjoyed the various activities which I could observe. After resting here a while I continued my walk-dream-flight until reaching a pump. Here I stopped a while and rested on a log alongside the pump and was much interested in observing the various groups of soldiers who came to the pump to secure a supply of drinking water. Shortly after this episode at the pump, it became dark and I then endeavored to retrace my steps to the quarters where I was encamped. . . .

After this I became quite sick and only remember in a vague indefinite fashion being carried or partially carried as I staggered along to the camp doctor. (Sullivan, 1927, pp. 120–121)

This soldier's description indicates that the euphoric feelings had precedence over the delusions. The euphoric state did not last more than a day and did not seem to be connected in any obvious way to the fearful delusions that developed during the weeks that followed.

Delusions Associated with Acute Alcoholism

Just as delusions may be secondary to major feelings of melancholia or euphoria, so may they be secondary to well-marked primary organic states such as alcoholism or drug addiction. In earlier chapters we have given examples of the onset of hallucinatory states stemming from overindulgence in alcohol. The hallucinations following alcoholism may develop into a total delusional confusion of delirium tremens. The following example is a condensation of an account published by Farrar describing the twenty-four hour period of delusional experience lived by a patient following overindulgence in alcohol. This patient had been a total abstainer for eighteen months previous to this episode until once, because of "social proclivities," he drank rather heavily for a fortnight and as a result acquired gastritis. During a week end at this juncture, he found himself alone in his home, the household servants having departed.

While thus employed [in going over my papers in my office] I suddenly became conscious of a conversation going on in the adjoining room. This was in itself a somewhat startling circumstance, for I had admitted no one and there was none who could properly be in the house without my knowledge at that time of night. The voices I recognized at once as those of the cook and one of my friends who lived hard by. What was still more annoying, however, was the drift of their conversation, which was about myself, and which they appeared to be at no pains to keep me from hearing. . . .

Frankly, I did not enjoy the talk. It seemed to me anything but complimentary, and while I might freely declare the self-same things and worse in remorseful self-reproach, yet I did not relish them from the lips of others. . . . These thoughts were all the matter of an instant and I proceeded at once into the room whence the voices issued, in order to give forcible expression to my objections.

It was to be expected perhaps that the conversation would cease as I entered, and for this I was prepared. But I was not prepared for what I did find, namely, *nothing*. The room was empty. There was no evidence of anyone having been there. . . . I was at a loss to understand how the speakers could vanish so suddenly and completely, but concluding that in the circumstances they had assumed the part of wisdom in avoiding my presence and a scene which might not have turned out to their advantage, I smiled contentedly and returned to the perusal of my mail. This accomplished, I glanced perfunctorily through the evening papers and retired worn and weary, to court slumber, which did not come. It was not late . . . possibly ten o'clock, and the street turmoil of the night of payday . . . co-operated . . . in banishing sleep. . . .

In the midst of the mêlée of confused sounds and more confused thoughts and feelings, I found myself listening all at once to a violent altercation which seemed to be taking place in front of the house. . . . This wordy strife soon drowned out all other noises, and I realized that it was myself who was again the subject of dispute. Thus was I tossed from the accusing points of my own thoughts to meet the sting of phantom voices still more merciless. . . .

Meanwhile the strife waxed hotter. Words gave place to blows. I seemed to be only a helpless auditor of the nearby struggle which was going against me, and for a brief space only the blurred sounds of conflict reached my ears. Then a painful pause. The issue had been determined. I already knew it when again the victor's voice became audible, as he protested to my fallen ally that he had hated to strike him down, but that he could brook no interference in the course he was resolved to pursue with reference to myself. From the other came no response.

Hostilities being concluded in this manner, I deemed the time opportune for action on my part. . . . I scrambled out of bed and proceeded to dress, with what haste I might, going now and then to the window to cast an anxious glance down on the street. Always my expectation was disappointed; I saw no familiar figure. (Farrar, 1911, pp. 573–575)

The account continued with a description of his escape from the house; how he met threatening figures; escaped but was pursued; and found refuge, but the voices remained just outside. After daybreak he partially reoriented himself although he could still hear the accusing voices. He worked at hard labor throughout the day but was tormented all the while by the imaginary conversations. Only in the evening did the reviling voices finally fade away. Of this point he wrote: "My insight was now complete—and just here comes in a very singular circumstance. I still heard the voices. I was thoroughly convinced of their imaginary character, yet I could not escape them."

Why such a delusional period failed to carry with it any real inner conviction of its essential truth is particularly puzzling. Usually delusions of persecution and reference, as far as the immediate experience is concerned, are experienced by the patient as being utterly real and convincing. The delusional experience does seem real to some delirium tremens patients, but even in the case of such convinced patients the experience is "corrected" when the acute phase is passed and remembered only as a vivid sort of nightmare. It should also be noted that this delusional episode had, as far as this patient was concerned, no basis in sensation or perception.

Delusions Which Derive from Hallucinations

Numerous delusions seem to develop out of hallucinatory experience. Some of these seem to follow in a logical fashion the hallucinations that are thought by the patient to have been the primary fact of the psychotic episode. In other instances the hallucinations and delusions are so intertwined that no guess can be made as to the temporal order of their appearance.

If on looking out of the window one sees a man standing under a tree and then hears him speak in a sensible fashion, and if at the same time others see and hear the same thing, everyone accepts the experience as real and relies on the actuality of one's senses. But if the same sort of an experience is had by only one person and no one else who is present can see or hear as does the afflicted person, then the experience is said to be a hallucination; if the person maintains his false conviction and the ideas associated with his experience, against all contrary arguments, the entire circumstance becomes a delusion. If he further draws in other experiences and ideas to bolster up and make the hallucination part of a system of behavior, then it passes on to paranoia. The following example is a description of the first two steps in this process written by an anonymous patient.

Suddenly, on looking out of one of the windows of my sitting-room, I saw standing under a cherry-tree within the yard at the side of my house a negro barber, with whom I had *scraped* an acquaintance in the course of frequent occasions to avail myself of his professional skill in shaving. He was arrayed in a blue dress coat, with remarkably bright brass buttons, dark pants, and a cloth cap. As I looked up our eyes met, and I distinctly heard him say, as he partially lifted his cap from his head, "Good afternoon, Mr. ———." I returned the compliment with a bow, and the exclamation, "How do you do, S———?" This attracted the attention of the watching one at my side, and she asked me what I meant. "Why," said I, "I was simply acknowledging the courtesy of S———." "Of who?" "Why, of S———." "Where is he?" "There, under the cherry-tree, looking up C——— Street. He spoke to me, and I replied. That's all. But I do wonder what he is doing there. He must be watching for somebody." All the arguments of my wife were unavailing to convince me that the barber was not there. I pointed him out to her afterwards directly under my window, standing between the building and the shutter of the window. All I could discover was the outline of his figure and the shining top of his glazed cap. My wife pointed out to me the impossibility of a man's being able to compress himself into so narrow a space. But, to me, it was all possible, all right, all natural. (Anon., 1857, p. 161)

This description is part of the record written by the patient whose experiences with synchronized visual and auditory hallucinations were cited in Chapter 6. He had many hallucinatory experiences of this kind and became wholly deluded, but never quite organized his delusions into a paranoid system.

I have already quoted in Chapter 2 the Rev. Trosse's description, from his autobiography, of the onset of his illness. It will be recalled that he was rather suddenly overwhelmed by the hearing of voices and by impulses of self-destruction. He continued his account of how this deluded state progressed into paranoid thought and behavior.

BEING in this miserable distracted Condition and refusing to make use of any suitable and proper Means, in order to my Recovery, my Friends had Intelligence of a Person dwelling in *Glastonbury,* who was esteem'd very skilful and successful in such Cases. They sent for him. He came; and engag'd to undertake the Cure, upon Condition that they would safely convey me to his House, where I might always be under his View and Inspection, and duely follow his Prescriptions. Hereupon, my Friends determin'd to remove me to his House; but I was resolv'd *not to move out of my Bed;* for I was perswaded that if I removed out of it, I should fall into *Hell,* and be plung'd into the *Depth of Misery.* I likewise apprehended *those about me,* who would have pluck'd me out of my Bed, to have been *so many Devils,* who would have dislodg'd me: Therefore I stoutly resisted them, with *all* my *Might* and *utmost Efforts,* and *struggled* with all Violence, that they might not pluck me out of my Bed and cloath me. When *one* of the Persons about me came behind me to hold me up in my Bed, I was under terrible Apprehensions *it was the Devil that seiz'd me.* And the same Thought I had of *all about me,* that they were *murtherous Devils;* and that they exerted *all their Power* to carry me into a *Place of Torment.* By their concurrent Strength they at length prevail'd against me, took me out of my Bed, cloath'd me, bore me out between them. They procur'd a *very stout strong Man* to ride before me; and when *he* was on Horseback, they by Force put me up behind *him,* bound me by a strong Linnen-Cloth to *him;* and, because I struggled, and did all I could do to throw my self off the Horse, they tied my Legs under the Belly of it. All this while I was full of *Horrours* and of HELL within: I neither open'd mine Eyes nor my Mouth, either to see what was done about me or to make any Lamentations; for still I look'd upon this as my *necessary Duty.* (Trosse, 1714, pp. 53–54)

Trosse, according to his autobiography, did not develop a systematic paranoid method of thinking that continued after he recovered from his acute illness, as is true for many such persons.

Schreber, whose *Memoirs* I have quoted in several previous chapters, recounted how his illness began with hallucinations that became delusions, which in turn developed into paranoia that was maintained throughout the remainder of his life. An excerpt taken from the final chapter of his *Memoirs* will illustrate the point.

Naturally I have also occupied myself with the question of future in a positive way. For several years after I had completely changed my ideas I lived in the certain expectation that one day my unmanning (transformation into a woman) would be completed; this solution seemed to me absolutely essential as preparation for the renewal of mankind, particularly while I thought the rest of mankind had perished. Indeed, I still regard this as the solution most in accord with the essence of the Order of the World. . . .

This raises the further question, whether I am at all mortal and what could possibly cause my death. From what I experienced of the restorative power of divine rays in my body I believe that ordinary illnesses, even external violence cannot possibly cause my death. . . . Therefore, it appears that I could only die from what is commonly called senility. Even science cannot say what death from senility really is. . . .

As regards the form my life will take until my death I believe I can expect . . . a certain amelioration in my external circumstances. . . . Whatever people may think about my "delusions," they will sooner or later have to acknowledge that they are not dealing with a lunatic in the ordinary sense. . . .

I consider it possible, even likely, that the future development of my personal fate, the spread of my religious ideas, and the weight of proof of their truth will lead to a fundamental revolution in mankind's religious views unequalled in history. (Schreber, 1955, pp. 211–215)

Viewed from the standpoint of intellectual development there is a sort of irrational, logical continuity from Schreber's hallucinations to his systematic paranoid ideas. As he explained events and their consequences to himself and rationalized the progressive disorders in his perceptual and emotional life, each event seemed to follow in a logical sequence.

Just what the expressed sequence of abnormal experience may have been in the excerpts I have sampled in this section, dealing with the relation of hallucination to delusion, is not always clear. Neither is it clear why some of the delusions continued to carry conviction while others were self-corrected at some later time. The mixture of disordered perception, false belief, and inner conviction seems to be an individual matter from which generalizations cannot be drawn easily.

Delusions Attributed to Compulsion

Some individuals develop delusions or systems of delusional ideas that seem to them to be derived from outwardly inflicted compulsive thoughts. In some instances these episodes start with a period during which the person becomes mentally preoccupied with "great thoughts." Such patients may feel that great mental powers have somehow been given them, as well as the strength of will to be able to solve many human problems or to proclaim policies, civil rights, divine revelations, and the like. All these solutions will become clear to them if they only set their minds to finding them. In the process of thinking, these ideas seem to break loose from self-control. They become autonomous and take on the ability of directing and eliciting all succeeding thought. Since these notions are by this time quite familiar, the patient accepts the control of ideas without resistance and finds himself following ideational directions in speech and action that are nonsensical and apparently delusional. For example, Clark published an account written by a patient about six weeks after his remission from an acute experience. The patient was a literary man, and wrote that he had been working steadily until one day he became rapidly convinced that he was somehow inspired with an insight which would enable him to solve the political problems of Europe. He thought that part of his personality had emerged into that of a poet and religious seer. He started writing out his solution and soon produced about a hundred pages of manuscript, which, when he recovered later from a psychosis, seemed to him to be comparatively realistic. But during the onset of the illness, as he continued to write, mystical and magical ideas crept into his production. He felt compelled to carry through certain rituals which, he was somehow convinced, would make his solutions more effective. These rituals led to the following thoughts and actions.

The rest of my manuscripts needed to be burned, and burning them would be a holy act—because a sacrifice and in obedience to God, not because they were evil. Sensing that all the manuscripts would not get burned, I arranged the manuscripts in a circle, in order, and decided to start burning the two ends. This would conceal beginning and end of my thought from any who might come. I started the fire by lighting the four sheets of the Sermon on the Mount, and with these lighting the rest of the New Testament, which rested on top of manuscripts in the stove. But as the third page burned it nipped my fingers before I let it go, and instantly the idea came that I should hold the fourth and final sheets in my fingers while it burned. I lit the sheet, and held it as the flame burned down to my fingers. The flame seared the first and second fingers and in a few days the nails were black half way back to their roots, and the fingers blistered. (Clark, 1946, p. 467)

In place of the pain bringing him back into contact with reality, this episode only led onto a more fantastic dreamlike state, during which he became more and more convinced of his own divinity and divine powers. Following this incident he developed a catatonic psychosis that lasted several months.

In his autobiography, *The World Next Door,* Peters wrote a description of the way in which his compulsive thoughts induced in him ideas of his own divinity. He had at first suffered from hallucinations and mental confusion, and then from a prolonged period of irrationality. He was filled with ideas of his own inner power, which went to the extent of conceiving that if he held the base of an electric lamp it might light up from the power stored in his body. Then he became, for a moment, self-critical.

My delusions, my own delusions . . . had . . . a kind of logic to them that was still very real to me. . . . And then Jesus Christ. What about that? I had not *thought* I was Jesus Christ when I had burned my hand. I had *known* that I was. It had been more than a conviction or a belief, and far simpler than either of those things. It had been knowledge in the same sense that I now knew that this was my right hand. In a sense it was a surer and more complete knowledge than that, or than the fact that I *knew* that I was David Mitchell. I knew my name only because it had been told to me, it was knowledge from the outside, whereas the knowledge that I was Jesus Christ had come from the inside, from the starting point of all knowledge. Was it not from within that we observed and knew . . . everything? The final confirmation of understanding did not come to us from the outside, but only from within ourselves. Was it then not only possible, but probable, likely even, that an impulse arising from the world within ourselves was surer and more to be trusted than any other knowledge? I could not say to myself honestly that I was not Jesus Christ reincarnate. I had no knowledge or understanding with which to oppose that one-time certainty. It was only the conventional world . . . that had made me disbelieve it. But again, disbelief was not knowledge, not certainty. It was only *doubt.* . . . Where is the barrier at which one can stop and conscientiously, honestly say to oneself: "I am against this but beyond here I will not fight it. There is nothing further I can do about it." (Peters, 1949, pp. 269–271)

Peters' mental argument was the beginning of the end of this particular delusional phase, which was the climax of his psychosis. He had been led by his inner compulsive thoughts to the conviction of being Jesus Christ. It seemed to him that his divine belief derived from a logical, rational process, while others considered that he had become paranoid. Finally, when some doubts arose in his mind he could then begin to question seriously his own inner convictions.

Delusions of Personal Power

In the development of these delusional trends of thought, some patients come to the conclusion that the acquisition of superior knowledge has brought with it a great inner power with which they can control the behavior and thoughts of other persons, both those near to and those distant from them. Their sense of inspiration and revelation carries the idea and the conviction of the reality of their inner power. This is but one stage in the development of their delusional system. Peters, whose delusion of divinity has just been cited, had at an earlier stage of his psychosis thought that by looking directly at any person he could control that person's behavior by means of a radar beam which he could manipulate and direct by staring.

My radar beam was a source of delight to me. Not only did it not diminish, but I found that I could exercise a certain control over it; I was able to summon it at will or to extinguish it. It had become very useful to me on the ward. I could repel attendants or patients at will. All that was necessary was to recognize the central source of heat in my solar plexus and move it into my eyes, stare angrily at my enemy and he would become pale, frightened and usually leave. Since the source of the power was definitely located inside me, in my chest, it must obviously come from the sun. Solar power, solar plexus. For this reason, whenever I was not engaged in some routine—eating, visiting the latrine, having my bandages changed—I gazed at the sun, absorbing its light and warmth. The skies were continually bright and cloudless. (Peters, 1949, pp. 143–144)

In this instance the idea of the source and control of the power, though bizarre, was well organized. More frequently, such ideas of personal power are rather vague and diffuse, although the belief in the reality of the power is just as intense in other patients as was Peters' in his radar beam. For example, Karpman's patient, who was obsessed by dread and guilt feelings, wrote as follows.

I am causing lots of people to become insane, accidentally, by reason of the power that leaves me and comes back—people are changing. This power causes railroad accidents, which is awful. My presence in the world is injurious to many people—I don't understand how; it is just an observation. . . . People's voices change when talking; sometimes they appear pale and drowsy, again peppy and full of life, and it seems to me that I am the medium of all that; it seems that I exercise some involuntary control over them. I know it to be imagination, yet it seems so true to me. . . . I imagine people losing their teeth; babies are dwarfed; people have nervous breakdowns, etc.,—all on my account. The blight seems to affect my two brothers; they, too, it seems are having physical and nervous trouble . . . I can't see how I could be such a freak of nature as to have these powers. (Karpman, 1953, p. 279)

In this instance there was a mixture of a feeling of power with a fearful sense of self-accusation plus some doubt, all of which created marked mental confusion. This confused state entered into the essence of his complaints throughout the several months of his psychotic episode.

Several instances from the account of a schizophrenic experience written by a social worker were cited in Chapters 2 and 5. This woman was quite sophisticated, so far as her knowledge of psychiatric illness was concerned. She said that her marriage became increasingly unhappy so that she obtained a divorce; following the divorce she entered into psychoanalytic therapy. As the therapy progressed, she soon came to have a pervasive feeling of mental and personal isolation that resulted in a state of panic, a condition that in turn became associated with an overwhelming conviction of her having discovered the secrets of the universe. These discovered truths she knew directly and with absolute certainty. But the panic mounted and she became terrified when alone. Then she found herself possessed by feelings of power, and these feelings seemed to defend her against her state of panic and persecution. She continued her account as follows.

During the paranoid period I thought I was being persecuted for my beliefs, that my enemies were actively trying to interfere with my activities, were trying to harm me, and at times even to kill me. . . . In order to carry through the task which had been imposed upon me, and to defend myself against the terrifying and bewildering dangers of my external situation, I was endowed in my imagination with truely cosmic powers. The sense of power was not always purely defensive but was also connected with a strong sense of valid inspiration. I felt that I had power to determine the weather which responded to my inner moods, and even to control the movement of the sun in relation to other astronomical bodies. (Anon., 1955, p. 681)

It is not clear whether these feelings of power and influence over others were merely defense mechanisms against feelings of anxious guilt and persecution or whether they grew out of the developing religious ideas that formed part of her defense against guilt feelings.

The mental processes giving rise to, or involved in, delusions described thus far, can be thought of as either secondary to some other disturbed intellectual or emotional process, or so mixed with other processes so that one cannot say which of many factors was the leading one. There are, however, many other accounts which seem to indicate that some delusions start with a peculiar pervasive feeling state of being unjustly accused, or of being the object of derogatory interest.

Delusions of Persecution and Reference

The onset of this peculiar feeling of self-reference and its pervasive spread in the mind of the individual may be either rapid or slow. The way in which each person reacts to the feeling depends on both the personality and character of the individual, as well as on the attending circumstances. If one may generalize from the many recorded accounts, the primary circumstances is an overwhelming peculiar feeling-state of being persecuted, while the following development of the paranoid state represents attempts to rationalize, explain, and justify this persistent inner feeling. Why the feeling-state occurs, whence it is derived and how it is maintained, have been topics of endless speculation. There is no firm evidence at hand to favor one theory rather than another. Whether the delusional systems that are attributed to hallucinations, compulsive ideas, personal powers, or euphoric states are really of the same psychological sort as delusions of reference and persecution is, in the last analysis, no better than a guess.

The description of the development of Renee's delusional system, recorded in the *Autobiography of a Schizophrenic Girl,* may be cited at some length at this point, since she was quite definite as to the order of the mental processes involved.

Very soon after the beginning of [psycho]analysis I understood that my fear was a cover for guilt, a guilt infinite and awful. During the early sessions, masturbation and the hostility I harbored toward everyone seemed to lie at the bottom. I literally hated people, without knowing why. In dreams and frequently in waking fantasies I constructed an electric machine to blow up the earth and everyone with it. . . . This was my greatest, most terrible revenge.

Later, considering them appropriate, I no longer felt guilty about these fantasies, nor did the guilt have an actual object. It was too pervasive, too enormous, to be founded on anything definite, and it demanded punishment. The punishment was indeed horrible, sadistic—it consisted, fittingly enough, of being guilty. For to feel oneself guilty is the worst that can happen, it is the punishment of punishments. Consequently, I could never be relieved of it as though I had been truly punished. Quite the reverse, I felt more and more guilty, immeasurably guilty. Constantly, I sought to discover what was punishing me so dreadfully, what was making me so guilty. . . .

Some time after, I discovered that the Persecutor was none other than the electric machine, that is, it was the "System" that was punishing me. I thought of it as some vast world-like entity encompassing all men. At the top were those who gave orders, who imposed punishment, who pronounced others guilty. But they were themselves guilty. Since every man was responsible for all other men, each of his acts had a repercussion on other beings. A formidable interdependence bound all men under the scourge of culpability. Everyone was part of the System. But only some were aware of being part. . . .

At this moment, the ring closed: the Land of Enlightenment was the same as the System. That is why to enter into it was to become insensible of everything except culpability, the supreme punishment, freely granted by the System. I was guilty, abominably, intolerably guilty, without cause and without motive. Any punishment, the very worst, could be imposed on me—it could never deliver me of the load. Because, as I have already said, the most dreadful punishment was to make me feel eternally, universally culpable.

It was only when I was near "Mama," my analyst, that I felt a little better. . . . I saw the room, the furniture, "Mama" herself, each thing separate, detached from the others, cold, implacable, inhuman, by dint of being without life. Then I began to relate what had happened since the last visit and relived it in the telling. But the sound of my voice and the meaning of my words seemed strange. Every now and then, an inner voice interrupted sneeringly, "Ah, Ah!" and mockingly repeated what I had said.

These inner voices had the aspect of the needle in the hay. They were affected, ridiculous. "Ah, ah! then the teacher said, said," and the voice dwelt stiltedly on "said, said." I struggled to repress them, to pay no attention. But they would not obey, the mocking repetitions continued. Often images were associated with the phrases. For example, if I wanted to recount that my German teacher had made some remark or that my little sister had made a row over going to school, I saw the German teacher gesticulating at his desk like a puppet, separated from everything, alone under a blinding light, waving his arms like a maniac. And I saw my little sister, rolling on the kitchen floor in a rage; but she too was changed by some mechanism, apparently purposeless. . . .

To get rid of these images, of these inner voices, I looked at "Mama." But I perceived a statue, a figure of ice which smiled at me. For I saw the individual features of her face, separated from each other: the teeth, then the nose, then the cheeks, then one eye and the other. Perhaps it was this independence of each part that inspired such fear and prevented my recognizing her even though I knew who she was. In the rest of the room, in the silence, everything was there, posed, congealed, stupid. And the terror, the mad anguish, mounted in me. (Sechehaye, 1951, pp. 27–30)

In Chapter 3 I included Renee's statement that the mental trouble, so far as she was concerned, began with feelings of unreality and *fear* which overwhelmed her completely, and these, so far as she could tell, were without reason or cause. Then after she began receiving psychoanalytic treatment she realized that the feeling was really one of guilt, underlying the fear; yet of what she was guilty, she still did not know. But since she felt so guilty the idea then came to her that the accusation must derive from a Persecutor. This in turn led to the idea that every person is responsible for every other person and hence all are part of one System. Her feeling and ideas were therefore part of the System, which she thought constituted what she called the Land of Enlightenment. Enlightenment had for her several meanings; a world with greater illumination, a greater understanding of her guilt; and the possession of a special sort of knowledge. Having somehow entered this Land, she felt more clearly the impact of her guilt. The realization of her guilt was in itself the evidence of the supreme punishment and she was therefore still more guilty. The pervasive feeling of guilt set her apart from the rest of humanity, including "Mama." Her guilt was reinforced by voices and distorted imagery. In addition to the overpowering guilt, she experienced hallucinations, feelings of isolation and unreality. Her confusion increased. Her strong inner compulsions led her to burn her hand in an open fire. She was in constant mental torture. All of this, so far as Renee was concerned, grew out of, and was maintained by, an overwhelming emotional state that she called guilt.

In Chapter 4 I cited the description Clifford Beers wrote concerning the end of his 798 days of persecutory delusions. His story about the way in which the delusion began is of equal interest. When he was a college student his brother developed a brain tumor that was at the time diagnosed as epilepsy. Several months after, Beers found that his mind was becoming more and more preoccupied with a generalized fear of epilepsy, which rapidly turned into the fearful conviction that he was to succumb to epilepsy and thereafter lose his mind. He described this feeling as follows.

For the fourteen months succeeding the time my brother was first stricken, I was greatly harassed with fear; but not until later did my nerves really conquer me. I remember distinctly when the break came. It happened in November, 1895, during a recitation in German. That hour in the class-room was one of the most disagreeable I ever experienced. It seemed as if my nerves had snapped, like so many minute bands of rubber stretched beyond their elastic limit. At this time, and on many subsequent like occasions, the one thought uppermost in my mind, though I gave no outward evidence of my great despair, was that my psychic convulsion would become physical. My imagination seemed to tear my body into shreds.

[In spite of this "break" he was able to continue his studies and to graduate from college. After graduation he secured employment and earned his livelihood, although his obsessive fear continued. Finally, he mentioned how the fear compelled him to stop work.]

On that day [June 15, 1900] I was compelled to stop, and that at once. I had reached a point where my will had to capitulate to Unreason—that unscrupulous usurper. . . . On this day several new and terrifying sensations seized me and rendered me all but helpless. My condition, however, was not apparent even to those who worked with me at the same desk. . . . I tried to copy certain records in the day's work, but my hand was too unsteady, and I found it difficult to read the words and figures presented to my tired vision in blurred confusion. . . .

After a hurried arrangement of my affairs, I took an early afternoon train, and soon found myself at home. . . . To relatives I said little about my state of health, beyond the general statement that I had never felt worse— a statement which when made by a neurasthenic, means much but proves little. . . .

On the 18th of June I felt so much worse that I went to my bed and stayed there until the 23rd. During the night of the 18th my persistent dread became a false belief—a delusion. What I had long expected I now become convinced had at last occurred. I believed myself to be a confirmed epileptic, and that conviction was stronger than any ever held by a sound intellect. The half-resolve, made before my mind was actually impaired, namely, that I would kill myself rather than live the life I dreaded, now divided my attention with the belief that the stroke had fallen.

[He was now so overwhelmed by the inner tension and conviction that he was surely going insane, that his mind dwelt continually on the idea of suicide. He finally did attempt suicide by dropping out of a fourth story window. However, he landed on his feet, which were broken, but suffered no other injuries. He was taken to a hospital for treatment of the broken bones. Nevertheless, his feelings of fear and guilt continued, but became directed in other channels.]

Knowing that those who attempt suicide are usually placed under arrest, I believed myself under legal restraint. I imagined that at any moment I might be taken to court to face some charge lodged against me by the local police. Every act of those about me seemed to be a part of what, in police parlance, is commonly called, the "Third Degree." The hot poultices placed upon my feet and ankles threw me into a profuse perspiration, and my very active association of mad ideas convinced me that I was being "sweated"—another police term which I had often seen in the newspapers. I inferred that this third-degree sweating process was being inflicted in order to extort some kind of a confession. . . .

While I was at Grace Hospital it was my sense of hearing which was the most disturbed. Soon after I was placed in my room . . . all of my senses became perverted. I still heard the "false voices"—which were doubly false, for Truth no longer existed. The tricks played upon me by my perverted senses of taste, touch, smell, and sight were the source of great mental anguish. None of my food had its usual flavor. This soon led to that common delusion that some of it contained poison—not deadly poison, for I knew that my enemies hated me too much to allow me the boon of death, but poison sufficient to aggravate my discomfort. At breakfast I had cantaloupe, liberally sprinkled with salt. The salt seemed to pucker my mouth, and I believed it to be powdered alum. . . .

My sense of sight was subjected to many weird and uncanny effects. Phantasmagoric visions made their visitations throughout the night, for a time with such regularity that I used to await their coming with a certain restrained curiosity. Although I was not entirely unaware that something was ailing with my mind, I did not accept these visions or any other abnormal effects of sense, as symptoms of insanity. All these horrors I took for the work of detectives, who sat up nights racking their brains in order to rack and utterly wreck my own with a cruel and unfair "Third Degree." (Beers, 1908, pp. 9–10; 13; 14; 15; 22; 30; 31)

Again, this delusional system began with an unreasonable and pervasive feeling-state of fearful apprehension rather than initial guilt.

The point is that a compelling, uncontrollable feeling occupied his mind and colored his entire mental life for several years. Had not his brother's illness been central in his thoughts at the time the feeling-state started, his feelings might just as well have been attached to some other idea. After the emotional turmoil became so acute that he was led to attempt suicide, there was no further mention of possible epilepsy. His deep inner fear was now combined with ideas of persecution and guilt. Visions, voices, and disordered perception added to the mental confusion. Yet all the while the feeling of guilty fear remained in the background, acting to distort ideas, imagery, perception, and beliefs. As he realized later, his ideas in relation to place, time, and persons became fantastically absurd, but the inner feeling was so strong that no matter how absurd his beliefs became the paranoia was maintained.

A third example of this pervasive feeling-state may be cited. Freyberg published the account of a male school teacher who began to feel that he was being persecuted by gossip, which he claimed must have been started by one of his assistants. At first he could not conceive the reason for this feeling nor why precisely this assistant should be instigating such a persecution of him. As time passed, it became increasingly obvious to him that more and more of his difficulties were attributable to a conspiracy led by this enemy. He became utterly convinced of the correctness of his private explanation but scarcely dared name the person since his wife continually insisted that he was incorrect, telling him that if he continued in his delusion, people would say he was crazy. His feelings maintained the false belief, and he became so disturbed that he finally attempted suicide but was unsuccessful. He was taken to a mental hospital where later he wrote a letter to his wife describing his mental state.

Everything that I do, that I think and say with respect to this or that is connected with a person which I did not name to you only once, but possibly ten times. That I went out as if on a search, that I took the same path twice in the same day or later on for very definite purposes, I have said, but I was not understood. I paid visits, visited physicians, etc. . . . all for the purpose of receiving an explanation about his, to me incomprehensible, personality. I named the person but no one believed me or could and would give me an explanation. During day and in the night I brooded and thought about this person who had interferred in my life, led me around as if on a string, made me ridiculous, tortured and tormented me so that I strayed from one job to another and yet did not achieve any security. I thought that I was overheard, spied upon, and yet did not see anyone near me. I was afraid of almost everyone and yet no one harmed me. I tortured myself with reflection, but did not arrive at any definite clear idea or conclusion. (Freyberg, 1901, p. 39)

The paranoid delusions maintained by this teacher became more fantastic and generalized during the three following years. At the end of five years his feeling of being persecuted slowly diminished. Why the feelings and convictions became less acute, or by means of what inner experiences, the patient did not state. However, after he left the hospital, he went to a great deal of trouble to obtain written evidence that would indicate that the cardinal points of his delusions were false; hence he finally became convinced that the delusions were not based on fact and regained his former sanity.

One of the anonymous patients whose hallucinatory experiences I cited in Chapter 6 may serve to illuminate the effect of delusions on behavior. She was an educated woman who had traveled from England to Holland in order to press her claims for a large sum of money. Her legal efforts did not meet with success. She caught a cold, accompanied by some fever, but continued her work nevertheless. Her illness, made worse by her continued disappointment, resulted, as she said, in her body and head breaking down, until fear carried her senses away. She became fearful of her own personal security because of the verbal attacks she had made on other people in attempting to regain her possessions. She got the idea that because she had registered herself with the police as Madame H. A. (her maiden name) rather than Madame H. B. (her married name), she was liable to be poisoned by her enemies. Hence, she ate very little and remained constantly in her bedroom, being increasingly the prey of a variety of fears and delusions.

After some time I was permitted to go to the garden; the open air soothed me, and yet everything around me was a source of illusion to me. The houses around the garden seemed to me to be prisons filled with prisoners. I fancied the kitchen of my landlady, in which a large pot was boiling, the place where the prisoners were put to the torture. The water of the pot in which they were going to throw me, I thought was boiling oil. Full of that notion, I tore the sleeve off my daughter's robe, desirous to retain it that she might not incur the hazard of being boiled alive. . . .

Most luckily I was left in the garden, though a violent storm was approaching. . . . But how different was that storm from that I had seen before, and those I have witnessed since. The clouds which rolled up from the horizon appeared to me to be the billows of the deep, rising o'er the banks of the Schevelingen to the skies, fighting in the air together over my head; while a flotilla of the enemy, on the margin of the river, carried on a deadly combat against the inhabitants. The last hour had struck for the prosperity of Holland. I did not hear any thunder; I did not witness any lightning; but I perceived the explosion of a hundred blazes of fire, the cannonade, ceaseless, reverberated in my ears; from which we may infer, with all certainty, that the ear and the eye of the insane amplify and enlarge whatever is heard or seen. (Anon., 1850b, pp. 393–394)

These misinterpretations of the reality of a thundershower were in a sense illusory experiences (the application of incorrect interpretations to factual sensory experiences). Her delusions, however, became more vivid and fantastic. Her account continued with the narration of her flight from feelings of persecution, which involved fears of imprisonment, torment, and possible death. Only after her husband had finally come from England, and found her and placed her in quiet and trustworthy lodgings did she start to regain a feeling of security and her usual peace of mind.

The onset of these feelings of guilt that lead to delusional systems is usually fairly sudden. Once the feeling has been started it is rapidly woven into the individual's everyday experience in a way that seems to others to be distorted and to overemphasize portions of experience in an odd, selective fashion. The feeling-state may very quickly become associated with hallucinatory voices or visions, mental confusion, and even acts of violence.

Patients frequently find difficulty in naming the pervasive feeling that seems to overwhelm them. Sometimes one can make a better guess at the nature of the feeling-state from the content of the account than from the direct words used in the description. For example, Fraser published the following retrospective account written by a 21-year-old single woman after her recovery from an acute psychosis, for which she had been treated with insulin coma therapy.

> On going shopping . . . with Mummy in the bus I felt faint, and we went into the house of some great aunts of mine who have always been very kind to us, and after lying down for a while and drinking some milk I went home again, and worried all day about having a baby. [A baseless guilt feeling.] G., another friend, who was in the house during that time and who helped by explaining that I would have to go to hospital for some time, advised my parents to take me to Dr. M., who asked me questions about the past. I was then taken to the hospital over the way, after a night at home when I thought I was going to die. There I remember a bell tolling all day, and the parting with Mummy, and being in a room with a very quiet nurse, and having earphones on, and hearing music and voices. I had a bell beside me which I rang and called out the names of people, and I remember seeing a building out of the window sink into the earth with Mummy standing straight at one of the windows, and Daddy waving to me . . . I had various imaginations or delusions such as being in a tomb, being a "bug in a rug," and being abroad. (Fraser and Sargant, 1940–1941, pp. 140–141)

It will be noted that she fails to say anything about her feelings other than that she "worried all day about having a baby," which according to the doctor was a baseless guilt feeling. Evidently she became so disturbed that she was admitted to a hospital the second day and very quickly plunged into a world of fantastic delusions.

One of the best and most realistic discussions of the phenomena of delusions I have found is that of Boisen, who has written at some length concerning the subjective form and content of schizophrenic thinking, from which I quoted in Chapter 3. He has in several contexts made the point that this disease usually begins with an intense feeling of pre-occupation concerning one's personal situation. The feeling-state becomes so intense that the individual is soon completely overwhelmed by it. Because of the emotional depth and intensity of the entire experience, the ideas seem to surge over him with such vividness that he can do no other than assume they must come from some outside source. The source of the entire experience is usually thought by the sufferer to be both supernatural and somewhat hostile. He easily becomes convinced that God is talking to him or that the Devil is after him. Being overwhelmed and confused, he may question, "'Who am I?" or "What is my place in this life?" Then the idea comes to him that he must make some great sacrifice, even give his own life for his own salvation as well as that of all mankind. In some persons the answer seems to be found in a sense of their own helplessness, which is so profound that quite often a suicidal attempt will be made. In other individuals there is a conviction that they have become the direct object of hostile forces against which they must struggle bitterly. It is this type of response to the overwhelming inner emotion which we have been trying to exemplify in the last four or five descriptions. Boisen commented on these phenomena in the following fashion.

More commonly the paranoic reconstruction is based upon delusions of persecution in which the personal self-respect is maintained through the device of transferring blame upon others. In any case a delusional reconstruction means not the breakdown of reason but its accentuation. The reasoning processes become the means by which the patient keeps his head above water. The ideas may be peculiar but the speech is coherent and the logic good enough, if only the premises could be accepted. Neither is there in such types any deficiency in affect. (Boisen, 1942, p. 26)

Boisen continued by pointing out that the schizophrenic delusion usually requires some transfer of guilt in order to maintain one's personal self-respect. The sequence of ideas at this point is, "I feel guilty; there-fore, I am hated; and I must hate back." However, the question remains "What gave rise to the feeling of fearful guilt and panic in the first place?" The mechanisms of defense or adaptation to the feeling seem quite understandable; but whence the original peculiar, senseless, object-less fear?

Patients' Attempts to Explain Delusions

It is apparent that delusions are rarely based on rational interpre-tations of ordinary experience. Something seems to be added to the ordinary processes of perception. This addition is, in a way, as disconcert-ing and puzzling to the person who is having (or has had) the experience as it is to other people who are dealing with him. The patient is puzzled when the delusion starts and he continues to be perplexed after the experience has ended or at least greatly faded. Many who have experienced delusions have attempted to explain or understand their occurrence. Graves' speculations about his psychotic episodes are relevant at this point.

I find myself entirely mystified by the appearance of hallucinations and I suspect occasionally that the appearances which have stood out and marked themselves upon memory were only a part of the total of falsity exposed. When events, appearances and statements were bizarre enough to cause wonder at the moment, or reflection later, I have labelled them as hallucinations. I do not find in myself in restrospect any emotions except wonder and suspicion. . . .

I am in utter ignorance, however, as to what the underlying emotions are in myself, except that in retrospect the delusion seems to be anodyne for fear, though it does not appear so during the period of its entertainment, when it is effective. . . .

My later aberrations have disclosed a shifting delusional system centered around a single stable concept—that the vagaries of conduct and ideas were produced by mysterious influences deliberately brought to bear upon my personality from the outside. To my view, some of these vagaries have indicated great intelligence, and some of them have indicated sheer imbecility. All of them I have tended to set apart from ideation and conduct originating from my own thinking, except in a secondary way. . . . At various times the origin of this influence, and its associations, would be placed in a different quarter, and the conclusions about it would vary. Throughout the shifting I would remain more or less possessed by the theory that my conduct and ideas originated from some source outside of myself, and yet more or less doubt would persist as to the state of fact. (Graves, 1942, pp. 679–680; 702)

Graves wrote these paragraphs rather late in life and after having been hospitalized eight times, usually because of clear-cut manic or depressive symptoms. In attempting to account for the hallucinations and delusions, it seemed to him that the experiences were impressed on him from the outside. He could not identify any underlying emotion except fear, and that fear, rather than having caused the delusions, seemed to him to have grown out of the delusion.

Davidson, after recovering from his second episode of schizophrenia, evidently meditated at some length in an attempt to understand his delusions.

I do not understand it; I cannot explain it; I can only remember it and relate it. What others cannot understand when they read, they will know in the day of their visitation . . . I have tried to write on very difficult and delicate matters as nicely and yet as fully as I can; if I have failed, my intention has been honest. . . .

I also know that there is only one thing that matters very much, and that is sin; and I am about as afraid of it as I am of cancer or insanity. I know that the spiritual world is far more closely connected with this world than most people imagine; and I know that if I persevere in doing good, after death I shall see men and women just as I do now, only perfectly happy and perfectly healthy, and with minds free from any bondage and from all inclination to sin. I do not think that everything I saw, or felt, or thought was real or true; I know there are such things as hallucinations, and I saw phantasms and suffered from delusions. Two sets of forces were at work, and because of my sin and want of self-control, the enemy had great power against me, especially in the way of trying to confuse matters, and giving the whole thing the appearance of nothing but insanity. But the most important things were real. My guardian in the asylum was real, and the insurance doctor was real; and my repentance was real, though it was also supernatural; and the voice, when I was partaking of Holy Communion for the sick, was real; and many other things besides. (Davidson, 1912, p. 267)

In brief, he was convinced of the supernatural and religious nature of his delusions. One can only respect Davidson's honesty and integrity of purpose as expressed in his autobiography. He recognized that much of the content of his insanity was fantastically delusional, but the remainder was to him divine revelation. His religious convictions grew out of his insistence that insofar as he was concerned mystical revelation was the only possible explanation. And one must be further impressed by the fact that his convictions are in accord with those of many others who have lived through similar experiences.

The attempts to explain delusional experience, such as those that Graves and Davidson set down, are very apparent efforts toward rationality. Each tried to separate the "plainly insane" from the personal, though supernatural, direction. For the sake of contrast, I submit the following portion of an attempt at explanation made by a patient of Nolan's who remained convinced of the reality of his paranoid delusions. A well-educated and widely traveled Irishman, aged 43, had been a patient in various mental hospitals for 20 years. He had been a junior Civil Servant in the Malay States when his delusions first developed. His original psychotic ideas had been concerned with religious matters. In the years which followed, his delusions became increasingly fantastic and irrational. He later wrote an *Exposure of the Asylum System* from which the following paragraph is taken.

Evil telepathists are rarely, if ever, so crude as to begin with the direct suggestion of a definite worded threat, insult, cajolery or flattery. They begin with the vague *suggestion* of undefinable evil, *with sensual*, not intellectual urgings to evil courses, or to lopsided exaggerated indulgence in good courses, with bringing about a *dreamy lackadaisical slowcoachy* way of going through the daily round. If possible, they propel towards *erratic ideas* and *habits* and *gloomy views of religion, to a sense of impending doom*, earthly or eternal, inexorable or only avoidable by *sacrificing the things that best make life worth living* or by *doing some appalling deed*. If they can drive an individual away from the herd into the desert they can the more easily *slow down and half paralyse* all the *processes of thought and volition,* and produce *a condition of apprehension of listening for suggestions not made by visible companions.* The suggestions gradually become more *emphatic* more *frequent* and more *definitely worded.* Should the victim take alarm, and strive to disattend to the uncanny suggestions, a *faint faraway* but *insistent ringing* is in his ears for *many seconds, even several minutes,* with *taunting* or *tantalizing or appealing voices* interjected and finally coming in a great volume of *objurgation* or *denunciation* or *prohibition,* accompanied by the most *awful bloodcurdling threats to the victim* and *all he holds* dear. (Nolan, 1928, p. 57)

Apparently, this patient was attempting to explain how evil telepathists operated to control his thoughts and direct his mind. Like others who have undergone similar experiences, he was convinced that these were outside influences which had gained control of his mind, a control they had maintained for many years. He was more explicit than some in his description of the subjective process. He regarded the outer control as essentially evil rather than divine. But to an outsider this explanation sounds more like the simple "raving of a lunatic" than it does an explanation of paranoia.

Development of a Paranoid System

Thus far I have tried to illustrate various phases and varieties of delusions with both brief and lengthy illustrative descriptions. This should afford some idea of the highlights, but it may fail to give an accurate idea of how the entire experience develops as part of a specific history. The experience of delusion may come to a person in a rapid fashion. Many of the illustrations given thus far were taken from rapid developments. But there are many individuals who are finally hospitalized because of psychotic behavior, whose history of delusional ideas extends back over many years, apparently having grown slowly during most of their lifetime. The following material is drawn from Peterson's publication of *Extracts from the Autobiography of a Paranoiac,* from which I have already drawn material in Chapter 5.

This work is given to the public as a lunatic's defense of his position. Every effort I have made hitherto to come to an understanding with my fellowmen, on things which I see to proceed from them, and which give my life its whole shape, has drawn out nothing more than blank denials of all knowledge of the things I spoke of. . . . (p. 196) I am not only a lunatic, but one of the class of lunatics having a controversy with the world in general; in other words, possessed with a monomania, or crazy one-sidedly, or on a single subject. . . . (p. 197)

I was always a shy, retiring child, not disposed to make myself free with strangers, not much given to prattle—in fact, one of the sad and silent sort from the first. I can remember some peculiar sensations which used to weigh on my mind, which go to show that the foundation of my mind-life was but imperfect from the first. I use to be troubled with very strange feelings when I was waking out of sleep, especially if I had been taking a nap in the daytime. It used to seem to me that I was floating in the air, and I often thought to myself: "Why, how queer I have been feeling!" It was as if I filled the whole room, way up to the ceiling. . . . I have heard this explained as due to a lack of simultaneity in the action of the two lobes of the brain, the tardy one remembering what had already passed through the other. My own theory was different, leaving the organ acting out of consideration. I only went so far as to look at it as a mistaken quality in the perception—an erroneous attaching of the nature of the act of remembering to what was really the act of thinking in the present.

I was very early in life an observer of my own mental peculiarities, to a degree which I think must be a very rare exception. I often used to be sensible of an unsatisfactoriness in my conscionsness of what surrounded me. I used to ask myself "Why is it that while I see and hear and feel everything perfectly, it nevertheless does not seem real to me? It is as if I were in danger of forgetting myself and the place where I am!" I often wondered even how I kept the run of things as well as I did. I always found myself holding on to the orderly and proper connection of my acts, and yet from my feelings I could not have answered for my own doing so. . . .

[He related at some length how as a child his mental life had been greatly influenced by the behavior of a great-uncle who lived on the farm where he spent the first 23 years of his life.]

My great-uncle . . . had roughed it a good deal in the world, had been at one time in his life a live-oaker in Florida. How his temper and disposition may have been at an earlier period I cannot say—I only remember him as a man possessed of the belief that a certain young man living on an adjoining farm had the power to torture him at his pleasure, both by bothering his brains and inflicting physical pain; which power he made use of to such good effect that the poor victim was almost constantly kept busy holding him at bay by means of cursings of the most fierce and vigorous description. While at work with the horses in the fields, and when driving, he would intermix his commands to the animals with savage execrations of the troubler of his peace. . . . Thus it went on day and night. He slept in a small room in one of the outbuildings, and often he could be heard a great distance off shouting out threats, sometimes throwing boots or boot-jacks against the boarded side of the building where he lodged. . . . Before I knew it I had gone a criminal length in my resentful feeling [toward my uncle]. I came at last to feel that a person of such a thoroughly savage character did not deserve more indulgence than a mad dog. My position from that time was one of contingent murder. . . .

[At age 23 or 24 he became so disturbed about his uncle's behavior that he forced his mother to move to a town some distance from the farm. Soon after moving to town he acquired a certain pulmonary illness, probably tuberculosis, which lasted several months.]

In the depressed state of my nerves I imagined myself much worse than I really was . . . I felt as if I was liable to sink away and die at any time. My disease was accompanied with periodical accesses of fever, and in the fictitious strength of excitement given by this, my mind seemed to gain an abnormal activity. It was at this time that I first received a revelation on the mysteries of the human soul that had an all-dominant effect on my destinies and the turn of my thoughts ever after. . . . My agitation was so great that my mother and the neighbors seemed to fear I was going crazy. I felt that I *had* been crazy for a long while and had just recovered reason. . . .

I strongly disliked many things I noticed in the manner and words of some I met, and there was nothing to prevent this dislike from occasionally being absorbed into my solitary musings, to find its final resolution in the passion of indignation . . . I have spoken before of my defective means of defense against "teasing" or mocking for the purpose of troubling. I was always terribly alert and sensitive to all kinds of "snubs" and sneers, and oblique remarks . . .

I went to a store and standing at the counter was noticed by one of the clerks, an Irishman, who came to me and said, "I always wait on the little boys first," and as I took no notice of the remark, seemed so determined his words should not be lost on me that he repeated them with the addition, *"like you."* . . . It produced no immediate effect, but it afterwards rose and rankled in my memory, and I was not able to keep clear of imagining vindictive things. . . . I felt that [his] blood would have been sweet to me. . . . My mode of thinking on these incidents no doubt had in it much of the character of insanity. . . . I never armed myself, or, in fact, went any further than to rehearse the drama of revenge in my own mind.

[He and his mother moved to another village, when he was 28 years of age, by which time even his relatives thought that he was insane.]

When my mother was making preparations for moving she asked me to help in packing up some chairs. I made an effort to apply myself to the task, but suddenly found myself overcome by my feelings, and before I knew what I was about I had shivered one of the chairs to fragments. . . . The fact is that I was and had been for some time in a state which any physician, knowing the facts, would have pronounced to be unmistakable insanity. But I had different ideas about what constituted insanity, and often thought to myself that if I did get put into an asylum, as had been threatened, they would not keep me, because they would see I was perfectly rational. I have learned more about the subject since. . . .

Along in June I had a worse spell than common of the kind of nervous stagnation or will-impotence . . . and perpetrated some quite irregular acts . . . In my despair I tore the collar from my shirt, tore the slippers I was wearing, dashed my fist into a tempting dish which my mother was offering me to eat, and other things of the kind. . . .

I passed the next day in brooding, silent, melancholy. It was a rainy day and in accord with my feelings. . . . That night I wrote a little statement to be left behind. . . . It cannot be said that I plunged thoughtlessly into the gulf of self-murder. I had from the first gauged the responsibility I was taking on myself, as fully as my mind was capable of doing . . . I went and took the pistol from the stand-drawer, put on a fresh cap, got into bed again and propped my head on the pillows, placed the muzzle of the pistol against the center of my forehead, and fired. . . . [He lost considerable blood from the scalp wound, but the bullet glanced off; he was up and about in a few days as usual, attending to his garden with bandaged forehead.]

I began to hear responses to and comments on my performances, and it gradually dawned upon me that I had been making myself a conspicuous object of curiosity to the whole neighborhood. . . . The comments heard grew more numerous and more and more derisive. . . . I had no suspicion at the time of any of the inspiration being drawn directly from my head. I do not say it was so. This is the debatable ground. . . . It was not until about a week later that it became evident to me that I was hearing my own thoughts given expression to by foreign wills and voices. . . . I heard a great deal about "inducting," "conducting," "sphere of influence," sometimes even "poles," positive and negative, and my brain was constantly compared to a magnet. . . . I could find no better explanation myself for a long time than the theory of a fluid, similar to or the same as electricity, uniting brains . . . After the whole earth had become pervaded with the magnetism from my head, it would be felt as long as I lived, and the instant of my death would be thus signaled all over the globe, and would be noted and used by all nations as a new era from which to reckon time . . .

[It was about this time that he was removed to the asylum at Pough-keepsie. After his arrival his delusions gradually became more systematic. He then wrote:]

But this is a very old story, and merely a re-statement of the perfectly well known features of my alleged monomania. Let me pass on and give as well as I am able my own theory on which I explain these phenomena . . . It is a question of personal identification. How does a man use his own brain? He can use it because it recognizes the actions of his members as belonging to the personal unit of which it forms the summit. Now the question is, cannot a human brain under certain circumstances become so perverted as to recognize for itself, and without the volition of its bearer, the acts of other individuals as belonging to its life, as falling within its own memory? And if so, would not those individuals become partakers of the intellectuality of that brain, know its conceptions and ideas, while it thus recognized their motions, and become able to share its walks and ways? Such I believe to have been the result in myself . . . But let us further suppose some little abnormality about the original con-stitution, a predisposition from a slightly dislocated arrangement of mind-apparatus and sense-apparatus.

Such, say I once more, I believe to have been the case with myself, and such to be the true nature and essence of the things which have constituted my insanity. . . . I do not deny the fact of insanity, but I firmly believe that it is and has been, since the summer of 1872, an insanity involving the will, ideas and acts of more than one individual.

Notwithstanding my full and necessary faith in the reality of things as I have reasoned to prove them, I am still willing to concede that there has been more or less of purely subjective illusion mingled with these dual realities. Under one aspect the whole of this train of mental images and impressions which has whirled through my head has consisted of insane delusion. The effect on the state of my system has no doubt been analogous to that produced by delusions, and the nervous condition which preceded it was such as eventu-ates in the rise of delusions. (Peterson, 1889, pp. 196–222)

I have selected certain portions from the autobiography that Peterson published, in which the patient presented evidence mainly to explain and justify his thoughts and actions. He recognized that he had at one time experienced delusions and hallucinations, and even supplied a plausible explanation in terms of a lifelong tendency to misinterpret perceptual events in the world about him. He noted that he was always shy and sensitive. On being teased, he never fought back but retired into daydreams in which he vented his resentment and hostility toward his tormentors. He also stated that he regarded some of his hallucinations as the hearing of his own thoughts. However, the delusions and the hallucinatory voices tended to break away from what should have been the obvious connections with his usual thoughts and from his "normal" perceptual world. Finally, in an attempt to find explanations for his mental peculiarities, he began to read the Bible extensively and from this reading he found "explanations" that were sufficiently satisfactory to provide him with a basis on which he could systematize his experiences into a theory. This theory said that his own destiny was connected with an ultimate religion for the world, an assumption which provided him with the idea that he possessed extraordinary powers and abilities. By this device he felt that he could encompass both the ordinary reality of the world and his own special abilities, particularly those abilities that had led others to believe him insane.

This description is typical of the slow development of the mental processes of many "chronic" paranoid patients. The development of emotional and thinking patterns seems quite as logical and rational as those of most normal persons. The patient's whole life history is somehow acceptable if one does not push for an accounting of incidents that the patient usually glosses over in his story, such as, in the case above, the breaking of dishes and furniture or the suicide attempt. Only when an observer attends carefully to the details does the entire history indicate the presence of basic disturbances, both in feeling and in action.

DISCUSSION

There is a vast difference between the meaning and significance of the term *delusion* to the person who is having, or has had, a delusional experience and the meaning the word conveys to everyone else. At the time the experience in question occurred, it may have seemed somewhat peculiar or unusual to the subject but he had no doubt as to the truth of the event itself. For example, a certain individual heard, clearly and distinctly, a voice which told him he was the Son of God and that he must carry a divine message to the world. He harbored no doubt or question as to the reality of the voice, or the meaning it conveyed to him. In fact, he believed that the voice must be obeyed and so he acted accordingly, trying to embark on a divine crusade. Others never did hear the voice even though they might have been present at the very moment when he said the voice was speaking. Nothing in the past or present behavior of the subject provided any justification for the fact that this ordinary man should have been selected by God to carry a divine message; hence, the public could only believe that the subject was suffering from a delusion. This is essentially a situation where a single man's perception and ideas are in direct opposition to those of the entire world about him. The one man may finally agree that his subjective perceptions and ensuing convictions must have been incorrect, and no matter how certain of the original experience he may have originally been, he says that he realizes its implausibility since everyone he knows tell him it cannot be true. In brief, he accepts the majority's opinion which holds that his own experience was false.

There are at least two major questions raised by these descriptions of delusional experience. First, whence came the idea or feeling that gave rise to the essence of delusion? Second, why do delusional experiences and ideas carry with them such intense internal convictions? The conviction is usually, though not invariably, coupled at least at first with some degree of doubt. The experience of an overwhelming inner emotional experience is usually phrased thus: "I am panic-stricken—but I know of nothing I should be afraid of." In delusion the frequent feeling is: "I am Jesus Christ, of that I'm certain, but why?" In the first instance there is a feeling of impending doom or an anticipation of some unknown event that is spoken of as "floating affect." In the second, there is a feeling of unknown fear but the fear is coupled with extraneous knowledge. The nature of the extraneous knowledge may change the feeling of fear to one of guilt, or to a feeling of unfounded persecution, or to a sense of impending mental and physical dissolution, and so on. As we have seen throughout our illustrative material, some patients remark that they find it difficult to give a name to the emotion which overwhelms them.

Many persons who have lived through delusional experiences have speculated on the origin and function of the feeling of conviction that is so frequently an essential element of the disturbance. Among the explanations that patients have offered are the following: the delusion was an anodyne for fear as such, and was therefore closely cherished; my convictions were ways to defend myself against the realization of personal sins; there was a split in my mind so that my will was not strong enough to correct my feelings or my convictions; my ability to synthesize my perceptions quickly and correctly has always been faulty; or there was a split between my ordinary capacity for self-criticism and the feeling of reality of perceptual experience.

There are, of course, many theories concerning delusions that have been put forward by philosophers, physicians, and psychologists as well as by patients. These theories may or may not be acceptable to persons who have experienced delusions. If the experiencer has no ready explanation (as is most often the case), he is usually willing to agree with any theory which seems authoritative enough, particularly if he is told that by agreeing his status will be ameliorated. At present there is no strong evidence that any theory or explanation relieves or corrects the inner conviction from whence the delusions take their strength.

This general consideration is illustrated by the argument that Moore advanced in his autobiography, *The Mind in Chains*. Moore was a "recovered" paranoid patient who during the course of his residence in a mental hospital had received insulin coma, metrazol convulsive therapy, and electric shock therapy. At the time when he was about to be released from the hospital, he wrote as follows.

All this [experience] I later reasoned into the pattern of [a] . . . "plot," . . . The "plot" put me in the State Hospital, and, I kept telling myself, "What a terrific scheme it is! . . . What a mental exercise! What a broadening experience! And when the truth is finally revealed to the world, what a terrific thing it will be!". . .

Only I guess I don't believe it any more. I'm not really absolutely sure, but now I don't think the whole thing happens to be the truth. I have thought this way since New Year's Day. Maybe I finally have been "brainwashed" by the truth.

The wise man, I am told, is he who is smart enough to realize that he really doesn't know everything. For over eleven months I thought I *knew;* . . . I still think it was a good theory, and as logical as most of them. I am even ready to believe it again should I think the facts warrant it. (In fact, I am ready to believe anything that I think the facts warrant.) Only next time I won't be so quick to tell others about it, and I'll check my conclusions more closely. How was it that finally I have been "brainwashed?" I'm not sure myself. It isn't that I see the fallacy of my previous arguments . . . I do not. They still sound like "sane" arguments to me. And I wish like anything that they were true. (Moore, 1955, pp. 211–212)

The correction of many delusions as expressed by the experiencer is in accord with Moore's statement, "Only I guess I don't believe it any more. . . . I have been brainwashed by the truth . . . I wish like anything that my beliefs were true." In spite of the suffering, the loss of personal liberty, and the social effect of having been certified as mad, all of which derived from his "terrific scheme," that is, his delusional system, at heart he continued to wish that the terrific scheme had been true. The "brainwashing" did have one real effect. He said, in passing, that if such ideas ever occurred again he would be most cautious in mentioning them to anyone else.

There seem to be three ways in which the victim of delusions may deal with the domination his false belief holds over all his thinking. He may suddenly recover (as after insulin therapy) and find that all the delusional experience has assumed the character of a bad dream he can easily forget. He may recover from the acute phase of the illness and yet retain the conviction that part of the episode was of a supernatural nature, a form of revelation, and still true, but to be kept more or less secret from everyone else. Or he may, as Moore did, arrive at the idea of a compromise by deciding that the belief and conviction had better be suppressed, although still thinking that the delusion is most probably true. If the delusional system does somehow lose its intensity of conviction and reality—becomes a bad dream—the patient has achieved the best practical solution for his future social readjustment. Neither walling off one's convictions or compromising with convictions has ever proved a lasting or satisfactory adjustment.

Because I know that time is always time
And place is always and only place
And what is actual is actual only for one time
And only for one place. . . .

(*Eliot*, 1936, p. 60)

CHAPTER *9*

Disorders of Memory

INTRODUCTION

Memory, as the word is commonly used, refers to a combination of cognitive processes: (1), the conservation or fixation in mind of certain acts and experiences, (2), the ability to recall and reproduce in mind these past acts and experiences, (3), the proper localization of elements of memory in time and space, and (4), the subjective feeling that the memory trace is correct. The first and second of these factors are necessary and indispensable for memory as such; the third and fourth are necessary for the proper relation of the remembered material to the experiencer himself as a person.

Since some of the disorders of memory are of the kind that may be objectively measured by a consensus of observers or by the comparison of recall with actual physical records, there exists a very extensive literature reporting observations, speculations, and theoretical formulations regarding these phenomena. The fact that an individual may, by his speech or behavior, indicate that he no longer recollects circumstances and relationships which at a previous time he was able to utilize in his direct contact with the world constitutes a form of memory loss detectable by direct observation which others can easily make and agree upon. Disorders of memory of this sort have been collected and classified under the rubrics of amnesia, dementia, and aphasia and have become part of the general scientific and medical literature on mental processes. Unfortunately, I have not found any systematic collections of such instances, or any theoretical formulation based on subjective accounts of amnestic experience. It seems obvious that records of memory losses or distortions by the experiencers themselves would be somewhat different from the accounts provided by outside observers. If there is a true lapse of memory, the experiencer may report that he remembers his past life up to a certain time and place, and then at another and later time and place his memory resumes, and he realizes that there does exist a gap between the two. If others say he has suffered from a distortion of memory, the experiencer may allege that his awareness seemed normal—that is, it was implicitly in agreement with general observations and statements made by others—but then gradually or suddenly his memory of events seems to have become different, confused, unreal, peculiar, or dreamlike and at variance with the external consensus. He may also say that at some later time his memory regained its quality of truth and accuracy so that, in general, it seems to conform with the recollection of others.

In 1871, Professor Griesinger summarized a common viewpoint on the nature of memory disorders. This summary is still valid.

As to memory it presents three notable differences in the insane. Sometimes it is perfectly faithful, for events of early life as well as for those which have occurred during disease. More often it is weak in some respects; this is especially the case in dementia. In other cases incidents of the former life are either completely effaced from the memory (which is very rare), or they are referred to such a distance (and this is more frequent) as to become so vague and strange that the patient is scarcely able to recognize them as having come within the range of his experience. . . . A person cured of insanity ordinarily remembers events which happened during the progress of the disease, and is often able to recount with surprising fidelity and precision the minutest incidents that took place, and to explain in detail the motives and disposition that governed his actions. . . . This is particularly noticeable in persons cured of melancholia or the less pronounced forms of mania; and less so in monomania, when the patient's recollections are usually much confused. (Griesinger, 1871, pp. 60–70)

Although Griesinger's summary has much to commend it I will organize my collection of subject reports in a somewhat different fashion.

Memory Lapses During a Psychosis

The anonymous author of *The Maniac* (p. 64), who suffered an acute psychotic episode marked by auditory hallucinations and delusions, recalled in writing her memoirs that one evening she suddenly regained consciousness and saw the doctor standing by her bed. He spoke to her and she replied, mechanically. Her attention, she said, had been caught by his watch chain which was in her direct line of sight.

"What a pretty chain!" As I was in the act of thinking that, a quite obscene thought seemed suddenly flung into my mind, without any volition of my own, from without. Instantly I pulled myself up, horrified, thinking—
"What am I thinking?"
And that same moment I was annihilated. My existence was extinguished as suddenly and utterly and completely as the flame of a candle, when it is blown out, is extinguished. That was the precise sensation. I suddenly and utterly ceased to be. . . . It is quite possible—in fact, most easy—to imagine and comprehend annihilation and nonexistence,after receiving actual, practical demonstration of them in one's own person. (Anon., 1932a, p. 135)

This account is interesting in that the lack of recall ended with a brief period of lucidity, which recall could not be then or later connected with her usual stream of consciousness. She said she was sure that it had occurred, yet when she wrote about it later she was unable to say when it had happened. Elsewhere in her account this woman told of remembering a slow return from blank unconsciousness to semiconsciousness, during which she heard voices talking, which in all probability were part of her own auditory hallucinations.

I could not open my eyes, or see, or make out in the least to whom this voice belonged; I was conscious of nothing whatever that was occurring in the room or to my own body—I was conscious solely of this talking voice and of my own arguments with it. . . .
But at this point my own consciousness began to ebb and ebb in the same slow manner in which it had previously crept in. I lost all power of arguing with the talking voice; I gradually lost power of distinguishing what it was saying; I receded inch by inch from the margin of conscious existence, leaving that unknown, unseen, unrecognisable stranger still talking without intermission upon that shore from which I had passed away. (Anon., 1932a, p. 97)

She went on to say that after her recovery she had questioned the nurse who had attended her. The nurse told her that approximately at this stage of her illness, she had talked aloud almost continuously. The patient was therefore unable to say whether part of the conversations she had heard had derived from her own voice or had been a product of her hallucinations. The major point to bear in mind is that recollection of events which occurred during a psychotic episode may be fragmentary but the fragment in itself may be quite clear.

Hackett related the onset of the psychotic break in his memory by giving the following account of certain days and nights, soon after he had been placed in a hospital.

I felt something strange was happening in my head. I felt drugged. I was at the end of a cliff, steeper than ever before, and I would fall and I could not save myself. I made myself sit up and look around. There were lights in the ceiling half dimmed but burning. Those sleeping near me were quiet except for the sounds of sleep. I sank back into the pillow and again had the sensation of falling. This was something of sleep and something of death. I was falling farther than ever before but I could not fight back. . . . I wrapped the pillow around my head and dropped from the cliff. . . . [When he continued with the thread of his account, it was apparent that he was confused and disoriented, for both time and place, He partially relocated himself in the following way.]

It was the Fourth of July. I figured out the day myself. It was the Fourth of July because we were out in the courtyard and a band was marching and they were giving out free ice cream. I did not know how long I had been here or why I was here, only that it was Independence Day and I was eating ice cream and a band was marching from the far end of the courtyard down toward us. Then the fear came. It was a trick to make me think it was the Fourth. . . . [The confusion continued. Fragments of memory were all that could be recalled.]

The rain did not help. I was in bed and I was depressed and even the rain did not help. . . . It was dawn and I lay awake in the white bed. How long had I been here? Days. Days that faded into night and nights into day. Some days, night would not fall. Some nights were unending. Some nights there was the moon; some days, the sun. There was no rain ever. (Hackett, 1952, pp. 16; 26; 34–35)

These reconstructions of scattered fragments of experience, full of blanks and uncertainties, are commonplace in the reports given by patients after recovery from a schizophrenic psychosis. There is usually a great deal of hesitancy concerning the proper relationships between person, time, and place.

In Chapter 4 I cited an incident recounted by a patient who had suddenly begun to experience persecutory delusions and quickly sought aid, only to lose consciousness before assistance could reach him. I mention it now because Mary Jane Ward tells of a similar experience in her autobiography, *The Snake Pit*. She had been slowly recovering from an acute psychosis, when one afternoon she was suddenly overtaken by the delusional idea that another patient had designs on her life. She ran to the nurse to seek protection and was asked what the matter was.

Virginia tried to think. It had been urgent, she knew, to reach a nurse but now she could not remember why. Something awful was going to happen to her. "Get a doctor, please. Get my doctor, please," she said, as the floor began to soften and swirl.

"Take it easy," said Miss Bixby. "It's all right. Just hang on. . . . Miss Jones! All right, Virginia . . . just hang on to me. Miss Jones, get . . ." They were fighting their way through the deep varnish of the hall now. "Just hang on," said Miss Bixby.

"It's never happened this way before," gasped Virginia. "I never had such definite warning. I never had warning before that I knew was warning.". . .

"Your doctor will be here in a minute. We'll go to meet him. We won't have any trouble at all. See, it's not far to the door.". . .

She spoke without conviction, all the time urging Virginia forward. Wants to get me out of her ward before it happens, wants to get me to wherever it is more convenient for them, wants to get me into his hands, slender hands for a man but they are strong. It was coming rapidly now. Could he come so fast? Miss Bixby opened the door. "You see," she said, "there he is. He is coming as fast as he can." Virginia could tell that he was running, but she knew he would not reach her in time.

[Sometime later.] The sun is shining. It is summer again. Again? Perhaps still. Now white flakes, like snow, began to dance in the sunlight. There may be a bonfire near by. I would like to see a bonfire. I would like to sit near it and get warm. . . . "I was wondering what time it was," said Virginia. High time. It must mean time for high tea. She frowned. She did not like to think about tea time. Why? I always used to like tea.

But then she remembered something. She had gone to a tea where an old woman had tried to knife her. She tried to kill me and I ran and ran and the Young Jailer came to my rescue. (Ward, 1946, pp. 196–198)

It will be noted that Virginia's memory of the manner in which this incident started was not too clear. She had been frightened by a delusional idea that may or may not have had a factual basis. Then there was a fairly detailed recall of the period of warning—and then no memory for a period of several months, during which time she had received a number of electric convulsive treatments. Her memory slowly returned, in an unclear and patchy fashion. In other contexts she made several interesting observations regarding her disordered memory.

She had no idea what day of the week it was, what week of the month, what month of what year. She tried to explain this to the nurse. "It isn't so much a matter of forgetting as it is of not knowing. When your memory is all tied up and separated from the rest of you, you don't forget. In order to forget you have first to remember, don't you, even though briefly?". . .

"There is something that bothers me a great deal," she said. "Seeing you I know I have seen you before. Many times. I mean, I know that I know you well, but I don't remember. Sometimes in the dining hall or on the walks or in the store I see people I know, that is, their faces are familiar, but I don't know why. I know I have been here almost a year and yet I remember nothing before last summer. And only patches since then." (Ward, 1946, pp. 93; 231)

Note the phrase, "In order to forget, you have first to remember." In effect, she is expressing the idea that if there is no registration of events in the mind at the time of their occurrence, there can be no recall. The next paragraph, however, rather casts doubt on this assumption. Her statement, "I know that I know you well, but I don't remember," implies that her present mental processes are in some way not properly associated with a series of past events with which connections should have been available for the proper elicitation of recall. The memory losses and disorganizations following psychotic episodes are not simple to unravel. They often confuse and bother the patient following recovery and have the effect of making many persons uncertain of the validity of their own recall.

Disorientation in Time

Some patients have special difficulties in recall since they cannot place such fragments of memory as they may retain into any meaningful time sequence. For example, Maude Harrison recorded the following comments in her autobiography.

I do not remember that first day in Five as a day. This is not surprising, because for a long time no day seemed to me like a day, and no night seemed like a night.

But this day, in particular, has no shape in my memory. I used to tell the time by meals, but as I believed that we were served with several sets of meals in each real day—about half a dozen sets of breakfast, lunch, tea and dinner in each twelve hours—this was not much help. . . .

I did not begin to believe in any real time until towards the end of May. Two birthdays, Barbara's and my niece Shirley's, I let slip by unobserved because I did not believe that either my friend or my niece was really having a birthday at all. It is on account of this continued confusion that my memory halts on looking back. (Harrison, 1941, pp. 32; 107)

In this instance the defect in recall seems to spring from the fact that the various units of memory were not attached to their usual time sequences. Night and day, mealtime, birthdays, and the like passed either unnoticed or seemed so indistinct that they were not perceptible. Probably the confusion of the voice, plus the pain and discomfort of the illness, had become uppermost in her stream of thought. All this served to blot out or at least to confuse the usual memory fixation points.

Jane Hillyer commented on these aspects of her psychotic experience and their relation to recall.

The next step in the process of dissolution was a complete snuffing out of my individuality. Life became, for short periods, a blank. One night coming to sudden consciousness in a flash of lightning, followed by a tremendous thunder crash, I called out, "Have the enemy gotten over? Are they bombing?" The nurses laughed. That was reassuring, though it made me a bit angry. I did not like being laughed at. Two of the nurses were talking in my room, one sitting on the edge of her bed combing her long, yellow hair. I looked at her. Who was she? Who was I? I did not know. Just this room, the storm outside, something that questioned . . . I was within four walls, companioned by two strangers; I existed, save for these, in unpeopled space. It was pleasant to "be back again." The two were nice to me, but rather superior in their attitude, and apparently amused at everything I said—it's good to be amusing, and yet there was something decidedly queer about this. . . .

The progression from this state of semi-cognizance and quiescence was rather gradual but steady; it is hard to trace. People and things counted less and less. I ceased to wonder. I asked a member of my family where I was and having received an answer, accepted it. And usually I remembered it, when I was in a state to remember anything objective. . . .

For a number of months, under such stress, I simply slipped back into the dark, as some people faint as the result of physical injury. I have but one other memory of that ward, though I think I was there some weeks. I stood in the doorway of the "porch," but only for a moment. I had been violently resisting all efforts to move me in any direction. . . . I had slipped into the realm of forgetfulness with a fixed determination not to talk, with a distrust and dislike of every one about me. (Hillyer, 1926, pp. 55; 69; 75)

It is apparent from Miss Hillyer's account that there was a dissolution of the continuity of conscious life throughout most of the four years of her acute psychotic episode, with little or no recall of anything more than a few fragments, which could not be correctly placed in time.

To return to the point of disorientation in time as a memory defect, there are accounts by patients which do indicate that losses of the usual temporal landmarks are certainly part of the difficulty, although the "time-cue" loss is complicated by many other factors which add to the problem of recall. Temporal distortions have for some persons a peculiar experiential quality that is reported in terms seeming to imply that time both moves and yet at the same time stands still. This adds a quality of unreality to the total experience of some patients. The difficulty thus generated can be illustrated by the following excerpt taken from the description of one of Fischer's patients.

I can no longer find my way about in the world, everything has vanished; I am no longer here myself. Before I was a person with body and soul and now I am only just a creature. I no longer know about anything. My natural life is deceased, the supernatural lives on. Before, I was a person like others, then a sick person when I was nervous because my child had died; but now only the body exists and the soul is dead. . . . I hear and I see but I know nothing; life is now a puzzle. Did you ever hear this: there is a moving belt on which the same object is always put—like in the factory. Time is now like a belt. But nothing is on it. It runs along and is always the same. . . . What about the future? One cannot reach it. One can speak about the present and the past, one cannot conceive of the future any more. One cannot picture it to one self and one has to sink back. Everything is like a question mark. Time is standing still; one is even swaying between the past and the future. Everything is so settled. Before it was backwards and forwards—Everything good, now it has, so to say, escaped the memory. (Fischer, 1929, p. 560)

This description, written by the patient while she was still psychotic, shows that part of her memory difficulties sprang from the fact that during her illness she was dissociated with regard to her regular stream of thought. Time ran along as it always had yet in some way she felt separated from it, she stood apart feeling unreal and alien, no longer a member of the world of reality around her.

The last three excerpts make evident the fact that memory lapses are not wholly due to periods of unconsciousness or to the failure of primary registration of passing events. It does not mean that the world went by while one was asleep or simply not attending. Rather, the world did go by but one was not consciously a part of it, one was in no way concerned with the passing show, and this lack of concern becomes manifest later in poor recall.

Fundamental Weakness of Memory in Psychosis

Some patients have mentioned during their illness an occasional difficulty in immediate recall. For example, Davidson wrote as follows.

I was far more given to talking than to reading; but noticing that my guardian, who was rather a silent man, read the papers carefully when the day's work was over, I tried one evening to read a short article. I could only read, word after word, slowly and with difficulty, like a young child. I found it strangely difficult to gather the sense of it, and as soon as I had read it I forgot it completely. I remember thinking this curious, for I could understand what was said to me, and I could follow with pleasure, and even learn off by heart, simple poetry like that of Bret Harte. (Davidson, 1912, p. 75)

As Davidson says, he thought that the inability to remember what he had just read was curious. When he wrote his *Remembrances* he certainly seemed to be able to recall in detail almost everything that had occurred to him. Whether the former was a real inability, or whether it simply resulted from lack of interest in the subject matter is impossible to assert.

A patient treated by Bockner commented on this point in the following fashion.

I can't argue with people because I can't collect my thoughts sufficiently. My thinking isn't clear and I forget the trend of a conversation. I don't think I am able to concentrate accurately on one subject. I don't feel able to put over my ideas or to make people understand what I mean. (Bockner, 1949, p. 970)

Lapses or weaknesses of memory or complete inability to remember may persist even after the patient has left the hospital and is presumably recovered. For example, an anonymous patient wrote as follows.

> I got an appointment as a collector for the Edinburgh Water Company. This, however, after a week's trial, I found so much beyond the compass of my strength and faculties, that, with feelings of deep mortification and disappointment, I was forced to relinquish it. I became perplexed with the simplest calculations. I lost money, and literally lost myself, having, on the last day of my collecting, become so bewildered in streets long familiar, that I could not discriminate north from south, or east from west, as if my brains were completely turned. (Anon., 1955, p. 20)

In an excerpt cited earlier in this chapter, Mary Jane Ward wrote: "It isn't so much a matter of forgetting as it is of not knowing. . . . to forget you have first to remember." In other words, there must be conscious attention and discrimination or there can be no fixation of a memory trace that may be brought to mind later. And yet, as Davidson pointed out, it is possible to learn "by heart, simple poetry," or on the other hand, as this last patient said, not to remember (recognize) one's way on well-known streets. Whether or not fixation takes place and why some experiences will remain fixed in memory and others will not, constitute part of the difficulty in understanding the problem of recognition and recall during and after a psychosis. A part of the trouble has been attributed by some of the individuals in question to *weakness*, a vague descriptive term which suggests only that the cohesive factor which causes memory images to adhere to one another has been weakened, and that ideas no longer cling together in a person's mental organization.

Obliteration or Active Forgetting

Several factors working against efforts at recall must be considered. First, there is, as a rule, a real physical and mental weakness following recovery from a psychosis. Recall often requires more voluntary effort than most patients feel they can command. Second, many of the experiences that might be recalled are of an unpleasant nature and therefore to do so seems pointless to the patient. Third, friends, relatives, and physicians all advise the patient to forget his psychotic experience. It is undeniable that most people are not too interested in listening to stories of someone's personal suffering. Both physicians and friends will join forces in saying: "You are well now. Forget the whole experience. Thinking about your past troubles and fears might only revive those thoughts which were so distressing to you." Fourth, the experiences, if and when recalled, have something of the quality of a suddenly remembered nightmare; they seem unreal, fantastic, foolish, and altogether unpleasant.

All in all, the general circumstances and influences of recovery from a psychotic episode conspire quite effectively to suppress the memory. This forgetting may be active—that is, an act of conscious repression or suppression; it may be passive, that is, the result of favorable circumstances.

These last points were very clearly stated by Custance.

But once I get out of a Mental Hospital all this changes. I find myself in a totally different "atmosphere." I cannot, however hard I try, get even my most intimate relatives and friends to understand or take any interest in what may or may not have happened to me during my "madness." Gradually the vividness of my memory fades; like my relatives, I try to put the whole experience out of my mind, and in fact it does to a certain extent disappear into "lower levels of my Unconscious." Then I find myself genuinely wondering whether these memories, so far as they are conscious at all, are not "delusions," "hallucinations," as "unreal" as the actual technical hallucination I know I have had. (Custance, 1952, p. 115)

In all probability this forgetting, whether repressed or suppressed, is a very common phenomenon in many persons who have lived through a psychotic period (excepting attacks of melancholia). The explanations that Custance gave all seem very reasonable and matter-of-fact.

One of the unpleasant experiences that may accompany electric convulsive therapy is a progressive loss of memory which the patient may experience when subjected to a long series of treatments. The patients are frightened by the idea of an application of an electric current across the head, a current strong enough to produce instantaneous unconsciousness. This sudden blackout is unpleasant, even though events that happened during the lapse are later not remembered. But more disturbing to the patient is the fact that when he regains consciousness after the shock, he finds difficulty in recalling who he is, where he is, or what has been occurring to him in the recent past. As one treatment succeeds another he finds it more and more difficult to recall the events of his past life. Actually patients regain practically all of their memories within two months after the treatments have ended. It is quite natural, though, that in most patients the temporary disorganization and loss of memory do induce fear. One of the theories concerning the therapeutic action of the treatment is that the patient is made "to forget his crazy ideas," a theory not borne out by fact. Peters commented on this experience of "forgetting" associated with shock treatment in the following way.

I feel sort of funny in my mind about that shock treatment, I keep thinking I'm wrong or that I don't know what I do remember, although everything seems to have come back to me now. . . .

My mind seemed almost to have a life and direction of its own, sorting and rejecting, fitting bits and pieces of memory together, recalling names and people, groping for exact sequence, questioning and doubting. I wondered if there was any such thing as total recall, or were there gaps that I did not recognize as gaps, holes which I would never be able to refill if only because I did not know they were holes? . . . How could anyone know that I would forget the right things and remember the right things? (Peters, 1949, pp. 263–264)

The questions Peters raised are really pertinent for the understanding of the normal process of memory as well as for the understanding of memory disorders. There are selective factors in fixation and recall in everyday life that are not fully understood. Why one set of facts will be remembered rather than another is not understood, any more than why one is quite sure that certain events recalled are true and will have one's doubts as to the veracity of others. In normal persons these doubts and questions may occur as another phase of the regular stream of thought. After shock therapy, these fragments recur suddenly without the usual interconnections or proper temporal attributes necessary in mental readjustment.

Amnesia Following Head Injury or Cerebral Accident

There are a number of personal accounts of complete loss of memory (amnesia) for varying periods of time. The amnesia following a head injury (brain concussion) usually runs a rather regular pattern. The following account written by Lombard's patient concerning his amnesia following head injury is excellent, the writer having given in considerable detail something of the mental processes involved in regaining his recall.

On the 18th of February 1921, while at Cambridge where I taught French in Newnham College, I fainted and had a nasty fall during which my head hit the pavement of a bridge; this resulted in an acute concussion of the brain and a hemorrhage in the right ear. The doctor . . . diagnosed a "slight fracture of the cranial base." I have recorded some of the psychological impressions which appeared after this accident. Of the ten days which followed I have no recollection except possibly a few vague images which came out of the shadows with the help of reports of others, but for which the authenticity is not rigorous. I returned to normality Monday the 7th of March.

During this interval, while I was rediscovering the capacity to remember I first became aware of things around me and of my own thoughts. Everything for me was unintelligible for I could not anchor anything to the past. I lived in a nightmare, and in order to get free from it, I applied myself as much as I could to find a valid explanation of the circumstances in which I found myself.

I was taken to the Addenbrooke's Hospital along the fence of which I had walked often; the name of which I knew. The first image which I remember was one of a vast hall in which there were many beds and a crowd of people. This image was abnormal, since my right eye having been displaced, the two visual images were not superposed [double vision resulting] . . . But all this had nothing strange about it, and especially nothing inexplicable; I felt that my right eye was injured, and that the eye created the double vision; I kept this eye almost constantly closed, and then everything seemed normal. . . .

What does this hall mean, and these beds, and these people? . . . All this should not really exist. There was no reason for me not to be at my college. I remember, without recalling all the details, trying out various hypotheses to justify my presence in this hall, and I ended with this one: I was at the college, in my room, and it was a dream.

But almost immediately, I became aware of the real passing of time: I was looking at a clock, and I was following attentively the hands of the clock . . . the movement which seemed to me to measure time with a prodigious slowness, the reality of which I did not doubt. Time was for me the only one of the past realities which overlapped into the present world. I could doubt the reality of the clock, I could think that the designation of the hours was inaccurate, but I could not think that the image of this movement that I was seeing was unreal, and it was too important for me to be disregarded. It was the only bridge with the real world. Very rapidly . . . this impression made me completely abandon the idea that I was dreaming. The night came, then the morning. A day went by and I was aware of it. I tried to remember the last of the essential events of my life.

"My students at Newnham?" A whole day passed without me seeing them again. I was surprised that they had not come. "The city?" No new image of the street since an evening when I saw a bicycle accident. (In reality, the eve of the accident which happened to me.)

I was aware of lying down, of a little pain in my eye; but I never questioned myself about it. It did not occur to me that possibly I might be sick. I have been locked up some place. . . . A little later, I asked that I be taken to the street; I wished to say "so that I may find myself in a familiar environment where my former life could continue," . . . (I always spoke English during all this period.) I lived for several days in a nightmare; I had the impression of being in hostile surroundings and that it was intolerable, in spite of all my efforts not to be able to anchor to anything I knew . . .

And then I was brought notes, flowers, my newspapers, my correspondence. My letters . . . what a surprise! Letters from my friends in France, full of warm sympathy and wishes of getting-well-soon. . . . They were touching, but seemed very much out of place.

Wednesday, March 3rd my mother came to see me. . . . When she arrived, I was not surprised and I was for an instant very happy. But the joy waned immediately. I recognized my mother at once. I believed momentarily in the reality of her presence: I asked her of news from home. Then I asked her the question which I had not dared to ask anyone and which was at the bottom of my problem: "Am I sick?" My mother did not understand the point of my question. She answered me as though I had said: "Do I look sick?" and to prevent me from any depressing thoughts, she told me that I looked fine. I was a little disappointed. The explanation was evasive. Later, as my mother spoke of leaving, I asked her the date, having in the back of my mind an idea.

This would be the first date that I would know and it would be a link between the world of the past and the real outside world in which I was living; "Friday the 4th or Saturday the 5th," my mother said as she left. I was not too disturbed by this. All of my sensitiveness, or at least all my conscious sensitivity, was reduced to the painful impression of living in the middle of an enigmatic state of affairs that I could not link to the past, nor to anything that seemed to be *true*. The explanation which should have come naturally to my mind did not occur. Not having given me an answer which would have allowed me to understand the situation, my mother, on leaving, took with her the proof of her own reality. I saw her leave; then, a little later, I asked myself if she really had visited me. I didn't think that I dared question the care-nurse about this, so I tried to prove things to myself. There was a date about which I was certain and which would serve me as a landmark,—Saturday, February 26. (I had been invited to attend an organ recital on that day.) If, beginning with Saturday the 26th, by counting days I should arrive at Friday the 4th, this would prove that my mother had really visited me. If the 4th was not a Friday, then I had imagined the date, the visit and the conversation with my mother. I therefore counted the days but I allowed 30 days for the month February and hence Friday was not the 4th, and my mother had not visited me. But during the following evening I suddenly realized that the month of February had only 28 days. I counted the number of days again. My mother had visited me. This was disturbing.

About the same date, the 6th perhaps, I was brought a visiting card bearing a name which surprised, pleased and amused me somewhat. I believed it for a moment, and then called my nurse. I always believed nurses!—Or at least, I have always asked them what I needed without questioning their reality . . . I called, therefore, my nurse to ask her if my card was a real card . . . She answered "Yes" and she turned immediately to speak to another nurse . . . I heard her and, I believe, I began to doubt the reasoning which had made me think that everything was unreal. . . .

On the 7th—I don't remember how it came about—the nurse asked me if I wanted to look at the Fitzwilliam Museum. I asked: "The Fitzwilliam Museum is across the street?" She raised me up in bed and turned me around so that I could see it. And I saw it—it was a reorientation.

"But then this is Addenbrooke's Hospital!" Everything was explained and, with the understanding of that instant came my belief in the reality of the world of sensation, the feeling of conviction and the sensation of finding myself, all returned. I immediately asked the date of the day. I also asked for explanations of the illness which had brought me there. They told me how I was found on Friday the 18th of February on the Silver Street bridge. I then recalled my morning errands, the beautiful morning, the river under the bridge that I had seen, the sensation which I had had on fainting, and the effort of trying to grab the railing of the bridge. I could hear myself saying: "Say! I am fainting." All memory of the past up to the moment immediately before the injury returned to me. (Lombard, 1923, pp. 651–654)

Part of the difficulty which disturbed this patient during the period of amnesia grew out of the fact that he could not establish any connections between the perceptual world in which he found himself and the familiar world of his past. The symptom of double vision he could accept and even correctly explain. Originally the hypothesis which had occurred to him concerning his loss of feeling was simply that he was dreaming. But then when he saw on the wall an actual clock face with the moving hands indicating the passage of time, he was not able to fit that image into his dream explanation. Having been kept in bed and supplied only with evasive answers led him to the idea that he was locked up. The total physical and psychological disorientation became a puzzling nightmare. He tried to lend reality to the situation in which he found himself by creating a temporal bridge, based on the dates of his mother's visit, but was unable to achieve this. Only when he had the opportunity for a successful *spatial* reorientation did things fall into place and he was thus able to regain the connections necessary for recalling both temporal and spatial relations. (Although his native tongue was French he always spoke English during his recovery, which was in itself a rather remarkable circumstance.)

The experience of a brain hemorrhage with some subsequent residual memory and speech disturbance was described by Forel, a famous neuroanatomist and psychopathologist of a generation past.

On May 17, 1912 . . . I found that I was extremely tired. I did not feel quite well, and I was conscious of a tingling and numbness in my right arm. When I began to dictate I could not find the right expressions, and this, in respect of the intricate subject with which I was dealing, was particularly fatal. In consequence of the defective ecphoria [recall] of my expressions I found the lucid formulation of my train of reasoning impossible. I felt almost desperate; I searched the dictionary for expressions which at other times were familiar, and while so doing I forgot what I wanted to say. After this the dictation passed off naturally, but I omitted a few words. The printed essay shows no signs of this, as I thoroughly revised it afterwards. My condition now seemed to me critical. The formication [tingling] in the right arm continued. It was obvious to those about me that I had difficulty in finding certain words. . . . I became suspicious, and began to think I had had a slight stroke. . . .

On May 25th . . . my impediment of speech recurred, and was more apparent. I fumbled for phrases, my speech became uncertain and indistinct . . . I was very tired and even rather dizzy.

Next morning, after a good sleep, I got up and went, half-dressed, to the water-closet. . . . I turned giddy, and fell down. I did not lose consciousness, but I felt very vague. . . . Supporting myself and swaying on my feet, I crept away. . . . However, I could still walk, dress myself, and even take my breakfast. My secretary told me later that I looked very absent-minded, and had spread the butter on my sugar instead of on my bread. (Forel, 1937, pp. 288–290)

In all probability there were memory gaps and distortions that Forel could not recall and hence did not report. His comments on the difficulty in speaking and thinking indicate that there were more memory disabilities than he himself realized. However, he did not lose the mental connections that supplied him with a feeling of continuity in time and place.

Amnesia Without a Known Basis

Complete loss of memory was described by an otherwise normal man as follows.

With an assurance to my wife that I would be back in a minute or two, I went out and failed to return.

The next thing that I remember is a sound of rifle shots and some short bursts of machine-gun fire coming from the other side of a hill on the right of a road on which I was walking. I was conscious of being dirty, unshaven and footsore. I did not seem to be particularly hungry or thirsty. I had a feeling of puzzlement upon my mind, not unlike that which one may experience on waking from a deep sleep in a strange place. Where was I? Who was I? Something was wrong, but what was it? I knew my own name and recognized my own writing when I jotted it down on a bit of paper, but everything else seemed uncertain and unstable. . . .

I had already realised that something extraordinary had happened to me, but I still felt as though I might wake up at any minute and find the whole thing a dream. It was some few minutes before I realised fully that I had absolutely no recollection of any course of events which could have brought me to the existing position. The immediate past seemed to be "a perfect and absolute blank," and when I had come to grasp that fact I found a little comfort in the thought that I was so far normal as to be able to recognise such a blank as being extraordinary. Evidently I had still some power of ratiocination and some standards by which to judge normal and abnormal happenings. I thought hard for a long time; I searched in my mind for any leading fact which might give me a clue to the business, but all I could get were distant but quite definite pictures of my home and people in East Anglia, and of certain phases of schoolboy life in term time and holidays. I recalled these things easily enough and in some detail, but at the same time I was aware that they were a long way off in point of time, and that they could have little bearing on the present. . . .

[With this realization he went to the police, who located his wife and family. The amnesia, which proved to be for the events of the past twenty years of his life, persisted. No reason for the amnesia could be found. He then placed himself under the care of a physician who used a modified psychoanalytic method to assist him in regaining his memory. He commented, as follows, on the way in which the regained material became incorporated into his life:]

I myself was never quite sure whether the story I was telling was a record of personal experience or not. The sense of memory was missing from them and in so far as my own feeling for them was concerned they might have been either versions of other people's stories the source of which was forgotten, or very plausible fictions developed by my subconscious mind to meet the needs of the moment. They continued to come with increasing ease and as I have said some of them were capable of confirmation, and others linked together in a way that suggested that they must have a basis in past experience, and all of them contained details that I could not have got from any of my recent excursions into history. . . .

My own impressions of these sittings was rather a curious one. I found them absorbingly interesting, but difficult to regard as a part of the serious business of life, and the recovery of my lost memory. While they were going on I felt as though I was looking at an uncertain and changing scene which required close concentration and attention if it was to be reported correctly to another party who could not see it. The words of description came slowly as a rule, but with irregular intervals and occasional little bursts of speed to describe particular and urgent points. I can imagine that someone observing a battle from a great distance and speaking his impressions into a microphone might produce much the same sort of jerky irregular story for his listeners. . . .

My reason could make me believe in them as being authentic memories because the evidence in support of them was so strong, but full memory is not a thing which needs this kind of support. It brings conviction without adventitious aids, and has a quality which distinguishes its working and results quite clearly from those of the reason or the judgement. I could remember the scenes in hospital as pictures that had come into my mind a few weeks before in response to a series of questions. They might almost have been the records of some other man's doings which I had heard about and pictured and had subsequently confirmed by independent evidence. . . .

[After several months of treatment plus several months of getting accustomed to this reconstruction of the probable events which had occurred in the amnestic period, he wrote:]

There was no feeling of strangeness about the restored memories; the whole mechanism of remembering seemed to be working as smoothly and normally as though there had never been anything the matter with it. I was a little hazy and uncertain about the sequence of events in the past eighteen months, but this was the only sign I could discover of my recent disability, and I supposed that it was no more than could be cleared up with a few hours of systematic effort. It did strike me that it was odd that these nearer events should be so much less clear to me than others which had happened years before them, but this by itself seemed a small matter beside the success. (Anon., 1932b, pp. 16; 17–18; 146–148; 218–219; 232–233)

This man's story indicates that he had lost all recall for a considerable portion of his previous life. He knew his own identity but all exact memory for the events of his life, for more than twenty years past, could not be immediately retrieved. By a process of association, and by making use of cues supplied or suggested by others, he was able to reconstruct a reasonably complete life history up to the period of eighteen months prior to the amnesia. His statement that full memory is accompanied by an inherent conviction of its truth, a quality over and above such components as reason or judgment, agrees with the reports of many other patients who have also been affected with amnesia. Full normal memory has as a component an intrinsic feeling of personal reality that connects all events in time, space, and person. In ordinary memory there can be no doubt, in the mind of the person who is relating the event, about the when, where, why, and true self-participation inherent in the experience. Should doubts occur, the recall will then usually take on a quality of unreality or, as one says, the experience itself was probably a fantasy and thus may not be true.

Attention should be called to the theory that amnestic lapses, such as the one recounted above, are of a hysterical nature and motivated by an unconscious desire to forget some part of one's past, or to suppress either some unpleasant past memories or present self-reproach. There was in this man's account no mention of brain injury or psychosis. Although he was able, with assistance, to reconstruct a "satisfactory" memory, he said that as far as he was concerned he never discovered a real basis or motive which had any explanatory value. The entire account of his memory loss and gain was never accompanied by a quality of possible reality or a conviction of truth.

Déjà vu *and* Jamais vu

Déjà vu is a name given to an actual perception that is felt to have been experienced before, although its possible previous occurrence cannot be explicitly remembered nor identified in time or place. This is an affective sort of experience where the feeling of familiarity becomes incorrectly attached to present recognition. This experience is not particularly uncommon in everyday life and has been recorded by many writers. MacCurdy gave an example of such a personal experience and analyzed the event in some detail.

On getting out of bed one morning I caught sight of my walking stick, hanging on a bookcase across the room. At once, I began to say to myself, "I have seen that stick before. I have seen it hanging there. When did I see it there?", etc. The ridiculousness of these speculations was immediately apparent, because I knew that I *always* hung my stick in that place and, of course, I had seen it precisely there a hundred times. Nevertheless, the peculiar feeling of *déjà vu* persisted. Then I tried to solve the problem by associating freely from "walking stick." Almost at once there came to mind memory of a complicated dream of the night before, several incidents of which had centered around the stick. Immediately the *déjà vu* disappeared. (MacCurdy, 1925, p. 429)

MacCurdy thought that this experience demonstrated two points. First, the peculiar emotional quality of familiarity may occur entirely independent of whether the memory of the previous experience is correct or not. Second, that some associated element of unconscious thought has been active before the *déjà vu* feeling was precipitated by some external stimulus.

The experience of *jamais vu* (failure to recognize the well known) is more rare than that of *déjà vu*. The following passage is taken from Burnham's study of *Retroactive Amnesia*. The account was by a professional man who said he had been overworked and that, in addition, it was possible that he may have been suffering from some nervous disease.

You have often experienced the sensation of *oldness* instead of *newness* when in a strange place—that is, the feeling that you had seen the same before [*déjà vu*]. Did you ever have the converse of that feeling? It has happened to me several times of late. Objects the most familiar all at once seemed wholly strange and altogether unrecognizable as never having been seen before [*jamais vu*]. One morning while on my way to the city I left the house and walked toward the place where I was to take the street car, a distance of four short blocks, a route traversed by me daily . . . and one quite familiar to me. . . I walked along absorbed in thought when I suddenly found myself in a strange place. I looked ahead, to the right and to the left, and then turned and looked back, but in no direction could I see anything I had ever seen before. I walked back to the street I had last crossed and looked up and down it but could see no familiar object. I then retraced my steps to the place where I had first stopped and looked about as before with the same result. Still it did not seem possible that I could have gone astray, as I could not have found strange ground by following the street I had started on . . . and I did not think I had been walking more than two or three minutes, and I did not think I had turned from that street. As there was nothing in sight which I could recognize I tried to recall the looks of the houses on my usual route and to compare them with those in sight, but I could not visualize them sufficiently to make a comparison. I, however, remembered a church which if I were on the right road should be about a block away on my left, with an open square between me and it, and I looked for the church. There appeared a church just where I should have located it but it was one I had never seen before. . . . though I scrutinized each part I could have sworn that I had never seen it before. . . . I concluded to go on, and did so, coming to a street with car-tracks within less than a block, but there was nothing familiar, in fact nothing I could recognize as having seen it before. I waited till a car came along and read on it the sign of the line of cars I was accustomed to take and so boarded the car and got safely to the city. I have since that had the same feeling several times. . . . I was not in the least excited on . . . these occasions but the first time I was very much surprised. (Burnham, 1903, pp. 119–120)

Whether this loss of a feeling of recognition in familiar situations is a true splitting of consciousness, an unexpected and unexplained partial loss of memory, or merely a defect in the apprehensions of meaning of well-known relations, is difficult to say. This experience is frequently mentioned as occurring during electric convulsive therapy. If further investigations of *jamais vu* phenomena following electric convulsive treatments are found to be relevant to the experience in general, then *jamais vu* may turn out to be no more than a process of fragmentation in which the elements of memory are not lost but partially obliterated, because whatever it is that holds memory together has been so weakened that it permits fragments of memory to appear in consciousness in a random sort of fashion. *Déjà vu*, in the same sense, could be thought of as a fragment of recognition separated from the main body of an otherwise usually well-organized conscious memory.

DISCUSSION

The general phenomena of memory disorders and disorganizations cover a wide variety of qualities and quantities. Forgetting and difficulties in recall are regarded as normal for the most part, in that they occur at one time or another in everyone's life. There seems no reason for regarding such losses or gaps as other than commonplace. The distinction between normal and abnormal memory losses is largely subjective. If one has no reason to think that the forgetting was unusual, or if there was no good reason for events to be remembered, then the lapse goes unquestioned. Often the lapse may be regarded as somewhat unusual by the outsider, while the person himself sees nothing strange about the circumstances. When events are such that an experience should ordinarily be recalled, but when there is an unexpected and absolute break or blank in the conscious stream of thought or a dissociation of consciousness so that either recall is nil or that which seems to be remembered is somehow vague, unreal, or unfamiliar, then the memory process is usually regarded by the patient himself as abnormal.

Since not only the present chapter but this entire treatise is based on personal reports of unusual experience, we must rely on the reliability and accuracy of the recall of individual autobiographical statements. If these remembrances suffer from gross omissions, inaccuracies, or distortions, there is no way for corrections to be made. It is a human characteristic to believe and trust in the accuracy of objective phenomena, meaning by *objective* those events on which there is an agreement among a majority of qualified observers. At the same time each individual person places the highest possible credence in his own private observances and memories. Present-day scientists are inclined to hold that only systematically organized objective phenomena are worthy of general belief. But at the same time, they must agree that phenomenal experience does provide relevant information to the individual and that such information can, in some way, be systematized. If, for example, we consider the two accounts of total amnesia cited above, we must realize that no amount of objective reporting by outsiders who might have observed the behavior of these two men would have provided the sort of information that was supplied by each of these patients. There is no reason for doubting the accuracy of either of these accounts. In all probability each of these individuals, in describing his own experiences, made an attempt to be accurate if for no other reason than to satisfy his own need to understand himself.

As I pointed out at the beginning of the chapter, the experience of memory depends on the conservation or fixation of a conscious record of certain events and experiences. For centuries, there has been theorizing about the problem of memory fixation. What will be, or may be, recalled? What conditions favor fixation in memory? How can forgotten events be brought back to memory? Generally speaking, events that occur while conscious attention is sharply focused on the situation are more apt to be conserved and recalled. If little or no attention is paid to the situation at the time of its occurrence, then conservation is more frequently doubtful and recall is not apt to be particularly accurate. However, this argument is often made in a circular fashion: that which was attended to will be recalled and recall will show that attention has been paid.

Among the excerpts supplied in this chapter are those that gave instances of failure of recall because of no original fixation on certain aspects of the past situation, and therefore no conservation; others illustrated failure of recall when the material should have been originally conserved; still others reported failures apparently due to an inability to ascertain whether the recall was accurate or not with respect to the time and place of the circumstances; and finally, certain disturbances were attributed to the failure to credit the recall with any conviction that the material was truly part of the person's past life (as in *jamais vu*), or on the other hand to a readiness to perceive the situation as having already been experienced (*déjà vu*).

As mentioned, the investigation of the memory disturbances, losses, and gains that tend to follow electric convulsive therapy, sheds some light on the nature of failures of memory in general. For example, Janis (1950) carefully questioned patients about selected portions of their memory before electric convulsive therapy was started and again several days after the therapy ended. He inquired about the details of events that were of an emotional nature as well as those emotionally neutral. He then requestioned the same patients after ten or more treatments, seeking evidence of defects in memory. There was no evidence that memories of emotionally toned events were lost more consistently than those of a neutral nature. He found that most of the failures in recall were temporary. The patient would often report, a day or so after the posttreatment interview, that a particular event was now recalled. Sometimes the patient said he had recognized and filled in the loss by a voluntary effort of recall; at other times he said that he had relied on hints or suggestions of other people.

Zubin (1948) found that if one required patients to learn lists of random words before ECT treatment, and then asked the same individuals to recall the lists after treatment, the patient would disclaim all knowledge of the learned material and would take as long to relearn the lists a second time as he had taken to learn them originally. On the other hand, he found that when he had patients learn lists of pairs of meaningful words (for example the names of cities paired with four-letter combinations of radio call letters) to a point where when shown a list of call letters the patient could anticipate and give the name of each city within a five-second interval. Upon repetition after treatment the patient would disclaim any memory of the entire material, as well as the fact that he had ever had to learn such a list. But if the investigator now showed each call-letter combination and asked the patient to *guess* the name of the city with which it might be associated, the patient would guess better than 95 percent correct, while continuing to insist that it was a pure guess, deprived of any feeling of time-place-person associated with his performance. This was interpreted as evidence that memorized material would become fragmented by the electrically induced convulsions but that these fragments had not been lost. What did seem to be missing in this case was the feeling of self-recognition in connection with the fragments; in other words, a *jamais vu* phenomenon had been produced.

In other chapters I have commented on the role of conviction in the mental life of the deluded patient. Most mental patients are utterly convinced of the truth and reality of the account they give in relation to their experience of mystic revelation, personal persecution, and so forth. This steadfast belief in the essential genuineness of the memory of their experience defies all argument, all evidence or negative demonstration. Even though the patient may recognize that the repudiation of his conviction would be to his own immense advantage, the belief will continue. This feeling of certainty is, from one viewpoint, a distortion of memory. If an ordinary man witnesses an automobile accident and gives an account of the event in some detail, he may later find that his recall differs in several important details from that of other observers. If others agree on the facts among themselves and call his attention to elements of his report which are implausible, he is apt to correct his recall and to doubt that his original conviction was true and accurate. The deluded person, on the other hand, is quite unable to amend his recall or his conviction of its veracity.

I will deal at length in Chapter 17 with the feeling of *Unreality*. There I will discuss how very real is the experience of unreality in the mind of the experiencer, and how this experience can be thought of as a disturbance or displacement of the feeling of time-place-person in the complex of recall and recognition. Both the memory of the past and the perception of the present seem not to belong together, nor to have linked to them the usual and properly attached feelings of self-reference. Why this dissociation takes place is still something of a mystery.

CHAPTER 10

Seizures

INTRODUCTION

Convulsive seizures or fits are often associated with lapses of memory and may or may not be regarded as mental aberrations. In grand mal attacks the onlooker sees a sudden arrest of the ordinary behavior of a hitherto apparently normal person, who may fall to the ground with severe convulsions followed by a period of somnolence, a dazed awakening, and a slow return to conscious behavior. The observer seldom hears specific complaints from the afflicted person. The epileptic patient experiences a sudden loss of consciousness, and when he slowly awakens finds difficulty in gathering his wits and often finds himself bruised and dirty as a result of his attack. Such patients encounter a lack of sympathy and evasive attitude on the part of most people. The sufferers understand one another's problems well enough but it seems to them that the world at large wishes to remain in comfortable ignorance of their plight.

The interruption of consciousness during the period of the seizure, the peculiar mental state just prior to and following the lapses in awareness, and the disorders of conscious life during so-called psychomotor seizures are all, in fact, a part of psychopathology. The memory lapses of the epileptic patients further justify the consideration of this topic as a special form of memory disorder. Epileptic seizures are of various kinds. The short lapses of consciousness with no (or only minor) motor involvement are known as *petit mal* attacks. The complete conscious blackouts with severe motor convulsions (epileptic fits) are described as *grand mal* attacks. Mixtures of partial or slight convulsive manifestations, accompanied by disturbed and confused states of consciousness, are termed *psychic seizures*. Finally, prolonged periods of unconsciousness and convulsions are called *cataleptic states*.

Petit Mal Attacks

A certain physician, a patient of Dr. J. Hughlings Jackson, described his first experience with petit mal seizures in the following fashion.

I first noticed symptoms which I subsequently learnt to describe as *petit mal* when living at one of our Universities, 1871. I was in very good general health, and know of no temporary disturbing causes. I was waiting at the foot of a College staircase, in the open air, for a friend who was coming down to join me. I was carelessly looking round me, watching people passing, etc., when my attention was suddenly absorbed in my own mental state, of which I know no more than that it seemed to me to be a vivid and unexpected "recollection;"—of what, I do not know. My friend found me a minute or two later, leaning my back against the wall, looking rather pale, and feeling puzzled and stupid for the moment. In another minute or two I felt quite normal again, and was as much amused as my friend at finding that I could give no distinct account of what had happened, or what I had "recollected." (Jackson, 1889, p. 201)

The man continued to have such seizures from time to time and, becoming interested in his own condition, he entered medical training and became a physician. The citation I have given, as well as the following two excerpts, are taken from a longer essay in which he reported on his own epileptic experiences, together with comments based on his observations of other epileptic patients. In describing the mental content during his seizures, he wrote as follows.

In a large majority of cases (seizures) the central feature has been mental, and has been a feeling of Recollection, i.e., of realising that what is occupying the attention is what has occupied it before, and indeed has been familiar, but has been for a time forgotten, and now is recovered with a slight sense of satisfaction as if it had been sought for. My normal memory is bad, and a similar but much fainter feeling of sudden recollection of a forgotten fact is familiar. But in the abnormal states the recollection is much more instantaneous, much more absorbing, more vivid, and for the moment more satisfactory, as filling up a void which I imagine at the time I had previously in vain sought to fill. At the same time, or perhaps I should say more accurately in immediate sequence, I am dimly aware that the recollection is fictitious and my state abnormal. The recollection is always started by another person's voice, or by my own verbalised thought, or by what I am reading and mentally verbalise; and I think that during the abnormal state I generally verbalise some phrase of simple recognition as "Oh yes—I see," "Of course—I remember," etc., but a minute or two later I can recollect neither the words nor the verbalised thought which gave rise to the recognition.

[He continued by giving accounts of the effect of petit mal seizures on certain mental processes during the period of lapse or absence.]

A *petit mal* has two or three times come on when I have been reading poetry aloud—the line I am reading or just going to read seems somehow familiar, or just what I was trying to recollect, though I may never have seen or heard it before. I recognise my morbid condition and stop, though I have generally sense enough to finish the line or even sentence, and remain silent for a minute or so; then go on again where I left off, recovering my sense of rhythm and metre sooner than my capacity of giving attention to or understanding the words. I do not remember to have made any deliberate effort to go on reading aloud, *coûte que coûte*, throughout a *petit mal*. I have made several rude attempts to go on writing, and have kept four or five specimens of what I have written. They were made in very slight *petits maux*. The writing was done slowly and in a fairly normal hand. I was in the main occupied with the usual impression of recollection, but was dimly aware that I was morbid, and attempted to criticise what I was writing. My impression at the time that I was writing was that the words and sense were quite reasonable, and that I had kept within very familiar and prudent limits of expression. I had found, I thought, just the words I was seeking for. A minute or two later I could see that some of the words were grotesquely *mal à propos*, though I think the grammatical forms of sentence were always preserved. I could not trace any undercurrent of thought or recollection from which the irrelevant words had come. (Jackson, 1889, p. 203)

This description of the effect of an epileptic lapse is particularly informative since the reporter was not only very well educated, but likewise, an excellent self-observer. Dr. Hughlings Jackson considered the patient's experience of recollection to be a variety of *intellectual aura*, which is a frequent but by no means a necessary feature of petit mal seizures. Experiences of this sort are sometimes described by patients as brief *absences:* by which they mean a lapse of consciousness, either with or without a pause in activity. Just as this physician could continue to read and write during a petit mal attack, so others will likewise continue to walk or work, and realize the *absence* only because of the changed position in which they find their body at the time when consciousness returns. As this patient indicated, during the lapse in awareness, the body or the mind may continue to operate in an automatic and mechanical fashion.

A sensitive and gifted poetess, Margiad Evans, has written an autobiography entitled *A Ray of Darkness*, which deals largely with her epileptic experiences and their effects. Her seizures began rather late in life.

[This sort of seizure] caused no pain, it lasted a few seconds, I saw and heard and moved while it happened. I have often crossed a room, and, while not losing sight or bearings, not know *how* I crossed it. The sequence of consciousness was so little broken by it, that after it had happened it seemed not an atom of time or myself had been missing, and I only knew it had happened again by the numb sensation in the centre of the brain which followed it. I do not get it now that the major attacks have superseded it; and that makes it still more difficult to be accurate in recollection. I do, however, remember laughing to my husband about my "little wheel," going off again. It seemed like a tiny wheel—the wheel say, of a watch, whirring at blurring speed, quite soundlessly, in my head while I went on with whatever I was doing, guided by *the consciousness left over* rather than the consciousness of the moment. The wheel would then cease, and there was a loud silence such as follows a blow on a drum, also in my head. A clanging ache followed that. The whole thing took about as long as for a normal person to walk five paces. (Evans, 1952, p. 39)

It is possible for an individual to undergo one or several petit mal seizures without having any conscious recognition of the blank periods. These blanks may be called to the person's attention by the remarks of onlookers. He may then recall that there had been periods during which he had experienced a fleeting queer feeling, or he may, on the other hand, never be able to recognize the fact that a lapse had occurred.

In an effort to retrieve whatever conscious content may have been existing during a petit mal lapse, one investigator attempted to induce hypnotic recall in patients known to suffer from such attacks. Under hypnosis, the patient was directed to report as much as he could about his most recent seizure experience. One patient spoke about a lapse that had been observed during his breakfast, at an instant just before he had reached out for an egg. Under hypnosis, he described his sensations as follows.

There is a slight sensation in the throat. I am looking at this particular moment at the bowl before me; there was some white cereal into which I had mixed an egg. [Next scene] I still see the bowl, with myself picking at it in a way with my fork. I have a sensation of lassitude, put my fork down at the right place. I see things now not as a whole but only that towards which my sensations are directed. I have slight sensations in my fingers. [Next scene] I seem to see the glass of water. The sensations are growing stronger. I can see myself holding the glass. I am sitting erect at the table, but I have the feeling that I am tipping back in my chair. [Next scene] I don't seem to see much but there is a tightening of the throat muscles, especially in the vocal region. My visual field tends to be luminous like a moving picture screen. A picture of a man comes into my mind. It is a man who is a colleague of mine. I seem to see him with a cigarette. It takes me back to my office, though it is in a different condition than when that man was there. [Next scene] There is a degree of numbness in the nasal region, a tendency to dilate and contract the nostrils. The visual field is dark or grey with a tendency to luminousness. Again there is that concentric affair, it now assumes the form of a grille in our kitchen. . . [Next scene] I am leaving the dining room, considering myself normal, though with sensations in my throat. Things are a little shadowy but I can localize fairly well. [Next scene] I am seated somewhere. I can see things clearly. I still have feelings in the throat; I did not feel it then. There is only that throat sensation. I approach someone and ask Mr. S. (another patient) whether I have not fallen asleep. I see him clearly. [Next scene] I seem to feel normal. He said that he left when I lifted a glass of water. I went on into the day-room. (Diethelm, 1930, pp. 549–550)

Several hypnotizable patients were investigated by this method. Dr. Diethelm reported that he found the replies usually indicated that during the attacks the patients had a change in conscious awareness and in bodily sensations, such as tenseness, tightness, and numbness, most frequently referred to the face, throat, neck, and hands. The visual field became constricted and the apparent brightness of the visual field changed from time to time. The level of consciousness varied from clear imagery to brief episodes that were essentially blank.

One gathers from this study that during a petit mal attack there is a distortion or a disturbance of consciousness, rather than a complete lapse. In addition the sensory input seems to become somewhat distorted. These experiences are usually recalled as consisting of a sudden change, an arrest or mental lapse, that may be partially revived by the device of an interview during an hypnotic state. Motor activity may cease momentarily or may persist in an automatic fashion without the patient's awareness. For example, the patient may continue to walk, but he does so mechanically, and is surprised to find when he "awakens" that he had moved elsewhere. A petit mal attack may cover a period lasting from a few seconds to about ten minutes. Many persons who have attacks of this nature report having felt a deep preoccupation with a variety of particular intrusive problems, thoughts, or sensations. This state actually characterizes the start of each period of absence.

Grand Mal Seizures

Margiad Evans, whose description of a petit mal seizure has been cited, later suffered also from grand mal seizures. She described her first grand mal seizure as follows.

I would make a cup of tea and go to bed. I made the tea, looked up at the clock—a strange chance—saw that it was ten minutes past eleven. The next thing I was still looking up at the clock and the hands stood at five and twenty minutes past midnight. I had fallen through Time, Continuity and Being.

My first thought was not that the clock had gone wrong, but that I had been asleep. I discovered I was lying on the floor on my back, my head against the rungs of a rocking-chair and my body, full length, crowded between the steel fender and the little table at which I had been writing. . . . After a fit, the one unforgettable sight is the first thing one sees *consciously* . . . I simply stared at it [the clock]. Then slowly mind and body began to try to come together and to work out a scheme for movement. . . .

Any idea, however ready-made, seemed fit for me then. After a few moments with open eyes, lying still, I began to feel very ill, sick and faint. And then I can remember my mind beginning to work, for it told me I must be ill and must go to bed.

Then came an extraordinary blank. I had reached the idea, the image, of bed, but where *was* bed? The next mental process is terribly difficult to describe, for, as after all my bad fits, the brain held and let go, held and let go, a confused mass of atmosphere and memory. It worked, but like an engine misfiring and unsteered. The idea of going to bed brought an extraordinarily vivid presentment of our childhood's room where I slept with my sister, gone these many many years. I saw the blue distempered walls, the tallboy. This floated in my head and vanished, to be followed by every room I had ever slept in, *except the present one*. But going to bed, and not knowing where to go raised a much more acute question—*who was I?* I seemed to think this over but in a casual sort of way, even with a certain amusement. . . . I went outside the door for air. . . . As the air touched me, I felt a cold dampness and it came on me stunningly. . . .

I realized the incredible, impossible, and ghastly truth—I had neither fainted nor been asleep: I had had an epileptic fit! . . . Searching the room I found everything confirmed my instantaneous certainty . . . I had fallen just as I was lifting the cup to drink . . . I had no memory of it. It had seemed as I have told—one moment filling the tea-pot and glancing at the clock, the next waking and still looking at the clock an hour later. (Evans, 1952, pp. 78–82)

This first grand mal seizure occurred when she was forty-one; similar attacks continued to occur at intervals thereafter. Then on one occasion a new feature followed the seizure. While still in the daze of returning consciousness, she realized she was weeping.

In that time my strange, unusual and terrible weeping did not cease, for I could hear it. It had never happened before; but it has done ever since, every time I have an attack. I sat there shattered, yet trying to tell myself why I was crying and sobbing with such utter grief. I told myself it was shock: I told myself it was because I had allowed myself once more to hope it was over. But I was certain within myself it was neither. It was certainly grief, the most profound, the most mysterious, but the cause was forgotten—was lost in those minutes of obliteration. So one will weep for awful loss, and the impetus of the emotion will go on even while in exhaustion the meaning of the tears that are still falling is forgotten. But I felt in some obscure way that my soul had been somewhere or seen some one who was Peace and completion, and that it had left that presence to come back to me. (Evans, 1952, p. 149)

Her grand mal seizures became increasingly frequent, so that her dread and fear continued. She asked her neurologist whether all epileptics suffered mentally from their fits as she did. He told her, "No"; that some patients actually enjoyed their fits. Then he asked what she meant by *suffering*, and she replied, "Only grief." During the months following she tried to understand the reason for her experiencing such a feeling of grief at the end of each seizure. She finally came to the conclusion that the grief grew out of her experience during the last seconds just before the convulsion started. She said that she would be moving about in the everyday routine of ordinary life; then she would become aware of a sudden stoppage and loss of ability to control her body. At that instant it seemed to her that her mind divided. Part of her stepped away while the other part gained a spiritual unity of a mystical sort. As consciousness returned, this spiritual feeling was no longer present, so that the loss gave rise to the grief.

She was treated with anticonvulsant drugs that greatly decreased the frequency and intensity of the seizures. With this decrease she was able to regain some part of her clarity of mind. She then found herself obsessed with ideas that were in some consistent way connected with *deceit:* "With *deceit* because the mind tries to deceive you; that you are not going to have a fit when you are." Her reactions to the seizures seemed to her to be fantastic at the start, each one being marked by a frightened withdrawal from all actions or thoughts that might have been in any way related to the attack or to its mental consequences.

To continue with our attempt to understand the certain aspects of the mental life of the epileptic patient, I may cite the following description written by an anonymous nurse-midwife of the experiences associated with her grand mal seizures.

It starts with a peculiar sensation in my chest, but before I can do anything about it I am unconscious. I know and feel nothing. On recovery, I have a feeling of extraordinary well-being; wherever I happen to be lying, whether on a couch, the floor, or even the roadside, it is as if I were lying on the most comfortable bed. I may hear voices asking if someone has injured herself and I wonder of whom they are talking. If I notice someone looking down at me with evident concern, I wonder at the anxiety shown. After a few seconds, I am completely awake; I find that I am lying on the floor, remember the aura, and I know that I must have had another fit. I feel myself gingerly to make sure that I'm whole, get up, and that is all. That is my version of the event, but what do spectators think? . . . The person with me wonders what would have happened if the fit had occurred a few moments earlier when I might have been with a patient, or an hour later when I might have been alighting from a bus in a busy street, and determines that I must not run such risks in the future. (Lancet, Editors of, 1952, p. 69)

This nurse had her first grand mal attack at the age of thirty. At that time she saw no reason for interrupting her professional work, but as the seizures continued and became more frequent her superior officers decided that she must change her line of activity. She resented this decision, feeling it to be an unfair ruling, yet as she said later, she gradually came to the realization that whether right or wrong, society, in general, does try to avoid contact with epileptic patients even though the epileptic is actually harmless to others. This conclusion regarding the social attitude gives rise to a feeling of being "picked on," amounting at times to a true paranoid attitude.

In 1798 an anonymous ("Diaetophilus") city official of Zurich published a two-volume work entitled, *Physical and Psychological Account of my Seven Years of Epilepsy*. In it he gave a general account of his life history, medical history, and his subjective impressions of the seven years of his life during which he had experienced sixty-five grand mal attacks and approximately two hundred *epileptoid phases*, as he called them, by which he probably meant petit mal seizures. He wrote that before the first major seizure, which occurred when he was almost thirty-three years of age, his health had been generally good. However, he said that at times he had experienced certain disturbances.

I had very rarely true headaches, but often felt a heaviness and "obscurity" hindering my thinking and especially my speaking and hearing. Oftentimes I could not recall frequently used words; or I could not pronounce certain words properly but uttered wrong sounds or had to spell words very slowly. . . . The sound of spoken words was often experienced as a hammering in my ears; or as a drumming, similar to the toys of my children making noises, or sometimes loud voices were painful to me. Mornings were apt to be much more difficult for me than were afternoons. (Diaetophilus, 1798, 1:20)

His first grand mal seizure occurred after a long working day that had been preceded by a sleepless night. It started with a feeling of a dreamlike weakness followed by loss of consciousness, crying out, and falling on the pavement. His description of another such seizure, which occurred in his later years, is as follows.

After forgetting my thoughts and living with agitated creatures of my imagination, over which I have very little control in such moments, the fit started. However, it seemed to have been somewhat weaker than any other previous fit. The cry which again was longlasting wasn't heard very far away in the house, but it seemed remarkable to me that I had heard the cry myself very distinctly and that I had the thought that a seizure was occurring, after which I lost all my thoughts. Since my wife was not present, not all circumstances can be related in a comparable way but as far as I know, at the beginning of my unconsciousness, my countenance had been very blue and my face became distorted, while my mouth foamed as usual. I woke up a little more rapidly than usually and was immediately fully conscious, and did not feel sleepy. (Diaetophilus, 1798, 1:122)

This man kept an elaborate day-to-day diary and a physical history. He experienced many petit mal attacks and believed that the occurrence of an *absence* usually preceded a major seizure. He was of the opinion that the combination of fear and his own imagination could give rise to a seizure, cold determination and self-control formed his best protection against fits, although somewhat ineffectual. Later in life, he said that he became completely free from all fits. Probably every epileptic feels at one time or another that were his self-control only strong enough, he could abort his seizures, but only rarely has any patient said that he was able to do so. Some patients claim that the seizures occur only when their attention has been diverted, so that the seizure, so to speak, "took advantage" of a momentary weakness in their attentive and cautionary control.

A grand mal seizure at the time of its occurrence is, strangely enough, much more disturbing to the onlooker than it is to the victim. The onlooker sees a person, apparently healthy and in full control of himself, suddenly and with no warning collapsing, making no attempt to avert injury. The fall is accompanied by a dreadful cry or scream caused by a spasm of respiratory inhalation. After falling there is an alternation of powerful contractions and relaxations of the whole body musculature; the face turns blue and is distorted, there is a frothing of the mouth and often a loss of bowel and bladder control. This active period lasts several minutes and is followed by complete relaxation into a flaccid unconsciousness and a deep sleep state. This period of seizure and flaccidity is succeeded by the slow bewilderment of awakening. The patient, having lost consciousness, is ignorant of the details of the seizure. He finds it hard to realize why others try either to avoid him or to interfere with his freedom. The onlooker, on the other hand, cannot understand why anyone, if aware of the possibility of such attacks, should rashly expose himself to possible injury or permit such a public display of his affliction.

Aura

Many patients who suffer from either petit mal or grand mal fits undergo what is termed an *aura* ("the breeze before the storm") a few seconds before losing consciousness. In a review of the histories of over 1300 persons who had suffered from grand mal seizures but who had never been confined to a mental institution, Lennox and Cobb found that

56 percent of the group reported having had an aura experience. However, there was a very wide variety of descriptions of the aura phenomena. The more common terms used to describe the experience were "dizziness," "ill-defined sensation," "mind adrift," "apprehension," "nausea," "headache," "faintness," and "peculiar sensation in stomach." The nature of the aura description is not related to the variety or course of the patients' seizures.

Mrs. Evans' description of her aura (her description of seizures has already been cited) was as follows.

There is a phrase . . . which describes the preliminary warning of an approaching epileptic attack . . . "the heart stood to meet its enemy." After this desperate stand comes a fluttering tremulousness of body and mind. The intensity varies; but it is physically like a breeze or a gale entering one and agitating all one's being . . . Because in the violent attacks one feels as though the body has been entered by a terrific alien power; and that that power is trying, after entrance to push its way out again. It is not unlike labour, but not so intelligent. If the consciousness is prolonged until the fall, as mine has often been, the flesh with its limbs and its orderly muscles seems actually to be entangled—the body is on the point of being blown aside.

To describe this, however vividly one may attempt it, is not to arrive at more than sensation. A terrific sensation, it is true, and one that is inaudible to the part of the brain which is still working, so *unlike life* is it. Possibly (I do not know) there *is* no part of the brain which is still working. The surprise may be registered by the mind, which my fits have made me believe, is separate from the brain . . . It travels, like sound, behind the jet aeroplane. Therein lies the danger; for the mind is still unbelieving of danger while the brain is losing, or has lost, control of the body. The mind reassures—its very incredulity is a delay of seconds which may mean the difference between safety and an accident.

Many people, of course, get fuller intimation of an approaching fit, and longer time in which to act. Again I only write of myself. I cannot act. That sight, hearing, memory, *personality* in fact, are intact almost to the last I have proved, but *speech* and *action* are both taken away. The power of speaking is wiped from the lips—the power of motion—or reasonable motion—is stolen. One hears people ask, "What is the matter?" One cannot answer, although one seems to know. One's eyes are nailed on an object or a face. This rigid attitude in which one seems to be listening to a call important beyond all human matters—there is of course no voice, but such is the effect, as if the last trump had blown—dissolves into a kind of hideous hovering. One turns round or away from helpers, if they are present, if not, from the presence of the appalling calamity in the room which is the body. The utmost source of terror to me was never the summons but this awful and yet *silly* moment, when the being tries to laugh it off, to leave it behind, to walk irresponsibly away. That ghastly moment is *funny* whether one can believe it or not . . . Whether or not my last sensation, and the one I most dread, the one which has most nearly touched me with true neurosis, the one I cannot forget, is that laughter, that shrugging it off. The next instant I fall into nothing. This horrible light-heartedness and ghastly gaiety are not sensual—they are emotional. . . . That is why they leave an impression which is ineffaceable, unforgettable and utterly fearful. (Evans, 1952, pp. 154–156)

Because of the perceptive and literary ability of the author, this vivid account is of more value than the more usual report of a "sudden headache," "a knot in my stomach," or the like that are given as descriptions by the more ordinary patient. The physical process of the "brain explosion" basic to the seizure has begun while the ordinary mental processes of consciousness went on as though nothing could happen, and then, in her case, her mind seemed to shrug its shoulders and leave in a jaunty fashion in a much shorter period of time than she later required to recount the experience.

Psychic Seizures

There occur a certain group of disabilities which differ somewhat from the more ordinary epileptic seizures in that the lapse of consciousness is not complete, while the motor seizure may be minor, incomplete, or atypical. Included in this variegated group are the so-called *fugue states*, during which the individual's mind seems to him to be clouded or obscured. Often while in this state he feels under a compulsion to wander aimlessly in a senseless fashion.

A young woman who suffered from such fugue states, with a pronounced impulse to wander, maintained the habit of writing down each evening in her diary phrases and sentences that were related to each day's experience. She told Dr. Stengel that generally her state of mind during this period of wandering was colored by a feeling of strangeness and was often somewhat hazy, but she did not believe that there was any true loss of memory. Dr. Stengel compiled the following excerpts from a portion of her diary that covered one of her fugues, which had occurred while she was a member of an English uniformed women's military service corps during World War II.

(11 August): Arrive at 1:30 and change for duty—frightful surging up inside—scramble out of uniform and bolt, get to N. *by train free*—steady as a die now. *Walk for miles, spend money, must spend it.* Bus to T., then another to P. (20 miles away). Beautiful trip—*wish I could go on forever moving*. It's all right then! Walk again at P. Gets dark. Find myself in terribly bombed part, empty hush and gaping ruins everywhere, refused to hurry, plod on in and out. Run into a middle-aged Irishman. *I invent some yarn*—apparently I am in D. Walk with him to station. No train till early morning. He insists in putting me up. In bed now writing, midnight.

(12 August): At T. station (50 miles from P) 8:30 hungry, *have been Irish all the way down*, gibbering to two Tommies, *am thinking of my home in Ireland and believe the yarns I have spun. Queer, almost happy,* just roaming

on and not caring what happens. *Gloriously light-headed, refuse to think at all. Walking, walking.* Just *in a cornfield* now, very wet and crickets are noisy. *Too dark to see,* about 10 P.M. Cold, shiver but not unhappy. Morning. Four o'clock has struck somewhere, have slept little, it rained. Strange experience. Oh I hope Daddy isn't driven frantic. What shall I do until it becomes inevitable to go back? *Yesterday was colossal. Never been through such varied emotions.* Interesting talking about life and religion to hard nut dockmen. Train journey to F. (40 miles further away). Sunset is too, too perfect. Spend last money. Cinema with an old country woman. Get talking to Welshmen, enjoy myself hugely. Cinema again. F. is very picturesque, give a little girl chocolate and cakes, like talking to her. Oh so much has happened. Can't put down hardly anything. Cramped day.

(13 August): Off in bus, big rolling country, get out and walk. Big cornfield. Too cold I think. *Rather hellish night though the sky is full. Too cold to sleep or think well.* Sirens in small hours. *Incredible feeling. Entirely alone in an unknown part of the world. Don't think of what might happen next but thank God for this strange excitement. This amazing dream*—how can it all end. Sleep on book to try to keep damp out. Skirt round ankles for warmth.

(14 August): *Start walking again. Strange, strange feeling. Hitchhike in vans to T.* Go over the Church. It is glorious, *read prayers, cry much.* Buy buns. Tea with a queer little man, amusing. Walk on main roads—get lifts. One of the fellows buys me a railway ticket and buns. On platform get talking to a fire party—tough language. God, it's all fun. Oh it is an experience to remember, meeting those tough hard nuts. The queer little man is still with me. Decent chap. Tries violent love. *Am so crazy, nearly let all morals go to the wind.* Just stop and slip away—sit in the waiting room of the station all night. Soldiers bringing in tea—all rather fun. Go to ladies' room to sleep, get little but am happy. Meet everything, these common people are good sorts. Gee, I'm grubby, filthy. . . .

(15 August): *Home now. Have hitch-hiked up. Dreadful feeling.* Don't want to ever wake up. It'll break me one day. Daddy is wonderful.

(16 August): Too floppy to worry, lie in bed all limp and sad, *waiting for it to come again, this urge, burst of energy and ideas and unable to check it.* Even if the doctor can help me he won't change *my fundamental make-up. Everything hazy and disjointed. Seem to be in waking up process. The last days were good to a point and so quick with the freshness and novelty with no bad conscience hindering, for there is too much to see and hear. It's gone. Miles away. Feel nothing but hell,* red hot and then an iceberg. (Stengel, 1943, p. 235)

This portion of the patient's diary describes part of what was probably her sixth fugue state. Her memory of the period seems fairly complete but somewhat hazy. She said that throughout the duration of any one of these fugue states the uppermost thing in her mind had been her feeling of bursting energy and ideas, plus the persistent impulse to move on. Only several days after military desertion, when she happened to hear a stranger mention the name of her home town, did she suddenly "awake" and then, realizing what had happened, she made her way home. On this occasion she remained home for three months, during which time she received psychotherapy and became somewhat relieved. After she returned to military service she was again taken by a four-day fugue. This seventh attack, like all her previous fugues, was marked by an overwhelming impulse to wander.

Dr. Efron published a report written by one of his patients who had suffered from both petit and grand mal seizures. The patient developed a different kind of seizure, characterized by its dreamlike quality (known medically as an *uncinate* seizure), and wrote about it as follows.

They are all like cars coming off the assembly line. I can't tell one from the next. . . . I can be perfectly well in every way when suddenly I feel snatched away. I seem to feel as if I'm in two places at once, but in neither place at all—it is a feeling of being remote. I can read, write and talk and can even sing my lyrics. I know exactly what is going on but I somehow don't seem to be in my own skin. Sometimes it wakes me up at night, but it usually develops during the day. When this feeling happens I know that I'm going to have a convulsion. I keep trying to stop it from happening. No matter what I do, it always comes. Everything goes ahead like a railroad schedule. At this part of my attack I feel very active. If I'm home I make beds, dust, sweep or do the dishes. My sister says that I do everything at breakneck speed . . . But to me it all seems to be in slow motion. I am very interested in the time. I'm always looking at my watch and asking someone the time every few minutes. That is why I know exactly how long this part of the attack lasts. It has been as short as ten minutes or may last the better part of a day; it is real hell then. Usually it lasts about twenty to thirty minues. All this time I feel that I'm remote. It is like being outside a room and looking in through a keyhole, or as if I'm God just looking down on the world but not belonging to it. This feeling gets slowly worse during this part of my attack. . . .

After this has gone on for some time, I seem to get what I call my "half-way point." I know just about when it is coming. When it happens I suddenly get snatched even further away. I am more remote than before. I still know exactly what is happening but now I don't give a damn. I'm no longer impatient. I don't care what happens. I feel like a piece of clay, inert. I don't try any more to prevent the convulsion.

It is also at the half-way point that I get a funny idea in my head. It is hard to put into words. It is just that I expect to smell something any moment, but I don't yet. I don't think that this is due to my having had so many of these seizures. The first time it ever happened, I was out in the country and I was feeling funny. I was in a field picking forget-me-nots. I remember very well that I kept smelling these flowers even though I knew thay had no odour. For about half an hour I kept sniffing them because I was sure they would begin to smell soon. I clearly remember telling this to my friend. I was somehow expecting them to smell even though I knew perfectly well at that time that forget-me-nots have no odour at all. When I'm getting this feeling of a smell coming I'm so far away from the world that I almost don't know I'm so remote, but yet a corner of my mind still knows I'm remote. I know it and don't know it at the same time . . . It is so intense that I don't seem to be aware of anything but this feeling of remoteness and the feeling that a smell is coming. This feeling gets worse and worse and I seem to be floating away. Yet I know what is happening all the time. I can read and talk but I don't feel like it. I used to read the Bible out loud at this state but gave it up because my family couldn't stand the monotonous tone of my voice. . . .

The part of the attack from the half-way mark to the convulsion is always shorter than the first part. It may be only five minutes long but is never longer than twenty to thirty minutes. I'm no longer interested in the time. I used to keep on working even though I felt this way but I had so many knocks and bad falls that I began to lie down on the floor. I push all the furniture away so that I don't hurt myself when it happens. Then, just when I seem to be as remote as I possibly could get I suddenly get a smell like an explosion or a crash. There is no buildup . . . It is all there at once. At the same moment that the smell crashes through, I'm back in the real world—I no longer feel remote. The smell is a disgusting sweet, penetrating odour like very cheap perfume. I just stop still when I smell it. Everything seems very quiet. I don't know if I can hear. I am all alone with the smell. I don't think this lasts for more than a few seconds and then the smell rapidly goes away. Then I find myself almost normal except that it still seems very quiet. This quietness lasts about five to ten seconds but I'm really not sure. Then I hear a voice off to the right calling my name, "Thelma, Thelma." It keeps calling. This is not like hearing a voice in a dream. It is a *real* voice. Every time I hear it I fall for it. It is not a man's or a woman's voice. I don't recognize it. There is one thing that I do know and that is if I turn towards the voice I have a convulsion. I try hard not to look towards the voice. I have often turned my head to the left to keep from looking towards the right. But the voice keeps calling my name, almost as if it wants me to turn to it. No matter how hard I try I have never been able to keep from turning my head towards this voice. I always feel that if I didn't look I wouldn't have a convulsion. But it is irresistible. As my head turns, it seems to start slowly, then faster and faster. Finally there is a big jerk and my head swings around to the right. Sometimes I am barely aware that my right arm flies up. That's it. I'm out. I have the convulsion after that. (Efron, 1956, pp. 270–271)

The remarkable thing about uncinate fits is that each seizure has the same *pattern* of experience. As this patient said, "They are all like cars coming off the assembly line. I can't tell one from the next." So far as the patient was concerned, the seizure was like witnessing over and over again the same sound-motion picture—always the same picture with herself playing the leading role. The long complicated experiential-behavior pattern continued, often lasting an hour or more, the behavior being more or less stereotyped.

Neurosurgeons have occasionally found patients who, during a brain operation, respond in a peculiar fashion. The surgeons report that if during an open operation, they apply direct electrical stimulation to the cortex of the temporal lobe of the brain, the patient may report a stereotyped fragment of a response pattern. For example, one patient reported every time the stimulus was applied to the brain surface, that she saw herself being chased across a green pasture by a red bull. This mental picture always occurred in the same way with each application of the stimulus. But such artificially produced experiences are rare and are nowhere near as elaborate as that of an uncinate seizure.

In other persons the psychic seizure takes the form of a "dreamy state." For example, a young man wrote to a neurologist, Dr. Dewey, complaining of the following symptom.

I am troubled with a feeling as though I were in a dream, which came on first one morning four years ago, while I was in the woods waiting for a rabbit which the dogs were driving out. I had been working hard on day previous and got up early in the morning and came up into the country for a day's sport rabbit hunting. Altogether I was pretty thoroughly exhausted, which, I suppose helped that feeling to take hold of me. This dreaminess stayed with me for the rest of the day, and I have had it occasionally since then. (Dewey, 1896, pp. 764–765)

In other parts of this letter he said that these attacks had occurred at intervals over the preceding four years. Physically, he said, he was in good health and strangers would never know of his affliction unless he mentioned it. He was greatly worried by these dreamy states although he could find no good reason for his worry. The physician prescribed a tonic and a regimen which the patient reported back as having made him feel better, though the "dreamy feeling will stay with me in spite of all I can do." These dreamy states are frequently forerunners of grand mal seizures.

Some persons who suffer repeatedly from migraine headaches have electroencephalographic records (brain-wave tracings) that resemble the tracing made by epileptic patients. Such headaches are characteristically very acute and are limited to one side of the head. They occur periodically. They often give rise to a rather stylized form of visual imagery. Migraine headaches are thought by some investigators to be a form of psychic seizures or to resemble closely a psychic seizure. For example, Dr. Lippman published the account written by a housewife, who gave the following description of the feelings that commonly overtook her during one of her migraine headaches.

Sometimes during a severe headache I have had the impression that my body was vibrating and moving like a very fast pendulum from myself on the left to a supposedly "other self" on the right, although I knew my own body was not moving. It was like watching Disney's "Pluto, the Pup" running at full speed toward an open gate, having it close, and he would collide with a solid object. His body would "z-z-z-z-ing-g-g" and vibrate from side to side until the force of the blow was over. I seemed to look at "the other self" on the right as though it were not part of me, and then when the "zing" motion stopped, I think we were still apart. This thought always occurred during intense head-ache, and probably only lasted an instant. Even so, my mind always seemed to be trying to find an explanation or comparison. (Lippman, 1953, p. 347)

It is to be noted that the experience reported above is of the pat-terned sort which usually characterizes a psychic seizure. It had occurred in much the same way at intervals over several years, but always in as-sociation with a violent one-sided headache.

Still another report was published by Dr. Lippman, written by an-other patient who had a somewhat similar sort of migraine experience, which she described as follows.

Well, for quite a long period of years . . . one of the premigraine mani-festations was the feeling of duality. My psychic or astral body would carry itself immediately above my physical body (that is to say, it would be directly above the real body, though sometimes at quite a distance). The "psychic" or "secondary body" actually seemed the more real of the two. It was the physi-cal body that seemed more illusory. During these interesting interludes, the psychic person was apparently endowed with mental volition of its own; thinking and observing quite independently—and concurrently. This detach-ment was accompanied usually with a distinct sense of coolness in the psy-chic body—though not with a chill, in the usual sense. This hallucination lasts a few seconds at a time. It comes and goes at irregular intervals for one to three days. It disappears as the ache in my neck and shoulders announces the onset of the terrible headache. (Lippman, 1953, p. 346)

In these descriptions of unusual migraine experiences which I have just cited, it should be noted that during or preceding the pain induced by the headache, the patients reported a feeling of mental duality or disassociation. This phenomenon of duality I will take up in more detail in Chapter 17, which deals with "Unreality."

Cataleptic Seizure

Nineteenth century literature contains many descriptions of the ex-perience related to a cataleptic state or seizure, which may or may not have been a form of what we now call epilepsy. The following excerpt from the account of a surgeon serves as an example.

Instantly I felt myself severely unwell. I went upstairs, and threw myself on my bed. In a few minutes I felt inexpressibly ill. The first sensation was an amazing weight on the chest, with difficulty of respiration; the carotids of my throat striking like hammers on my head, and a feeling as though torrents of air were rushing into my brain, and the head were itself expanding. The agony became insupportable, and I knocked for someone to come to me. . . . In this state I lay for hours. Meanwhile my sister, alarmed by my knocking, had come and found me speechless. . . .

Towards the evening, however, a relapse took place, with phenomena essentially different. Beginning with the same contraction of the chest as before, there followed tetanic spasms—a violent jerking of the upper part of the body from side to side, interrupted by quiet intervals, sometimes by a complete rigidity of the neck and the spine. So sensitive was I to touch, or to the impression of a breath of air that the approach of anyone evincing an intention to disturb me would throw me into convulsions. (Anon., 1854b, pp. 380–381)

This account was part of a self-description written by a surgeon who said he had "undergone marked spiritual changes." He also said that he had been working very hard and for long hours just before the occurrence of this seizure, which marked the onset of an acute illness. He continued for four days in a stuporous condition with occasional seizures. He saw visions, heard voices, and concluded that he was close to death. Then, he said, Jesus appeared to him in a vision. After the vision he speedily recovered and remained convinced thereafter that Jesus had chosen to save his life.

At the present time, such cataleptic experiences are usually said to be related either to religious ecstasy or to acute delusional states, although some neurologists consider that they consist of the so-called epileptic equivalent states. The experience itself is probably qualitatively no different in the twentieth century from that which was recorded in previous centuries, but the medical explanation and religious frame of reference of the cataleptic patient has changed.

DISCUSSION

In spite of the fact that seizures have been recognized as well-known afflictions of mankind for thousands of years, their physical basis is not clear and their effect on the mental life of the sufferer is but little understood or appreciated by the majority of the population, including most physicians.

The experience of the aura is most puzzling. Every individual who experiences this phenomenon has the identical experience each time a seizure occurs. It is as if the same phonograph record were invariably turned on and played just prior to the onset of the seizure. No relation has been established between the particular nature of the aura and the life history of the individual.

It is apparent from the accounts of seizures given by the patients themselves, that they commonly experience the feeling of being "possessed"; a feeling that some sort of overwhelming power has been completely and irresistibly forced upon them from the outside. As the power takes over, each patient experiences a complete lack of self-control and self-direction. Indeed, it is in a sense surprising that the person who suffers from repeated seizure is as "sane" as he is. The sudden mental invasion, the striking down, the social isolation and opprobrium are all factors that mitigate against sanity, and yet very few persons who suffer from seizures ever become insane in the usual sense of the word.

Not many years ago it was a generally accepted idea that there was a specific personality type termed epileptoid. The epileptoid personality was said to be inflexible and bigoted, with a tendency to religious fanaticism and imperiousness. It is possible that many persons who had suffered from seizures for some time, and who had been more or less segregated from society, may have responded in such a fashion. Nowadays the great majority of persons who have seizures are treated with one or another of several drugs or chemicals that prevent or greatly decrease the frequency and intensity of seizures. In the past, it was all too common for persons who suffered from continuing seizures to slowly become more and more "demented," to lose gradually their intellectual abilities to such an extent that institutionalization became necessary. The symptom-picture of the epileptoid personality may, in fact, be said to have characterized a goodly number of such institutional patients. Today, however, through drug treatment, the frequency of seizures of almost all epileptic patients can be controlled, so that mental deterioration is very rarely encountered.

What is it like (you ask perplexed), this fear?—
Fancy yourself compelled to walk a plank
From cliff to lofty cliff with reeling shank;
Fancy yourself a swimmer, in the rear
Of some white ship that nevermore draws near;
Fancy yourself entangled in the dank
Morasses, with the elephants that sank,
As sole companions, save the moon's half-sphere—
'Tis like such times.

(Leonard, 1925, p. 99)

CHAPTER 11

Fear; Phobia

INTRODUCTION

The preceding chapters have dealt with disorders in which the cognitive functions of consciousness seemed to be the primary processes involved in the psychopathological experience. However, one can never say with certainty that only one aspect or attribute of the mind is the most important feature of psychopathology. The reader probably has noticed, in most of the excerpts cited where disorders of perception and of memory have constituted the patient's basic complaints, that there was frequently much concomitant evidence of the patient's realization of his inability to control his behavior, coupled with a pervasive fear regarding the outcome of his disability. In such complex mental turmoils, it is usually not too clear or certain whether the primary disorder is cognitive, conative, or emotional in nature. There are mental aberrations in which the expressions of certain emotions and subjective feeling states do seem to be the primary phenomena of the pathology. These are states in which fear or phobia, melancholia or depression, mania or ecstasy, hopelessness or despair, love or pain, as well as other recognizable emotional experiences, seem to dominate the entire psychopathological picture. In these instances the patient usually finds little difficulty in naming and describing his experience, while the on-looker can frequently name correctly the behavior that he may observe. There is usually no doubt in anyone's mind as to the nature of the feeling concerned when another person says, "I am afraid." Essentially, fear is the inner feeling and the outer behavioral expression aroused by an ac-tive or imagined threat to one's safety and well-being. The emotion of fear is very often blended with other feelings and expressions, gaining therefore, as the case may be, many names—dread, terror, apprehension, horror, appall, aghast, and so on. With differing degrees of intensity, fear, or blends of fear, may take on still other names—panic, haunt, hesitation, anxiety, peril, stampede, and so on. The word phobia is used to describe a persistent feeling of intense fear that attaches itself to any one or com-bination of life experiences over a period of time.

Most accounts of mental disorders make mention of fear or some variety of fear. The essential difference between normal and abnormal fear does not lie so much in the experience itself as it does in the at-tendant circumstances. If the fear is provoked by some real, imminent threat or danger, it is considered normal; if it has no apparent basis in fact, it is usually considered to be abnormal. Peters neatly phrased this distinction in the quality of the emotion by saying,

The only thing a madman attacks instinctively is the *presence* of fear. A "normal" man attacks the *thing* he fears. There is a difference. (Peters, 1949, p. 301)

The Nature of Phobia

The description of the experience of fear or of phobia is a favorite literary device, usually aimed at the arousal of sympathetic fear in the reader; as, for example, in the horror story or the thriller. These literary productions are obviously not comparable to the descriptions given by persons who have in actuality experienced either true phobic states or the panic and terror that arise during a psychotic episode. To clarify this point, I will cite from descriptions given by persons who have lived through neurotic phobic experiences.

An anonymous surgeon, who related his experience of an anxiety state that was complicated by feelings of unreality and of depersonaliza-tion, spoke of his anxiety and fear in the following way.

It is as difficult to describe to others what an acute anxiety state feels like as to convey to the inexperienced the feeling of falling in love. Perhaps the most characteristic impression is the constant state of causeless and apparently meaningless alarm. You feel as if you were on the battlefield or had stumbled against a wild animal in the dark, and all the time you are conversing with your fellows in normal peaceful surroundings and performing duties you have done for years. With this your head feels vague and immense and stuffed with cottonwool; it is difficult, and trying, to concentrate; and, most frightening of all, the quality of your sensory appreciation of the universe undergoes an essential change. (Lancet, Editors of, 1952, pp. 83–84)

Note that this surgeon spoke of a feeling of an internal, pervasive *alarm* which persisted, though he gave no outward evidence of the inner turmoil. Notice also that he felt an inability to concentrate his thoughts and that his sensory world seemed to be constantly changing.

Another description may be cited from the autobiography by W. E. Leonard, *The Locomotive-God.* As its central theme, the book deals with the nature of the author's phobia and his attempts to conquer his phobic neurosis. One of the several descriptions of his agoraphobia (fear of open places) which he tried to reconstruct, was as follows.

We start with a state of terror generated by past experience. The past experience itself remains in the subconsciousness. At times this emotional effect remains merely a diffused state of terror, in intensity running the whole scale from vague anxiety to intensest feel of impending death; and the agonized mind stands balked of any explanation whatever; except perhaps (as formerly with me) that the state is a premonition of the organic breakup of death. The bottom is knocked out of all security, as when, in an earthquake, chasms suddenly open all about one . . . except that in an earthquake the mind knows the fact *earthquake,* and in my case, it once knew no fact at all. But oftenest the subconscious experience in addition to terror generates in conciousness some specific *form* under which the terror manifests itself, a form of course symbolically, even literally, simulating the original experience. My central, dominating phobia of distance is as good an illustration as one will find. But the *form* of itself will lack adequate motivation for consciousness. So the mind feigns motivation. And so friendly counselors ask, "What is there to be afraid of?"—and add to the grievous burden by laughter. (Leonard, 1939, pp. 320–321)

Leonard's descriptions of his phobic attacks always suggest the implication that the phobic state itself resembled a seizure, a stoppage, or a blank area in the stream of consciousness. The terror disturbed his mental functions to such an extent that he seemed at times to recall little of the outward manifestations.

As a contrast to these descriptions of neurotic phobias, I present the following description of an extreme fear induced in an otherwise normal young man. About a century ago, when chloroform was first used as a surgical anesthetic, many introspective accounts detailing the resultant experience of loss of and return to consciousness were published. Such was the case of a certain university student whose account Herbert Spencer later published. Part of this production reads as follows.

I began to be terrified to such a wonderful extent as I would never before have guessed possible. I made an involuntary effort to get out of the chair, and then—suddenly became aware that I was looking at nothing: while taken up by the confusion in my lungs, the outward things in the room had gone, and I was "alone in the dark." I felt a force on my arm . . . keeping me down, and this was the last straw which made me give in, the last definite thing . . . I remembered outside my own body. Instantly I was seized and overwhelmed by the panic inside. . . . I could feel every air-cell struggling spasmodically against an awful pressure. In their struggle they seemed to tear away from one another in all directions, and there was universal racking torture, while meantime the common foe, in the shape of this iron pressure, kept settling down with more and more irresistible might into every nook and crevice of the scene . . . I recognized some different parts of my body, and felt that the pain in one part was not the same as that in another. . . . A chaotic roaring ran through my brain, innumerable drums began to beat far inside my ear, till the confusion presently came to a monstrous thudding, every thud of which wounded me like a club falling repeatedly on the same spot. (Spencer, 1878, pp. 555–556)

This description of an intense fear aroused in the student by the chloroform-induced anesthesia while he was restrained in a dentist's chair, demonstrates Peters' point that the normal man attacks the thing (circumstances) he fears, whereas, as we have seen, the madman attacks the fear itself. The student whose account I have just cited had the experience of being slowly suffocated by the gas, so that he attempted automatically to escape from the chair. He was acutely aware of the various parts of his body, as well as of painful throbbing in each limb and muscle; deep terror engulfed the entire situation, which terror he could not control, so threatening was it to his life.

The acute anxiety of the surgeon and Leonard's phobic terror were experiences by which each found himself possessed. Each had an inner feeling for which he could not find or recognize an adequate stimulus. Each man, including the student, was terrified, yet somehow knew that his terror was essentially pointless and recognized it as such. The "feel" of the fear was, so far as anyone can tell, of the same quality in all three instances. The feeling muffled their ordinary thought processes, distorted sensory and perceptual experience, and disrupted self-control. However, only for the student was there a tangible basis for the fear; for the surgeon and for Leonard, none was known.

The Role of Fear in Neuroses

It has been intimated in previous chapters that a valid psychological distinction may be made between the psychopathology of neurosis and that of psychosis. This distinction is partly a matter of both the intensity and the quality of the disturbance. In addition, the distinction rests on the insight of the individual (the neurotic patient being able to recognize the lack of a rational basis for his disturbance). Finally, a difference lies in the combination of the interference with voluntary self-control by fear in the development of the aberration. It is to this last point that I now turn.

As a rule, *neurotic fear* begins rather early in the life of the individual. The neurotic patient usually states that the first panic or terror episode occurred during childhood and that episodes or "spells" of the same senseless panic states have occurred from time to time ever since. A confession was published by an anonymous patient, "Vincent," telling of his agoraphobia, from which he had suffered throughout most of his life.

I am now in mid-life and I have not seen a well day since I was about twelve years of age. Before I experienced any of the symptoms of agoraphobia I recall that a strange affliction came over me, an affliction that seemed to baffle the country doctors who were consulted. I was taken suddenly with "spells" which lasted about thirty minutes. During these attacks I was entirely conscious and rational. As I remember the affliction . . . a sort of "coldness" that produced a very unusual sensation, or perhaps a *lack* of sensation would describe it more accurately. . . . When my strange illness came upon me, I worried over it, fearing that I should die in one of the attacks. . . .

There was a high hill not far from my home in the country where we boys used to coast in the winter time. One evening while coasting, in company with other boys of the neighborhood, I experienced an uncomfortable feeling each time we returned to the top of the hill. It was not a well defined symptom of this horrible (I use the term deliberately) malady, but later experiences have taught me that it possessed the unmistakable earmarks. As the months went by the symptoms developed, with the result that I avoided hill-tops, so far as possible. Later, perhaps a year or so, I commenced having a dread of wide fields, especially when the fields consisted of pasture land and were level, with the grass cropped short like the grass on a well-kept lawn. I likewise commenced to dread high things, and especially to ascend anything high. I even had a fear of crowds of people, and later of wide streets and parks. . . . But the one thing that I would make plain is that the malady is always present . . . I am conscious of it . . . during every hour that I am awake. The fear, intensified, that comes over me while crossing a wide street is, it seems to me, an outcropping of a permanent condition . . . When I think of the agony which I have experienced for many years I am astounded at the endurance of the human spirit. (Anon., 1919, pp. 295–299)

"Vincent" mentioned elsewhere in this confession that he was in good physical health so that he had never been rejected when applying for the purchase of life insurance. He had not consulted a physician concerning his phobia since he had left his parents' home at the age of eighteen. In brief, he apparently dwelt in a state of constant anxiety marked by spells of terror and panic, for which he was unable to discover a reason. Fortunately, the internal anguish and fear did not prevent him from earning his livelihood.

Another somewhat more detailed account of a phobia was written by Mrs. F. H. in the form of autobiographical notes that she sent to a physician-friend, Dr. Earl Bond, whom she had consulted professionally some twenty years before. Mrs. F. H. had received psychotherapeutic treatment from several reputable physicians and had a record of several stays in clinics and hospitals. Her phobia centered on the act of going out-of-doors into full daylight. Mrs. F. H. wrote an extensive account of her fifty years of terror, when at long last, through her own self-analysis, she considered that she had conquered and put an end to her phobia. The following is a condensation from her notes, which provides some knowledge of the nature of the fear she had experienced, as well as the self-established routine she followed in her attempt to gain control over her phobia.

For many years I had been burdened by fears which prevented me from going about in the daytime, and which continually kept me in a state of anxiety so severe as, often, to practically paralyze me for hours as I lay racked and tortured on my couch. . .

My phobias were concerned with a good many things, but the central one, the core of them, was an abject fear of light. This fear was so overpowering that I darted out into the daylight only to be driven back, as if by an Unseen Force, into the darkened room where I could find a comparative peace and feeling of safety, although even there I had to fight off periods of intense fear . . . [which sprang up] like jack-in-the-boxes . . .

But one day, suddenly, without warning, a blob of buried stuff cut itself loose from its moorings in the hinterland of my unconscious, and came out into the open. What I saw, I saw clearly, and *without fear.* In the days that followed, I took counsel with myself and argued that if a certain part of the content of my unconscious had broken out of its Pandora's box, then it was possible for more to be discovered. So I decided to get along with the job of trying to track down the horrid "appearances" which troubled me, to find out what they were ,and to rid myself of them. It was a challenge that I had to accept, and I accepted it. . . .

Since walking alone in broad daylight was my worst hazard, I set myself the task of going out every day in order to bring up my fears in all their might. For many years it had been impossible to walk farther than a square in daylight, for my mind would get into such a state of fuzziness that it was not safe for me to be abroad alone in the streets of a city . . .

I [now] found that the fear of not being able to get home was also one of my most terrible fears. It seemed that there was something which interposed between my home and me; not being able to get back had an element of fatefulness . . .

It was what light might reveal that stirred up a sense of horror in me, the horror of the things that were hiding in the corners and culs-de-sac of my mind. Light was the Great Revealer; in the manner of a giant searchlight, it focused upon the contents of my mind and brought out what was in that dark uncharted hinterland . . .

For several days, I walked abroad as one entranced, with the same words beating upon my inner ear: "You will have to go on forever and ever! You will have to wander the face of the earth like a lost soul"—the first theme with variations, yet even more fearful. There were other ideas that came to mind as I tried to push through to the meaning which eluded me. One day I was afraid that a spell had been put upon me, that I would turn into something not myself, a lower animal, or would be transported to the underground garden of the Old Witch where people became partly human with heads of wolves or jackals, as in fairy tales. But even more frightening was the thought that I might turn into a ghoul. . . . Thus my rampant unconscious, once the lid was off, led me into the very heart of a country where bleak fear reigned supreme . . . My fear of not getting home meant that something I had done, or thought I had done, was separating me from "the place where love is"; something sinful and forbidden was preventing me from being able to get home. . . .

And then, one day I automatically slipped into what felt like an almost hypnotic state from the moment I left my door. I fell into a slow, rhythmic gait without meaning to do so. I felt that I was wearing a fixed stare, a look of utter vacuity. . . . As I proceeded, the feeling grew. I felt controlled by an unseen force, by something quite outside myself. That I was scared is putting it mildly; I felt as if I were possessed . . . [but] once home the [panic] ended.

After about a week of peace, I suddenly ran into a veritable whirlwind of a panic. I was walking in a near-by square, when all at once I felt I was in imminent danger. So poignant was this feeling which gathered force by the second, that I almost cried out, "Save me! Save me! ." . . . In this experience, unlike most of my experiences, I was unable to see beneath the surface of my fear. The sheer terror of it was almost paralyzing. How I ever arrived at my apartment, I will never know, but within its safety I brought up the whole fantasy. . . .

As to this feeling of utter unworthiness, I know that all neurotics believe, when the neurosis is upon them, that each one of them is, in fact, the wickedest person in the world. They are blind, for the duration, to the fact that the world is full of real offenders who are going about their business unperturbed and imperturbable. . . . Throughout the period of my neurotic illness, this idea weaves in and out; and the intense craving I had to get back to the halcyon days before the fall was manifest in the fear that I would never get back home, and in the seeking of someone who would fulfill the prerequisites of a mother or father surrogate. Thus when I found myself surrounded by strangers, with no means of escape, I was thrown into a panic. . . .

I wanted, frantically, to run away as fast as possible. In interpreting my own fear . . . I discovered a concealed wish to return to a non-moral state in which our time-encrusted mores would no longer operate, and one could become an uncivilized being again. . . . I have often wondered how many others have felt such urges translated in fear of places remote from humankind . . . This brings me to the end of my story. I managed to come out into the light unafraid. I was able to take up my life again without crippling fears. (Anon., 1952, pp. 162–176)

Mrs. F. H. was a writer. She had gained her vocabulary and background of psychological reference from the several psychoanalytical therapists who had treated her. I mention these points so that the reader may more clearly understand the reason for the phraseology she used so freely. Her self-analysis finally led her to recall an incident that had happened when she was four years old. A baby sister had been born of whom she disapproved and she had innocently suggested to her parents that the sister should be drowned by her father, as she had seen him do to a litter of kittens. Because of this childish remark she was not only spanked and called a murderer, but she was also partially ostracized by her parents. Her self-analysis indicated that this childish incident, magnified by the stern parental behavior, had terrified her and filled her with guilt feelings, so that she dared not face the light of day or go out-of-doors, lest others might also call her a murderer. It is interesting to note how the terror gradually became generalized and attached to other ideas that interfered with her attempts to break through the barriers the phobia had imposed. Mrs. F. H.'s history is one of the very few autobiographical accounts of a phobic state I have found in which the sufferer considered the phobia to have disappeared and her recovery to be complete. How long the recovery continued and how complete it really was, cannot be told from her report.

I cited a few pages back an excerpt from W. E. Leonard's autobiographical book, *The Locomotive-God*, which deals largely with his practically lifelong phobia. His graphic descriptions of various aspects of his phobic experiences are illuminating and interesting. The following series of excerpts from his book will provide further information. For example, he described a typical phobic seizure as follows.

Well, here is what happens always. First, the seizure happens—as well say, nothing happens, if a red-hot-iron is run down the throat, even though it should miraculously leave no after-effects. The seizure happens; the acutest agony of the conscious brain happens. Second, the seizure leaves me always far more exposed to phobic seizures for weeks or months; increases my fear of the Fear; and, as in the distance-phobia, robs me of a goodly part of what little freedom of movement on street and hillside as I have. . . .

[In another connection he characterized a phobic seizure which occurred during his childhood:] The alien spell that had seized me [before] seizes me again. I recognize it for the same. I think, "That passed, this will." But it does not pass. It surges with an indescribable intensity of Horror. Home again becomes immeasurable distance, only more immeasurable. And the distance of three blocks to the railway-bridge girders is, I feel, an infinity of street in the sun. I totter. I fly. I open my shirt to get air on my bare chest. There is a white hitching-post by the gutter near the end of the block. My imagination creates that as its goal, as its refuge. If I can get to the hitching-post, I am saved. I get to the hitching-post. There is a pile of bricks on the tree-lawn and mortar in a mixing box. I stumble on a pail. I fall down on the gravelly sidewalk. All my strength is gone, but with it something of the seizure of panic is gone. . . .

[He described some of the more common physical components of his panic state in the following terms:] In my seizures I sometimes feel faint but never faint away. I never have shrieked but once—as I stood on the bluff before the vision—and then I was shrieking for specific help; I become white in the face and speak (if another is with me) with a very agitated plaintive quiet, like a dying man who is trying not to make a fuss about it. I never have nausea or any other disturbance of the digestive tract; and headaches or other nervous disturbances follow only rarely. . . . One other was a nervous dread that I was about ready to fall down. One other still was the sensation of retching . . . that I had to make the best of during many hours. . . .

[He contrasted his childhood panics to his adult phobias:] The [adult] phobic phenomena were not simply infantile clinging to parents and house. The central terror—craving for safety, reducible ultimately to the fear of death —spread over my entire consciousness, over my whole environment. Every fear known to timid childhood was mine—fear of darkness, of thunder-storms, of dogs, of bodily pains, of blood. And many fears that only maturity has the knowledge to fabricate—as of symptoms of imagined diseases. The hideous components of this three months nightmare . . . thereafter mitigated but never entirely eliminated from the abiding core of the distance-phobia . . . were of diverse origins. . . .

My mind found diabolically cunning ways of rationalizing all my [adult] terrors into secondary forms, pseudo-explanations, as plausible as horrific. For, not having the true explanation, the reason still insisted by its own instinctive urge upon some explanation. So it was with the innumerable phobias that beset me. Such is the mechanism in phobias generally, I believe. The real causes are unknown to the sufferer; and he makes up his causes. If he is of low intelligence, he makes up palpably foolish causes; if he is of high, then more plausible causes. Let us say both have a phobia of darkness; in both the real cause is forgotten childhood trauma, from a fright in a wood; the former will explain it as fear lest some goblin thrust out a white hand from the blackness; the latter as a fear that some disease may attack him, appendicitis or spasm, with no one near to help in the night. (Leonard, 1939, pp. 322–323; 64; 421–422; 317; 320)

It is evident from these excerpts that Leonard was an intelligent and gifted man who unfortunately had been, and continued to be, greatly handicapped by his phobias. He repeatedly had recourse to medical and psychiatric advice and treatment. He read very widely concerning the phenomena and theories of psychotherapy. He made several determined attempts to solve his problems, both with the help of therapists and through self-analysis. He finally came to believe that his original terror dated back to an occasion when he had, as a young child, stood close to a locomotive as it entered a railway station. The sights and sounds surrounding this event had terrified him. In spite of his self-realization of the original fear-producing incident and the insight into the meaning of the terror itself, Leonard was never able to gain control of his phobic seizures.

Another aspect of everyday life experience that may become linked to neurotic phobic phenomena is the way in which such phobias frequently affect the professional career of the afflicted person. The following extract, written by one of Dr. Clevenger's patients, describes the effect of his phobia on his career.

The detriment that this malady has been to me, aside from the physical and mental distress, has been almost incalculable. It has throttled all ambition, killed all personal pride, spoiled every pleasure. To my acquaintances I have been a veritable puzzle. A thing of this kind, cannot, of course, be explained to every individual who may chance to notice my idiosyncrasies. One cannot wear his heart upon his sleeve all the time, and with a few exceptions I have never attempted to make people understand what the trouble was, for I realize how hopeless the task of making them comprehend the matter sufficiently to enlist their sympathy. Most people with whom I have been brought into contact have called me a "crank," and intimated that I was irremediably crazy. Others have insinuated that the memory of some dark crime committed in early life, was the cause of these personal peculiarities. Others still have attributed it all to natural indolence and a desire to shirk work and the ordinary duties of life. Perhaps they are all right; perhaps all wrong—I merely know that it has ruined all my prospects in life, and that, endowed by nature with a mind more than usually quick and retentive, I find myself now, at an age when the opportunities of youth have pretty well slipped by, forced to contemplate a future which bears no prospect of pleasure or profit. (Clevenger, 1890, p. 540)

The author of this statement has clearly pointed out the way in which a persistent and recurrent phobia may act as a most effective handicap in normal life activities. The spells of terror amount to a form of inexplicable self-torture which in varying degrees often continues throughout a lifetime. The limitation in activity, the lack of any understanding or sympathy from others, the inner conviction that the fear is "senseless," all combine to produce an irritating and pervasive pessimism that on occasion leads to suicidal attempts. The problem seems much too simple to the onlooker who says, "It's all in your imagination. Snap out of it. Use your self-control." The neurotic individual has discovered long ago that such observations and well-meant advice are of no assistance whatsoever. Even more discouraging is the fact that he has very frequently found that long, tedious, torturing efforts at psychotherapy likewise fail to bring him relief. Neurotic phobias, of varying degrees of intensity, are not uncommon in the general population; they do account for much loss of human health and happiness.

Fear in the Psychotic States

Concerning the qualitative manifestations of the emotion of fear itself, there seems to be little difference between its nature in neurosis and psychosis. The overwhelming, pervasive, distracting turmoil of the phobic neurotic differs from that of the melancholic or paranoid patient mainly in terms of the insight or meaning the sufferer attaches to his inner feelings. This observation does not mean that neurosis and psychosis are nothing more than manifestations of the same pathological process, any more than an elevated body temperature could be taken as evidence that typhus and tuberculosis have the same pathological basis.

Peters made an important observation in his comment on the role played by fear at the onset of his psychosis. Note that, in this description of a state of fear, part of the difference from those previously cited rests in the expression of a feeling of unreality.

The warning in the trees, their branches twisting against the coming of the night . . . is already too late. . . . Fear comes suddenly, chilling and shocking. But in this there is no bold stroke, only the slow preparation of terror. What child has looked upon his first complete day and not felt the slow agony of nightfall wresting it from him? With it come uncertainty and new shadows —shadows with movements and hidden life, the life of the small nighttime enemies: rodents, insects, marauders, and . . . and what? The sounds and movements of people are contained and stifled, the cry of alarm dies in the throat of a victim, the child looks quickly over a shoulder for what is not there, and the gesture is stealthy, ill. (Peters, 1949, pp. 1–2)

Fear had crept into the mind of this psychotic patient, fear accompanied by feelings of the weird and unreal—a world of unreal evil that terrified him. For the neurotic patient, the phobia constituted a sudden spell or seizure, only rarely described as unreal or evil. The psychotic patient, on the other hand, finds himself in a world of magical or unreal fear that has overwhelmed him slowly and that he may be convinced will eventually destroy him.

Lenore McCall's comments on the part played by fear during her four-year period of melancholia supply further illustrative material.

There is no emotion in life more paralyzing than fear, no element more devastating. It is the archenemy of man and from the time [my illness started] until I recovered it was my constant companion. I learned to know it in all its aspects, real and imaginary, and as it stalked my footsteps I did not have to look back to be aware of its presence for its heavy, chill hand was always on my shoulder.

Beside that foreboding figure there walked another in due time, a kinsman of the first, betraying their relationship by many mutual characteristics; at times so similar that their identities were merged. The name of the second companion of my descent into the unknown was horror. I grew to know it as intimately as fear and I was to reach the point where their combined presence was the only link between me and reality, the only terms by which I was able to translate my existence.

My fear was based fundamentally upon a terror of myself, of what was happening to me, of the helplessness which was overpowering my faculties, and it manifested itself first in a mounting fear of everything about me. I began to be afraid of people, of my family and my friends; not because of what they represented, I soon learned, but because of my own inability to cope with ordinary human contacts. The world which others inhabited, and to which I rightly belonged, was becoming unreal to me and I felt myself an alien as I trudged farther and farther into weird and unknown terrain. (McCall, 1947, p. 8)

This description was particularly related to the days and weeks of the beginning of her depression. But the same fear and horror accompanied her through all the years of her illness. As she experienced it, her fear seemed to stem out of her inability to cope with her own everyday life, with its duties and responsibilities. She could not think clearly or consecutively. Whether her inadequacy was due to the feelings of fear, or whether the fear was secondary to her inadequacies, is impossible to say; either way, the end result remained the same.

This description of fear in a case of melancholia may be compared to the fears of a patient who had suffered from episodes of both mania and depression. We allude to Custance, who suffered from both manic and depressive episodes, and who wrote most of his account while he was in the process of recovering from a maniacal state. The manic states he characterized as "Universes of Bliss" and made no reference to fear. But concerning the role that fear played during his episodes of depression (Universes of Horror), he wrote as follows.

I lay in my bed in the ward of the Hospital dominated above all by an overpowering sense of fear. At first I did not know exactly what it was that I feared, except of course that my mind, which I strove as hard as I could to keep blank, would insist on working about the ordinary, human fears . . . Wisely, no attempt was made to get me up, and I lay as motionless as I could, covering my head as a rule with the bedclothes, partly to shut out the sights and sounds of the ward, and partly as a sort of instinctive reaction. . . .

I had reached [finally] the extremity of fear. Paroxysms of terror overcame me, and I nearly jumped straight out of the window with the idea of killing myself with the broken glass. But the fit passed, and looking back I date my improvement and subsequent recovery from that moment. . . . My soul had plumbed the lowest depth. . . . Although for months . . . my mind went on revolving in the same channels of fear and despair, the weight of the anticipated horror and pain seemed to be lifted, to recede as it were. (Custance, 1952, pp. 64; 75)

In the case of Custance, the paralyzing fear and horror of depression gave rise to suicidal tendencies. Fear in depressive states is usually combined with an equally overwhelming *horror*. I take it that horror, in the context used by melancholic patients, means horror of death, of insanity, and of physical dissolution.

In several previous chapters I have availed myself of excerpts from the *Autobiography of a Schizophrenic Girl*. It will be recalled that Renee's earliest complaints were based on a sharp feeling of unreality and of perceptual distortions that waxed and waned from time to time after the age of five. During her adolescence she developed active tuberculosis and was hospitalized in a mountain sanatorium. Both her physical and mental health improved during the hospital stay so that she was able to return to her parents' home.

It was New Year's when I first experienced what I called *Fear*. It literally fell on me, how I know not. . . . Suddenly Fear, agonizing, boundless Fear, overcame me, not the usual uneasiness of unreality, but real fear, such as one knows at the approach of danger, of calamity. . . . I remained unaware of the basis for the fear which from then on came over me at any moment of the day. . . .

During the earliest attacks of Fear and intense unreality, I sometimes uttered these . . . words: "I should prefer to escape into madness to avoid this consuming fear." Alas, I did not know what I was saying. In my ignorance I believed that madness was a state of insensibility . . . [and] no responsibility. Never . . . had I even imagined what "to lose one's reason" actually meant. . . .

In the endless silence and the strained immobility, I had the impression that some dreadful thing about to occur would break the quiet, something horrible, overwhelming. I waited, holding my breath, suffused with inquietude; but nothing happened. The immobility became more immobile, the silence more silent, things and people, their gestures and their noises, more artificial, detached one from the other, unreal, without life. And my fear increased, became inexpressible, shattering, intolerable. (Sechehaye, 1951, pp. 13–14; 23; 25)

The experience of sudden overwhelming fear and unreality that Renee described is not an uncommon occurrence in schizophrenia. The usual account given by schizophrenic patients includes an initial state of mental confusion, then a complex web of feelings of unreality and great fearfulness. The idea which very soon rose in Renee's mind—that madness would be an excellent defense against the fear and unreality—is an interesting one. The wish to seek this "defense," however, indicated the lack of realization that she had already "lost her mind." The intense fear and loss of contact with reality gradually overwhelmed her until her "defense" became a catatonic rigidity, since this permitted her to block out from awareness almost all external sensory stimulation. Yet, as one may suspect, her fearful state persisted in spite of the catatonic defenses.

The role played by fear in many instances of mental disturbances was neatly summarized by a patient at the Utica State Asylum in a speech he delivered to the group of inmates in April 1856. His style was somewhat oratorical but his observations were acute.

Practical Insanity, Proteus-like, assumes a variety of forms, but its principal phase is fear. Fear is its presiding deity: the fear of death in some terrible shape. This apprehension is riveted in the minds of the insane, and underlies the disposition to commit suicide, although suicidal intentions are ofttimes to be traced to a desire to rid one's self of the world and the world of one's self.—"The spirit of man will sustain his infirmity; but a wounded spirit who can bear?"

I speak the truth in a mystery; I knew a man—whether in the body or out of it he could not tell, at entering this retreat, to suffer, in imagination, all the horrors and tortures of the damned,—apprehensions of violence, of a horrible end,—proneness to commit suicide,—compassed with an everlasting chain of plots, plotters, and counter-plots, loud menaces and whispers murdering sleep; mine eyes have seen it, mine ears have heard it, and the half is not revealed. (Anon., 1856b, p. 75)

Only very rarely do depressive or schizophrenic experiences occur without including a large element of fear, and most frequently one or another form of fear constitutes the major disabling component. The experience of fear or of feelings akin to fear usually involves large elements of anticipation of the future, in which death, disease, and disaster constitute the storm center of the fear. Since a large part of the mental content of a psychosis becomes a distorted connection to present and past reality, the fear is all the more unbearable. The patient cannot easily or with any sense of certainty, associated with his past, experience a reasonable future for himself. Everyone recognizes the inevitability of death, yet the actual thought of death is almost universally blocked out of the ordinary human mind by a multitude of suppressive devices. When psychosis or neurosis intervenes, the suppressive devices fail.

Fear Mixed with Other Emotions

Fear—pure fear—is a rare experience. Fear is usually blended with other emotional states, such as unreality, curiosity, anger, or reverence, or it is so bound to its circumstantial context that the situation itself designates the feeling. For example, *terror* is fear of impending destruction, whereas *guilt* is fear of possible punishment. Dr. Oliver phrased it as follows.

Fear has torment, we all know that. But fear . . . is intimately connected with punishment; it is, in a sense, its own punishment. It carries, inevitably, its own curse with it. . . . Fear results in a sort of checking of the mind, in inhibitions; that it brings with it its own special punishment or curse. (Oliver, 1928, pp. 248–249)

It is for these complex, blended, fearful states that both the experiencer and the onlooker find difficulty in securing adequate labeling words. For example, a woman who was undergoing psychoanalytic treatment with I. P. Glauber developed peculiar panic states. She reported her feelings during one of these attacks as follows.

The frantic panic occurs when I feel I must continue, go on and on. I must feel that there is a definite termination of my working in view. There is a feeling of panic, palpitation, blinding. It actually blurs my vision and my head feels closed in and smaller when I am near a person for whom I feel aggression, and at the same time, a feeling of clinging. . . . She mustn't leave me—but I must have the power to leave her. This is true of men as well—anyone upon whom I depend for a feeling of belonging. I feel real only when I'm close to someone—actually kissing them or holding their eyes with mine. But at the same time I want to run away for fear they will leave me first and I'll be alone, proven worthless, unlovable. . . . I hate them for seeing me as I am —and playing on it. It seems torturous to me. I fear working in the office and I fear not working; it all seems outside of myself. I'm all walled in within myself and I must fight my way out—groping to belong to reality. (Glauber, 1949, pp. 76–77)

She spoke of the feeling as one of over-all panic, yet there is a mixture of feelings of hate, dependence, love, unreality, and depersonalization, together with some perceptual distortions. Strong fear was probably the essential component in her agitated state, yet it was not the only disturbance or her main symptomatic complaint.

In a reply to a question asked by Morton Prince, "What is your mental state? Anxiety, curiosity, or what?" another phobic patient described her panic state as follows.

Trying to look into the mysteries of the world, as to what air is and the planets, and that sort of thing. In other words, it comes to me now that it is largely trying to investigate and not succeeding, and from the fact that I do not succeed it makes mental conflict. It is this way: I try to find out what something is like, so to speak, and I cannot find out what air, for instance, is like, and because I cannot give myself a satisfactory definition or answer it makes conflict. I see now quite clearly certain things. It has come to me that what it is is more or less of a temper fit, as if you were very angry and wanted to strike someone and you do not strike him. It is the same way about this. I want to feel the air and I cannot, and it is a mild temper fit. I do not think it really is anger. It is *annoyance*, irritation. In other words, it is trying to do something that you cannot. I have *since* had repeated attacks of the same kind of unreality, but *they never frightened me*, only annoyed me. First it is a feeling of *annoyance*, later, in the major attacks, comes the panic. (Prince, 1912, pp. 263–264)

In this instance the panic or groundless fear was said to be secondary to an anger, annoyance, and sense of unreality that of themselves did not give rise to fear; but the combination of feelings, lasting over a period of time, did incite fear, panic, and finally phobia. Dr. Prince thought that the feeling of the unreality of air, of which the patient complained, was the expression of a fear of death. While it is true that suffocation is an adequate stimulus for producing fear and panic in any person, this woman's panic may have been related to either a real or imaginary sensation of suffocation. This is not what the patient reported, however. She said her attacks were akin to the temper fits of frustration which were eventually built into a feeling of panic.

Another way in which fear, fatigue, and pain may intermix to produce a state that actually disables the person was recounted by Margaret Cleaves, a practicing physician, in her *Autobiography of a Neurasthene.*

I began to feel very strangely, but I relaxed none of my effort in bringing my work to completion. Finally there came to me a sense of dread and terror beyond my comprehension. My eyes caught the muscles of my colorless hands quivering one day similarly it seemed to me as the fibrillary contraction of a progressive muscular atrophy. I was saturated with the atmosphere of organic nerve conditions clinically as well as in the work I had been doing. It struck terror to my heart despite the fact that I had often been so worn as to have other muscles quiver, but I never before had known the strange incomprehensible feeling of desolation and danger. . . .

[After several weeks she went on a vacation but gained no real relief. Subsequently, hoping that a real change of scene would benefit her, she went to France where she rented a cottage. Of this she wrote:]

I was utterly unprepared for the sensations I experienced immediately I was within its four enclosing walls. It was one of nameless horror, a feeling as though they were crowding in upon me with crushing force not only upon every side, but from above as well. I never was, nor am I in the habit of giving up when I undertake to do a thing. I felt as though I could not remain long enough to attain my purpose, but I tried the old trick of setting my teeth together and saying "I will." It was no use. The sense of dread, horror and impending danger of what I knew not, as well as the increasing helplessness of my right leg was so great that I turned to the door and fled incontinently. (Cleaves, 1910, pp. 60; 107–108)

According to her account, Dr. Cleaves had been a hypochondriac since childhood, but had always been able to drive herself to accomplish any task, no matter what her physical complaints may have been. The incidents that are cited happened on occasions when her inner emotional turmoil overwhelmed her volitional strength. At the time of the first of these incidents, she said, she was filled with a feeling of dread, terror, and desolation in which fear seems to have been the core. During the second incident the fear was certainly in ascendency, to such an extent that the phobia of closed places blotted out all her usual devices for exercising conscious voluntary control.

Fear and Sex

Psychoanalytic theory, which has dominated psychiatric thought for the past quarter century or more, holds that psychopathology is essentially a breaking through into conscious life of the disguised energy and affect of repressed instinctive sexuality. This theory was commented on at some length by Leonard in relation to his own phobia.

This [theory] for a time convinced me that the phobia was somehow rooted in sex; while, on the other hand, the phobic seizures in their analyzable emotion were so damnably obvious as expressions of the self-preservation instinct, I vacillated for years between sex and self-preservation as the leitmotif. . . . But all observations for eleven years had got me nowhere. And all the explanations of amateur or professional psychologists and neurologists in the vicinity had got me nowhere, being inconsistent or superficial, or frankly tentative. And all my varying technic of cure had got me nowhere. . . .

[His first wife committed suicide. This tragedy made his agoraphobia more acute and circumscribing. Four years after the suicide he remarried. Of the second marriage he wrote as follows.]

This most private experience may still be considered scientifically as one more experiment in phobic phenomena. And it shows: (1) that suddenly breaking phobic bondage . . . may not really break it at all; (2) that even a half-hour's entire release from phobic emotion under conditions where otherwise most intense [feelings dominate] . . . presages no inevitable cure; (3) that in changing the environment I *carried with me* essentially unchanged (except for reduction of intensity, itself due to another stimulus and another support) the characteristic phobic need of a center of safety; (4) that the love-stimulus, helpful beyond any other, was itself only peripheral to the trouble. And the next twelve years show that even the stimulus of marriage and a new home could not withstand the phobias, least of all under any worries and any emotional stress . . . and there can be no twelve years on earth without these, even where without phobias. (Leonard, 1939, pp. 390; 349)

From Leonard's experience, as well as from other similar reports, it becomes apparent that fear and phobia are much stronger emotional drives than either love or sex. A spouse may provide a haven of comparative security, but only for short intervals since the shelter of marriage in no way mitigates or cures the fundamental fearfulness. Dr. Oliver commented on this point in the following way.

People trifle with love. Now I deny that love is a strong passion. Fear is the strong passion. (Oliver, 1928, p. 121)

It is indeed astonishing to discover the number of autobiographical accounts one can find in the literature where the sufferers, particularly those patients who have lived through full-blown psychoses or neuroses, question the relevancy of repressed sexuality to the core of their psychopathology.

Fear During Heart Disease

It is an ancient medical observation that certain patients who suffer from one or another of the various forms of heart disease undergo, at intervals, periods of panic or of melancholia. One such patient, Mrs. Pastorelli, who had suffered panic attacks in connection with her heart disease, wrote about the experience as follows.

Is there really nothing which can prevent me feeling my heart—that vital machine whose slightest deviation from the normal is enough to upset the entire body—suddenly give out, get painfully irregular, to be thrown for hours into an unimaginable state of crazy fear, while at the same time the lungs seem to be turned into cotton-wool which lets no air pass, and in a few moments a glacial cold, such as I have never experienced at any other time, penetrates the whole of my being and turns it into a block of ice? Shall I then always be liable to those states of collapse when, in indescribable agony, gasping and feeling death imminent, I find myself as incapable of resistance or defence as a plant whose stalk is suddenly cut? (Pastorelli, 1936, pp. 32–33)

A panic of this kind may seem "reasonable" to the onlooker, who must, however, understand that it is subjectively determined by the objectively imminent possibility of sudden death. Fear may be very acute in a variety of situations and conditions, but it always seems more tolerable when an objective explanation is at hand.

Discussion

Surveying in a more general way these autobiographical accounts of pathological fear and of phobia bring several points into clearer light. *Fear is the strong passion.* In the presence of great fear all other feelings, emotions, intellectual barriers, and volitional efforts collapse. All interest and motivations based on hunger, thirst, or sex become ineffective. All of mankind's intellectual defenses, such as turning one's thoughts to other subjects, attempting to divert the feeling of fear from consciousness, efforts based on the premise, "I've always been master of my own mind"; all these vanish in the face of great fear. Fear is all-pervasive and all-powerful. It blots out hope. It destroys inhibitions. It cannot be denied. It is beyond bravery and cowardice. It distorts all the usual orderly mental processes, eventually erasing both memory and conscious existence.

When in the throes of fear the sufferer seeks a "center of safety"; or when such refuge does exist, he strives to "huddle in a corner," waiting in despair till the paroxysm passes. While the paroxysm of terror continues, the person is unable to question or consider its possible causes. But once the phase of acute terror has waned, there still lingers in its wake a dread or horror, from which he occasionally may attempt a self-explanation. The dread—the horror—continues essentially unchanged because one cannot even find a really adequate explanation for the paroxysm. The person is only cognizant of the fear that descended on him and that possessed and overpowered him. With a tangible source that one can recognize as an adequate stimulus, one flees if one is able, or if cornered one fights. But, in pathological fear there has been no recognition or realization of an adequate stimulus. There has been no detail in one's surroundings or in one's memory that could, in any way justify the fear. One fights to become free from an unknown source of fear. One can only appeal to magic, to superstition, or to ritual to ward off future paroxysms. Lacking any really satisfactory, self-evident explanations, one is often willing to believe all the explanations advanced by anyone who is endowed with an authoritative manner. But with every recurrence of the panic, such welcome but dogmatic explanations somehow lose their reassuring qualities.

In many ways, an overwhelming state of panic is similar to an epileptic seizure. It happens. One does not know why. One tries to avoid, insofar as possible, the various attendant circumstances that immediately preceded and seemingly led to the more recent attacks. One finds oneself inevitably forced to believe that fear is inflicted from without, or born from some inner and totally involuntary mechanism. The panic is frequently accompanied by a feeling of injustice, since one can conceive of no possible reason for having to endure such an affliction, from which most of one's fellows appear to be free. "Why has the Lord afflicted me?" is the common complaint of both the phobic and the epileptic sufferer.

Phobia, like melancholia, is regarded as an overwhelmingly real experience by each phobic patient. The feeling of a specific avoidance may be illogical, so far as the surrounding circumstances are concerned, but he cannot escape the certainty of its presence. Others may tell him that his fear, his phobia, his panic, is silly and nonsensical, that it is strictly imaginary, and that he should exercise his will power and rise above it. He may agree with these suggestions, but only on an intellectual level, for he has repeatedly found that his conscious efforts do not modify or banish the pervasive and demanding inner experience.

The comparison between the phobic experience of the neurotic patient and that of the psychotic patient is an interesting one. In all likelihood, the fear itself is qualitatively similar in both conditions. But the reactions to the emotional experience do differ. The neurotic is overwhelmed and disabled, yet retains sufficient mental integration to maintain his capacity to adjust, in one way or another, to most situations of everyday life. He realizes his handicap and lives with it as best he can. The psychotic patient, however, is gripped by terror in addition to being in a state of melancholia, mental turmoil and confusion, and so forth, all together precluding even partial adjustment to the outer environment.

The psychotic patient is mentally and emotionally unable to function, his fear being the leading element of his almost total mental disintegration.

Many psychotic and neurotic patients arrive at the conclusion that their fear is basically a fear of death, that somehow the innate terror which every person feels of his own inevitable death has broken loose and overwhelms them. But why in him, rather than in any other person should fear break loose; such is the question for which each patient seeks to find an answer.

Between the idea
And the reality
Between the motion
And the act
Falls the Shadow . . .
(Eliot, 1936, p. 58)

CHAPTER 12

Melancholia; Depression

INTRODUCTION

The shadow that melancholia casts on the mental life
of any human being is the oldest concept of psychopathology that is still as current in modern thought as
it was at any time in the past. The feelings that characterize this experience are typically sorrow, fear, and
hopelessness. Because of its outward manifestations it
is quite easily recognizable by observers. The specific
causes of melancholia are as debatable today as they
were three millenia ago.

In the fourth century B.C., Hippocrates, known as
"the father of medicine," wrote a treatise on melancholia. He taught that health and disease were governed by the balance between the humors or juices of
the body. To each humor there corresponded a particular temperament; for example, the "melancholic"
temperament and melancholia were ascribed to the primacy of black bile in the body (*melancholia* = black
bile, Greek.) Another of the basic humors of the body,
blood, was reflected in the sanguine temperament, a
notion that gave rise to the medical treatment of
bleeding as a method to counteract disease. For more

than two thousand years the doctrine of bodily humors was the conventional and accepted basis of medical thought. It became part of the general common sense of mankind. Only the scientific advances of the nineteenth and twentieth centuries led to serious doubt concerning the veracity of this ancient medical and psychological theory.

In 1621 Robert Burton first published his classical book, *The Anatomy of Melancholy,* which constituted a survey and critical evaluation of almost everything that had been written about melancholia in the western world since the days of Hippocrates. Burton considered melancholia to be the most universal of human afflictions, holding that there is no person who does not, at some time or other experience it, to some degree, in one or another of its changeable forms. He noted that many authorities had limited the true nature of melancholia to one consisting of fear and sorrow, which were assumed to be inseparable companions in forming the common basis of all depressions. In spite of this authoritative limitation, Burton reviewed not only these two more familiar emotions, but a multitude of other symptoms as well.

The four and twenty letters make no more variety of words in divers languages, than melancholy conceits produce diversity of symptoms in several persons. They are irregular, obscure, various, so infinite, Proteus himself is not so diverse . . . as a true character of a melancholy man . . . Who can distinguish these melancholy symptoms so intermixt with others, or apply them to their several kinds, confine them into method? "Tis hard, I confess; yet I have disposed of them as I could, and will descend to particularize them according to their species. . . . Not that they are all to be found in one man . . . but some in one, some in another, and that successively or at several times. (Burton, 1927, pp. 347–348)

Burton's statement remains valid. The descriptions and analyses of the experience of melancholia that I will present are quite diverse in nature and rather difficult to organize in a systematic fashion.

The Nature of Melancholia

The state of melancholia is not a simple emotional experience or intellectual disturbance. Different persons use a variety of terms to describe their experience. Traditionally, the feeling is said to be a mixture of sorrow, hopelessness, and fear, including a train of other similarly unpleasant and distressing feelings. On the physical side, insomnia, weariness, tension, weepings and sighing are frequent external symptoms. Hallucinations are rare. Delusions regarding other people seldom occur but delusions concerning one's own person are commonplace. Thoughts of suicide and suicidal attempts (often successful) are frequent. Because of this complexity of feelings and manifestations, it is not possible to summarize in a series of citations the entire range of melancholic complaints. Custance, whose descriptions have been quoted several times in other connections, wrote the following in an attempt to define the essence of the nature of melancholia as he, himself, had experienced it.

If I were asked to characterise in the briefest possible way, the whole experience of the depressive phase, I would describe it as a total reaction of repulsion between those fundamental poles of all being as we perceive it, which can be roughly and variously designated as the individual and the environment, the "I" and the "Not I," the ego and "the other," the perceiver and the perceived (including inner perceptions), or even as the soul and God. The basis of that repulsion seems to be fear, or "anxiety," to use the word generally employed to translate the Freudian concept of "Angst." And in the last analysis, as I have tried to show, the fear or anxiety seems to resolve itself at the climax into the fear of physical pain in the most terrifying form.

There is something quite logical about this. . . . Certainly it seems to me that my reactions in the depressive phase are crude . . . or "total" . . . There is little or no discrimination; everything is abhorrent to me, everything repels me, everything frightens me. My consciousness has as it were regressed to that earliest stage of the simple organism which, finding its environment unpleasant, wants to get away at all costs. I want to get away into the nothingness of annihilation, hence my suicidal impulses. Yet the unpleasantness of my situation thrusts itself upon my consciousness with all the intensity and with all the endless variety and refinement of torture made possible with the vast and intricate development of the nervous system in man. Infinite possibilities of horror and pain occur to me. If I have the slightest pain, that pain becomes in anticipation infinite and increasing, absorbing my whole consciousness. Every unpleasant reaction or thought is magnified to the limit. . . .

The sense of sin . . . in depression is dominating and all pervading. . . . It can reach incredible extremes . . . As far as I can analyse it, the sense of sin . . . was dominated by two factors. The first factor was a tremendous sense of repulsion . . . [and] guilt. . . . The second factor was an overwhelming sense of sexual sin. (Custance, 1952, pp. 76–77; 79)

Onset of Melancholia

The following may be considered as one of the typical modes of onset of a depression. It was described by the nurse whom I have already quoted in Chapters 3 and 4.

I was seized with an unspeakable physical weariness. There was a tired feeling in the muscles unlike anything I had ever experienced. A peculiar sensation appeared to travel up my spine to my brain. I had an indescribable nervous feeling. My nerves seemed like live wires charged with electricity. My nights were sleepless. I lay with dry, staring eyes gazing into space. I had a fear that some terrible calamity was about to happen. I grew afraid to be left alone. The most trivial duty became a formidable task. Finally mental and physical exercises became impossible; the tired muscles refused to respond, my "thinking apparatus" refused to work, ambition was gone. My general feeling might be summed up in the familiar saying "What's the use." I had tried so hard to make something of myself, but the struggle seemed useless. Life seemed utterly futile. (Reid, 1910, pp. 612–613)

It will be recalled that the writer of this excerpt had been a charge-nurse in a general hospital. The onset of the depression was rapid, and her loss of self-control, together with the realization of her own insanity, took only a few days to develop. The fatigue and inner tension led to an agitated state, which made her admission to a mental hospital imperative. In a matter of weeks, she passed from the agitated depression into a maniacal state. As she recorded her account of this episode, it is apparent that her first symptoms were undue weariness, tension, and insomnia, leading to an apprehensive fear and mental confusion which eventually culminated in strong feelings of hopelessness and futility.

In *The Varieties of Religious Experience*, James included a chapter on "The Sick Soul" which deals largely with the phenomena of melancholia. He cites the following quotation from a manuscript that had come into his possession.

Whilst in this state of philosophic pessimism and general depression of spirits about my prospects, I went one evening into a dressing-room in the twilight to procure some article that was there; when suddenly there fell upon me without any warning, just as if it came out of the darkness, a horrible fear of my own existence. Simultaneously there arose in my mind the image of an epileptic patient whom I had seen in the asylum, a black-haired youth with greenish skin, entirely idiotic, who used to sit all day on one of the benches, or rather shelves against the wall, with his knees drawn up against his chin, and the coarse gray undershirt, which was his own garment, drawn over them inclosing his entire figure. . . . *That shape am I,* I felt, potentially. Nothing that I possess can defend me against that fate, if the hour for it should strike for me as it struck for him. There was such a horror of him, and such a perception of my own merely momentary discrepancy from him, that it was as if something hitherto solid within my breast gave way entirely, and I became a mass of quivering fear. After this the universe was changed for me altogether. I awoke morning after morning with a horrible dread at the pit of my stomach, and with a sense of insecurity of life. . . . I remember wondering how other people could live, how I myself had ever lived, so unconscious of that pit of insecurity beneath the surface of life. . . . I mean that the fear was so invasive that had I not clung to scripture-texts . . . I think I should have grown really insane. (James, 1902, pp. 160–161)

Again the fearful feeling of insecurity and hopelessness with the attendant horror and sorrow took hold of his sick soul and, as he said, "fell upon me without warning." This man thought that he had saved himself from true insanity by mentally clinging to scriptural texts, a common defensive device but one that has failed many another person who has been similarly overwhelmed by fear.

Not all depressions start as suddenly as those I have depicted. For example, the development of the melancholia described by Lenore McCall (see pages 22, 46), grew in intensity over a period of approximately six months before the break with sanity actually occurred. During these six months, much of her inner life grew to include the elements of weariness, mental confusion, desolation, fear, and despair, which typified her final condition of melancholia.

Major Varieties of Depression

From the collection of autobiographical accounts of melancholia or acute depression I have assembled, it seemed to me that four major classifications may be used to characterize the material. It is possible that the emotional core is quite similar in all varieties of melancholic experiences, yet I have found it emphasized differently, as a function of the status or other problems of the individual; hence, accounts written by (1) religious mystics; (2) passive, depressed, psychotic patients; (3) the patients who suffer from an agitated depression; and (4) the more fragmented or schizoid patients; all four types seemingly present the same core of melancholia, but each type appears in some way in a different light.

MYSTICAL OR "SICK-SOUL" EXPERIENCE

The reports given by mystics emphasize sin, evil, and the like; there is usually not much reference to physical conditions or complaints. The intrusion of religious experience into psychopathology may be illustrated by portions from a journal kept by a middle-aged man under the pseudonym "Nicodemus," whose private mental world figuratively collapsed at the same time as the military collapse of France early in World War II.

I am lost; I am damned; I am dead; only Thou, O Christ, can quicken these dead bones. I am a crawling mass of corruption; every thought, every act, every wish, every willing of mine is corrupt—I can do no good thing. Even this contrition, this horror of myself is rotten with sin and self-will. Slay me O God, and remake me! I pray for no less than that. And, in an hour, even that blinding knowledge will be lost to me and I shall slide back into the foulness, the pettiness, the futility of self. Except Thou save—except Thy fire shall not abate, shall consume me utterly, purge me thoroughly. O God, take not Thy fire from my soul! Save me from the hell of indifference and compromise! Save me—and I shall be saved. Heal me and I shall be healed. There is no other saving; I cannot save myself. . . .

I know too, as matter of cool self-observation, that this that has happened to me, is no "neurosis." There is no phrase which fits it more nearly than the old phrase which has seemed so often so hollow, of "the hand of God."

For this has come *to* me, not *from* me; it is the action of some transcendent power upon me, not merely the explosion of forces immanent within me. . . . That is as nearly as I can tell this state in words. And it is now constantly at call. Anxieties, annoyances, the hate and horror which are the burden of all news now, are no more than, as it were, winds ruffling the surface of a fathomless and illimitable sea. The intolerable tension, the sense of doom, the contrition which rent the soul asunder—all these have passed. It is a state which I have never known save in moments and is, I know, foreign to my natural temperament and one which I neither conjure up myself nor could conjure. (Nicodemus, 1942, pp. 66; 67; 128)

This melancholic experience is that which has been characterized as part of the mystical experience of the "sick soul," which he maintained stemmed largely from a sense of sin. But note that the sufferer wrote, "This has come *to* me, not *from* me." As is so often true, the individual who recounts his pathological experience will state that the disturbance came upon him from the outside. Indeed, in most instances of psychopathological experience, the sufferer finds himself in a world of experience that he never conjured or imagined, and that he never conceives as having arisen from within.

The evangelist John Bunyan wrote the following paragraph on his feelings of unworthiness in his *Grace Abounding in the Chief of Sinners* (I quote from James). Bunyan was a sensitive person continually concerned with the flow of his spiritual vitality.

But my original and inward pollution, that was my plague and my affliction. By reason of that, I was more loathsome in my own eyes than was a toad; and I thought I was so in God's eyes too. Sin and corruption, I said, would as naturally bubble out of my heart as water would bubble out of a fountain. I could have changed heart with anybody. I thought none but the Devil himself could equal me for inward wickedness and pollution of mind. Sure, thought I, I am forsaken of God; and thus I continued a long while, even for some years together. (James, 1902, p. 158)

The essence of Bunyan's melancholia James termed "the vanity of mortal things," referring to the concern the sufferer feels for the state of his own soul.

A certain peculiar mental state has been repeatedly mentioned by several devout followers of mystical practices who hoped to achieve true ecstasy by long devotional exercises and meditations. It is described as a condition that is gradually reached, in which they would find themselves in a state of sorrow likened to the darkness of night, and during which they experience a certain "dryness of the soul." As an example, the description of such a state as related by Madame Guyon may be given here.

Loaded with miseries of all sorts, weighed down with the burden of continual crosses, I at last gave up hope. The darkness of an eternal night settled upon my soul. Looking upon myself as a victim doomed for destruction,

I had not the least expectation of emerging out of the distressing state, in which I found myself. As in the case of the Saviour in the extremity of his sufferings, God seemed to have forsaken me. But thanks be to his grace, my heart bowed in entire and holy submission. Lost as I was, or rather as I seemed to myself to be, I could not cease to love. Believing, as I did, in the strange position of my mind, that I could never again be acceptable to God, and never received by him, I distinctly and fully recognized his justice and goodness; and could not repress the longing desire I had to do something, or to suffer something, to promote his glory. I could praise the name of the Lord out of the depths, to which no lower deep seemed possible. (Upham, 1849, p. 182)

Madame Guyon's depression continued throughout several years of her life. It lifted suddenly with a feeling of revelation, grace, and ecstasy, and she regained an inner assurance that God's salvation had been given to her. The sorrowful feeling of the loss of self-esteem without the mention of fear seems central in this variety of mystical depression.

Other mystics have spoken of the lethargy and weariness of the soul as leading features of the melancholic state. MacCurdy supplies the following citations from the early Church Father, St. John of Damascus.

A sorrowfulness so weighing down the mind that there is no good it likes to do. It has attached to it as its inseparable comrade a distress and weariness of soul, and a sluggishness in all good works, which plunges the whole man into lazy languor, and works in him constant bitterness. And out of this vehement woe springs silence and a flagging of the voice, because the soul is so absorbed and taken up with its own indolent dejection, that it has no energy for utterance but is cramped and hampered and imprisoned in its own confused bewilderment, and has not a word to say. (MacCurdy, 1925, p. 343)

To sum up the leading features of the melancholic experiences of religiously inclined or mystical devotees, I may point out the following: (1) loss of self-esteem, (2) sorrow, (3) a mental weariness and feeling of inner tension, (4) inability to carry on with one's duties and obligations, (5) feeling of being lost from God's goodness, (6) feeling of horror at one's own unworthiness, and (7) hopeless despair and a sense of doom. There is little mention of states of fear or thoughts of self-destruction. There is no mention of divine punishment; rather, though God has somehow withdrawn His Grace, there yet remains a steadfast feeling of an abiding trust.

PASSIVE DEPRESSION

This type of melancholy is the one commonly experienced by manic-depressive patients during the depressive phase of their illness. For reasons not understood, this passive depression yields rapidly to electric shock therapy in a very specific fashion. Patients suffering from this affliction were formerly found quite commonly in mental hospitals, being residents for periods varying from several months to several years. Nowadays, this condition is not common in mental hospitals, since such individuals are usually treated either in a doctor's office or in a general hospital, where a limited number of shocks (or one of the newer drugs) ends the melancholic process rapidly and completely.

Custance's account of his depression was cited previously in this chapter. He wrote further concerning this experience.

I seem shut into myself, withdrawn from real contact with the outer world as also from contact with God; the sun does not really shine, the trees and fields are not really green; I am shut in with my thoughts, always of a depressing and melancholy nature. . . .

This state is so exactly what is described by the mystics that I will give two quotations. . . . "everything seemed to me full of faults; my charities, my alms, my prayers, my penances; one and all they rose against me. Either by you, O my God, or by myself, or by all creatures, I felt myself universally condemned." . . . "All the favours ever granted me were swept out of my memory. My mind was so greatly obscured that I stumbled from doubt to doubt, from fear to fear. I believed myself so wicked that I regarded my sins as the cause of all the evils, and all the wickedness that afflicted the world." . . . [This is] exactly what happens in my mind as depression progresses. [St. Theresa wrote] . . . of her mind being "obscured." That is what is happening to my mind at the very moment I am writing. Instead of the light of ineffable revelation I seem to be in, perpetual fog and darkness. I cannot get my mind to work; instead of associations "clicking into place" everything is an inextricable jumble; instead of seeming to grasp a whole, it seems to remain tied to the actual consciousness of the moment. The whole world of my thought is hopelessly divided into incomprehensible watertight compartments. I could not feel more ignorant, undecided, or inefficient. It is appallingly difficult to concentrate, and writing is pain and grief to me. As for wickedness, although my mind has not reached the stage of regarding myself as the most wicked person in the world and responsible for all the sin and evil afflicting mankind, I know too well that it can do so. That appalling self-centredness is the reverse of the delusions of grandeur and power. It leads to the uttermost depths. (Custance, 1952, pp. 61–62)

In a depressed state such as that Custance has just described, there is a loss of all the ordinary pleasures of existence; there is no sunshine, no pleasure from music, salt loses its savor and flowers their perfume. The patient becomes certain that he has been forever lost because of his unforgivable sins. He fears his imagined inevitable doom, and frequently voices his wish that death might put an end to his suffering.

William James included in *The Varieties of Religious Experience* a translation from a letter written by a patient in a French asylum that details further the suffering of the passive melancholic patient.

I suffer too much in this hospital, both physically and morally. Besides the burnings and the sleeplessness (for I no longer sleep since I am shut up here, and the little rest I get is broken by bad dreams, and I am waked with a jump by nightmares, dreadful visions, lightning, thunder, and the rest), fear, atrocious fear, presses me down, holds me without respite, never lets me go. Where is the justice in it all! What have I done to deserve this excess of severity? Under what form will this fear crush me? . . . Eat, drink, lie awake all night, suffer without interruption—such is the fine legacy I have received . . . There are limits to everything, there is a middle way. But God knows neither a middle way nor limits. I say God, but why? . . . After all, I am afraid of God as much as of the devil, so I drift along, thinking of nothing but suicide . . . As you read this, it will easily prove to you my insanity. The style and the ideas are incoherent enough—I can see that myself. But I cannot keep myself from being either crazy or an idiot; and, as things are, from whom should I ask pity? I am defenseless against the invisible enemy who is tightening his coils around me. I should be no better armed against him even if I saw him, or had seen him. Oh, if he would but kill me, devil take him! Death, death, once for all! But I stop. I have raved to you long enough. I say raved, for I can write no otherwise, having neither brain nor thoughts left. O God! what a misfortune to be born! Born like a mushroom, doubtless between an evening and a morning; and how true and right I was when in our philosophy-year in college I chewed the cud of bitterness with the pessimists. Yes, indeed, there is more pain in life than gladness—it is one long agony until the grave. (James, 1902, pp. 148–149)

From this letter one may gain some understanding of the feeling of evil, the hopelessness, the fear, the querulous, irritable temper, and the mental confusion that mark a passive depression. The entire experience is of a sense of sin and evil with a persistent inner frustration. The passivity is both a result and a cause of the distress.

AGITATED DEPRESSION

Some melancholic patients are possessed, in addition to their fearful sorrow, by a compulsive and restless agitation that drives them to incessant activity (for example, walking and wailing) for long periods of time. This variety of depression is not infrequently an outstanding feature of involutional melancholia. The Reverend William Walford described, in his autobiography, this aspect of his melancholia, which marked the sixth decade of his life.

The agitation and restlessness that affected me were so great, that I was unable to sit down, as the moment in which I attempted to do so brought an increase of misery; and I was kept pacing up and down my parlour from the time of getting up until going to bed. I was so intensely wearied by this incessant going to and fro, as frequently to scream with anguish. In consequence of this painful excitement, I seldom rose from my bed before noon, as I was able to continue this posture without additional pain. As soon as I came down stairs, I hastily swallowed my breakfast, standing, and then the endless movement began. While my body was thus occupied, my mind was the seat of the direst contemplations, revolving the past and the future, until sometimes, when thinking of my pious friends who were no longer living on earth, I loudly bid them to an everlasting adieu, as I was never to be admitted to the rest to which they had been conducted . . . On such occasions, sighs of distress, so deep from my bosom, would involuntarily escape, as too plainly indicated the profound sorrow that affected me. (Walford, 1851, pp. 185–186)

The condition of being driven to continual activity is, in a sense, the vivid outward expression of inner tension. As noted in several of the descriptions of melancholia given above, the patient complained of an inner tension from which he could find no relief. The agitation usually takes the form of an endless pacing the floor. Some patients also express their oppressive tension by wringing the hands, continuous gesturing, or plaintive crying.

In his autobiography, *A Mind Mislaid*, H. C. Brown relates how at the age of 65, he found himself in a state of agitated suicidal depression. He attributed this mental break to frustrations in his career. He recovered after some three years of hospitalization. Since much of his account is not relevant to his own experience, I have somewhat abridged his description in the following.

I am utterly powerless to describe the abject terror which seized me when I realized I was within the four walls of a madhouse. . . . I do not recall that I was ever muddled in my thoughts, but I certainly suffered from a depressed state of mind that was so severe as to make me utterly indifferent to muddles or no muddles. In that state you seldom speak to any one, and then only to snarl. A constant state of hostility would perhaps define the attitude. . . . I was perfectly aware at all times of everything that was going on around me and do not recall a single moment when I was confused or didn't know what I was doing. I do know that I was simply sick of living, that nothing interested me. . . .

Nevertheless, my frightful mental depression persisted. It was utterly impossible for me to dispel the gloom. . . . The power to work, the will to work, was temporarily gone . . . life had lost its savor. . . . I just didn't want to get well. I would much rather be dead. . . . This struggle to conquer fear was a bitter one. To return to the world meant facing a terrible ordeal. Life just couldn't be faced, that's all there was to it. . . .

It was thoughts like these that produced agitation; that compelled me to walk unceasingly and breathlessly all my waking hours. . . . I went at break-neck speed, I would say five miles an hour would be a conservative estimate. For two years . . . not eight hours, but nearer twelve a day. If you are fond of figures, you can multiply . . . and you get a very respectable total of 43,-800 miles for my two years performance. (Brown, 1937, pp. 19; 74; 77; 78; 80; 82; 168–169)

Brown's estimate of the number of miles covered by his walks is probably no exaggeration. As he has said, the progress of the agitated patient is not a slow melancholic stroll, but a rapid dog-trot which continues throughout the waking day and on into part of the night. One might think that such activity would be thoroughly fatiguing, yet actually such patients sleep poorly and fitfully and often have to be restrained in order to keep them in bed for more than a couple of hours at night. The endless pacing the floors, the sighing and dry-eyed moaning, the irritation the patient expresses when there is any thwarting of his activity, contribute to a truly astonishing performance.

Most attacks of agitated depression occur during the involutional period of life. However, such symptoms have also occurred before the age of fifty. I may cite an example recorded by an anonymous patient of a period of acute agitated melancholia that overtook him in his late twenties.

The everlasting reflection of [my frustrated ambition in] its fiery form inflamed my brain—every thought became agony, and I went mad. My spirit was impaled upon the instrument on which it had so sinfully leant—hope fled, and in her place reigned that sleep-hating demon despair. Agony-driven, I hurried ceaselessly on through that room till every foot mark of my bruised and blistered feet could be traced in blood and water upon the floor. Sleep, that oil, that priceless balm for the weary soul, had entirely departed; and my parched brain glowed like a furnace. Were any one to ask me how long I travelled upon these bruised and bleeding feet—how long my glaring eyeballs refused protection from lids that felt like fire, my answer would break his faith in my veracity forever. (Anon., 1947, p. 17)

In this instance the agitation lasted only a few days, since as the depression deepened he became more deluded and disoriented, finally drifting into a stuporous state from which he eventually recovered.

The hopeless despair, the sense of sin and fearfulness are as prominent in the mind of the agitated depressed patient as they are in the mind of the mystic and the passive sufferer. Inner tension seems to be present in the complaints of every variety of melancholia, but in the agitated patient it is so strong that it breaks through all ordinary barriers of inhibitions and becomes the most overt symptom.

SCHIZOID OR FRAGMENTED DEPRESSION

In some patients, usually schizophrenics, the depression may differ somewhat from the varieties of melancholia considered so far. In these schizoid cases the sadness seems to be a part of a larger emotional upheaval, in which hostility, anger, and fear play a complex role. Schizoid thinking usually becomes disconnected so that the coherent associations which ordinarily exist among thought processes are missing or, at least, are no longer apparent. For example, Hackett wrote as follows.

That night, the creeping tide of depression washed away the sand of self-esteem. I was a fool to think I could win. There was no victory for such as me. I was a crippled puppy running by the road, dust on a cathedral floor, a blind lion, for me there was no hope. Was there anyone at all? There was no one at all. My wife had betrayed me to my enemies. I was separated from my family, afraid for my children. I looked about the room in which I lay. . . . I was the king of the insane . . . I was the king in exile; this was my throne room; I was the giant of cardboard and this was my jail. All was depression. Days during which it was ever night, sleepless nights unending, and I did what they told me . . . I was silent . . . others made jewelry or wallets, but I made nothing. . . . It was as if they had been there forever . . . just the setting for my own struggle. The depression was with me and the terrible feeling of being caught. It was not the feeling of being caught that comes when you are tired of running and hiding and questioning; it is the feeling of being caught that comes the first time you are caught. (Hackett, 1952, pp. 86–87)

Other schizoid patients have emphasized the growing mental weakness and the feeling of automaticity that seems to attach itself to all their actions. This mechanical feeling seems to depend largely on a gradual loss of finer shades of feeling. Fear and automatic, nonvolitional action alone remain.

A certain patient treated by the renowned French psychiatrist Janet phrased the experience as follows.

The further I go the more my mind weakens; the more complicated an act the more I dread it. I stop before the least obstacle without knowing what to do. My parents, who see me do something from time to time, are deceived and think that I am really acting. What I appear to do is not done by me; it is done mechanically, as if it were done by some one else who had control of me. I prefer to do nothing at all, rather than feel within me these actions performed by another, which are as if inspired or forced by some one, God or devil. It is too sad not to do anything of oneself; it is too humiliating. I am ashamed, too, afraid of being laughed at, and I prefer not to stir rather than act so. . . . I but half feel things; I am in a world which I do not understand, which does not exist, and which inspires me with a vague fear. . . . I can no longer speak to living beings; in the first place I do not know whether they are alive; and in the second I no longer belong to the same world with them; they humiliate me when they speak to me; I am going to withdraw into a corner where there is absolutely no one; I do not live, I cannot live, I do not wish to live. (Janet, 1921, p. 11)

Both this and the excerpt just preceding bear the marks of melancholia, but the experience reported in both cases is more that of a secondary development which grew out of the person's self-realization of mental disintegration.

Other Common Features of Melancholia

It is possible to pick out the more common complaints that accompany the melancholic state. I have given examples of sorrow, hopelessness, fear, guilt, lack of energy, horror, grief, repulsion, agitation, and finally, despair, resulting from the loss of self-control. To these I should add specific descriptions of persistent lassitude, self-reproach, insomnia, and contemplation of suicide.

LASSITUDE

A symptom from which many patients complain is inertia, lack of energy, or an indolent lassitude. Reid's patient, who had several episodes of depression, wrote as follows.

> In recent years the depressions have appeared suddenly. One day I went to town to do some shopping for a friend. I went to a grocery store to make some purchases. It suddenly occurred to me that I could make these to much better advantage at the market only a block away. Suddenly I realized that I did not have sufficient energy to go to the market, and that another depression was upon me. It was with the greatest difficulty that I ordered the goods, paid for them and came home. At these times my brain feels paralyzed. . . . I have the impulse to act, but it seems as if something shuts down and prohibits action. (Reid, 1910, p. 619)

Several of the excerpts I have given earlier in this chapter have mentioned the weariness of depression. The patient just cited said that the lack of energy was the first and most obvious indication of the onset of her depression; in other words, the physical lassitude preceded the feelings of despair and hopelessness. In other instances, patients who have had repeated periods of melancholia usually report a slowly mounting lethargy as each of their attacks started.

SELF-REPROACH

As all of the excerpts indicate, the melancholic person is dominated by fear, sorrow, and hopelessness, to which are added the experience of mental confusion and a felt deficiency of available energy, the entire complex constituting an ill-defined feeling of sinfulness and sloth. This state is further aggravated by a confusion of intellectual processes, which the patient vaguely recognizes as an inability to think, to remember, and to make decisions. Many of these patients will gradually cease complaining of their unbearable sorrow or depression and seldom utter spontaneous complaints of any sort. When questioned, they speak slowly, and with many sighs, of having sinned, of being eternally damned, and of their inability to concentrate and remember.

James cited the following portion from *The Life and Journal of the Rev. Henry Alline,* an eighteenth-century evangelist.

> Everything I saw seemed to be a burden to me; the earth seemed accursed for my sake: all trees, plants, rocks, hills, and vales seemed to be dressed in mourning and groaning, under the weight of the curse, and everything around me seemed to be conspiring my ruin. My sins seemed to be laid open; so that I thought that every one I saw knew them, and sometimes I was

almost ready to acknowledge many things, which I thought they knew: yea sometimes it seemed to me as if every one was pointing me out as the most guilty wretch upon earth. I had now so great a sense of the vanity and emptiness of all things here below, that I knew the whole world could not possibly make me happy, no, nor the whole system of creation. When I waked in the morning, the first thought would be, Oh, my wretched soul, what shall I do, where shall I go? And when I laid down, would say, I shall be perhaps in hell before morning. (James, 1902, p. 159)

In a sense, this inner conviction of sin and unworthiness is a strange mixture of feelings of self-reproach and self-importance. How could any one mortal being cause the earth to be so accursed? The guilt-laden sinner can conceive of no adequate and sufficient punishment for his nameless crimes. One of Davidson's observations from his *Remembrances* casts a special light on this point.

Few people know what a punishment a short period of real madness is, or even a period of deep depression. We must each one of us, at his or her appointed hour, stand alone, not in the middle of a crowd, before the judgment-seat of Christ; and He requires truth in the inward parts. No saint could wish for greater joy; no sinner could fear a more dread apocalypse. Even the most blood thirsty conqueror and dissolute pagan would hesitate, if he knew that his latter end meant an ever-lasting headache; and it is worse, far worse, than that. (Davidson, 1912, p. 276)

The torturing punishment of self-reproach is, as many patients have testified, so great that all regard for the welfare of any other person is of little or no importance, as one's own soul must come to its own final judgment.

INSOMNIA AND DISTURBED SLEEP

The feelings of guilt and the state of agitation are in part strengthened by the difficulty in sleeping that the depressed patient often has. Many melancholics suffer from insomnia, or when they do sleep their sleep is broken by bad dreams and nightmares, so that they awaken in the early morning hours filled with self-torturing thoughts from which they find little relief, either by daybreak or the activities of the day. Benson in his account, *Thy Rod and Thy Staff*, wrote of this aspect of his depression in the following way.

The symptoms of a persistent sleeplessness, a perpetual dejection, amounting at times to an intolerable mental anguish . . . I used to wake, morning by morning, in my pleasant room, and hear the drowsy twittering of birds in the great plane-tree . . . and wonder half-bewildered where I was; till the old horror rushed back into the mind. (Benson, 1912, pp. 1; 3)

Sleeplessness and disturbed sleep constitute prominent complaints in melancholia, particularly acute during the early phases of melancholic episodes. Unfortunately the sleep disturbances usually remain and continue in some degree throughout most of the illness.

SUICIDAL THOUGHTS AND ACTIONS

Many depressed patients become quickly convinced that suicide is the ultimate answer to their hopeless condition. They see no reason for the prolongation of their present state of misery nor can they find any reassurance in the conventional belief that life beyond the grave can be better. The "logic" of this feature was brought out by Custance in the following statement.

First of all, I had by now become quite convinced that I was finished for good and all. There was no possible chance of my coming out of the Hospital alive. In fact though not actually dead I was as good as dead. For some inscrutable reason, perhaps because I had committed "the unforgivable sin" or just because I was such an appalling sinner, the worst man who had ever existed, I had been chosen to go alive through the portals of Hell, in an ordinary English lunatic-asylum. Therefore it was obviously too late for repentance. . . . All this I kept to myself, of course; I did not argue with [the Anglican parson] about it. Nor did I tell the doctors. . . . My wife, who visited me nobly at least twice a week for the whole eleven months of my confinement, never could understand the logic of this attitude. She was the only person to whom I dared confide my horrors, and I tried hard to show my train of reasoning. Roughly it was that I was a sort of opposite of Jesus Christ. Satan's job had been to catch a man, get him to sell his soul to him completely and utterly, like Faust, and then take him down alive into the pit. That was a sort of necessary counterweight to the resurrection of Jesus and the elect. I was the man. But if I could only kill myself, it might blow up the whole Universe, but at least I would get out of eternal torture and achieve the oblivion and nothingness for which my soul craved. I did in fact make three attempts at suicide, the most serious of which was when I tore myself from my attendant and threw myself in front of a car. (Custance, 1952, pp. 66–67)

Because of the persistent feelings of hopelessness and futility, most depressed patients seriously consider suicide and a proportion of the group actually do commit suicide. Indeed, in the past, most psychiatrists regarded every depressed patient as a potential suicidal risk. The risk has always been greater during the days or weeks of recovery; at that time there is a decrease in lassitude with periodic recurrences of acute melancholia.

DISCUSSION

Melancholia is the oldest concept still in common use for describing a special and definite variety of pathological mental phenomena. Its psychological nature and physical presence are well known and easily recognized. The onset of melancholia or depression may be sudden or gradual as far as the experiencer is concerned. This shadow falls upon the sufferer and clouds his mind like a heavy fog. The fog cannot be voluntarily resisted or diverted.

We have seen that there are at least four major groups among which melancholic patients may be differentiated; the mystic, the passive, the agitated, and the fragmented. This division is based in part on the surrounding circumstances, but is principally derived from the course and outcome of the illness. As far as the actual core of the inner experience is concerned, there are probably little or no important differences among these groups.

As Burton pointed out more than three hundred years ago, the terms that have been used to characterize the melancholic experience are practically infinite. In the autobiographical material I assembled it seems that the more frequent complaints involve feelings of fear, sorrow, and hopelessness, together with feelings of rejection and repulsion, lassitude and weariness, unworthiness and guilt.

This material was not organized around such experiences as sadness, hopelessness, feelings of unreality, retardation, and inadequacy, as they are blended in varying proportions. I did not avail myself of such an organization mainly because of the indefinite way in which such terms have been used. For example, in everyday usage, *sadness* has a wide variety of meanings. It may connote heaviness, lethargy, mournfulness, or simply a lack of ability to respond. Likewise, the word *hope* implies that at some time in the future one's present desires have a chance of being fulfilled. *Hopelessness* implies that there is no belief or faith that the future will bring the fulfillment of one's desires. To a large extent, the hopes of mankind center around the continuation of childish wishes, such as, "When I grow up, I'll be . . ." Some of these hopes have been achieved, others forgotten; still others have been quieted by religious faith—"There will be a better world hereafter." The depressed patient finds that he has lost his faith in both earthly and heavenly reward and says, "I am a failure," "I'm eternally lost," "There is no hope."

Hopelessness carries with it a feeling of unreality. As the excerpts in this chapter indicate, the depressed patient complains that food has lost its taste, the world is clothed in mourning, his body feels lifeless and wooden, and so forth. Intellectually, the melancholic person may know very well that his environment has not changed. But his emotional relation to the world has become different so that he feels unreal. He can no longer maintain an interest in life or in the world around him. How can he respond adequately when he feels there is no zest left inside him, and that he is sodden with lethargy and overwhelmed by the conviction of his own unworthiness? The feelings of sadness, hopelessness, unreality, and unworthiness together result in a loss of faith, the faith that St. Paul defined as, "The substance of things hoped for, the evidence of things not seen."

I will return for a moment to the consideration of the more discriminable elements that are blended in the experience of melancholia. Various writers have pointed out that the process of depression closely resembles what is called "an attack of conscience" in normal everyday experience. During such an attack of conscience, there is a conviction of having sinned, a feeling of lethargy and a fear of the hitherto not appreciated consequences of some past act or thought. One suddenly becomes poignantly aware of the possible consequences of the action, idea, belief or whatever; in a word, some of one's personal ethical or moral lapses become vividly present in the consciousness and expiation seems highly desirable. Ordinarily, if the person has already recognized his responsibility, he tries to modify his thoughts and behavior, so as to expiate the sin or offense. The depressed patient has no conscious knowledge of a moral lapse, of any real sin that might have been of sufficient magnitude to justify the intensity of the depressive guilt feelings. Hence the patient is, in a sense, justified in complaining of having committed "the unpardonable sin," by which he means the unknown sin. An unconscious and unknown sin can neither be condoned nor expiated. Essentially, the patient is saying, "I don't know what I did, but it certainly must have been immense and unforgivable; unknowingly, I must have sold my soul to the Devil; anything I try to do can only make it worse; I am afraid and horror-stricken; I may be going mad." This is, to put it simply, the essence of the thought process that the depressed patient follows when trying to explain to himself his innermost feelings of guilt and melancholia. At this point, one is reminded of Peters' observation I quoted in Chapter 11, on fear: that there is a real difference between the fear of some outside object and the fear which has no real object.

The experience of melancholia has, in the minds of many, come to be thought of as an essential part of religion. Hence, the argument has developed that depression expresses either a visitation or a withdrawal of divinity, or is a signal of divine concern, either of approbation or of retribution. Many thinkers believe melancholic persons are not really insane, and that they are in need of moral and ethical guidance rather than medical care.

This point was considered by James in *The Varieties of Religious Experience*. Since James himself suffered one or more periods of depression, his remarks, although he did not directly refer to himself, become more significant.

The normal process of life contains moments as bad as any of those which insane melancholy is filled with, moments in which radical evil gets its innings and takes its solid turn. The lunatic's visions of horror are all drawn from the material of daily fact. Our civilization is founded on the shambles, and every individual existence goes out in a lonely spasm of helpless agony. If you protest, my friend, wait till you arrive there yourself! . . . It may indeed be that no religious reconciliation with the absolute totality of things is possible. . . . But provisionally . . . since the evil facts are as genuine parts of nature as the good ones, the philosophic presumption should be that they have some rational significance, and that systematic healthy-mindedness, failing as it does to accord to sorrow, pain, and death, any positive and active attention whatever, is formally less complete than systems that try at least to include these elements in their scope. (James, 1902, pp. 163–165)

In other words, whether melancholia is pathological or not, the experience exists and in no sense is it philosophically irrational. The healthy-minded man must make a place in his rational philosophy and religion for sorrow, pain, and death.

There remain several other considerations that must be borne in mind when considering the psychology of melancholia. For example, there is the undoubted fact that many patients have oscillated between states of melancholic depression and mania. In the following chapter I will present some descriptions written by persons who have lived through manic episodes. To anticipate this material I may say that, psychologically speaking, melancholia and mania are not exactly the opposite sides of the same coin; that understanding something of the psychology of depression does not necessarily enable one to predict the psychology of mania, despite the connection between the two processes.

Another puzzling point arises from the behavior of agitated melancholic patients. That the depressed person should feel inadequate, both physically and mentally, seems to come in a natural sequence from the inner tension and other handicaps which accompany the feelings of sadness and hopelessness. But, if this be true, why do the same intense sadness and hopelessness underlie the overwhelming compulsive agitation and endless activity of some persons, which is in utter contrast to the mute suffering of the passive patient?

CHAPTER 13

Mania

INTRODUCTION

The word *mania* comes from the ancient Greek, meaning *madness*. Mania is used today to describe the psychopathological state marked by a combination of overactivity, excitement, elation, distractibility, loss of inhibitions, flight-of-ideas, imperception, and irritability. Experientially, the manic state consists of a kaleidoscopic period that is later only partially recalled. The experience of mania partakes of the symptoms of practically every other psychopathological experience, but includes much of the odd affective quality of elation. Elation does not mark the experience of *every* manic patient, nor does every person who experiences elation necessarily belong in the manic category. But it is significant that practically the only state that is ever characterized by mental patients as being somewhat pleasant is that of elated mania. The elation is usually of short duration; it may be mixed with irritation; it is seldom said by a patient to be completely desirable; but its unique and exciting quality has been remarked on by all who have experienced it.

In contrast to most other aberrant experiences, mania may be likened to living in a whirlwind. Usually the person suffering from one or another variety of insanity describes his experience as though it proceeded "in slow motion, in a dark dangerous swamp." The protracted suffering, the immobility of terror, the feeling of unreality, and the unending grief are common symptoms of most psychopathological conditions. In mania, associations change rapidly, no experience lasts very long. Images are hurried and the connection of one idea to the next is often unclear or not apparent. The manic individual is overwhelmed by his feelings, both inwardly and outwardly, as if carried away by a hurricane. Graves, who suffered from several manic episodes and later tried to describe the elusive nature of mania, remarked as follows.

Why the emotional change in mania from extreme to extreme is so fast is more than I know; it just seems insanity. (Graves, 1942, p. 670)

Attacks of mania do occur as episodic phenomena uncomplicated by other forms of psychopathology, but more commonly mania and depression follow each other or are interspersed between periods of sanity. In melancholia, thoughts of death, feelings of hopelessness and devastating fear are practically constant, whereas in mania, fear is seldom mentioned, inner security is usually present, and the temporary, but pressing, feeling of having almost achieved Paradise is commonplace. While in a manic state, the patient has very little or no insight into his own condition. He feels healthier and more capable than ever before.

During a period of maniacal excitement, hallucinatory experiences are not common, and such hallucinations as do occur are usually disorganized and unsystematized. Anger and irritation are transient. Manic patients seldom hold grudges or build up paranoid ideas. However, religious ideas and delusions are quite common. The press-of-activity and the distractability remain as disrupting qualities throughout most of a manic episode, although the degree of disturbance and excitement may vary from mild hypomania to an acute frenzy.

Because events, both inner and outer, do seem to the patient to move so rapidly and disconnectedly during a manic episode, it is difficult for him to remember and to analyze his experiences. From the available autobiographical accounts, I have selected the more common and oft-repeated elements with the caution that this selective process presents only the commoner fragments of the total experience of mania.

The Nature of Manic Experience

In previous chapters I have quoted from Custance's account of his experiences during both melancholic and manic episodes. His summary of the main features of his manic episodes is the most systematic presentation of its sort I have found.

I have endeavoured to describe . . . the main characteristic features of the manic state. They are . . . (1) Intense sense of well-being, (2) heightened sense of reality, (3) breach in the barriers of individuality, (4) inhibition of the sense of reality, (5) release of sexual and moral tension, (6) delusions of grandeur and power, (7) sense of ineffable revelation. In addition to these, a number of other symptoms and sensations are not without significance. (Custance, 1952, p. 55)

Although this is a first-hand formulation, Custance has emphasized several symptoms that are not very frequently mentioned by other patients, as well as glossing over several symptoms that other patients have emphasized. I have reorganized Custance's recapitulation of the main features in mania and will present the material under the following headings: (1) well-being and elation, (2) heightened reality, (3) delusions of power, (4) revelation, (5) overwhelming emotion, (6) breached individuality, (7) loss of inhibitions, and (8) excitement, confusion, amnesia, and dementia.

Well-being and Elation

Usually the manic patient states that he feels fine, healthy, wonderful, better than he ever felt, and so on. This well-being may become tedious and wearying to the patient after a time, particularly if he gains some self-realization of the fact that he is in an asylum and some appreciation of the silliness of his own behavior. Graves' description of this feeling of well-being (associated with weariness) during an excited period reads as follows.

Now came phantasmagoria and complete wildness, in recounting of which I still find deathly weariness. I detected only one line which might have been a communication, to the effect that "You are being scientifically tested but there are some effects not understood." During the extended raving I caught myself inviting the doctors to "split a personality if they wanted to," walking from end to end of the confined space and calling out my own name and that of the nom de plume I was accustomed to scribble under. I lectured at length on the proper handling of the insane, remarking that a "new era is coming when only really insane will be confined, and each one of these will consider each attendant to be God, thus offering complete and willing cooperation." . . .

In fact, I was tossing mentally to and fro upon a sea of shifting delusion, occasionally controlling my physical action, but with a hectic imagination offering and getting partial acceptance and various explanations for my plight and conduct which are just too silly and too nebulous in memory to set down. (Graves, 1942, pp. 300; 302–303)

This passage is illustrative of the confused mental content of the maniacal state, which reached the level of disoriented delusion marked by a feeling of healthy elation. Whether Graves' "deathly weariness" mixed with "a hectic imagination" was present during the episode itself, or whether these critical ideas are but part of the later account, is difficult to determine.

A description of the feeling of well-being, which alternated with intervals of melancholia, may be drawn from a patient's account that was first published in 1796.

> I always waited with impatience . . . for the coming of the paroxysm of agitation which lasted ten to twelve days, more or less, because I could enjoy during its duration a sort of beatitude; everything seemed to me to be easy; no obstacle theoretically nor almost in reality could stop me; my memory acquired all of a sudden a singular perfection; I remembered long passages of Latin authors; I have difficulty ordinarily to find two rhymes, and I wrote at this time in verse as fast as in prose; I was sly, even shrewd, prolific in devices of every kind. The complacency of those who, in order not to push me to the breaking point, let me give free rein to my fantasies reinforced in my mind the conviction of my superior capacities, and sustained my boldness; my insensitivity to cold, to warmth, to the little inconveniences of life justified it also; finally a deep and concentrated egoism made me think of everything in terms of myself. (Anon., 1849b, pp. 386–387)

This patient said that during his periods of depression, interrupted by the beatific intervals he described, he felt timid, ashamed, cowardly, and full of self-reproach. The states shifted from one to the other overnight, each state lasting from ten to twelve days.

Dr. Anderson reported the case of a young woman, aged 23, who had become overactive and elated to the extent that it became necessary for her to seek hospital admission. She was, as most manic patients are, rather a nuisance in the hospital until she finally experienced a state of religious ecstasy, upon which she characterized her feelings as follows.

> I just didn't mind anything; nothing mattered which anybody did to me, it didn't disturb me. I just felt at the time it was a right state to be in and that everybody ought to be in that state. I thought I was even going to become weller than even people who thought there was nothing the matter with them any way. . . . The thing is that when I'm feeling miserable I think to myself, "Is the whole thing a dream?" I can't come to a true realization of my troubles. I'm absolutely certain it's wrong when people say it's too good to be true, for the happier I am the more I'm conscious it's real. . . . You absolutely have to be living in the present to get that feeling. . . . You just have a feeling you're part of the earth, not a person on your own, sort of melt into it. (Anderson, 1938, p. 82)

This patient not only mentioned certain aspects of well-being and elation, but also commented on her concept of reality and on the break in the barriers of personal individuality. After the period of quiet ecstasy, she recovered her sanity rather rapidly and was soon able to leave the hospital.

Custance described and emphasized the way in which his feelings of well-being were related to particular physical sensations.

Often the physical sensations make themselves felt well in advance of the corresponding thoughts, and sometimes even without the thoughts becoming conscious at all. Thus at the onset of phases of manic excitement I have sometimes noticed the typical symptoms, the pleasurable tingling of the spinal cord and warm sense of well-being in the solar plexus, long before any reaction in the mental sphere occurred. . . .

First and foremost comes a general sense of intense well-being. I know of course that the sense is illusory and transient, and that my behaviour while it persists is so abnormal that I will have to be confined. . . . The pleasurable and sometimes ecstatic feeling tone, remains as a sort of permanent background of all experience during the manic period. . . .

The intense sense of well-being, which is physical as well as mental, is not wholly illusory. My digestive system functions particularly well, without the slightest trace of constipation or diarrhoea, and I have an inordinate appetite. Metabolism is rapid. I can stand cold without difficulty or discomfort; an inner warmth seems to pervade me. I can, for example, walk about naked out of doors on quite cold nights—to throw off my clothes is incidentally a strong impulse and presumably symbolises the freedom from restraint which is a feature of the whole condition. (Custance, 1952, pp. 16; 30; 59)

From these descriptions and many other similar ones, there can be no doubt that the general feeling-tone during mania is, for the most part, pleasurable, characterized by euphoria and physical strength, coupled with an inner certainty of one's own exalted mental abilities.

These feelings of well-being and exaltation are accompanied by the patient's discovery that the sensory world about him is clearer, brighter, more colorful, and full of delightful odors and tastes. Remarks to this effect may be found in the citations already given. In many cases, pain loses its potency, even wounds, cuts or bruises are ignored and allowed to go unattended in the rush of elated activity. Hypersensitivity to sensory stimuli may be so vivid that they take on an illusory character. For example, Graves recorded the following experience.

I had been accustomed to find surcease in absorbing sun rays, and had discovered odd and meaningless symbols apt to form behind eyelids in its light. I glanced at the orb, stood a minute in its light, and was pleased and surprised to find a renewal of the spectacle in elaborate form. A series of golden yellow bars flashed before my eyes, much like the rounded end strips which a medic uses to hold down a tongue in throat inspection. One of these perched on the City Hall; another as I swung around, draped itself over the center of the Court House; a third dropped nearly to cap the Morning Herald Building. As I swung around to develop the display, one similar shape in green, and a fifth, in red, dropped over each other to form a kind of moon track over the Parkway, the blend making a deep purple. (Graves, 1942, p. 448)

Graves' visual experience occurred during an ordinary working day and its vividness greatly impressed him. Added to other mental peculiarities, the illusions led him to the realization that mania had overtaken him again, so that he decided to seek the refuge of a hospital.

Heightened Sense of Reality

In the ordinary course of existence we take our experience of reality for granted. So little special attention is ever given to it that if a person starts complaining that he has feelings of unreality or of heightened reality, the complaint itself is so unusual that we may conclude that it may be indicative of psychopathology; and if such complaints continue, we become increasingly certain that some essential pathology is involved.

The rapid and confusing changes in the stream of conscious thought of the manic patient lead to a peculiar experience of uncertainty with respect to reality. There is a continuous shifting of ideas and an intrusion of new experiences and sensations mixed with the usual association of everyday life, so that recognition and familiarity no longer play their usual role. Stated somewhat differently, the lack of recognition and the break in the accustomed meaningful connections between ideas, together with the seeming rapidity of ideational changes, make it impossible for the patient to sustain or recall the ordinarily organized associations in thinking that underlie his "sane" feelings of reality. Of course, many of the experienced ideas are subjectively recognized as fantastic and unreal, but the speed of the process provides the patient with no opportunity to evaluate the phenomena properly.

Custance described how his manic attacks began and how this experience was accompanied by a loss or disturbance of his feelings of reality.

One begins to slip; the world about one changes imperceptibly. For a time it is possible to keep some sort of grip on reality. But once one is really over the edge, once the grip of reality is lost, the forces of the Unconscious take charge, and then begins what appears to be an unending voyage into the universe of bliss or the universe of horror as the case may be, a voyage over which one has oneself no control whatever. . . . First . . . comes the general sense of well-being . . . which . . . remains as a sort of permanent background. . . . Closely allied is . . . the second main feature . . . well described . . . as a "heightened sense of reality," . . . [which] consists of a considerable number of related sensations, the net result of which is that the outer world makes a much more vivid and intense impression on me than usual. . . . The first thing I note is the peculiar appearances of the lights—the ordinary electric lights in the ward. They are not exactly brighter, but deeper, more intense, perhaps a trifle more ruddy than usual. Moreover, if I relax the focusing of my eyes, which I can do very much more easily than in normal circumstances, a bright starlike phenomenon emanates from the lights, ultimately forming a maze of iridescent patterns of all colours of the rainbow, which remind me vaguely of the Aurora Borealis. (Custance, 1952, p. 29–31)

According to Custance, the heightened sense of reality is not a feeling of unreality, but rather a quality of vividness that is somehow added to all the ordinary primary sensory experiences. Sensations are not only more intense and vivid, but also have the extra quality of being more pleasurable.

MacCurdy supplies us with an account of this state by a well-educated patient.

On the whole, I feel that when I am exhilarated, my mind occupies itself, for the most part, with its own affairs. And its inspiration and motives for action are self-creative and come from within. It is, as a rule, too busy, and in too much of a hurry, to stop and make minute, rational, and detailed account in passing of external objects. Its tendency is towards flightiness. . . . Though, of course, if observation be for the moment, its special occupation, as when acting as a coast pilot . . . it might be capable of observing and regarding with abnormal minuteness and accuracy.

. . . The point seems to be, so far as I grasp it, that during an exhilaration the mind penetrates infinitely more deeply into all things, and receives flashes of almost divine light and wisdom, which open to it, momentarily, regions of thought hitherto difficult or impossible of penetration. But, except in the milder form of the exhilaration, the mind's own restlessness, and impatient activity, interfere, for the time being at least, with the just application and the rational and appropriate, not to say the sane, use of what it has thus acquired. . . . Naturally the more exhilarated I become the more difficult it is for me to reason to myself and to admit the insanity of my projects and hence to be willing to renounce or break away from them. (MacCurdy, 1925, p. 301)

This description, which mentions well-being and exhilaration, lack of inner inhibitions, overactivity, flightiness, and the like, attributes to the heightened sense of reality, the deeper penetration of the mind, which then results in the experience of divine light and wisdom. The ordinary checks and balances of perceptual processes are weakened or missing, a fact that allows the sensory experience, not being subject to inhibitions, to have an extraordinarily vivid quality, sometimes leading to the occurrence of an ineffable quality of religious experience.

In the final chapters of his lengthy book, *The Eclipse of a Mind*, Graves attempted to summarize the psychological features of his frequent manic and depressive experiences and their interrelationships.

The hallucination incidents [in the last two hospitalizations] were sufficiently depersonalized so that the personality surveying them always retained a question as to the reality. That is to say, the hallucinations I have experienced did not necessarily appear to have relation to me. . . .

The conscious mind, except for brief periods, was presiding over the personality, though it had lost contact with reality, possibly more definitely than in previous attacks. . . .

In depression all emotions are more or less tepid, and the outlook on reality is clear and as accurate as it normally is, whereas in mania the emotions are all strong, though erratic, and the concept of reality is disturbed in greater or lesser degree. It is nonsense to set down emotions as clear and definite in any case; my experience is that they are always mixed. (Graves, 1942, pp. 668; 669; 677)

From Graves' viewpoint the disturbance in reality feelings during his manic attacks was of different origin from the unreality feelings that are common in schizophrenia or in depression. In another connection, he compared the manic state to the exhilaration of alcoholic intoxication, speculating as to whether mania might likewise be a toxic state.

Delusions of Power and Grandeur

The delusions which occur during mania differ qualitatively from the delusional experiences which mark many other varieties of psycho-pathological experiences, in that manic delusions are not persecutory or hateful, but expansive and grandiose. As a usual thing, the manic patient reports that he frequently realizes that the delusions were imaginary or that they were dreamlike in nature. Custance made this point in the following way.

A main . . . feature . . . consists in the delusions of grandeur and power which are perhaps the most typical feature of manic-depressive insanity. They are closely connected with the first feature, the "elation" or sense of well-being which is a background to the whole state. . . .

I feel so close to God, so inspired by His Spirit that in a sense I am God. I see the future, plan the Universe, save mankind; I am utterly and completely immortal; I am even male and female. The whole Universe, animate and in-animate, past, present, and future, is within me. All nature and life, all spirits, are co-operating and connected with me; all things are possible. I am in a sense identical with all spirits from God to Satan. I reconcile Good and Evil and create light, darkness, worlds, universes.

Of course it is all a dream, a vision, pure imagination if there is such a thing. I know perfectly well that in fact I have no power. . . . I can truthfully say that never in the midst of the wildest flights of grandiose ideas have I ever allowed myself to forget that. (Custance, 1952, pp. 50–52)

If one recalls for a moment the descriptions of delusional experience I have cited in previous chapters, where the delusions almost always in-cluded ideas of evil, of unwarranted attacks on one's life and security, or of attack by the sufferer on men or spirits who were oppressing him, then by contrast it appears that maniacal delusions are essentially "playful" daydreams which carry but little conviction in the minds of the patients.

Even the more grandiose maniacal delusions of power and knowledge possess little or no conviction of their essential truth. For example, in his book, *A Mind That Found Itself*, Beers wrote the following.

After all, delusions of grandeur are the most entertaining of toys. The assortment which my imagination provided was a comprehensive one. I had tossed aside the blocks of childhood days. Instead of laboriously piling small squares of wood one upon another, in an endeavor to build the tiny semblance of a house, I now, in this second childhood of mine, projected against thin air phantom edifices, planned and completed in the twinkling of an eye. To be sure such houses of cards almost immediately superseded each other, but the vanishing of one could not disturb a mind which had ever another interesting bauble to take its place. And therein lies part of the secret of the happiness peculiar to that stage of elation which is distinguished by delusions of grandeur,—always provided the afflicted one be not subjected to privation and abuse. (Beers, 1908, p. 193)

There is a distinct difference between the experience of delusion in mania and the more common forms of schizoid delusions. Manic delusions are saturated with uninhibited euphoria; they are unlimited rosy dreams of personal power. The well-being of the patient overflows into ideas of grandeur, ideas that are never considered by the patient to be exactly real or completely convincing, but rather, as forming part of a "playful" mood susceptible of modification or correction. Most schizoid delusions involve fear or anger coupled with a compelling necessity for self-defense. Mania has at its core very little fear and hence the expressions of delusion are basically different from those that involve fear.

Revelation and Beatitude

Manic patients tend to lose contact with the real environment around them. I have cited the description given by Custance (1952) that began, "One begins to slip; the world about me changes . . ." The manic elation and heightened sense of reality lead quickly to delusional thoughts of power and grandeur, which may, in turn, sometimes give rise to ideas of Divine revelation and beatitude.

The way in which these ideas may develop, particularly at the onset of a manic episode, was rather strikingly described by Dahl in the form of a soliloquy in his autobiography, *Breakdown*.

Well, now! You will become whole by becoming holy. You will become a saint! And in your sanctity, most certainly, you will be a marvel of fine health in ways emotional and mental! . . . In your knocking at the door, you have opened the door! A man who is very good is a man near to sanctity. Perhaps, you are nearly a saint right now! Perhaps you ARE a saint right now! In the making!

. . . And, oh, now, how good you are beginning to feel and oh, now, how good you do feel because you are good. Oh, what a happiness it is to be good! And, oh, how happy you are becoming!

And now it is that as your goodness grows and your happiness increases, your eyes are unblinded more and more and your ears are undeafened more and more. As all resentments leave you. all hate, all angers and all contempts, how you grow to love yourself and your fellows and how now as this happens it also happens that you have eyes that see and ears that hear and more, so many things more, do these eyes see and hear, as in a revelation, than do the eyes and ears of your poor fellows

How doth wisdom pour now into your soul, your psyche, your soul-psyche, your psyche-soul, your wholeness, your holiness. You see God in all around you and you can feel His Goodness outside you and in and now you speak. Or is it you speaking? Could it not be God speaking in you? . . . For men to hear! That they, too, may know the joy you know. (Dahl, 1959, pp. 153–154)

The rather grandiose line of thought, the inversion of phrases, the rhyming expressions and the fashion in which ideas build up to beatific sanctity are all clearly expressed in this citation. Dahl's thoughts ran along like an uninhibited daydream, his elation carrying him to the point of belief in the achievement of religious revelation.

Another citation, this time from Custance, illustrates how the elation and beatific feeling influence the manic's stream of thought and his perception of the world.

I can testify from experience that these are the actual sensations accompanying the delusions of power so common in asylums. The sense of being intimately in tune with the ultimate stuff of the universe can become so overwhelming that those affected naturally proclaim themselves to be Jesus Christ, or Almighty God, or whatever deity they have been taught to look on as the source of all power. In my own case I was fully convinced of my supernatural powers, and attempted to test them in various ways, mainly by somewhat childish experiments in sympathetic magic . . .

In that peace I felt utterly and completely forgiven, relieved from all burden of sin. The whole of infinity seemed to open up before me, and during the weeks and months which followed I passed through experiences which are virtually indescribable. The complete transformation of "reality" transported me as it were into the Kingdom of Heaven. The ordinary beauties of nature, particularly, I remember, the skies at sunrise and sunset, took on a transcendental loveliness beyond belief. Every morning, quite contrary to my usual sluggish habits, I jumped up to look at them, and when possible went out to drink in, in a sort of ecstasy, the freshness of the morning air. . . .

A sense of ineffable revelation persists in varying degrees throughout the state and seems to be intimately linked with the delusions of power. It seems to me as though all truth, all the secrets of the Universe were being revealed, as though I had some clue, some Open-Sesame to creation. (Custance, 1952, pp. 20; 46; 52)

Custance's description of mania closely resembles some accounts of mystical experience written by devout followers of religious practices. It is necessary to look at the entire history of a manic episode in order to come to a decision as to its frame of reference.

We may add one more description of beatific feelings as they were related by a case of Dr. Anderson's.

I just felt very peaceful and happy, very contented; and I felt that every little thing I did, things that were ordinarily irksome, were a joy to do; and because I loved God I felt He was in me and I felt I wanted to go out and tell the world about it. I didn't actually see a Cross, but I was always conscious of the Cross and from it came the most amazing love and power. . . . everything seemed to speak of God. The Presence was real. (Anderson, 1938, p. 83)

Beatific experiences during a manic episode are not common nor do they last for any considerable period of time. They seem to consist of the experience of being overwhelmed by an inner elation which is so powerful that it conceals any self-recognition of the overactivity and feelings of frustration or irritation which are quite often a part of the manic experience.

Overwhelming Emotion

Together with the feelings of elated euphoria, heightened sense of reality, delusions of power, and occasional feelings of beatific revelation, there is also present the experience of no longer being able to direct or control the surging of emotional experience. This loss of control has been described in various ways. Graves spoke of it as the *naked emotions* that completely overwhelmed his intellect, and discussed them as follows.

The conscious mind—with me—crumbles in every direction—and the stream of naked emotions continues to induce speech and activity which range just off the imbecile level. "Naked emotions" is a rather happy term I hit upon to cover a portion of the manic ebullition. It describes and diagnoses succinctly. In normal conduct emotions are covered over, disguised, and sometimes redirected by the operation of the rational mind. In mania they are uncovered, defectively related to other elements of existence, and expressed in action and speech without either disguise or order. (Graves, 1942, p. 305)

It is precisely this overactive display of emotional expression that impresses the outside observer. The observer sees a man whom he knows as a previously restrained, orderly member of the community and who

is now behaving and speaking in a disorganized, uninhibited fashion—
in fact, exhibiting an overflow of naked emotions. This lack of control
experienced by the patient is one which he neither can, nor does he really
desire, to alter. The entire experience seems to the patient, at the time, to
be very pleasant.

The activity which Graves spoke of as naked emotions leads onto
behavior and thought processes which are difficult to describe in a succinct fashion. The following citation has been pieced together from
fragments of Dahl's account of the onset of his attack of mania and his
consequent committal to a state hospital.

> Inside me a dam had broken indeed. Now I talked as I wrote, with a
> swift fluency. . . . [He visited his former physician, and said to him], "I'd
> hoped . . . to make you human, in my book. . . . I had this thought that you
> might be a ghoul—your life and health sustained through your feedings upon
> the sick souls of patients such as I. You are so cold. And yet so interested in
> me. . . . Tell me you are human and not a ghoul?"
>
> [He conceived the notion that he possessed divine inspiration, through
> which he could reorganize the world. When he explained this idea to his wife
> and friends, he found them skeptical. The following phrases express his emo-
> tions at that time.] "I was in a fury with her" . . . "You have betrayed me!" . . .
> From now on I was going to speak the absolute truth to everybody. . . . but
> have you ever tried telling people just exactly what you think of *them?* . . .
> "My friends, they say they love me so much but that they would destroy me.
> They kill me. They slay me. They give me a pain in the neck" . . .
>
> The attendant looked at me and smiled. "Why did you say your name
> was Bob Hope? Because I really am. I'm a clown. I have to be. Or else I'd cry
> myself to death." . . . I was aware of these great changes in me. . . . Now it
> was demonstrated in . . . a leaping out, a looming over. Now I run to attack.
> . . . With great relief I realized that the unknown horrors I had imagined now
> had become real, and since they were real, I could fight them . . . I was ag-
> gressive, wrestling with a strong combination of desperation and confidence
> . . . (Dahl, 1959, pp. 158; 169; 173–174; 175; 192; 195; 199; 200)

Dahl's account provides some idea of the emotional turmoil through
which he passed at the onset of his psychosis. There was nothing mild in
his experience. He scorned, he attacked, he fought, he insulted in an uninhibited way. He was quite certain of the clarity of his mind. He realized
in a vague way that his ideas and behavior were inappropriate, but felt
under no particular obligation to restrain himself. Others might be certain that he was insane; but his inner revelations were more important
to him than any external consideration. Dahl's account does illustrate
this typical feature of manic pathology: that of being overwhelmed by
emotional processes, which block or conceal all intellectual understanding and volitional control. (Note, however, that certain memories of the
episode were no longer available to him.)

Breached Individuality

Another aspect of manic experience that many patients relate is described by Custance in the following fashion.

It is difficult to know just how to designate it, though it is closely allied with the [sense of well-being] . . . Perhaps it can best be described as a "breach in the barriers of individuality." . . . The shell which surrounds the ego and so often gets harder with the years is pierced. The experience partakes of the nature of the good-fellowship produced by alcohol; it also constitutes in some degree a regression to a childish faith and confidence in the benevolence, the "akinness" of the surrounding world. . . .

This seems to be quite common among manic-depressive patients; only the other day one said to me that he could converse with "any old spirit." I hold imaginary conversations—which appear absolutely real to me—with all my favourite historical characters, notably anima-figures (in Jung's sense) like Cleopatra and Mary Magdalene. These figures actually appear to me in visions, and so do my own ancestors, in whom I take far more interest when in the manic-state than at any other time. (Custance, 1952, pp. 36–37; 38)

In a way, this merging of individual consciousness—a melting of personal individuality—into a universal consciousness is akin to the feeling of ineffable revelation. For example, one of Dr. Anderson's cases reported the breaching of individuality in these terms.

I seem to merge into everything. [There was] an intense consciousness of power and absolute ecstasy. I am awake all night if I happen to have it, sometimes it wakes me up. It comes in a sort of flood . . . over the body. A terrific consciousness of power in surges, like the sea coming against you. . . . I feel calm as well. Things appear more real, as if you were just becoming alive and had never lived before. The whole being expands. If you are alone and you yield to it the more it grows over you, and you feel you can't keep on the ground. Everything is much more intense; I notice everything I haven't seen before, lights and sounds. . . . You want to give yourself up to it because it seems as if something finally happened you would lose yourself, but it seems as if will seems to get in the way. . . . Everything is absolutely new, every minute is as if everything has just started. . . . I seem above time and yet it was intensified in some way. I could see time for what it was. It seemed like something which served a purpose, which was used to divide, to limit something, but not real. (Anderson, 1938, p. 85)

The breakdown of one's feeling of individuality is sometimes associated with the intense elation and beatific revelation, but this association is not always true. The breached individuality is sometimes reported as being part of the confused excitement and press-of-activity. The experience of depersonalization, which I will consider in Chapter 17, differs from breached individuality in that depersonalization is a *loss* of one's individuality, while breached individuality is an *expansion* of one's feelings of self so that there seems to be a fusion of several minds.

The relation of this confused, excited, agitated experience to the patient's prior everyday life constitutes an additional puzzle for him. Like the features of mania that have already been discussed, the flood of emotions and the feeling of elation swamps the critical basis for judgment by which one ordinarily distinguishes self from nonself. In the mystical sense, one loses oneself and merges into the greater self of all mankind. Perhaps this feeling of having been merged with the greater soul of all existence is in part due to the disappearance of fear and to its replacement by a feeling of complete inner security. If true, one might think of breached individuality as the complete fulfillment of hope, in contrast to the complete loss of hope that marks depression.

Loss of Inhibitions

It should be apparent to the reader that the various phenomena of manic experience discussed thus far are qualitatively different from the phenomena which enter into almost all other forms of psychopathological experience. There are only two abnormal states in which patients ever relate an experience that is in any way pleasant or desirable. These are, first, the grandiose state of general paresis (of which we have found no published autobiographical account) and second, the elated phase of mania. Unfortunately, both of these grandiose and elated states carry with them behaviors which are so truly antisocial that the experiencer must be segregated to protect not only society but also the patient from himself. Exaggerated elation as well as other manifestations of mania cannot exist within the usual rules and regulations—cultural inhibitions —upon which all social life depends.

The loss of conventional inhibitions on the part of the manic patient is an easily recognized phenomenon. Manic patients speak freely and extensively on any unconventional topic; they exhibit themselves, both mentally and physically, without shame, and they are not repelled by situations that are ordinarily repugnant. From the standpoint of such a patient, Custance commented as follows.

The inhibition of the sense of repulsion extends to all objects which would normally provoke repulsion, and constitutes [a] . . . peculiar and distinctive feature of the manic state. . . . In the manic phase repulsion gives place to attraction. I have no repulsion to excreta, urine and so on. I have no distaste for dirt. I do not care in the least whether I am washed or not, whereas I am terrified of the slightest speck of dirt and continually wash my hands like Lady Macbeth when in a state of depression. At the same time I feel a mystic sense of unity with all fellow-creatures and the Universe as a whole; I am at peace with myself; and I have no sense of guilt whatsoever. . . .

[There is also] a release of moral tension, particularly in the sexual sphere. The normal inhibitions disappear. . . . This was very clearly illustrated by the course of my first really intense manic period, the first time my mind really slipped over the edge of the plateau of "reality" and penetrated into the infinite regions beyond. . . .

One of the most interesting features of this experience is the light it throws on the nature of the sexual urge in mania. This urge is almost entirely impersonal. The question of selecting an attractive girl, which normally plays a large part in sexual adventures, did not trouble me in the least. I was quite content to leave it to chance. Moreover it would be quite wrong to dismiss the whole episode as just a matter of unbridled "lust." Lust is something very different. (Custance, 1952, pp. 41; 42; 44; 49)

This loss of conventional inhibitions refers not only to moral standards, but also to such ethical matters as truth and falsehood. A patient of MacCurdy's made the following observation.

During the heat of the telling I may be said, in a limited degree, and momentarily, to believe my own stories. I am not, however, sufficiently carried away to prevent my taking account of stock soon afterwards, and to separate the truth from the falsehood and to experience a definite regret for the latter. I have sometimes asked myself by what stretch of the imagination and silencing of my own conscience I could possibly, for example, aver ownership to real estate which I had in reality merely viewed and talked of buying; or assert a complete mastery of branches of learning whose merest rudiments I was perfectly well aware only to have examined superficially. And I have, at such times, detected myself explaining it all to my conscience in some such way as the following: "That I could easily, should occasion require, or were it in any way to become necessary for me to back up my statements, buy the land in question, or study the subject under consideration until I had mastered it." Thus I try to soothe my conscience with the thought that I never assert things which are not, at least, within my power, and which I might not perfectly well have done, or indeed can do if necessary, or may even at the time perhaps fully intend to do. And in this way I excuse myself to myself, by imagining that I am in somewhat the same category as the merchant or broker, who undertakes to deliver, at some future time, articles which he has not yet bought, or makes prices on things which do not belong to him. For, we both undoubtedly think that we can produce the goods when called upon to do so. (MacCurdy, 1925, p. 302)

The manic or hypomanic loss of inhibition is, as the citations indicate, not due to ignorance; neither is it due to simply another phase of the elation. The loss seems to be evidence of a peculiar change in the person's personality. The manic patient seems free from the inner fear, dread, or anxiety that more or less pervades the mind of most human beings. The manic, being free from fear, has no inhibitions against following the many ideas that occur to his excited mind. He ventures into the exploration of ideas and behavior, which conventional restrictions make taboo in everyday life.

Excitement, Confusion, Amnesia, and Dementia

The very obvious restless overactivity and press-of-activity of a manic patient invariably impresses the observer. The patient himself finds that his mind is unusually clear and full of brilliant new ideas. He feels full of energy and has a compulsive need to talk about himself and his brilliant ideas. He must rush to create a brave new world. Each new idea seems to spring full-formed into his mind. He is usually irritated by not being able to complete the action demanded by one train of thought before several fresh ideas surge over him. To him everything seems crystal clear, and yet, at the same time, confused; confused because, no matter how much he hurries, not enough time is available to bring anything to the desired goal. After recovering from his fourth attack of mania, Graves wrote the following description of his excited and confused experiences.

The first three episodes disclosed a degree of physical agitation, and some outbreak of verbal expression, as to the exact nature and persistence of which my conscious memory is very far from clear. I recollect only by fits and starts, with complete gaps. Irresistibly, the state reminds me of that experienced during a serious alcoholic bout, and possibly compares with the experience of drug taking. The appearance of frenzied dementia, of "coming back" to myself, and recognizing a stream of language, of floor pacing, once of head-knocking against the wooden cover of a radiator, all constitute items . . . which led me to classify the manic outbursts as probably based on intoxication. The chief symptom, possibly, is that presented by a fellow in surprise and shock listening to himself emit sounds, perceiving himself engaged in actions, without memory of preceding events or conduct, and with a complete realization of the insane nature of the proceedings apprehended. The state of waking from a dream isn't a very close comparison, because the memory after dreams is occasionally very good, while the memory of the manic conduct is absolutely cut off. (Graves, 1942, p. 668)

This is a representative account of a patient's recollection of a period of acute mania. Memories are fragmented and so disconnected that much of the episode seems senseless. The EDITOR process of his stream of consciousness, which ordinarily censors and rationalizes his memories, no longer has possession of memory traces from the past.

A common feature of these periods of acute mania is a flow of conversation composed of more or less complete sentences or parts of ideas, often without any apparent connections with each other. This phenomenon is often termed a *flight-of-ideas*. Custance tried to write down such an experience. He considered that this record was an example of "directed" rather than "phantasy" thinking.

I have to choose my words very carefully. For what I am doing is, I believe, something which has not very often been attempted (BEELZEBUB

ON BED in form of blue fly). It is to think at precisely the same point in the space-time continuum by both methods of thought (coughing, running at the nose, bottom of feet wet) (blue check handkerchief)—inductive and deductive (so hot, have to remove coat and purple pullover query CAESAR'S) artistic and rational (itching), negative and positive—in the terminology expounded [previously]. . . .

First of all it seems to be (had to open window owing to extreme sense of heat query "real"?) essential to fix my exact position (fly on pipe) in the space-time continuum, at any rate by what the sailors call D.R. (dead reckoning query alive or dead?) . . .

Now I called this statement a statement of position by D.R., or dead reckoning. I did this instinctively; that is to say I wrote it down without fully reasoning out in my head what its implications were. It was therefore a statement as it were from the negative or inductive side of things represented by the (-) sign, and I must now reason out positively, or rationally, exactly what I meant. (Custance, 1952, pp. 138–139)

This excerpt, in addition to illustrating the confusion, distraction, and continuous shifting of the patient's focus of attention, has some of the qualities of compulsion together with a blurring or loss of the main stream of thought. In everyday life our attention—the center of one's conscious awareness—is focused on one aspect of the environment, which may be either the outer or inner environment. Depending on circumstances, the focus of attention is more or less well defined and clear. If circumstances demand, the point or area of focus changes, the process of change being termed distraction. In mania the focus is not only continually changed, but also is blurred by overlap of ideas. Normally, when one becomes distracted, there is an apparent time lag between each successive point of focus. In mania, each new focal point is sharp, but the mental connections between successive points are unclear because of a seeming overlapping of images. This overlap is not too apparent to the experiencer.

This persistent process of distraction in the flight-of-ideas is at first attractive and amusing to the patient, but as it continues, day after day, with only a few hours of restless sleep intervening at night, it becomes wearying, tiresome, and unpleasant. Graves characterized the entire experience of mental turmoil as imbecility.

In mania, with imbecility succeeding to all of the personality control position, the emotional flow is so irrationally fast (for reasons quite beyond my understanding), the change from extreme to extreme is so fluid, that any sort of definition or judgment about it is impossible. Actually, in mania, the width of the attention of the afflicted person seems to be reduced to nil. That is, the immediate stimulus to action or expression, whether that stimulus comes from external circumstances or from the chance flow of thought, is momentarily brought to represent the total of pressure. Balancing considerations, which might induce the emotional swing to be in another direction, or to modify the rise of emotion, are pretty well extinguished. (Graves, 1942, pp. 671–672)

In connection with the weariness and pain, Graves commented on his attitude toward death and suicide and the role it played during his manic periods.

I can only conclude that my last three demonstrations of marked manic disturbances have been so closely associated with the consideration of suicide —which is one form of approach to death—as to have this topic pretty clearly in the foreground. However, the mania betrays some reverse of the normal approach, and such euphoric display as is present arises obviously from the escape from the necessity of suicide by escape from the restriction of reality. While the intoxication of mania lasts, I for one have no disposition to embrace death. After the intoxication is over, my chief emotional reaction is shame and disgust with myself, and a wonder that my fear of death could be so wonderfully and idiotically twisted. That the facing humiliation, of despair, of deprivation should produce a desire for death is quite natural; but that this desire for death should of itself be over-matched by the frantic and silly construction of an "escape" into insanity puts the last item of proof into semi-recovered rationality that tolerance of life in good sense is no longer practical. Thus "depression" means the recovery of normality, though of course it does not mean the recovery of the full mental structure which might have been displayed in the successful previous period of competitive life struggle. (Graves, 1942, p. 669)

Death-wishes and contemplation of suicide are a commonplace part of mental life during depression. But like the emotion of fear, the idea of self-destruction is not a commonplace part of manic experience. Graves was both intelligent and well read so that his "normal" attitude toward life was one of skeptical pessimism; thus depression and depressive ideas were understandable to him. But mania seemed to him incomprehensible; the escape from his manic ideas by the act of suicide seemed irrational, but suicidal ideas during depression actually appeared to lead him toward the recovery of his sanity. It is worth noting that patients who have experienced both mania and depression place quite different negative values on one or the other state. Custance when depressed said he was in a kingdom of horror; while in mania he was in a realm of bliss. These values were exactly reversed in the case of Graves, who felt that his depression was not too far removed from his normal condition, whereas mania was a wearisome state of imbecility. Graves summarized his concept of the undesirability of mania, in the following way.

From my viewpoint, I was a somewhat shaken individual who had been seized, confined, cut off from access to friends and means, and subjected to galling and extraordinary cruelty. I was guessing wildly, ever more wildly, as to reasons, utterly devoid of judgment as to relative weights and proper associations. Memory and hallucinations, reality and theory, all participated in a wearisome confusion of ideas. I grow tired of extricating the small seed of fact from which my imagination would engender an oak tree of imagined silliness, of the boiling out of all my aversions and clashes in a busy life into "explanations" which would satisfy the temporary maniac I was. (Graves, 1942, p. 261)

Not only were the periods of mania unpleasant and undesirable, but, after having lived through several of these, Graves was of the opinion that the episodes had led to a certain amount of mental deterioration, and gave some evidence to back up his opinion. There has long been a question in the minds of many observers as to whether or not repeated manic and depressive episodes bring about a greater mental deterioration than that which one would expect to find in the same period of time and which could be attributed to the normal process of aging. The following excerpt from Graves is the only first-hand self-observation relevant to this point that I have found.

Evidence of mental deterioration in myself. . . . My own tests of the loss of capacity are these: 1. Concentration upon written matter, habitual in former occupation, is relatively poor. . . . In conversation there is a lapse of attention, and a presence of inattention to the statements of others. 2. In transcribing written work in forms—incident, for instance, to hospital files—I note that my memory is only with ease capable of carrying a single date, a single set of symbols, a single name, if accuracy in presentation and spelling is to be attained. Formerly, I could carry a full line of familiar material, I believe. 3. Formerly I was an exceptionally good card player, and still retain much of the capacity. Yet I noticed recently that in shifting from one type of game to the other, I became—by my own standards—more than a little confused. . . . 4. Physically, my nervous correlation, never very good, has become markedly worse. I am clumsy, slow, and liable to come to full stops in the performance of the most mediocre household duties. . . .

My impression is that of slowed and dulled mental operation. Underlying the process, a matter of volition, is a distaste for activity, the symptoms of which are remission to the will of others in details of living. (Graves, 1942, pp. 532–533)

Whether these changes were greater than those he would have experienced simply by growing twenty years older, without having suffered mental illness, is difficult to say. It may also be true that this was written in a period of depression following a hypomanic incident. Actually, many patients have described a mental "slowness" during the period of convalescence which follows a period of insanity, but such descriptions usually imply that this mental lethargy or weakness is a transient phenomenon.

Manic confusion is often exaggerated by the shift from the retarded, lethargic state of depression to the contrasting state of elated well-being, or vice versa, a shift that often takes place rather rapidly. Several excerpts from descriptions of this transition from melancholia to mania have been included in this chapter, but I will add one more description that is particularly relevant. Dr. Blalock published and discussed this autobiographical account of a manic-depressive case.

"Last October [during a period of depression] . . . I felt funny feelings in my eyes. A change in the optical nerves was taking place, a rotting. I just felt myself rotting and decaying away, a sort of change in the nerve structure causing tension. I'd walk about and feel the cerebral hemispheres go bing. I was having headaches. Then suddenly [one morning] I came out of it. There was a reconnection. The nerves of the eyeball were reintegrating. I've been drinking a lot of water. That helps the nerves. At that time I felt the segments of the brain were piecing together, emotionally speaking. I felt just good, not exhilarated, mind you. There was a religious experience. . . . At that point I was thinking of 15 things at once. . . . I was nervous rather than sincere. . . . Perhaps I can come to it from that point. . . . It may have been a matter of glandular disturbance all around. A man can pull himself up by sky-hooks, that is, if he has the right kind of imaginations. (Blalock, 1936, pp. 322–324)

From this account it would seem that the somatic delusions which accompanied the depression changed rather rapidly and dropped completely out of his thoughts, so that he found himself thinking of fifteen things at once. He first attempted to account for the change in terms of a glandular disturbance, but then shifted rapidly to the magical idea of "sky-hooks"; then to religious concepts and then to an over-all confusion.

DISCUSSION

Generally speaking, patients who suffer from mania realize that something new and different has occurred within them. They usually reject what they conceive of as an *accusation* made by others to the effect that they are insane. Manic patients realize their unusual elation and extraordinary feelings of well-being. They may or may not object to hospitalization, to seclusion, and to restraint. In the early stages they usually realize that something has been changed (if they have had a previous attack they know what is happening), but they will nevertheless insist that they are still capable of adequate self-care. In brief, there is usually a fairly good realization by the patient of the condition in which he finds himself. He soon finds, however, that he is incapable of self-control and of properly caring for his own personal welfare. The depressed patient is very often a danger to himself because of his preoccupation with suicidal thoughts. The manic patient is in danger because of his overactivity, distractibility, overexertion, insomnia, together with his disregard for the welfare of both others and himself. Patients in a manic state are seldom a direct threat to others. They rarely attack others, except with words, the verbal assault itself being more of a bombastic, irritating, and teasing nature than a hateful reprisal. Manic patients may be very troublesome on account of their noisiness, overactivity, and lack of inhibitions, but they are not, truly speaking, troublemakers.

One of the mysteries of the experience of mania is the fact that mania often shifts to depression, the same holding true for depression and its relation to mania. There are not too many elements in common between the two experiences; neither are they completely opposite. Indeed, as the autobiographical excerpts show, subjectively, mania is not exactly the antithesis, or the absence, of depression. Mania is not necessarily a "pleasant" state; it may be accompanied by a great deal of unpleasantness and physical pain. The manic patient finds that his strange perceptions and emotional experiences usually mystify him. The limitations that others impose on his behavior and verbal expressions often irritate and frustrate him. The self-realization (usually vague) of the senselessness of his speech and actions during an attack may give rise to feelings of self-reproach. Even during the very peaks of ecstasy and elation, there may be elements of feelings of frustration and unwarranted constraint.

Manic states have been said to represent sublimations, often direct unconventional sublimations of repressed desires. Though this may have some element of truth, one must point out that the interpretation is not one spontaneously offered or readily accepted by patients. The patient finds his experiences going faster and faster. He finds himself overwhelmed by ideas, new associations, unsuspected physical strength, uncritical answers to age-old problems of human existence, all occurring in the semblance of a colorful kaleidoscopic illusion. He often wishes the show would slow down or end, for it is both tiring and bewildering. As Graves said when he commented on the ever-changing focus of attention: "It just seems insanity."

At the core of melancholia lies fear, sorrow, and hopelessness. It is more difficult to identify the core of mania. There is little or no fear during mania. On the contrary, there is an overwhelming feeling of elation and well-being. There is often a breach in the barriers of individuality, with experiences of beatific revelation.

In the sense that the manic patient is free from hope and fear, he should be happy. He has a feeling of well-being and believes that he is thinking clearly. Many of the deepest secrets of the universe seem suddenly quite plain and open to his conscious mind. It seems to him that every man should be his friend. There are no more inhibitions. He feels free to express himself frankly and directly. And in spite of it all, only for short moments does he experience unendurable pleasure.

If we take phrases from the descriptive excerpts included in this chapter, to show that the experience of mania is not unalloyed pleasure, we find the following items: "In mania the emotions are all strong, though erratic, and the concept of reality is disturbed"; "In mania emotions are uncovered, defectively related to other elements of existence"; "These periods of intense excitement were followed by great nervous prostration"; "Complete wildness, in recounting of which I still find deathly weariness"; "Thus I try to soothe my conscience"; "In mania the afflicted person seems reduced to nil"; "I participated in a wearisome confusion of ideas," and so on. Mania is therefore not a period of complete happiness. It may entail a freedom from hope and fear and even from too much love of living, yet it is certainly not Paradise.

*The utility of pain lies in the warning it gives: in trying
to escape pain we escape destruction. . . . The bitterest
quintessence of pain is its helplessness, and our incapacity
to abolish it. . . . This baffling quality, so conspicuous in
extreme agony is present in all pain and is perhaps its
essence. . . . The horror of pain lies in its intolerable
intensity and its intolerable tedium.*

(*Santayana,* 1920, p. 27)

CHAPTER **14**

Pain and Suffering

INTRODUCTION

That psychopathology is almost always attended by
pain and suffering is a point frequently overlooked by
medical and psychological writers. Almost every autobiographical account of mental illness repeatedly tells
of sharp pains and physical suffering, but most textbooks dealing with psychopathology gloss over the
facts of the patient's inner torment. The acute mental
and physical pain and suffering that become such a
constant complaint have been, and continue to be,
passed over or dismissed with the comment, "It's all
imaginary and unimportant."

The intensity and the bodily location of the pain
reported varies among mental patients but, so far as
any individual is concerned, the reality of the pain is
beyond question. Being told that there is no basis for
his pain or that it is purely imaginary only accentuates
the patient's misery and frustration. It is rare to find
an account that does not stress the occurrence of pain
and insomnia.

Because the varieties of pain and suffering are
so diverse, it is difficult to present this material in any

systematic fashion. The two kinds of suffering most frequently mentioned are headaches and stabbing pains, the latter being similar to those produced by electrical stimulation.

Headaches

Many different kinds of pains in the head have been described. The following excerpts give a more or less random sample. In her book, *Reluctantly Told,* Jane Hillyer relates that when she had been in an excited, agitated state she had been placed in complete restraint (tied down in bed). She described her growing suffering, particularly the pains in the head.

The ache started in my shoulders and went down my spine, vertebra by vertebra, as if it were walking downstairs. It increased the dull pain, which I had continuously at the back of my head. It was rather nice to ache; it kept one from wondering so much about "dumb" things. In a little while the pain at the base of my brain became so severe it occupied my exclusive attention. A definitely outlined area felt very hot, rimmed as if with still hotter wires, burning white. It was a steady ache, no throb, no sharp darts, just ache like a heavy volume of sound. (Hillyer, 1926, 50–51)

This distressing experience might in part be attributed to the physical restraint, which served to accentuate the dull headache from which she had been suffering for some time.

Hackett mentioned in his account, *The Cardboard Giants,* how he suffered from a persistent dull headache. On one occasion when he had been more stuporous and out of touch with reality than usual, he became aware of and very concerned about certain remarks made by another patient. His concern, he says, gave rise to a different sort of headache.

The headaches came with a small bubble of pain over my right ear, and the bubble grew like a goiter growing inward until it was as though everything inside my head was being forced out through my eyes. All the matter and tissue and cells and blood were being forced through my eyelids, which I dared not even blink lest my head explode from the congestion. (Hackett, 1952, pp. 182–183)

He said that he then began to feel cold and numb as he regained his self-control, even though he was still fearful and full of resentment. These bubbles of pain were, he said, associated with the surges of violent anger.

Pain in the head formed part of an acute phase of Dr. Margaret Cleaves' neurosis. She describes this in the following fashion.

At the same time that the conditions detailed in regard to pain, sleeplessness, congestion of my sensory cortex, with profound circulatory disturbances and the sensation of hot blood pouring into my ear with great weakness especially of right side, I had a constantly recurring dream out of which I always wakened in a condition of terror and which left me shaken and trembling for hours dreading with a nameless dread to go to sleep again. This was of a mad cat gnawing at my head always at the one spot and that directly over the middle lobe of the right half of my brain. Why a mad cat I do not know any more than I can understand why a medical man, also a neurasthene should have a dream of a vampire fastening itself upon him at the base of the brain, nor why that vampire should take the form and features of a medical man of his acquaintance. In both instances the distress was great. (Cleaves, 1910, p. 73)

This is the kind of description that leads those who attach symbolic meanings to patients' reports, to say, "This account is very significant." Whether it actually has symbolic significance is not, as far as the present study is concerned, essential. Our point is that acute suffering was involved. Whatever symbolic implication one may gain is unfortunately all too apt to divert the attention of the listener from the actual torture the patient experienced.

Stabbing Pain Akin to Electrical Stimulation

Sharp, stabbing, needle-like cramps, similar to those which are produced by the discharge of an electric current through the body, are, next to headache, the commonest complaints of pain recorded by psychotic patients.

Dr. Devine's patient complained endlessly of being under the influence of "The Strengths," which governed his thoughts and behavior throughout his waking hours. The Strengths also afflicted him with special forms of pain.

[The Strengths] struck me in Paris for the first time; they struck me in the form of a battery. He showed this form of strength because he knew I had put coins in a machine which gave electric shocks. At times he says he will strike me as I have struck others. I have the sensation of being struck in the bones or flesh. They do not often knock me over in their angered states; they merely apply strength. They give me the sensation of being crumpled up; the bones and all have that feeling—not broken but crumpled up . . . a sensation of becoming a bag of powder. (Devine, 1921, p. 234)

A military man who was held in a mental hospital because of persecutory delusions related the way in which he was tortured by electric shocks.

The one which is specifically used on me consists of a violent electric shock applied to the heart almost every night, after about four hours of sleep, by means of electromagnetic instruments which the secret police activate. This shock which is ordinarily followed by one or many others after a few moments drowsiness, makes me bleed in this region and gives me a most painful disturbance. I undergo also the effect of an electric current which strikes me very frequently on the head, as would a borer that would be used to pierce my head. Under certain circumstances I have forced ejaculations which necessarily bring about in me a most unfortunate exhaustion, and which has happened to me three times in five nights. I must also point out to you intestinal pains which force me to go too often to the toilet, an electric current which is applied to my left foot and gibberish in my ears which is as much inopportune as it is continuous. (Cullerre, 1886, p. 224)

This man went on to complain of other physical and mental indignities which the voices compelled him to endure and in which he was urged to participate. All of these evil thoughts and commands were communicated to him by a woman's voice.

No physical basis could be found for these stabbing, electrical pains. No actual muscle spasms could be seen or felt by outside observers.

It may be recalled that in Chapter 6 I presented Lang's account of pain in connection with hallucination, where he said that he experienced sharp, stabbing, spasmlike pains usually associated with auditory hallucinations. He noted that the pain could sometimes be somewhat relieved by rubbing his hand over the area where the pain seemed to be localized.

Painful Tortures

Haslam published in 1810 an account of the medical history of a Mr. Matthews who had been held as a lunatic at Bethlem Hospital since 1797. There had been some medical and legal dispute with respect to Matthews' sanity or insanity. Matthews maintained that he was constantly being assailed by a gang of villains who tortured him by means of an "Air Loom," an instrument which resembled a pipe organ. When the loom was operated the villains could affect the mind of any selected victim who might be within range of the instrument, so that thoughts could be stolen or new and false ideas implanted in the mind of the victim. Still worse, the loom could bring to any selected victim a wide variety of physical suffering or "assailments." Matthews described these assailments in the technical terms he said were used by the gang that was torturing him. The list is, as Haslam said, a formidable catalogue of human misery and calamities for which no remedy was known. We have selected the following from Matthew's original list.

Fluid Locking.—A locking or constriction of the fibres of the root of the tongue, laterally, by which the readiness of speech is impeded.

Cutting soul from sense.—A spreading of the magnetic warp, chilled in its expansion, from the root of the nose, diffused under the basis of the brain, as if a veil were interposed; so that the sentiments of the heart can have no communication with the operations of the intellect.

Stone-making.—The gang pretend they can at pleasure produce a precipitation in the bladder of any person impregnated, and form a calculus. They boast of having effected this in a very complete manner for the late Duke of Portland. . . .

Kiteing.—This is a very singular and distressing mode of assailment, and much practised by the gang. As boys raise a kite in the air, so these wretches, by means of the air-loom and magnetic impregnations, contrive to lift into the brain some particular idea, which floats and undulates in the intellect for hours together; and how much soever the person assailed may wish to direct his mind to other objects, and banish the idea forced upon him, he finds himself unable; as the idea which they have kited keeps waving in his mind, and fixes his attention to the exclusion of other thoughts. He is, during the whole time, conscious that the kited idea is extraneous, and does not belong to the train of his own cogitations.

Sudden death-squeezing; by them termed *Lobster-cracking.*—This is an external pressure of the magnetic atmosphere surrounding the person assailed, so as to stagnate his circulation, impede his vital motions, and produce instant death.

In short, I do not know any better way for a person to comprehend the general nature of such lobster-cracking operation, than by supposing himself in a sufficiently large pair of nut-crackers or lobster-crackers, with teeth, which should pierce as well as press him through every particle within and without; he is experiencing the whole stress, torture, driving, oppressing, and crush all together.

Stomach-skinning consists in rendering the stomach raw and sore, as if it had been scalded, and the internal coat stripped off.

Apoplexy-working with the nutmeg-grater consists in violently forcing the fluids into the head; and where such effort does not suddenly destroy the person, producing small pimples on the temples, which are raised, and rough like the holes in a nutmeg-grater: in a day or two they gradually die away.

Lengthening the brain.—As the cylindrical mirror lengthens the countenance of the person who views himself in such glass, so the assailants have a method by which they contrive to elongate the brain. The effect produced by this process is a distortion of any idea in the mind, whereby that which had been considered as most serious becomes an object of ridicule. All thoughts are made to assume a grotesque interpretation; and the person assailed is surprised that his fixed and solemn opinions should take a form which compels him to distrust their identity, and forces him to laugh at the most important subjects. It can cause good sense to appear as insanity, and convert truth into a libel, distort the wisest institutions of civilized society into the practices of barbarians, and strain the Bible into a jest book. . . .

Bladder-filling is filling the nerves of the neck with gaz, and by continued distension, effecting a partial dislocation of the brain. This frequently repeated, produces weakness of intellect. . . .

Bomb-bursting is one of the most dreadful inflictions performed by the infernal agency of the air-loom. The fluid which resides in the brain and nerves, the vapor floating in the blood-vessels, and the gaz which occupies the stomach and intestines, become highly rarified and rendered inflammable, occasioning a very painful distension over the whole body. Whilst the assailed person is thus labouring, a powerful charge of the electrical battery (which they employ for this purpose) is let off, which produces a terrible explosion, and lacerates the whole system. A horrid crash is heard in the head, and if the shock do not prove instantly fatal, the party only recovers to express his astonishment that he has survived the murderous attempt.

Gaz-plucking is the extraction of magnetic fluid from a person assailed, such fluid having been rarified and sublimed by its continuance in the stomach and intestines. This gaz is in great request, and considered as the most valuable for the infernal purposes of these wretches. They contrive, in a very dexterous manner, to extract it from the anus of the person assailed, by the suction of the air-loom. This process is performed in a very gradual way, bubble by bubble.

"The explanation of the forementioned terms will enable the reader sufficiently to understand others which belong to the science of assailment, as *foot-curving, lethargy-making, spark-exploding, knee-nailing, burning-out, eye-screwing, sight-stopping, roof-stringing, vital-tearing, fibre-ripping,* etc." (Haslam, 1810, pp. 30–38)

The action of the air-loom was made more effective, he said, by means of *brain-sayings,* that is, a communication of thought between the gang and their victim. The thought exchange was particularly effective because the victim was impregnated with the magnetic fluid produced in part by the air-loom. Matthews sketched a picture of the air-loom and the gang which operated it, which drawing Haslam included in his book. Haslam pointed out that, in spite of the dreadful suffering which Matthews had experienced, the latter appeared to derive some consolation from the sympathy which he said existed between himself and the gang which operated the loom. He said he watched the operators carefully and often, when they were about to assail him, he would brace himself and so partially avoid the imminent pain.

Not only is the list of tortures impressive but the fact is interesting that a special vocabulary or terminology was furnished "by the operators." This interest is reinforced by the fact that I have found several vocabulary lists which other tortured patients have supplied.

In the supposedly autobiographical account, *Operators and Things,* "Barbara O'Brien" similarly gives a set of definitions, which according to "her" was dictated by the "Operators" (the same word that Haslam's patient used) for "her" to deliver to the psychiatrist. Physical pain, as such, was not the central theme of "Miss O'Brien's" account.

Matthews' and "O'Brien's" accounts have much in common. In neither is there a religious or mystical element. Both suffered from becoming the object of "operators," who were defined as the unknown persons who had selected them as objects for experimental purposes. In spite of being subjected to personal persecution and mental distress, neither seemed distraught.

Schreber devoted part of a chapter in his *Memoirs* to listing the varieties of the "miracles" that God had inflicted on him during the years of his illness. Portions of these descriptions may be cited.

I may say that hardly a single limb or organ in my body escaped being temporarily damaged by miracles . . . Even now the miracles which I experience hourly are still of a nature as to frighten every other human being to death; only by getting used to them through the years have I been able to disregard most of what happens as trivialities. . . . But this does not exclude that *temporarily* most serious damage is caused and very painful conditions arise giving the impression of extreme danger. [Following is a list of these.]

Various changes in my *sex organ* . . .

The removal by miracles of single *hairs* from my *beard* and particularly my *moustache:* finally a *change in my whole stature* (diminution of body size) . . .

I once had a different heart . . .

My *lungs* were for a long time the object of violent and very threatening attacks. . . . A "lung worm" was frequently produced in me by miracles. . . . its appearance was connected with a biting pain . . .

My *ribs* were sometimes temporarily smashed . . . One of the most horrifying miracles was the so-called *compression-of-the-chest-miracle,* which I endured at least several dozen times . . .

I existed frequently without a stomach . . . I could not eat because I had no stomach. . . . Food and drink taken simply poured into the abdominal cavity and into the thighs, a process which . . . was beyond all doubt to me as I distinctly remember the sensation. . . .

The *gullet* and the *intestines,* which were torn or vanished repeatedly, further the *pharynx,* which I partly ate up several times, finally the *seminal cord,* against which very painful miracles were directed . . . I must further mention . . . the so-called *putrifaction of the abdomen.* . . . that more than once I believed I would have to rot alive . . .

The miracles directed against my *head and the nerves of my head* happened in manifold ways. One attempted to pull the nerves out of my head . . . These attempts caused fear [and] . . . an unpleasant tension in my head. . . . Attempts are made to paralyse my fingers when I play the piano or write, and to cause some damage to my knee-cap to make marching impossible when I walk about in the garden . . .

The most abominable of all miracles—next to the compression-of-the-chest-miracle . . . was "the head-compressing machine". . . . There had appeared in my skull a deep cleft or rent roughly along the middle, which probably was not visible from outside but was from the inside. The "little devils" stood on both sides of this cleft and compressed my head as though in a vice by turning a kind of screw, causing my head temporarily to assume an elongated almost pear-shaped form. It had an extremely threatening effect, particularly as it was accompanied by severe pain. . . .

In the foot bones particularly in the region of the heel, *caries* was often caused by miracle, causing me considerable pain . . . A similar miracle was the so-called *coccyx miracle.* . . . Its purpose was to make sitting and even lying down impossible.

[In a later portion of his *Memoirs*, Schreber made still another detailed statement relevant to the many forms which his physical sufferings assumed.] I also suffered from sciatica, cramp in the calves, states of paralysis, sudden attacks of hunger, and suchlike; earlier on lumbago and toothaches were frequent. Sometimes the lumbago was so painful . . . that I could only lift myself from the bed with simultaneous cries of pain—half *voluntarily* uttered; the toothache was also at times so severe that it made every mental activity impossible. Even now I suffer from almost uninterrupted headaches of a kind certainly unknown to other human beings, and hardly comparable to ordinary headaches. They are tearing and pulling pains . . . The bellowing miracle . . . causes . . . a very unpleasant concussion of the head: if it occurs while I am eating I must be very careful not to spit out what I have in my mouth. This rapid change in my condition gives the overall impression of madness and my whole life therefore carries this stamp, the more so as my surroundings are made up mostly of madmen who themselves add to all sorts of mad things happening. (Schreber, 1955, pp. 131–139; 201–202)

Schreber went on to say that because of the interferences and distractions caused by his aches and pains, he could seldom remain very long at any one occupation and hence had had to fill his time with trifles. He felt best when carrying out menial jobs or when playing the piano. The headaches were usually so distracting that he could perform no task which required any protracted mental effort. In summing up, it is interesting to note that the descriptions of pain experiences are in each case confounded by the patient's account of his delusions and hallucinations.

Schizophrenic Pain and Suffering

Most accounts written by patients who have been said to have suffered from schizophrenia dwell on the suffering they have endured. The widest varieties of pain and discomfort have been related. The excerpts that compose this section have been chosen to illustrate in some degree these varieties.

Davidson, in his *Remembrances*, related many instances when he was seized by agonizing pain, usually in connection with some hallucinatory experience. The following is an example.

That evening I felt the remarkably unpleasant sensation of a clamp round my head. It was more pronounced than before, and, in addition to this, I heard and felt the beating of what seemed like huge wings in my ears. Headache and heavy throbbing in the eardrums keeping exact time to the shadows caused by the flickering of a dying lamp in a dark room might correspond to the sensation; but the lamp was not flickering, and I saw and knew that others in the room were not experiencing any sensation of shadowy beatings. At last, for a few short moments in which I felt I must sink to the ground and die, I felt appalling agony, as of two horns being rammed down from above, through the front top part of my skull, right down into my very brain, while a rusty red light seemed to be closing in on me choking me. I was just able to keep from shouting out with pain; and as I felt myself sinking off my chair, I offered a fervent short prayer to God for help. A second more, and I must have shouted and terrified everyone in the room; when suddenly I felt that something had gone into my head which strengthened it most marvellously against what was pressing down into it. The two horns seemed forced up at once; the fearful pain, red glare, and beating noise left me completely, and I felt cool, comfortable, and relieved; such sudden relief as I had never known in my life before." (Davidson, 1912, p. 150)

These spells of suffering usually consisted of a generalized and agonizing crushing that weakened his strength, and he would fall as though pressed to the ground. The acute suffering never lasted for more than a few minutes; there were no physical aftereffects.

Still another account of a patient's mental torture can be taken from Maude Harrison's *Spinners Lake.*

I could fill a volume with the Voices, but it would become monotonous. There was nothing of which I was not accused, nothing, nothing . . .

All the other things of which I had been accused had a remote basis, or possible basis in fact. I had been afraid of war; I had received money from my firm which I had not earned; I had said I was ill when presumably I wasn't; married men had made love to me. But I could find nothing on which this last charge could be based. I tried to find something. . . . At last [I] found it. . . . When I made my discovery I shrieked. . . . I knew that the Voice would make this into sadism as certainly as he had made the acceptance of my salary while ill into thieving. I shrieked and fell half out of bed. . . . I still had much through which to live. But this was the nethermost pit. No turn of any material rack could have hurt worse than this. I was in hell, and all Heaven was in a rage." (Harrison, 1941, pp. 59–61)

Evidently both physical pain and the torture of mental suffering are intrinsic parts of the schizophrenic experience. The endless accusation of the voices are exceedingly unpleasant and uncomfortable, even when they do not involve actual physical pain. Mental distress in other varieties of illness is equally difficult to endure, though it is not related so closely to auditory hallucinations, but rather to other psychological processes.

Pain and Suffering Associated with Melancholia and Depression

Suffering has been invariably concomitant with melancholia. In 1621 Burton wrote in his great study, *The Anatomy of Melancholy,* that the suffering of the melancholic man constituted "the cream of human adversity, the quintessence, the upshot; all other diseases are but flea-bitings."

They are in great pain and horror of mind, distraction of soul, restless, full of continual fears, cares, torments, anxieties, they can neither eat, drink, nor sleep for them, take no rest, *neither at bed nor yet at board, will any rest despair afford*. (Burton, 1927, p. 946)

Fear and sorrow are at the core of melancholia, and suffering is an attribute of both these qualities; indeed, sorrow, fear, and suffering are inseparable.

Late in the sixteenth century, the great mystic St. John of the Cross set down his conceptions of melancholia in *The Dark Night of the Soul*. The following excerpt describes the suffering he said was pertinent to melancholia.

A description of this suffering and pain, although in truth it transcends all description, is given by David, when he says: "The lamentations of death compassed me about; the pains of hell surrounded me; I cried in my tribulation." But what the sorrowful soul feels most in this condition is its clear perception, as it thinks, that God has abandoned it, and, in His abhorrence of it, has flung it into darkness; it is a grave and piteous grief for it to believe that God has forsaken it. (Juan de la Cruz, 1953, 1:385)

The melancholic's complaints involve fear of death; inner torture associated both with his present status and the fear of Hell to come; the self-accusations of having lost his inner grace as well as being abandoned by God; the feeling of despair based on the certainty of being plunged in darkness forever; and the clear perception of the utter hopelessness of his present and future.

Excerpts from the autobiography of the Rev. William Walford illustrate the painful conditions through which he lived during his twenty years of melancholia.

. . . almost incessant headaches from my infancy, but soon after my settlement in Yarmouth it assumed a new form. I was attacked by paroxysms of despondency, which during their continuance rendered life a burden almost intolerable. I could give no account of the reasons of such disquietude, and was at a loss to devise any probable means of relief. . . .
Similar feelings constrained me to shun the converse of my friends, though I was passionately desirous of their converse. I could compare myself only to a human body, the skin of which having been stripped off, no part can be touched without inflicting agony. This condition at length increased to such a degree, that I could not bear the ordinary conversation of the members of my family, whether they were sad or cheerful. The light of day so distressed me, that I had all my windows blinded: the sun, the moon, and stars filled me with inexpressible dread, and I beheld them as seldom as was possible. All ornamental furniture, especially looking-glasses, was especially offen-

sive to me, and was removed from the apartment in which I lived. My own personal appearance was neglected to the utmost; I should never have shaved myself, or changed my clothing, but for the affectionate remonstrances of my wife; nor could I endure the thought of having new clothes made. (Walford, 1851, pp. 147; 184)

A portion from a letter written by a patient to her physician, Dr. Hughes, conveys much the same story.

Oh! I cannot tell you how I have borne it so long—this is the strangest part of it all when it seems utterly impossible to endure the moments as they come. Oh! I have wept and prayed and importuned my Heavenly Father to let kind death relieve me, but no answer comes and every day is but a repetition of the past, for nothing breaks the awful monotony. My tears are like rivers and my prayers are continual and importunate. There is the most startling horror on my soul, and when I would end my sufferings death startles me. Any death would be more welcome than this existence. Food nor sleep do not seem to be essential to such an existence. When I take neither, I get along as well as when I have a little of each. I cannot engage in any of the duties or pleasures of life. I cannot have one moment's relief from my anguish, consequently cannot read, nor see, nor converse with a friend, nor with my own, dear, devoted children. There is a most terrible ringing and popping noise in my head; as of a thousand insects at a little distance. It never ceases for a moment, and a tremor is felt over the whole system. My trouble seems to originate in the head. My brain is so disturbed and my head feels like a tight bandage was tied around it. When I lie down on the bed, I feel like I press it so hard, as though I would go through it. (Hughes, 1885, pp. 85–86)

In all these accounts of melancholia, the pain and suffering are not (and cannot be) referred to any recognized physical basis, and are, therefore, referred to delusions or to hallucinations. The patient may recognize this fact and hence conclude that the suffering is imaginary, but this realization accentuates rather than diminishes the suffering. It would be easier to bear were there some anchorage or sensible reason on which he could depend to explain the suffering.

The only statement we have found in which an attempt was made to compare the mental and physical pain is the following by Graves.

I have said that mental pain can present a close simile to physical pain. . . . In trying to force myself to set down the self-accusatory descriptions of insane conduct and thought, I have encountered the sensation of extreme lassitude, of weariness of mind, accompanied by sensations that I think most people treat as headaches. It has been my aim all through life to be stoical, and to disregard sensation, sometimes pleasant as well as unpleasant sensations. I think I have sometimes achieved a good discipline in that matter, though I have also memory of frequently falling short. So I simply cannot tell how real are these sensations; how much actual suffering they occasion. My experience is that they are much less poignant than the pains from a tooth drawing or the breaking of a bone, but that they have as much shocking power as a light fist blow. (Graves, 1942, p. 695)

This comparison with the shock of a fist blow is interesting, since, as we have shown, many patients do speak of certain aspects of their pain as sharp spasms or electrical shocks, in contrast to the shock of a light fist blow. In any event, Graves implied that so far as he was concerned, the pain was really not as severe as many other patients have claimed.

Pain and Suffering in Neurotic Conditions

In other chapters I have given examples of the disability and handicap that phobia and compulsions may bring to the sufferer. The following is an excerpt from a letter written to Dr. Clevenger by a phobic patient, in which general irritability is emphasized.

The first noticeable symptoms which manifested themselves were extreme nervous irritability, sleeplessness and loss of appetite. Any excitement would throw me into a state of almost frenzy, so completely would I be overcome. Palpitation, spasmodic breathing, dilations of the eyes and nostrils, convulsive movements of the muscles, difficulty in articulation, etc., were the most prominent features. A sense of impending danger seemed ever present, spoiling every pleasure, thwarting every ambition. The dread of sudden death which was at first marked, gradually subsided, giving way more to a feeling of dread —not of dying suddenly—but of doing so under peculiar circumstances or away from home. I became morbidly sensitive about being brought into close contact with any large number of people. Finding myself in the midst of a large gathering would inspire a feeling of terror on my part which could be relieved in but one way—by getting away from the spot as soon as possible. (Clevenger, 1890, pp. 538–539)

This man, like many other neurotic patients, seemed to suffer from an increased sensitivity to every variety of sensory input. The ordinary range of stimulation became qualitatively intense and unbearable. Whether this factor represents a lack of inhibitory control or a real increase in sensitivity makes little difference—the experience is one of overreaction to all stimuli. The elements of physical pain were not mentioned in this citation but there can be no doubt about the psychic suffering involved. Other neurotic patients have spoken of their experience as being true physical pain.

The physician, Dr. Margaret Cleaves, who termed herself a neurasthene and from whose account I have already quoted, did speak of her suffering as true pain.

I was in constant and severe pain. There was not a nerve trunk but cried out night and day with the anguish of it all. The sense of cerebral and spinal exhaustion was extreme, and to make it all worse there was congestion of the sensory cortex which made me intolerant of the vibrations of light and sound, in fact—the external world—but I could not get away from them. Had it not been for the financial losses to which I have just referred, I could have stopped before it was too late—perhaps. At this time I seemed to never sleep, the mental and physical anguish were too great, my eyes were ever ready to fill with tell-tale tears, my nights were spent in weeping and my days in hard work, giving to others in trouble all I had of strength and courage. (Cleaves, 1910, p. 70)

In this excerpt there is little or no mention of fear or phobia. Rather, the fatigue attributed to overwork seemed to the sufferer to be the basis of her trouble; yet the mental difficulty and the pain persisted as strongly at the end of a restful vacation as they had during long and concentrated working hours.

Leonard, whose comments on his lifelong phobias have been quoted at some length in Chapter 11, on Fear, also complained of the prolonged pain he endured.

My eyes had troubled me for the first time . . . Aching and aching, month after month, for two years of unrelieved pain. . . . The cause of the aching was certainly neurotic. . . . the association of the aches with miscellaneous bodily aches, in thigh, arm, or neck . . . I suffered for two weeks a pain in my left jaw for which the dentist could find no physical cause. In twilight sleep one afternoon, it grew of an instant fiercely more acute, as I felt myself hit by a tin can and heard it, in a dream-noise, bang along before me in whispering metallic repercussions. Instantly in the midst of the most violent bodily shudders the memory of a moment . . . in the school fright and flight returned, and the pain disappeared. (Leonard, 1939, pp. 248–251)

Leonard is one of the few we have found who consistently spoke of his pains as "neurotic," that is, he considered the pains to be secondary to his phobias. He had consulted many medical specialists and had gained no relief from his suffering. He did report that he had found from experience that very often his more *immediate* discomfort was relieved when he gained some degree of understanding of the unconscious association that seemed to exist between the pain and a forgotten memory of some childhood fright. However, these insightful discoveries did nothing to bring about any permanent relief.

Pain and Alcoholic Hallucinosis

The horror, torture, and pain experienced during delirium tremens or alcoholic hallucinosis have been described many times, both by those who have lived through such an episode and by writers of fiction. A particularly vivid description was written in a letter published by Dr. Mann, from a lawyer who had suffered an attack of delirium tremens.

He wrote that while in the delirium he developed the delusion that he had been sentenced by a court to be thrown into a den of serpents. There he was to be left, so that he might during the next twenty-four hours attempt to fight his way out to a boat which would convey him to safety. He thought that the sheriff of the court took him to the serpents' den and gave him a bottle of brandy.

I seized it and quickly draining its contents, sprang in among the hissing serpents. They leaped at me and entwined themselves around my legs and arms. They environed my body and tore and lacerated my flesh. I tore them from me and flung them into the darkness. Seizing a large heavy one, I pulled off its head, and used its body for a weapon. As I would spring towards them, they would retreat, but others would grasp me from behind. I would turn and stamp and crush those in the rear, only to find them closing in upon me in front. Thus I fought them with every muscle strained to the utmost tension. Wounded and bleeding I passed down beyond the half-way mark; two-thirds of the distance had been reached. I was growing faint from loss of blood; my overtaxed muscles were growing weak and feeble. I paused for a moment to breathe when the boatman shouted, "Courage! Courage! you have three hours yet." I renewed my struggle with desperate effort . . . I had almost reached the water's edge . . . I had only one more monster between me and safety. . . . I caught it in my hands. "Too late! too late!" said the boatman, and as I flung the serpent behind me the boat moved off." (Mann, 1890, pp. 445–446)

During a toxic delusional episode of this sort the sufferer is completely "out of his mind." He behaves as though his delusion were actual reality. He becomes greatly excited and agitated. He attacks persons and things in his environment in a violent manner. If placed in restraint, he will continue to struggle. Actually, it is not uncommon for patients to struggle so violently that they undergo a physical collapse, endangering their own life as a result of the combination of terror, suffering, and exhaustion.

Pain Associated with Opium Withdrawal

There have been several published accounts describing the suffering and physical pain associated with the breaking of the opium habit. In his book, *The Opium Habit*, F. Ludlow relates in detail how he reduced himself, over a period of 39 days, from a daily intake of 80 grains of opium (2000 drops of laudanum) to no opium at all. In the following excerpts one may observe the process of withdrawal and its various effects.

Two days more and I had come down to twenty-five grains. Matters now began to look a good deal more serious. Only fifteen of the last forty grains had been dispensed with; but this gain had cost a furious conflict. A strange compression and constriction of the stomach, sharp pains like the stab of a knife beneath the shoulder-blades, perpetual restlessness, an apparent prolongation of time, so much so that it seemed the day would never come to a close, an incapacity of fixing the attention upon any subject whatever, wandering pains over the whole body, the jaw, whenever moved, making a loud noise, constant irritability of mind and increased sensibility to cold, with alternations of hot flushes, were some of the phenomena which manifested themselves at this stage of the process. . . .

From the point I had now reached until opium was wholly abandoned, that is, for a month or more, my condition may be described by the single phrase, intolerable and almost unalleviated wretchedness. Not for a waking moment during this time was the body free from acute pain; even in sleep, if that may be called sleep which much of it was little else than a state of diminished consciousness, the sense of suffering underwent little remission. . . .

The tenth day of the experiment had reduced my allowance to sixteen grains. The effect of this rapid diminution of quantity was now made apparent by additional symptoms. The first tears extorted by pain since childhood were forced out as by some glandular weakness. Restlessness, both of body and mind, had become extreme, and was accompanied with a hideous and almost maniacal irritability . . .

During one of the last days of this protracted storm my old nervous difficulty returned in redoubled strength. Commencing in the shoulder, with its hot needles it crept over the neck and speedily spread its myriad fingers of fire over the nerves that gird the ear, now drawing their burning threads and now vibrating the tense agony of these filaments of sensation. By a leap it next mastered the nerves that surround the eye, driving its forked lightning through each delicate avenue into the brain itself, and confusing and confounding every power of thought and of will. . . .

During the five days in which I was descending from the use of six grains of opium to two, the indications of the changes going on in the system were these: The gnawing sensation in the stomach continued and increased; the plethoric feeling was unabated, the pulse slow and heavy, usually beating about forty-seven or forty-eight pulsations to the minute; the blood of the whole system seemed to be driven to the extremities of the body; my face had become greatly flushed; the fingers were grown to the size of thumbs, while they, together with the palms of the hands and the breast, parted with their cuticle in long strips. The lower extremities had become hard, as though the agency of some compressed fluid. A prickling sensation over the body, as if surcharged with electricity, and accompanied with an apparent flow of some hot liquid down the muscles of the arms and legs, exhibited itself at this time. A constant perspiration of icy coldness along the spine had also become a conspicuous element in this strange aggregation of suffering. The nails of the fingers were yellow and dead-looking, like those of a corpse; a kind of glistening leprous scales formed over the hands; a constant tremulousness pervaded the whole system, while separate small vibrations of the fibres on the back of the hand were plainly visible to the eye. To these symptoms should be added a dimness of sight often so considerable as to prevent the recognition of objects even at a short distance. . . .

Although the opium habit was broken, it was only to leave me in a condition of much feebleness and suffering. I could not sleep, I could not sit quietly, I could not lie in any one posture for many minutes together. The nervous system was thoroughly deranged. Weak as I had become, I felt a continual desire to walk. (Ludlow, 1868, pp. 18; 19; 21; 28; 32; 43)

The pain and suffering endured by persons who try, or are compelled, to break their addiction to opium are traditional, and at the same time, mysterious. No well-recognized physical pathology can be regularly determined that is attributable to the use of opium. The intake of opium does affect appetite and sleep habits, but why lower dosage or deprivation from opium should give rise to such intense suffering and exquisite pain remains an enigma. Although the withdrawal of opium furnishes an objective basis for the ensuing psychopathology, the resultant suffering is no more comprehensible than the suffering of the schizophrenic or melancholic patient.

DISCUSSION

Much of the distress and painful experiences that have been detailed as forming part of psychopathology has no known physiological basis. It consists of a disturbed emotional experience or some specialized form of hallucination, since there is rarely anything in the objective situation that can be considered an adequate noxious stimulus. As far as the sufferer is concerned the acute experience of pain seems to belong in the same class of experiences as hallucinatory voices and visions, smells, and tastes. Indeed, pain is often inextricably associated with varieties of hallucinatory experiences. The sufferer is often unwilling or unable to reconcile the evidence of his senses with the subjective pain he has undergone or is undergoing. He may attempt to account for the experience with magical or mystical ideas, such as poisoning by witchcraft or by "miracles." But in any event, he is certain of the pain, even of its location, extent, intensity, and duration. To tell him that the pain is all in his mind, that it is imaginary, is, so far as he is concerned, a clear indication that the other person does not understand his problems. He suffers from actual pain and the pain is often one of the major reasons for seeking relief. The fact that the pain, in someone else's eyes, seems extraordinary and beyond belief supplies him with no basis for rejection of his own experience. He has suffered from all possible sensations of burning, stabbing, aching, dismemberment, mutilation, and crushing. The torture and agony are real; the fact that he is still alive and functioning only proves to him that he is a very unusual person.

The pain and suffering that accompany psychopathological conditions are undoubtedly leading symptoms in the actual life of the individual. They are part of the problem of reality *vs.* unreality feelings that concerns every mental patient. The patient says, "I hear voices and see visions"; "I am convinced I am the object of a great plot of evil"; "I am in constant fear and terror"; "I am tortured by stabbing pains and endless suffering." The outsider, on the other hand, says "I neither hear the voices nor see the visions of which you complain, in fact I must tell you there is no objective factual basis for your complaint; it's all in your mind or in your imagination." And yet the experience continues, unrelenting, and in no way can the patient deny its subjective existence. The conflict between the facts of outer reality and inner certainty of experience is the essence of the dilemma of the mental patient.

Thus the most important part of man's existence, that part where he most truly lives and is aware of living, lies entirely within the domain of personal feeling. Reason is used only to satisfy feeling, to build up a world in which feelings can be gratified, ambition realised; and, as we see in history, even then it has very little power in conflict with any strong emotion, any powerful symbol like a flag, the mere name of a country, even one invented last week, or words like "freedom." (Cary, 1958, p. 24)

CHAPTER 15

Other Feeling States

INTRODUCTION

It is apparent from previous chapters that much of psychopathological experience consists of disordered and disturbed personal feelings. Any comprehension of the introspective descriptions of these states is hindered by the patient's attempts to find words with which adequately to designate the feeling and to convey to others some idea of the nature of their experience. Thus far, I have dealt with the topics of psychopathological belief, depression, sadness, elation, fear, ideas of persecution, and suffering. There remain accounts of some other subjective feelings that do not belong anywhere in the foregoing list.

Those feelings that are identified as anger, hatred, and hostility are most frequently associated with paranoid states of the variety I included in Chapter 8 on "Delusion and Paranoia." As a rule, the accounts of anger show that this emotion is not part of the essential or primary abnormality but occurs rather as a secondary feature of the basic emotional turmoil. For example, anger and hatred arise when provoked by the voices and delusional ideas that assail the patient. Or

317

the patient is angered by misinterpretation of the intent of the actions of physicians and attendants, or he has, in fact, been abused.

Hate and Hostility

Excerpts from the descriptions given by patients in which they express resentment and hatred directed toward others, especially relatives, doctors, nurses, and attendants, may be cited to illustrate this point. These hostile feelings are, so to speak, normal, in that many patients believe, sometimes with good reason, that they have been unfairly treated. Examples of maltreatment are commonplace, one of them standing out quite clearly in Beers' book, *A Mind that Found Itself*.

The head attendant and one of his assistants passed my door. They were returning from one of the dances . . . While they were within hearing I asked for a drink of water. It was a carefully worded request. But they were in a hurry to get to bed, and refused me with curses. Then I replied in kind.

"If I come there I'll kill you," said one of the attendants.

"Well, you won't get in if I can help it," said I, as I braced my iron bedstead against the door.

My defiance and defences gave the attendants the pretext for which they had been waiting; and my success in keeping them out for two or three minutes only served to enrage them. . . .

The door once open, I offered no further resistance. First I was knocked down. Then for several minutes I was kicked around the room—struck, kneed and choked. (Beers, 1908, pp. 162–163)

The defiance and hostility Beers expressed in this incident were those that any normal man under similar circumstances might have experienced. The actual pathology in Beers' case, however, consisted of a long and continued belligerent attitude, throughout which he deliberately sought occasions in which he might provoke a fight.

More exceptional are the accounts of resentful feelings that apparently arise from within the patient's mind and that are unattached or only partially attached to the surrounding circumstances. For example, a female patient of Dr. Kindwall told of her feelings when being admitted to the hospital.

Although I was quite willing to acknowledge that the hospital was doing the best that it could, nevertheless suspicion was there too, and I was eager to support it. The best that could be done! Just that had been known to fail so often! Surely there might have been some other way! All the while, down underneath there was resentment, seething, turbulent, threatening, something unaccountable that thumbed is nose at mental processes and formulae. Just then I wanted more than anything else, someone who would question the judgment of the hospital, someone who would dispute it to the bitter end. There came back to me a well-remembered saying of Dr. Meyer's: "The

psychosis is an experiment of nature." The phrase which I had always enjoyed, now roused a violent protest. "Why should I be one of nature's guinea
pigs?" Feebly, the logical counter query rose: "Why, pray, should I not?" I
had no satisfactory answer for either question. . . .

   During the days and nights that followed, the resentment and bitterness . . . continued. Only when I could get off somewhere by myself and
could lose myself in my own fantasy creations did it subside. At other times,
everything that was said seemed an insult; every nurse who came near me
an enemy with diabolical intent. I seethed with hatred. What was it that
these women were after? What was it that I had done or not done? As they
struggled to get me into a pack they seemed to me fiends, a sort of human
embodiment of all that was hateful. Resistance at such times became a virtue
and I felt that somewhere, in some larger accounting, my struggles were
recorded; that some power or force that was quite outside myself and something within myself were in essential accord and would finally come into their
own." (Kindwall and Kinder, 1940, pp. 529; 531)

   As she says, the patient had no rational basis for her pervasive
hatred and resentment. The basic hostility she attributed to the feeling
of having become "one of nature's guinea pigs" together with the interference exerted on her usual freedom of action. Eventually she became so
overactive and destructive that she had to be placed in physical restraint.
It is possible that the anger and resentment were unconsciously motivated, but this possibility was not hinted by the patient's account of her
experience nor does it add to our general comprehension of the patient's
feelings.

   Dr. Hayward's patient discussed her emotional experiences during
the period when her doctor was trying to employ a psychotherapeutic
procedure.

   I hated you when you first came. So many doctors had tried things
with me and got discouraged that I had thought that now at last I would be
left alone, in peace. But you just wouldn't go away so I wanted to kill you. . . .

   Hate has to come first. The patient hates the doctor for opening the
wound again and hates himself for allowing himself to be touched again.
The patient is sure it will just lead to more hurt. He really wants to be dead
and hidden in a place where nothing can touch him and drag him back. The
doctor has to care enough to keep after the patient until he does hate. If you
hate, you don't get hurt so much as if you love, but still you can be alive
again—not just cold and dead. (Hayward and Taylor, 1956, pp. 216–217)

   In this instance the feeling of hate was attributed by the patient to
the fact that she did not want to be disturbed by a prying doctor. She
had undergone much of the agony of mental suffering and now her only
desire was to be left alone to protect herself from any chance of increasing or reinstating the bitter anguish already endured. This "leave-
me-alone, I hate-you-for-disturbing-me" feeling may become so intense
that it reaches murderous levels.

A transcript of the actual conversation of a resentful patient with his physician, Dr. Cohen, when the latter was attempting to initiate psychotherapy, reads as follows.

Well, I don't want—ah, ah, ah, I really regard you as an enemy, see? You know, and I really, I guess really I want to murder you. You, you you're, you're a good guy, you know, and you let me sit in that chair, you know, that that is sort of a desire I have, you know, upon you, see, see, because, you, you, really treat me well for that, see. For, you know, the fact that I want to do that to you, see [hesitates] ah, ah, that is really a criminal act see. I, well, what the h——, I really want to do it to you, see? And ah, and ah, well ah, ah, I don't like you anyway, that's all, and ah, what the hell, I just don't want to swear, to make no, I don't want to swear at you, that's all. . . . Well, ah, I want to sw——, sw——, swear, the whole G. D. thing at you, that's all. Well, let's see, ah, ah [hesitates]—I really, I really, I really feel like I want to kill you off altogether, that's all, that's all. I feel like doing to you, that's all. [Softly.] For—[hesitates a long time and stutters] I really, ah, ah, feel like doing that to you that's all. It is the first time I really felt like that towards you, you know. I mean I am really o——, o——, open on it now. I never felt like that before. (Cohen, 1956, p. 315)

This patient evidently was in a disturbed, confused, and somewhat inarticulate condition at the time this transcript was made. He was not too sure of why he hated the doctor, but there could be no doubt about his hostile attitude. He asked for nothing more than to be allowed to sit in a chair and be left alone. When urged to "open up" and tell about his troubles, his resentment expressed itself in a desire to murder the doctor.

Some psychiatrists who have commented on these states of hate and hostility have insisted that the basic personal feeling which marks the hostility is that of an unorganized and largely unverbalized anger. They go on to insist that it is a generalized anger which breaks through all conscious processes and colors all ordinary mental processes. This contention seems plausible but it cannot be directly inferred from the statements of the patient himself, and does not account for the fact that nonpsychiatric medical practitioners may have no difficulty with such patients or the patients' day-to-day variations.

Generalized Feeling-State

Some bewildered individuals describe a state of "just feeling," without any other mentation, such as thinking, knowing, willing, or imagining. This peculiar state is usually related as having occurred during an acute phase of the illness, and especially when the person is in a condition of semiconsciousness. From the descriptions, one gains the impression that these generalized feeling-states might have been specifically identified as fear, anger, religious contemplation, and so forth, but for some obscure reason the person hesitated to give the experience a name. For example, Jane Hillyer described one period of her illness in the following way.

> Lying there I came as close, I think, as I ever have to a state of emotion unaccompanied by thought. I simply *felt*. Again, I have never learned words to describe sensations so far removed from what is called normal. General misery, physical discomfort, degradation not born of intellectual concept, but a deep, bodily and inner mental state; a feeling of being lost, lost utterly with no sense of place or time, no idea as to whom voices belonged, no clear realization of my own identity, lost in mind and body and soul, lost to light and form and color; a distinct, acid nausea of self-revulsion—all these were in the feeling that swept over me. But they do not describe it any more than a list of ingredients describes any assembled whole. It was all the more complete in that I was not conscious of intellectual activity of any kind. My whole being was given over to feeling. I had not the slightest defence, either within myself or without. The sensation grew, rolled upon me like a gigantic wave. I gasped, struggled; there was a sickening, acute moment, then a welding. The emotion became *me*. (Hillyer, 1926, pp. 71–72)

Miss Hillyer was in a state of physical exhaustion and only partially conscious during the period she described. The strength of the various emotions battling inside her and her intense suffering had conquered her ability to think in any rational fashion. Descriptive terms such as "helplessness" and "hopeless suffering" might have been used to name her experience at this stage of her illness; in retrospect, however, these straightforward concepts were apparently of little value in her attempt to explore the very depths of her past experiences.

That such a generalized state is more than a period of disorganization which anyone might have before lapsing into unconsciousness may be illustrated by the following description offered by Peters.

> During this entire period, I identified everything by its feeling. . . . The people themselves were identified for me only by the sensation or feeling of their presences. Not their physical presence, but something which was communicated with great force, as fear is communicated silently to an animal. Instantaneously with my first vision of another person would come the conviction through the senses that he was good or evil, frightened or to be feared, kind or cruel, cunning, trustworthy, false, angry, pleased, or any one of dozens of other categories. (Peters, 1949, p. 46)

Some patients have spoken of this feeling as an animal-like mental state. They have said that each outside person seemed, when they came into sight or hearing, to be good or evil. This is said to happen in the same instinctive way that a dog might judge anyone who approaches it as a person to be accepted, fought, or feared without any rational basis derived from the behavior or from what might seem to be the intentions of the person in question. This generalized feeling state may be, and probably is, a condition in which the person's mental faculties are so disturbed that no complex intellectual discriminations can be made.

Another aspect of this type of generalized emotional state that some patients have tried to describe is the feeling the person says is characteristic of the mental illness itself, a feeling in contrast to the general one of well-being that characterizes health and sanity. Dr. Rows' first patient, whose account I cited previously, went on to say that she had been disturbed, and then had seemingly partially recovered and was allowed to leave the hospital for a trial visit home. She described her feelings as she left the hospital in the following way.

The feeling I had at the gates was, am I going to be ordinary, or were these things going to assert themselves again? . . . I began to do funny things again; then I knew I was just as bad as when I went in. Well! I don't think I gave you clearly to understand the symbolism, but it was this; the spirits came out of utter darkness; they had been in utter darkness for ages; I inhaled them into me, breathed them in; then a stop would come, and I felt queer internally; then another detachment came, just a little different to the former one. . . . I had all the symptoms of being horridly sick, but was not actually . . . I was doing peculiar things in B., and the first day at home—it seemed to me that everyone, that things were coming in a funny way—a glorious dream, and yet not a dream, but a feeling . . . I had no feeling of spirits, but I knew they were acting. (Rows, 1914, pp. 198–199)

This woman's description was related to the contrast between her feelings when mentally deranged and when well. She distinguished an inner feeling that she thought characterized the severe phase of her mental illness. On leaving the hospital gates to return to the home of her parents, she realized that she still had this feeling of being horridly sick and that she was not yet in control of herself. She realized that the mental illness continued. The feeling was clarified by the act of leaving the institution.

Only a few descriptions have been found of the way in which a generalized feeling-state shifts in quality from one of pleasantness to unpleasantness, or vice versa. Lang's descriptions of hallucinatory experience have been cited at some length in previous chapters. He has offered a very good description of these shifts in affect in his discourse on *The Other Side of the Affective Aspects of Schizophrenia*.

On ten or twelve occasions I have experienced interesting phenomena in connection with the rapid shift of halaffective states [hallucinations combined with marked emotions] in response to a direct suggestion by thoughts-out-loud [hallucinations]. The following example may illustrate the condition: I am engaged in activity which is affectively indifferent. A thought-out-loud stating "Let's make Johnnie feel happy" penetrates the conscious field. Immediately my affective tone shifts from one of indifference to one of pleasure. Then a thought-out-loud will state. "Let's make Johnnie feel sad." Immediately the affective state shifts to one of sadness. Further shifts back and forth may follow. Beyond the verbal suggestion of the thoughts-out-loud, the affective shifts lack basis in a change of the stimulus situation. The duration of any single affective state of the series varies from a few seconds up to several minutes; it may differ from one state to another in the same series. . . .

On certain special occasions, however, the hallucinary pain is accompanied by an intense feeling of pleasure which dominates the central conscious field and seemingly spreads throughout the organism. . . . The most important form of religious experience in that period [of my illness] was religious ecstasy. The attempts of the thoughts-out-loud to persuade myself to adopt a messianic fixation formed the hallucinary background. In affective aspects, a pervasive feeling of well being dominated the complex. I felt as though all my worries were gone and all my problems solved. I had assurance that all my needs would be satisfied. Connected with this euphoric state, I experienced a gentle sensation of warmth over my whole body, particularly on my back, and a sensation of my body having lost its weight and gently floating. (Lang, 1939b, pp. 198–199)

There are several points mentioned in this portion of Lang's account that deserve further consideration. The thoughts-out-loud hallucinatory experience was one over which Lang was never able to exercise any voluntary control. He was certain that these hallucinations were thrust upon him from some outside source and that his mind was taken over by compulsory ideas which he could neither select nor direct. Occasionally, the changes in compulsory thoughts anticipated a shift in the quality of the generalized feeling-state, this state bearing no particular relation to the thoughts or to the general mental state created by the compulsory thoughts. The feeling of pleasantness associated with an experience of pain also gave rise to a peculiar state—one that was seemingly self-contradictory. Finally the complex sensory qualities (marked pain plus intense pleasure) which accompanied the state of religious ecstasy is worth noting, because the ecstasy is usually said to be linked with the feeling of pleasure rather than that of pain. Experiences of this sort indicate that emotional qualities (pleasantness, unpleasantness, pain, fear, hate) can be dissociated from sensory and ideational processes and may be just as irrational to the sufferer as any other aspect of his psychopathological experience.

Feelings of Isolation and Lethargy

Differing from other feeling states is a condition characterized by the patient's complaints of feeling shut off from human contact and of finding himself isolated. In addition to the sense of isolation there are usually complaints of a loss of energy and interest. Others have called this a lassitude plus an inability to regain a feeling of being part of the life scene of the world about oneself. For example, the Rev. William Walford wrote as follows.

I began to shut myself up in solitude, as walking or riding through the streets made me feel as though every one I met was acquainted with my wickedness and misery. I could not endure to look anyone in the face, and ere long, the sight of my own face filled me with fear and aversion, as I considered myself to be wholly a reprobate, forsaken of God and odious to man. This unhappy sentiment originated in an irrepressible notion that I had been unfaithful in the performance of my duty, especially that which was connected with my college residence. Every instance of languor, deficiency, and imperfection which came to my remembrance, was so magnified and exaggerated as to appear of the most criminal and unpardonable nature. . . .

Taciturnity, irritability of temper, an unnatural and diseased sensibility of conscience, and such a degree of indolent lassitude as rendered every mental occupation distasteful, increased over me, to such a degree, as to alarm me lest the sanity of my mind should be subverted. At times my thoughts were so agitated and my conceptions so disturbed, as to make me apprehensive that some foreign invisible agency was acting upon me; imaginations of the most extraordinary nature often darted upon me with such rapidity, as left me without control over them. (Walford, 1851, pp. 179; 148)

This particular description was part of an account of a prolonged and acute depression. These feelings of isolation are usually reported as part of the process of melancholia; although they may also occur as part of other varieties of psychopathology. At no time did Walford consider himself to be truly insane; hence the disturbing fear that he might lose his mind was always with him.

I have drawn in previous chapters from Lenore McCall's autobiography dealing with her four years of melancholia; she spoke of her feeling of isolation as follows.

But I *am* alone and no one can help me. Don't you understand that's the worst of it? Even my children have slipped away from me. I can't hold on to them in my mind; I can't reach even my husband. I'm shut away by myself where everything is dim and queer. The only thing that's real now is the horror I'm in. (McCall, 1947 p. 52)

Another description of this intricate experience of inner isolation was given by a schizophrenic patient to Dr. A. Lewis.

I am more and more losing contact with my environment and with myself; instead of taking an interest in what goes on and caring about what happens with my illness, I am all the time losing my emotional contact with everything, including myself: what remains is only an abstract knowledge of what goes on around me and of the internal happenings in myself. . . . Even this illness which pierces to the centre of my whole life I can regard only objectively. But on rare occasions I am overwhelmed with the sudden realization of the ghastly destruction that is caused by this creeping uncanny disease that I have fallen victim to. . . . My life has something unreal, strangely unnatural about it now. . . . This dead emotionless attitude towards myself is almost as though I were protecting my nature against myself. With the numbing of my feelings I am as though half drugged: only in the rare accesses of anxiety I awake from this dream life and with torturing clearness I become aware of my actual state. . . . My despair sometimes floods over me. But after each such outburst I become more indifferent. I lose myself more in the disease, I sink into almost oblivious existence. My fate when I reflect upon it is the most horrible one can conceive of. I cannot picture anything more frightful than for a well-endowed cultivated human being to live through his own gradual deterioration, fully aware of it all the time. (Lewis, 1934, p. 346)

That this feeling of hopeless isolation waxes and wanes is worth noting. The patient seems to be saying, "The background of everyday emotional experience has changed so that I have become vegetable-like. I know that the background of ordinary well-being is missing; in its absence I feel overwhelmed by despair and fright because of my isolation which is over and above any personal change or changes in the world about me." In this case, the isolation feelings surged up and down as the patient happened to compare his feelings at the time to those he remembered before the illness began.

One of Dr. Bockner's patients, an elderly woman, described this feeling (which the physician had called emotional shallowness or depersonalization) in the following way.

My husband and I have always been happy together, but now he sits here and might be a complete stranger. I know he is my husband only by his appearance—he might be anybody for all I feel toward him. That's what worries me most of all. How can my feelings for him have changed after all these years? I was always soft and feminine, but now I feel hard, as though nothing could shock me any longer. I'm beyond feeling. Meeting a friend I say the conventional things, but feel nothing and don't mean what I say. A comedian on the wireless I normally like immensely just doesn't amuse me now. I laugh politely with everyone else, but feel neither joy nor sorrow. I hear the birds singing in the morning, but my hearing of pleasant sound is affected as badly as all my other feelings. (Bockner, 1949, pp. 969–970)

Such feelings of isolation are peculiar states, which, as I have said, usually follow or are part of prolonged despair. It is as if the persistent emotional storm had exhausted all deep feelings, leaving the person isolated, in a state of lethargy and lassitude; a feeling of "I have suffered too long and too intensely so that now I am set off apart from others, and nothing matters any longer."

It will be recalled that Dr. Rows' second patient was a former schoolteacher, whose entry to a mental hospital was precipitated by the sudden schizophrenic delusion that she was the reincarnation of Jesus Christ. She wrote the following description for her physician after having been in the hospital almost a year.

I have made a big effort the last two years to break out of that solitariness
. . . but I am becoming more isolated . . . I feel that I have not a single friend
in the world, but I make no complaint. I feel I have not a scrap of affection
for anyone, but I feel no bitterness—it would not matter to me if any acquaintance or I myself were removed by death. . . . I can't think how I can be
aroused, surprised, or offended. I am not interested in other people or in
myself . . . I don't care. (Rows, 1914, pp. 201–202)

This description of the feeling of schizophrenic isolation seems
similar to that which is often related by melancholics. For example, this
patient stated that she had suffered too much and too long and that she
was now too exhausted to evince further interest in friends or events.

In dealing with the topic of compulsions, Janet cited a description
made by a woman physician who had at one time been a dipsomaniac.

Nothing interests me any longer, I am weary of everything,—to be
interested in nothing is insupportable; it makes me nervous. Nothing is worth
the trouble of an effort. I can no longer even get angry, for nothing is worth
getting angry about, and I am astonished when I see people who have the
courage to get angry. All things are well enough; the children are brought up
well enough for what they have to do; the servants are satisfactory enough;
everything in life is passable, and it is very wearisome. To be neither unhappy
nor happy, to desire nothing, is very discouraging. You cannot imagine this
feeling of a shadow which, little by little, invades the whole of life, like an
eclipse of the sun. (Janet, 1906, pp. 8–9)

This feeling of isolation seems to resemble an absolute exhaustion of
emotional feeling that surprises the patient, particularly since there is no
necessary physical or mental fatigue connected with it.

Anhedonia or Apathy

Isolation is the feeling-state of being set aside or out of touch with
the usual contacts with persons and events, while there still remains some
awareness of the inappropriate feelings that still continue. The feeling of
isolation merges into another condition, that of a total lack of any feeling;
this condition was named *anhedonia* by the French psychopathologist
Ribot, almost a century ago.

Anhedonia (if I my coin a counter-designation to analgesia) has been
very little studied, but it exists. . . . A young girl, suffering from congested
liver and spleen . . . and thus, for a time, modified her constitution. . . . She
ceased to feel any affection for father or mother; would play with her doll,
but could not be brought to show any delight in it; could not be drawn out of
her apathetic sadness. Things which previously had made her shriek with
laughter now left her uninterested. . . . Esquirol has recorded the case of a
magistrate, a very intelligent man, suffering from a liver complaint. "Every
affection seemed to be dead in him. He showed neither perversion nor violence,

but there was complete absence of emotive reaction. If he went to the theatre (as he continued to do from force of habit) he could find no pleasure there. Thoughts of his house, his home, his wife, his absent children, affected him no more, he said, than a theorem of Euclid." (Ribot, 1914, pp. 53–54)

This condition of an absence of all, or practically all, appropriate affective responses was further described and explored by James in his *Varieties of Religious Experience*.

The world now looks remote, strange, sinister, uncanny. Its color is gone, its breath is cold, there is no speculation in the eyes it glares with. "It is as if I lived in another century," says another, "things are not as they were, and I am changed."—"I see," says a third, "I touch, but the things do not come near me, a thick veil alters the hue and look of everything."—"Persons move like shadows, and sounds seem to come from a distant world."—"There is no longer any past for me; people appear so strange; it is as if I could not see any reality, as if I were in a theatre; as if people were actors, and everything were scenery; I can no longer find myself; I walk, but why? Everything floats before my eyes, but leaves no impression."—"I weep false tears, I have unreal hands: the things I see are not real things." (James, 1902, pp. 151–152)

It is evident that different persons use different phrases to describe this condition of greatly reduced affect. It is so unusual that some patients use terms which either imply or directly state ideas of unreality and depersonalization (see Chapter 17). An instance of this variety was supplied by Dr. Angyal in paraphrasing a statement made by one of his patients.

He has various symptoms of depersonalization which are very striking. He feels that his "personality is like a shadow on the ground," "like a stick of wood in the wind"; pointing to himself he says: "That is only my name, not me." Most of his complaints refer to the experience that he is divided into many persons who interfere with each other. For example, he says: "I am half. I am 50 per cent somebody else. There is an extra one, another A.D." (patient's name). "You ask questions from me, and the other answers it." "I can't do anything; if I want to do something they abstract it from me and add it to the other." Pointing to himself he says: "This person is not the same any more. Every day another person comes in this room." "They put me in two or three parts, in two or three figures." "They knock me in so many pieces that I can't get hold of myself." (Angyal, 1936, p. 35)

I have cited this example in its present context to show how anhedonia, isolation, and depersonalization overlap.

Several examples that may be more clearly representative of anhedonia may be given. An inspirational essayist, Benson, from whose book *Thy Rod and Thy Staff* I have quoted before, wrote as follows.

How can I express the inexpressible? No analogies will make it clear. The soul seemed to inhabit my body as a man inhabits a house; but though the house seemed ruinous and tottering to its fall, squalid and darkly shuttered, the inhabitant seemed in no way disconcerted or concerned, but preparing, if need was, to leave it. I had no sort of hope of recovering my health or activity. I simply looked forward to some hideous collapse of brain and body alike; and meanwhile the inhabitant held on his way, executed his designs, and gave no hint of his will. When I reproached myself with my heedless and trivial life, my foolish passing-by of opportunities, my dulness and perversity, the soul said nothing either of comfort or of blame. (Benson, 1912, p. 52)

This analogy is picturesque yet it also manages to convey an idea of the lack of any feeling state, either appropriate or inappropriate. Benson seemingly considered his behavior to be impersonally mechanical.

A widow wrote to Dr. Hughes describing the mental state she had been in since the death of her husband. This description seems to portray another variety of the "mechanical" condition of anhedonia.

I experienced a most sudden and violent change or revolution, a complete breaking up or giving way of the whole nervous system or inner man, and since that dark and sad hour I have never had a natural feeling or sensation. Everything is wrong, the whole sympathetic system completely paralyzed. Every feeling and sensation that makes life is completely annihilated. I have not even the common sensations of hunger, thirst, or any sensation whatever of sleep. All is gone, and every act of my life is now purely mechanical. I, of course, take food, and sometimes have a kind of sleep, but entirely devoid of sensation or desire, and therefore painfully mechanical. (Hughes, 1885, pp. 84–85)

She wrote that this condition had continued for several years. In spite of her insistence on the lack of feelings she did complain about the hopelessness and loss of interest that pervaded her mental life. It is difficult to infer exactly what the trouble was from which she was suffering.

According to Dr. Starobinski, a male patient, who alternated daily between manic and depressive phases, described the depressive phases in terms of apathy or loss of feeling rather than in the more usual terms of hopeless sadness.

The bad day is for me a state of complete apathy, the best thing being for me to be left alone; it begins during the night when I awake around two, three or four o'clock; I doze then until the morning and this light sleep is adorned with black thoughts or sad ones. Almost regularly I am sorry for all the things I have done or said during the preceding good day, but I hasten to add that 24 hours later when the good day has reclaimed its rights, I regret rarely or disapprove rarely what I have said or done previously: (I don't want to say by this that I approve completely what I have done; on the contrary, *the feeling of my inadequacy and of my awkwardness prevails in me during the good or bad days,* but I should accept myself as I am, having, however, tried to correct myself). Let us continue with the bad days. I have a good appetite and I am almost ashamed of it; also the meals are the only acts which will make me walk; but I don't go gladly to a table d'hôte. Conversation is for me unpleasant and painful especially when it is not elicited by a useful and clearly fixed subject, as for example, the visit of the doctor or a friend. It is very hard for me to correspond or to do any work which involves thought. I could do this work but with an effort which tires me very much and which irritates me or annoys me. (Starobinski, 1921, p. 345)

The affectless state is sometimes reported by schizophrenic patients. For example, a patient wrote Dr. Heveroch about his mental condition while in a hospital, saying in part as follows.

I am without psychic feelings; if I speak or do something, I don't feel that I am speaking or doing something at the same time; that is terrible for me. I am living and actually not living. In writing and figuring my pencil moves swiftly. The thought to write comes to me by itself without previous decision. My thoughts germinate so quickly, that I am unable to follow them, but conversely: I cannot pursue a longer trend of thought; everything escapes from my senses and my body is surrounded by a numb fog. (Heveroch, 1913, p. 426)

This description, like several that preceded it, emphasizes the mechanical nature of the person's actions and thinking. For this patient life went on without the appropriate feeling states, although he did say that the experience was a "terrible" one for him.

Finally, a description of this condition related to Karen Horney by a neurotic or anxiety-phobic patient may be cited in order to show that anhedonia is similar in both neurosis and psychosis.

Now, for the first time I saw it—I was literally unable to *feel* anything. (Yes, for all my famous super-sensitivity!) How well I knew pain—every pore of me clogged with inward rage, self-pity, self-contempt, and despair for the last six years and over and over again and again! Yet, I saw it now—all was negative, reactive, compulsive, *all imposed from without, inside* there was absolutely nothing of mine! There just was nothing. Had I been a little less numb I suppose I'd at last have cut my throat. (Horney, 1949, p. 5)

Present-day systematic psychiatric observation has repeatedly emphasized the occurrence of so-called emotional blunting or loss of affect, particularly among schizophrenic patients. This does not imply that a condition of true anhedonia obtains, but rather that an appearance of inappropriate or inadequate emotionality marks the patient's behavior. Lang, whose experiences have been cited earlier and at length, commented on this point in the following way.

My experience has led me to the conclusion that the seeming loss of affective capacity so often reported . . . is not so much an actual loss of capacity as it is a shift in the direction of affective discharge. Affectivity becomes centered around ideation. Ideas rather than sensory and motor phenomena form the focus of affective activity. Another factor which tends also to lead to an exaggeration of the loss of affective capacity is the degree of cortical dominance present in the patient. Often I have had the experience of feeling an affective response, but having trained myself to favor ideation over emotion, I have tried to block the affective response from showing any outward sign. This repression of the outer expression of an affect may lead an outer observer to the view that the affect itself is missing when actually it is not. (Lang, 1939b, p. 197)

If one may speculate concerning the nature of the feeling-states that have been considered thus far in this chapter, it may be that much of this phenomenology is founded on a generalized emotional state which seems inappropriate to the patient himself. This state could be attributed to a loosening of the bonds of psychological associations within the person's mental organization. In any event, the result is a disorganization, in which the usual relation between external circumstances and inner feelings does not exist. The particular name an individual gives to the feeling, such as resentment, hate, guilt, and isolation, is probably related to the circumstances that govern the perceptual world at the time, or possibly to his habitual emotional state. For example, a generalized disorganized affective condition might be labeled as a feeling of guilt, if circumstances were actually such that other persons seemed to be reproachful or if the usual attitude of the person were inclined to be intrapunitive. Irrespective of its origin, the feeling is nevertheless recognized by the patient as being peculiar and different. The fact that it possesses these strange qualities leads him to report the state as unusual and indefinable. Or the patient might agree with Lang and say that he had more interest in ideas than feelings, particularly since the feelings seemed to be so changeable and unreal.

DISCUSSION

It is difficult to assign a name to certain subjective emotional experiences. For example I may say, "I'm afraid" when I am in physical danger. Others may comprehend the meaning of my statement because they can easily observe the conditions surrounding me and my behavior at this particular time. These other persons remember how they felt when in somewhat similar circumstances. In an absolute sense this similarity does not justify anyone in saying that what I feel when I say "afraid" is identical with the inner feeling which he calls fear. However, in actual practice such similarities are sufficiently meaningful so that we achieve interpersonal understanding concerning personal feelings with but little difficulty.

Difficulties do arise when a person tries to describe a feeling-state that occurred during some period of either physical or mental illness. It is apparent that each person whose experience we have cited in this chapter was groping for the proper words with which to clothe his experience and was not particularly satisfied with the final description he had given. The generalized feeling-state seems different from the normal feelings of anxiety, discomfort, and despair, or any other of the more ordinary affective experiences. Some patients will say, "When I have this or that peculiar feeling I know I'm very ill or even insane; when I do not have it, I am sure I'm well and sane again." In a way, this identification of a strange feeling-state seems akin to the aura or feeling-state that precedes an epileptic seizure. It has a distinctly sensory-affective quality that the individual can discriminate in himself but that is difficult or impossible to convey adequately to others.

Another difficulty in communication that the mental patient experiences arises from the lability of his feeling states. He finds himself pervaded with an emotion that is, so far as he is concerned, new, distinctive, and different. Then this feeling-state vanishes (for little or no comprehensible reason) and he finds himself pervaded by yet another very different feeling, or, in some instances, by an absence of any emotion at all. One of the patient's major difficulties in this connection derives from the fact that these experiences seem to him to arise involuntarily from within himself, or to be inflicted from without so that the effect in either case is inappropriate, involuntary, and overwhelming. The patient usually attempts to rationalize the experience by saying that it is due to one or another set of circumstances, but when he does he will usually remain more or less dissatisfied with his own explanation. Furthermore, the EDITOR function—that curious dissociated state—seems to stand at one side observing rationally the peculiar changes which are going on in the remainder of one's mental life.

Why some persons seem possessed by such a generalized state of anger, resentment, and hostility constitutes a special problem. The patient may correctly appreciate the situation in which he finds himself, the unfairness with which he has been treated, and the futility of his efforts to make himself understood—all of which are circumstances sufficient to arouse irritation, anger, and resentment. But over and above this, some patients do consider the resentment they feel as too great for the circumstances and that the anger has somehow been pushed on them by outside forces. The feeling of hostility seems to be a feeling-state distinctly different from that of guilt, self-condemnation, or isolation. The feeling of angry hostility overwhelms the individual in an involuntary and unreasonable fashion, just as guilt or fear may do.

In contrast to the more unusual and recognizable emotional states of fear, anger, suffering, and lust, with their host of variations and combinations, are the states that are characterized by the decrease, loss, or absence of emotion. In this category I have placed the phenomena that go by such terms as isolation, apathy, and anhedonia.

These affectless states are not limited to any one diagnostic group. We have cited reports given by a wide variety of types of mental patients that convey the same basic idea. The condition may be experienced for a few hours or for months. One might think that the affective void would result in a truly neutral feeling—neither pleasant nor unpleasant. Actually, every citation here presented, as well as every other description of this sort that we have come across, conveys the general impression that the patient does not like the experience—he finds it unpleasant—despite his paradoxical complaint of an utter lack of feeling.

The feeling-state of isolation seems to be in large part a characterization of mental exhaustion following a period of intense turmoil. It carries in addition the element of unreality that is so characteristic of changeable psychopathological states. Whether the complaint will be one of isolation or of apathy seems to depend upon individual peculiarities rather than on any particular pattern of mental processes, at least as far as present-day diagnoses are concerned.

Whether there is a true difference between anhedonia and apathy is impossible to say. In all likelihood, anhedonia refers to the condition where a patient says, "I can't feel," whereas apathy refers to a state where the report should be, "I don't feel because I don't care." Probably because anhedonia is an uncommon, technical word, I have not found it employed in any actual report of a patient.

In the reports of these deficient affective states there is usually included a statement to the effect that the surroundings seemed to the person unreal and alien. Whether it is the lack of feeling that gives rise to the strangeness of the surrounding world or vice versa is impossible to say, though it is apparent that feelings of unreality do sometimes occur in association with normal emotional experiences—for example, "Things seem unreal and that frightens me."

Finally, a comment is desirable on the so-called generalized emotional states. First, there are reports of conditions where only emotions remained in the consciousness of the individual. These states seem to be largely characterized by a stuporous semiconsciousness. Secondly, there are reports which imply that the psychotic state has a different and distinctive "feel." This is an important point, if true.

The patient says, "I cannot"; his family says, "He will not";
the fact is, "He cannot will." (*Author unknown*)

CHAPTER 16

Disorders of Volition

INTRODUCTION

Previous chapters have been concerned with disorders
of emotion, perception, and thought—that is, with
emotional and cognitive disabilities. Obviously, no part
of this material dealt solely with either emotion or
cognition, since the emotional and cognitive elements
of experience are closely interrelated and in addition,
knit with the conative (striving) aspects of experience.
Reports that have emphasized volitional disabilities
may next be considered.

In Chapter 2 I demonstrated repeatedly that
many psychiatric patients first became aware of their
mental disturbance and acknowledged the fact when
they realized that they could no longer exert voluntary
control of their thoughts and behavior. I have also
cited many excerpts made by individuals who might
admit that their perceptual and intellectual functioning was faulty and confused, and yet continued to
insist that they were in control of their mental faculties
and that they were in no sense insane. Similarly, other
patients have related how they became overwhelmed
by senseless fear or anger but still continued to insist

that they were never really abnormal. Only when a patient realizes that he has lost his self-control will he admit that he is probably deranged.

Every person believes that he can, by using his own will power, control and direct his thoughts and behavior. Furthermore, he is confident that he, and only he, is responsible for his inner life and external behavior. If unreasonable and pervasive thoughts or feelings intrude into his mind, or if he finds himself behaving in some peculiar way, he rationalizes both the event and the surrounding circumstances; that is, he quickly supplies an explanation (which may or may not be true) that satisfies him (or others) and that fits the event into the more usual and acceptable categories of experience. The major function of this rationalization process is that of adjusting successive phases of inner experience into the reasonable, self-consistent stream which is part of the broad stream of the person's mental life. But when the patient finds that his own thoughts and behavior proceed in an uncontrollable fashion for which he can no longer find a "reasonable" basis, he becomes convinced that his mind has come under some external or supernatural control, more powerful than any strength of will or volitional process he may possess. For example, visual hallucinations, persistence of hallucinatory voices, compulsions, and unnatural feeling-states will compel the person to realize that mysterious outside governing forces are more powerful than any self-generated, internal control. At this point he will usually retreat, saying that he is no longer responsible for his mental life and social behavior. Such an admission generally makes "sense," both to the afflicted person and to everyone else, since a mental illness is popularly regarded as a disruption of psychological processes that results in a loss of control.

But what is will power? How can I, or anyone else, recognize the qualitative or quantitative aspects of the experience of will? Volitional experiences do not bear self-scrutiny or prolonged introspection. The experience is tenuous, fleeting, and fluid. It affords little or no basis for rational or objective verification. This tenuous quality is so generally recognized that further analysis or explanation is rarely requested. There are many varieties of mental experience, such as fragments of remembrances, memory traces of decisions, fleeting feelings, patterns of preconceptions, and other tricks of mind, that are ordinarily neither scrutinized nor scrutinizable. We can only accept such experiential material as part of the qualitative stuff that complicates and "flavors" conscious awareness. Everyone recognizes the elusive nature of such fragments of conscious experience; if these experiences do not continue for too long and are not too intrusive or demanding, they are usually ignored. The volitional capacity (whether for simple movements or complex deeds) must neither be absent nor grossly interfere with the general mental processes. If the volitional quality is persistently absent or intrusive, the afflicted patient recognizes the disturbance in his will power. Depending on the over-all effect of such abnormalities in the desire or intention to act, the psychological state that results may be anything from mere annoyance to complete disability.

Disorders of volition have received various designations, depending on the circumstances of their occurrence and the effect on the person having the experience. Among the terms used in this connection are fixed ideas, obsessions, compulsions, irresistible ideas, imperative commands, and abulia.

Fixed Ideas

In order to gain some understanding of the nature of these types of volitional disabilities—minor obsessions—examples were collected by Berry from a group of normal college students. Berry requested the students to provide him with answers to two questions: first, "Do you have or have you had any fixed ideas?" and second, "Do you have any ideas which involuntarily come to you when you are fatigued?" The following are a few of the answers he received to these questions.

I used to have a fixed idea of a monstrous stone so high that I couldn't see its top, and the stone would begin to roll toward me menacingly. I haven't had it, however, since I was a little youngster. So now it is very vague. Only the fearful sensation remains.

I have . . . a fixed idea . . . I don't remember ever being seriously injured with a knife . . . I can't imagine where I ever developed such a feeling of perfect terror for that object. The thought of it comes at most inopportune times when there is no occasion at all for is appearance. I can be talking on an apparently interesting topic of conversation when all at once without any warning, whatever, I shudder as I feel the blade of a knife hurting me. I know it is ridiculous to imagine that I am being cut, but I cannot help being frightened. . . . Sometimes I can feel the sharp blade in my mouth and I am perfectly certain that in real life it never was there. I haven't told anyone of the queer sensation for I do not wish to be considered abnormal. . . .

When I was about eight years of age I had a fixed idea. I thought I was going to cut my throat from ear to ear with a certain large butcher-knife in my grandmother's kitchen. I couldn't throw off the idea. I was afraid to go near the knife. This persisted for about two weeks, then gradually wore off. When fatigued certain combinations of words or letters recur again and again. Often I am wholly unaware of their origin. For instance the words "sy," "cip" have come to me over and over the last few days, and I am absolutely ignorant of where or when I heard or saw them. . . .

I am not sure the following would be designated as a fixed idea, but I have never been able to discover any reason for the occurrence. My home for several years was on a farm. I never went into the large barn alone that I did not feel impelled to look at the rafters to see whether there was not some one hanging there. I realized the foolishness of the idea but could never drive it away, and in spite of all my resolutions to the contrary I invariably looked almost before I realized what I was doing. The impression was not nearly so vivid when others were present. . . .

I do have fixed ideas . . . When I am at a railway station watching a train come in I have a desire to jump in front of it and I never have been able to get rid of this feeling. The same thing happened when I saw Niagara Falls this summer. I felt as though something were urging me to jump into them. (Berry, 1916, pp. 19–22)

Fixed ideas similar to those described by Berry's subjects are not uncommon in the everyday life of the normal individual. The experience is often reported to be mildly unpleasant, intrusive, and of unknown origin. Although fixed ideas are largely conative in nature they cannot be started, modified, or stopped voluntarily. During an individual's life span, experiences begin, run their course, and slowly lose their emotional impact over a period of time. Fixed ideas of this degree of intensity cannot be considered as pathological per se. They seem to differ from true pathological experience largely in terms of intensity or of the extent to which they complicate the general mental functioning of the individual.

Obsessions

When a fixed idea or feeling continues to intrude into a person's thinking, often it may lead to behavior which that person comes to regard as unreasonable and annoying. This continuous condition is termed an obsession. We may illustrate this concept from the account of a general surgeon who, after entering the British Army during World War II, found himself overtaken by feelings of anxiety and by obsessive ideas. He found that these ideas forced him to attempt to restrain his thoughts and behavior during his professional work. Finally these ideas compelled him to seek psychiatric assistance. He later described his experiences in this way.

Acute visual obsessions were terrifying, both because of their apparent meaninglessness, and because of their independent existence. I often had the most acute image, for instance, of a hammer and screwdriver working away at my skull, or of my skull being forced open and spat into, perhaps at a moment when an observer would only have noted me as a surgeon doing some operation or talking to my commanding officer. I would be opening an abdomen, for instance, and would have the most vivid hallucinosis of eyes looking at me from within the cavity. At night I was driven to distraction by thoughts of self-destruction—not by the wish to do so but an accurate representation of suicide in various unpleasant ways—and I took elaborate precautions to guard against this. Silly jingles and rhyming phrases said themselves over and over again in my head. Every now and again, of course, all this boiled up to an unbearable intensity. (Lancet, Editors of, 1952, pp. 84–85)

This surgeon became convinced that he was losing his mind, and that he was beyond ordinary medical help. His surgical work continued to be satisfactory but his loss of self-control became so unbearable that he had to be invalided from active military service in order to seek intensive psychotherapy.

Another description was written by a patient who, having over-worked for many years, finally consulted a physician because of stomach pains. During the medical treatment Dr. Baillarger found that the patient had many hypochondriacal complaints and obsessions and had written a manuscript detailing both his physical and mental symptoms. Portions of this manuscript were published by Dr. Baillarger, from which the following is a relevant excerpt.

If I decided to go horse-back riding I would see myself falling on my head and breaking it on the rocks; the ideas of a boat excursion brought without fail the idea of being ship-wrecked. In the country, it was the fear of snakes that would pursue me; it seemed to me that there were some even in my bed. Whatever security my room offered me I could not go to bed without first making a thorough search and it is with difficulty that I would fall asleep. This fear of snakes would follow me even to the city. Sometimes I would imagine that somebody was hidden under my bed in order to stab me; the slightest noise would keep me awake and provoke in me fears, and I would never consent to sleep alone in a house. I always bear in mind objects, people and even the places I am being told about and if I am told about a scene I immediately see all the characters appear. If I am told, for example, of the death of some woman, I see that person immediately, she is being placed in a coffin, I assist at her burial, she is lowered into the grave and *all this is in my mind.* Often I have seen myself dead and assisted in advance at my own funeral procession. (Baillarger, 1856, p. 56)

Dr. Baillarger considered that this patient's complaints were a form of monomania and wrote at some length concerning the automatisms involved. It is obvious that the patient was overwhelmed by obsessive fears—particularly fear of death—and that he had no voluntary control over his intrusive and obsessive thoughts. At the time this report was published (1856) the patient was certainly disturbed and handicapped in his everyday activities, but he was not considered to be candidate for admission to an asylum.

However, there have been instances in which obsessions may, if sufficiently acute, lead the individual to believe that his mind has gone astray and that he should be hospitalized as one who is mentally incompetent. A patient who had been committed to a mental hospital because of obsessive ideas and compulsive behavior, which led to general mental confusion, wrote a description of his troubles, from which an illustrative portion published by Dr. Zeifert may be cited.

> I'm constantly afraid I'm going out of my head. . . . Anything that comes up in my head I try to remember. If I walk the street I try to remember everything I see. There is no reason for my doing it except that I must remember it. . . . Since I have been in the hospital I have had all sorts of compulsions. . . . The worst of it all is, Doctor, that I feel I have to remember. I'll be unhappy all day now because I'll try to remember everything I said to you and everything you said to me. . . .
>
> I am forced to remember everything; I hear something on the radio and then I have to know all about the words of that song; when I look at the window I have to keep counting all the windows and try to remember them; when I go to bed at night I have to keep repeating the names of the patient on my left and the one on my right for fear I won't remember them in the morning and this keeps me from sleeping; I know I am incurable; this drives me mad. (Zeifert, 1940, p. 295)

As far as one can judge from this patient's account, his depression and anxieties were thought by him to be secondary to the driving force of his obsessions and his inability to exercise any control over them. It was as if compulsive questions and doubts had overwhelmed him in most of his activities, both physical and mental. Although he realized the absurdity of his obsessional ideas, he could not by his own will control or change them. Generally speaking, obsessions are intrusive, irrational, and uncontrollable mental states. Even if a patient does recognize some of the aspects of the origin of his trouble, he remains unable to control the persistent ideas or emotions and cannot resist actions that grow out of the obsessions.

Compulsions

The terms *obsession* and *compulsion* are used somewhat interchangeably. *Obsession* implies a persistent, unavoidable, haunting idea, usually motivated by fear, while *compulsion* implies a more definite force that acts against the will and, in turn, leads to overt action. Since both terms are used in trying to describe persistent and unwelcome feelings that tend to lead to action, neither term can be expected to convey much descriptive precision or clear understanding.

A forty-year-old patient wrote Dr. E. Straus a description of the development of a compulsive system of ideas and behavior that had overwhelmed her. While ill in a hospital some fifteen or twenty years earlier, a visitor had placed a bouquet of flowers on her bed. Her cousin had removed the bouquet saying that flowers should not be placed on an invalid's bed. This cousin had a three-year-old son who died several weeks after this incident. The patient then became obsessed by the idea that touching or being touched by flowers might lead to death. She had loved flowers but found she could no longer touch them or allow them to be brought into her home. Since she lived not far from a cemetery, where friends and acquaintances were in the habit of decorating graves with flowers, on occasion they would visit her while carrying bouquets. Such visits led to the development of further compulsive acts.

If one of these [neighborhood] people touched me, I would have to wash the affected garment with soap flakes or benzine. Or someone who had been there [the cemetery] would come to our house, and then I cannot move around properly. I have the feeling as if the rooms were becoming too narrow and I were hitting everything with my dress. I have to go through the door sideways. In order to find peace, I wash everything in soapy water and, depending on the circumstances, I also have to wash the dress which I wore at the time. Then everything becomes large and wide again and I have room. If I go shopping and someone is in the store, I cannot go in, because I might either be pushed by the people there, or receive the money that had belonged to them. Thus, I am anxious the whole day long and this anxiety drives me hither and yon. Now I have to wipe away or wash something here, then over there. . . . I do not find peace anywhere. . . . I am also disturbed by pictures in newspapers and magazines where such things are portrayed. If I happen to lay my hand on them I again wash it with soap. . . . Inwardly I am constantly agitated and the beautiful saying suits me well: "Where thou art not, there dwells peace!" (Straus, 1938, p. 64)

According to Straus, this woman's basic obsession consisted of a senseless but pervasive fear of death. This fear spread to germs and contamination and then generalized to a fear of contamination of any sort. Although she realized intellectually that her fears and compulsive rituals were nonsensical, she was not able to exercise sufficient self-control to maintain her peace of mind.

When obsessions and compulsions characterize the individual's reaction to internal conflict and anxiety, as in Straus' patient, the condition is generally referred to as obsessive-compulsive neurosis. The actual symptoms, however, are not restricted to this diagnostic category. Some psychotic patients, particularly schizophrenics, live through periods of incessant, obsessive mental activity. Schreber, for example, complained bitterly of his mental disturbances that were created by such compulsive behavior.

This [divine] influence showed itself relatively early in the form of *compulsive thinking*—an expression which I received from the inner voices themselves and which will hardly be known to other human beings, because the whole phenomenon lies outside all human experience. The nature of compulsive thinking lies in a human being having to think incessantly; in other words, man's natural right to give the nerves of his mind their necessary rest from time to time by thinking nothing (as occurs most markedly during sleep) was from the beginning denied me by the rays in contact with me; they continually wanted to know what I was thinking about. For instance I was asked in these very words: "What are you thinking of now?"; because this question is in itself complete nonsense, as a human being can at certain times as well think of *nothing* as of *thousands of things at the same time*, and because my nerves did not react to this absurd question, one was soon driven to take refuge in a system of *falsifying my thoughts*.

Compulsive thinking . . . contravenes man's natural right of mental relaxation . . . it disturbs the "basis" of a human being. My nerves are influenced by the rays to vibrate corresponding to certain human words; their choice therefore is not subject to my own will, but is due to an influence exerted on me from without. From the beginning the *system of not-finishing-a-sentence* prevailed . . . the words so produced contain not mainly finished thoughts, but unfinished ideas . . . It is in the nature of nerves that if unconnected words or started phrases are thrown into them, they automatically attempt to complete them to finished thoughts satisfactory to the human mind. (Schreber, 1955, pp. 70; 171)

The experience Schreber said would "hardly be known to other human beings" has actually been recounted by many other persons, both normal and deranged. Psychotic compulsions differ from the typical neurotic's compulsions in that the former usually attributes the irresistible demands and orders to an external force. Also, in obsessive-compulsive neuroses there is a continuum between the persistent thought and the act —both seem to originate from one single dynamic cause, as seemed to be true for Straus' patient. In contrast, Schreber's compulsion seemed to be related to his over-all psychotic disturbance rather than to some specific fear. When one recalls that Schreber had been the Presiding Judge of a high court, his lack of volitional and intellectual control becomes yet more impressive as a form of disturbance.

Obsessive ideas do in some cases become so intense that the person fears his own impulses, which may become homicidal. In 1882, a physician who had testified in the trial of a man accused of attempting to take the life of the Queen of England, received a lengthy letter signed "Sufferer," which he submitted for publication. The letter was concerned with a strong compulsion to commit murder that the writer said he had experienced for many years. Some passages are of unusual interest.

Now, sir, *I am a Homicidal* (and sometimes Suicidal) *Maniac*. Up to the present time I have only *thought* these awful thoughts, I have never put them in *action*, but at the same time it is quite true that I cannot control them (the thoughts). But for God's help (in answer to agonizing prayer) I know not where I might ere now have been. It is awful to contemplate.

To go back. It is now 17 years since I had an attack of nervous debility, brought on by working overtime to help my dear old parents (curse overtime). One night my mother was away from home, and I slept with my father. There was an old Dagger in a cupboard in the Room, and my thoughts went unconsciously and without any will, wish, or control of mine to that, and I felt an almost irresistible impulse to get out of bed and murder my father with the dagger, but I did not. I laid and trembled, and after that fell asleep. From that moment to this I have been a different creature . . .

Go where I will, be where I may, in Church, Chapel, Street, House, or public Meeting of any sort, the same ideas pursue me. *I hear* NO *voices.* It seems an IMPULSE, as in other people there is an impulse to go whoring, &c., when no object is present to give rise to the thought. But I argue this way. Sins of the flesh, avarice, ambition, &c., are *natural,* my mania is *unnatural;* and whatever is unnatural must be wrong. Still it is all of no use. However I will hope, strive, pray, and endeavour by God's help not to fall. I am certainly in Hell. Such thoughts form a Hell to anyone who has just sense enough to know they are wrong. (Manning, 1882, pp. 370–371)

This letter leaves no doubt about the compulsive tendencies which the writer had up to that time successfully resisted. The writer was certain that his impulses were evil and unnatural, but was skeptical of being able to keep up his resistance.

We may mention another oft-cited example of homicidal mania, the case of a Frenchman named Glenadel. He had always been very devoted to his mother, but at the age of sixteen he became obsessed with the idea that he might "accidentally" kill her. This obsession was most repugnant to him, and to relieve his guilt he somehow shifted its object, so that the compulsion was directed toward his sister-in-law. In order to avoid committing an actual murder, he enlisted as a soldier; while in the Army, however, he found himself continually obsessed with the idea that he might desert in order to return home and carry out his tormenting impulse. After several years word reached him that his sister-in-law had died, upon which he accepted a furlough and returned home. To his horror, he found his sister-in-law and mother both alive and well. In an attempt at self-protection, Glenadel had himself roped in bed and then requested that he be committed to a mental hospital. When the examining health officer asked him, among other things, whether he had any complaints against his mother, he replied as follows.

No, monsieur, I loved her very much; thus, before starting, I said to myself [in 1812], "Shall I kill that mother who has exercised so much care over me during my infancy, and who has loved me so well, although I have entertained this fatal thought against her? I will not do it, but I must kill some one." It was then that the thought of killing my sister-in-law first occurred to me; I have a distinct recollection of this, I being at that time in Dax, and it was in the year 1832. It was then [1837] announced to me that my sister-in-law was dead, which was a mistake, it being another relative who had died. I then accepted the furlough they had offered me, which I should by no means have done, had I known that my sister-in-law was still living. When I reached my home, and was informed that she was not dead, I experienced such a sinking and depression of spirits, that I became quite sick, and my idea resumed its course. (Anon., 1850d, p. 49)

At the time of this examination, 1839, Glenadel had been suffering from the same compulsive homicidal urge for 26 years. During all these years he was able to resist the idea and conduct himself rationally. On the evening of his admission to the asylum he wrote to the physician-in-charge saying that he would behave himself at all times, and continuing, "You will think me cured. At moments perhaps I shall pretend to be so. Never believe me. Never let me out on any pretext: The only use I shall make of my liberty will be to commit a crime which I abhor."

That such compulsive ideas may actually break through all barriers of inhibition and self-restraint is illustrated by the case of a patient who shot and killed a surgeon who had previously treated her. When asked why she killed him, she replied as follows.

Because I couldn't get him out of mind: and this from the time I left the hospital; that made him a victim too. I couldn't understand why I was so attracted to him. I could control myself before that; what I mean, I couldn't stay away from him. That person was always in my mind! Before the operation I could have kept from thinking about him, but afterward I never could. And I couldn't stay away from his office. I knew that as long as I was in the city that I'd always think of him. I thought that was the only way to get him out of my thoughts. . . . I'd give anything I could ever have to be what I was before the operation. That is, able to work, able to control myself, rid of the numbness and cramps in my arms and legs, and the ideas, too. . . . The feeling like wanting the Doctor, and wanting to be near him and all that, these caused me the most trouble. I thought that was the only way to get him out of my thoughts. That was the biggest reason—to get him out of my mind. My mind since, is relieved. I don't think about him as much as I did before. (Rathmell and Corrin, 1940, pp. 318–319)

This woman was said by the police to be partially deranged after the murder. She had yielded to her obsession, believing that overt action would drive the idea of the doctor out of her mind. Although she said in this interview that her mind was relieved after the murder, her subsequent behavior gave evidence of the persistence of further compulsions and destructive tendencies. The psychiatric report of her case brought out the evidence that from childhood the patient had been a lonely, unloved person. Her development, physical and psychological, was considered to be abnormal. With respect to the murder, the court psychiatrist concluded that during her period of aftercare from surgery, when she had received understanding and sympathetic treatment, she had fixated her need for affection on the surgeon, and, the need remaining unfulfilled, her emotional cravings and morbid ideas had led her to commit murder.

Obsessive ideas and compulsions may lead to criminal acts other than homicide or suicide. *The Autobiography of David* is the life story of a man who, from early adolescence, had suffered from an unreasonable fear of open spaces. His phobia was so pervasive and compelling that, at times, he was unable to work to earn his livelihood. To this phobic affliction was added the compulsion to expose himself.

I was out one day a little further from home than usual and resting against a railing, when opposite me at a groundfloor window I saw a young woman. She was standing just between two lace curtains and looking at me. Suddenly the thought flashed into my mind: "What if that girl should see me naked?" The idea was ridiculous, I knew, but my limbs began to tremble, and a cold sweat broke out over me. "What if I could not control myself, and I were to unfasten my clothes before her," was the next thought. I became torn with a panic of fear. . . . From that day this new dread was added to the others. For about a year I never went out of doors without the fear that I might expose myself. The acuteness of the agony that this cost me was probably greater than any of my other dreads. . . . Sometimes when very bad I would make a pretence of going down the stairs of an entry to the basement where the cellars were. I had often done this to get away to absolute quietness. Now in my extremity, I resorted to this means of escape and while there my strength failed me. I did that which I had feared [exposed himself], for facing me at the other side of the garden upon which the basement opened were a number of houses, their windows looking towards where I stood. (Raymond, 1946, p. 59)

When the spasm was over, David found himself lying on a rubbish heap, dazed and exhausted. To save the scandal of open court proceedings, he was certified as mentally irresponsible and committed to a mental hospital. The court and physicians held that his was a case where the temporary inhibition of will power resulted from "acute nervousness." The disability caused by the fear of open places had somewhat subsided before the act of indecent exposure, but during and after hospitalization all his phobias returned in full force.

It is apparent that there is little essential difference between a fixed or perseverative idea and an obsession or compulsion, except that obsessions and compulsions are usually much more socially harmful and disturbing. These disorders of volition usually involve great anxiety and fear, but the anxiety and fear are not of themselves reported by the sufferer as being the primary motivating force of the disturbance. The onset and course of disorders of volition may be experienced and described somewhat as follows: "For reasons I do not know, I found myself possessed by a feeling of being compelled to think about some specific idea and then to act upon the idea. I could not and cannot control this compulsion; rather, it controls me. I usually realize that the compulsion has no logical or rational basis, but it forces me to think and behave unreasonably. Usually I am aware that no positive gain will result from anything I may do as a consequence of my compulsion. My actions only partially appease the queer feeling. When the compulsions first began they were associated with a rather limited group of circumstances; for example, a fearful feeling which I attributed to the idea that eyes were watching me as I worked. This feeling tended to spread from the idea of eyes to other ideas. Then it became attached to many other ideas. It now complicates almost everything I do. I know that all this is unreasonable and foolish. But I can't stop the feeling. It's stronger than I am."

Irresistible Impulses

The experience of quite suddenly feeling compelled to perform some involuntary action—against one's better judgment—is termed an irresistible impulse. The impulse—for example, an unreasonable fit of anger—is usually described as coming into the mind abruptly and overriding all other thoughts. The concept of irresistible impulse has some status in courts of law, which implies that it has happened frequently among the general population as well as among deranged persons. The following account recorded by an anonymous writer is typical.

One night, after a number of weeks of fearful suffering, as I was lying in bed tossing, sleepless and despairing, a most horrible impulse seized me, an impulse impelling me to destroy one who of all living beings, most deserved my love. I buried myself under the bedcloths and struggled with the hellish impulse till the bed shook. It still gained strength. I sprang up, clung to the bedpost and sunk my teeth, in the agony of despair, into the hard wood. It was uncontrollable. I shut my eyes, bowed down my head for fear that I should see her, and rushed out of the house. Bare-footed, with no covering save a nightshirt, I ran through the streets to the Police Office and implored them to lock me up. Fortunately the officer on duty was a humane and sensible man. He gave me a watch-coat to wrap around me, kept me under his own eye, and, I suppose, sent notice to my friends, for my wife and sister came with clothing. The paroxysm had passed, and gasping, panting for death in any form, I accompanied them home, steeped to the lips in despair. (Anon., 1947, pp. 17–18)

The major difference between an experience such as this and an obsessive-compulsive tendency is the *rapidity* with which the former seizes the individual and his almost complete inability to exercise self-control. In this case the destructive urge formed part of the onset of a total breakdown; in spite of the kindly action of the police, the patient's continued agitation led to his early removal to an asylum. In such a situation the word *asylum* is actually more appropriate than the word *hospital*.

Inner Commands

For the most part, the involuntary actions and disrupting conative experiences we have considered, thus far, have been instances where the underlying motivation seemed to the sufferer to be nonspecific. Another variety of such disorders describes feelings that are related to an *inner* compulsion, an *inner* force or urge, an inner feeling of *"I must."* Some patients, particularly those suffering from auditory hallucinations, attribute the impulses to certain statements or commands given by these voices. The commands lead to thoughts and behavior which may be much the same as those related to nonspecific feelings; but, in this case, the patient feels that there exists a real basis (or what seems to him to be a rational basis) for his essentially involuntary thoughts and actions.

Perceval recounted the extent to which his behavior during his mental derangement resulted from commands issued by the voices. He rejected or tried to reject many of them, particularly since at the beginning of the episodes the voices often seemed to provide irrational commands. Several incidents may be cited to illustrate the interaction between the hallucinatory commands and Perceval's bizarre behavior.

A spirit came upon me and prepared to guide me in my actions. . . . I heard voices without and within me . . . I understood that I was only saved by the mercy of Jesus . . . Actuated by the same spirit, I took a like position on the floor, where I remained, until I understood that the work of the Lord was perfected. . . . The guidance of the spirit left me, and I became in doubt what next I was to do. . . . After some hesitation, I heard the command, to *"take your position on the floor again." . . .*

Returning to the common room [after meals], I always attempted to wrestle with, or asked one of the patients to wrestle with me, I was then locked into my seat. If my arms were at liberty, I would occasionally seize one or two of the patients to wrestle with me as they passed by me. I had no malicious motive; I did it in obedience to inspiration, and imagined they were inspired to know what I was commanded, how I obeyed, and how to act in consequence. My attempts at wrestling were however inculcated by the spirits on more practical grounds than ordinary. They told me that it was necessary "for the *keeping me in a right state of mind,*" in other words, "to keep my head to my heart, and my heart to my head"; that I should be suffocated, or strangled, or violently exercised, or at least perform one act of obedience to the Lord Jehovah supremely Omnipotent, in a certain rhyme or measure once or twice through the day . . .

Another delusion I laboured under was, that I should keep my head and heart together, and so serve the Lord, by throwing myself head over heels over every stile or gate I came to; the condition here was as before, on its being done *in precision and decision.* I often attempted and failed, getting smart strokes from the cane of Herminet Herbert [his attendant]. I knew it was dangerous, but I expected to be miraculously preserved if I did it aright. At last I did it outright, and my head struck upon a stone, on the other side.

The blow stupefied me: finding no advantage, I did not attempt it heartily again. (Perceval, 1838, pp. 38; 117; 125)

Explanations such as these given by Perceval for his behavior are illustrative of the inner conative struggles of many psychotic patients. The voices, stating that they are of divine origin, give orders which may seem somewhat foolish to the patient, but an order from God is a command which constitutes both an inspiration and a threat. If the patient does not comply at once and wholeheartedly, the voices then tell him that he will be punished. Not only will he himself suffer, but because of his doubts or lack of conviction, other people will also suffer and die. The patient's dilemma is further complicated by the fact that the commands are often ambiguous and unclear; suggestions are given and rewards promised, but once the command is followed through, involving personal danger and humiliation, the patient finds that nothing has changed. Hence, having obeyed the orders he attributed to supernatural control, the patient is at a loss, for he is informed by the voices that he misunderstood, did not wholeheartedly comply, and so forth. All this adds further to his confusion, so making any exercise of self-control even more difficult.

An example of a similar unsuccessful struggle was related by Renee in the *Autobiography of a Schizophrenic Girl*. How she finally did succumb is told in this excerpt.

I received orders from the System. I did not hear the orders as voices; yet they were as imperious as if uttered in a loud voice. While, for example, I was preparing to do some typing, suddenly, without any warning, a force, which was not an impulse but rather resembled a command, ordered me to burn my right hand or the building in which I was. With all my strength I resisted the order. I telephoned [her analyst] to tell her about it. Her voice, urging me to listen to her and not to the System, reassured me. . . . but unfortunately only for a moment.

An indescribable anguish squeezed my heart, an anguish no resolve could allay. If I refused to obey, I felt guilty and cowardly for not daring, and the anguish mounted. Then the order became more insistent. If, finally to obey, I went to the fire and stretched out my hand, an intense feeling of guilt overcame me as though I were doing something wicked, and the anxiety waxed in proportion. I should say, however, that the latter alternative provoked the greater disturbance, for I felt that if I obeyed the order, I should commit an act irreparably damaging to my personality. . . .

I had, too, the conviction that my behavior was deceitful. In reality, it wasn't anything of the kind. I was deeply sincere. But if I disobeyed the System to maintain the integrity of my personality, I was deceitful since I acted as though I had no consideration for the order. If I obeyed it, I was equally deceitful, since I did not agree to burn myself. I suffered horribly from the orders and from the feeling of treachery so contrary to my character. . . .

One day, trembling, I placed the back of my right hand on the incandescent coals and held it there as long as possible. By thinking of my duty to the System . . . I was able to stand the pain. (Sechehaye, 1951, pp. 36–39)

Undoubtedly, Renee did struggle against the inner commands and impulses. She succumbed to them in the vain hope that the inner tension would be relieved. She, like most other similarly afflicted persons, reported that little or no relief of tension was gained from following such orders. The particular impulse itself may become less demanding, but the anxiety continues; and now, added to the tension, is the demoralizing knowledge that one was foolish and weak enough to follow the dictates of a senseless command.

Abulia

In contrast to the inner force exerted by compulsions and obsessions, there may exist a state of complete inability to exert one's will power, or of having no will power to exert—that is, an experience of *abulia*. The various disorders of volition considered so far have been characterized by a feeling of being prompted by some external force, so that the person experiencing it was no longer completely under his own self-control. The individual was acting, so to speak, "against his will." Abulia, in contrast, represents a total lack of will to direct or resist any kind of internal or external impulse. An example of such a condition was described by Dr. Heveroch's patient.

I am absent-minded, without energy or will. It is impossible for me to reflect about something at will. My head feels like a washcloth. I have the feeling of a madman, I don't perceive my will and do everything mechanically. I can't get my eyes to stand still, don't know how to turn myself around; I do everything without thought or feeling. If someone speaks to me, I am as if without consciousness, without thought, and am unable to give an answer. . . . I, myself, can't bring the sensation of will, that is the sensation of the expression of the will to the level of consciousness. (Heveroch, 1913, p. 427)

The experience of abulia is not just that of a simple loss of will or will power. Every description of abulia I have found seems to have been complicated by the addition of other experiences. The patient just cited used the following phrases; "Everything in me is asleep," "Everything around me is enveloped in a fog," "My hands are the hands of a ghost," "My mouth begins to speak without my knowing about it," and so on. Not only is the experiential quality of will lacking, but feeling of unreality and other inappropriate emotions act to complicate the entire experience.

I have cited part of Renee's description of her inner struggle to resist an "order from the System to burn my right hand." Somewhat later in the course of her illness she found herself gradually enveloped in a state of apathy and abulia. She described it as follows.

I no longer received orders from the System: there was much less anxiety, and the fear too affected me rarely. My usual keen sense of responsibility was gone; I did not raise a finger to find work or to help my family. For the greater part of the day I sat in a chair, gazing fixedly before me, or plunged in the absorbed contemplation of a tiny spot, . . . but with what weariness! The slightest movement required extraordinary effort, particularly to overcome the first inertia. Once I had begun things became easier, but then I could not stop. (Sechehaye, 1951, pp. 56–57)

Abulia, like apathy or anhedonia, is described as a dreamlike state of unreality, in which the EDITOR function of ordinary consciousness remains semivigilant. The EDITOR notes some fraction of passing events and retains partial memory traces of them, thus providing a hazy record of the total experience. But the EDITOR function has no control nor is it in any way identified with the passing show. During abulia and apathy the EDITOR is limited in its capacity of awareness and fixation, since it plays no active part in the interaction between the apathetic organism and his environment.

It will be recalled that Perceval doubted (but tried to obey) the inner spirits or voices he heard. Many of the commands involved actions that were dangerous to his welfare. On one occasion the conflict between the orders and his own safety led to the following experience.

At last, one hour, under an access of chilling horror at my imagined loss of honour, I was unable to prevent the surrender of my judgment. The act of mind I describe, was accompanied with the sound of a slight crack, and the sensation of a fibre breaking over the right temple . . . accompanied by an apparently additional surrender of the judgment. In fact, until now, I had retained a kind of restraining power over my thoughts and belief; I now had none; I could not resist the spiritual guilt and contamination of any thought, of any suggestion. My will to choose, to think orderly, was entirely gone. I became like one awake yet dreaming. (Perceval, 1838, pp. 60–61)

Perceval's sensation of something physical breaking or snapping is not unique. Such an experience has been mentioned in several other autobiographies as having occurred when there was some marked change in mental content or experience. Whether the actual sensation occurred or whether the description is no more than a figurative way of saying, "My will was broken," is impossible to say.

DISCUSSION

Will or volition are terms used to designate a mental function ordinarily related to experiences such as choosing, delaying, deciding, and directing. In phenomenological accounts of an individual's mental life, will and volition are rarely mentioned as independent functions or processes. Volition is an attribute of experience in the same fashion that pleasantness and unpleasantness are attributes of feelings, ideas, images, and thoughts. When a person feels that he has decided among several alternatives or made a choice between ideas or actions, then he reports having exercised his freedom of will. An act of will is usually followed in temporal order by a sense of, or feeling of, responsibility.

Disorders of volition are subjectively self-evident. Others may come to gain knowledge of their occurrence, either by inference from behavioral observations or by taking stock of the verbal descriptions of the experiencer, and by comparing these descriptions with the memory of their own experiences.

Disorders of volition are of two major sorts: (1) a need for greater effort in the achievement of an act of will (decision) due to an unusual force that opposes the normal mental process involved in such acts, and (2) the weakening or loss of the mental capacity to exercise an act of will. In both varieties the disorder is associated with a feeling of weakened personal responsibility and a constriction of freedom in decision-making.

The experience of the increase in volitional effort that is required to exercise one's will is associated with certain states and behaviors called fixed ideas, obsessions, compulsions, irresistible impulses, and inner commands. The differences between these phenomena depend largely on the timing and vigor of the opposing force against which the will must operate. There is nothing to indicate that weakness of will is of itself pathological in any of these circumstances. The conditions under which these difficulties in conation arise may or may not be abnormal. The state becomes abnormal to the experiencer if it results in the feeling of loss of or interference with his sense of responsibility. Fixed ideas, compulsions, and the like are usually regarded by the experiencer as nuisances; they interfere with his peace of mind but are of themselves no indication of "loss of mind." Only when certain ideas, impulses, or commands overwhelm the totality of his better judgment does the experiencer agree to the possibility that for a shorter or longer period he had indeed lost his mind.

Most psychopathological experiences involving disordered volition are reported by the experiencer as possessing one or more of the following features: an imperative, distasteful idea demands an inner strength to resist that is near to or beyond the limit of his ability; the idea, thought, or impulse intrudes on him persistently and he cannot stop, divert, or redirect it; not only is he unable to control the idea, but, rather, he finds himself controlled by it; most of his thoughts or impulses seem to him utterly senseless, deprived of all ordinary values or meanings, so much so that many become positively repulsive and cause him to behave in ways contrary to his accustomed better judgment and desire. Disorders of volition engender or carry with them feelings of anxiety, fear, and dread that tend to make the total experience itself more vivid and confusing.

Abulia, the feeling of having lost one's will, is subjectively different from those experiences that bear the necessity of increasing or using more of one's volitional strength and is usually accompanied by other complex and unusual inner states. Descriptions of lack of will are frequently associated with descriptions of anhedonia and feelings of unreality. The abulic individual complains of having lost all human feelings; he says he is operating automatically, much as a mechanical man might do. Abulia may overtake an individual suddenly, but the more usual account indicates that it is realized only after a long inner struggle between the person's normal inhibitions and the ideas, impulses, and commands that he feels are externally imposed on his mind.

. . . human kind
Cannot bear very much reality.
Time past and time future
What might have been and what has been
Point to one end, which is always present.

(*Eliot*, 1936, p. 118)

CHAPTER 17

Unreality and Depersonalization

INTRODUCTION

Concepts having to do with the nature of reality, unreality, self, and not-self have been a matter of
philosophical debate for centuries, but discussions of
them have practically disappeared from modern psychology texts. This disappearance has not been due
to solution of the problems, but rather to an inability
to conceive of objective methods for investigation. The
glossing over of these problems has left our understanding of the experiences essentially in limbo.
Patients still speak of feelings of unreality and
depersonalization, even though modern psychiatry and
psychology find no well-defined place for the concepts.

Everyone knows the difference between reality
and unreality and between the self and the not-self.
The ordinary man recognizes these differences if he
stops to think about them. He knows too that small
children frequently have difficulties in distinguishing
the real from the unreal and self from not-self. A little
girl will cry when she is stuck with a pin and wonder
why her doll does not cry when it is stuck with a pin.
Adult common sense supplies an explanation which

351

implies that each individual "learned" these differences as he grew older. The distinction between real and unreal are usually conceived in intellectual terms. For the adult, sensations and perceptions, as they occur, are real. The EDITOR process constitutes a running self-critical censorship of immediate experience that may be followed by doubts, uncertainties, or a correction of the immediate feeling of "reality." For example, the whisper that apparently called me becomes, after a few seconds, recognized as the rustle of leaves stirred by a breeze; and I conclude that no one called me.

There are many occasions in everyday life when the distinction between real and unreal, usually so clear to the self-critical EDITOR, blurs, and one is left with an increased feeling of uncertainty. If one has lost sleep or has otherwise become fatigued, the certainty of what is real or unreal waxes and wanes. A well-trained and quite well adjusted introspective psychologist wrote as follows.

To begin with, how, from the introspective standpoint, shall the feeling of reality be defined? It is, as it were, psychical solidity: not merely vividness of experience but, rather, density of experience whether that experience be perceptual, ratiocinative, or emotional. With the loss of the sense of reality, tangibility and meaning evaporate from experience.

In my own experience the feeling of reality rises and falls. . . . Lack of sleep reduces the feeling of reality; so too, in even greater degree, does muscular fatigue of the eyes. . . . At such times the external world seems to lack solidity: it awakens no interest; people appear as trees walking; thought moves sluggishly; indifference to the consequences of actions ensues; consciousness of self ebbs. . . . The haze of an autumn day that makes objects seem far-off, immense, veiled, has the same effect upon mental experince. . . . The roar of a big city, the presence of a crowd of people reduces the sense of reality. . . .

Not only do sense stimulations bring on a feeling of unreality that extends from the sense world to the world of thought and emotion, but the reverse may happen. Prolonged reading or thinking on philosophical topics has the same results. Not only do conclusions seem to lack validity, but the world of daily experience also grows thin, dreamlike. This state, which is rather unpleasant, seems more akin to emotional than to mental fatigue. Again, the reading of certain sorts of poetry . . . reduces the sense of reality. . . .

The predicate of unreality has attached itself to certain things in a seemingly arbitrary and uncomfortable way. A voice over a telephone has no body, messages so received make no impression on me. . . . Social invitations fail to convince, particularly if given orally. I always experience a feeling of surprised relief when I find that I didn't dream it. (Downey, 1905, pp. 298–299)

These experiences of a blurring between reality and unreality were described as feeling-states but were in no wise thought to be pathological.

It is apparent that introspective training in a normal person can bring about a clearer awareness of reality–unreality feelings. The pathological feelings of unreality may in part be due to the fact that the ordinary human being has never specially attended to these aspects of his mental life.

Varieties of Reality–Unreality Experience

The difference between imagining a thing and believing in its existence, between the certainty of reality and the uncertainty of unreality, is dependent upon mental processes or psychic states than can be studied by careful introspective analysis or by the examination of the way in which the mental processes came into being, that is by the study of the histories of these states. I have just cited an excerpt from an introspective account of the operation of the reality–unreality process. The implication of the report was that reality–unreality, in its inner nature, is a particular type of feeling or emotional state.

In contrast to this introspective description of reality–unreality feelings made by a trained psychologist, I will next present part of an account by an alcoholic patient who had been hospitalized because of his acute condition, in order that both his physical and mental health might be improved. On the first sleepless night of the "cure" he became partially delirious. He attempted to ascertain whether a figure he saw in the doorway was real or imaginary. He reported as follows.

That shadowy figure of a man, faintly smudged against the door of my darkened room, and I, lying there in bed a few hours after my entrance, watching him curiously. *Is he real?* No matter what appeared or happened—*is it real?* Black, electric-eyed rabbits scurrying around the floor—*are they real?* Kick them and find out. They are *not* real. All right. Try to sleep. That man, now—is he real? I see his bulky figure, swaying gently. Yes, he must be real. There is a crack of light along one side of the door which is not entirely closed. Yes, when he moves toward the right he blots out part of that crack of light. He is real, all right.

He is smoking! I can see the glowing end of his cigar moving in his left hand. There—it goes to his lips. He draws on the cigar, the glowing end brightens. He seems to enjoy it, too. I wish I had a smoke. Against the rules here, they tell me. . . . Well, if *he* can smoke, I can, too. They'll smell the smoke—I'll blame it on him. Ah, I have my wits about me, all right. But—is he real? Are you sure he's real? Are you sure? (Owens, 1929, pp. 95–96)

In this account, the process of reality determination was more of a sensory-perceptual intellectual process than it was a feeling-state. The decisions and classing of the experiences as real or unreal depended not on his feelings, but on a process he thought to be a rational one. For this man, the sense of reality was an intellectual judgment.

Still another variety of unreality experience has been reported by

Janet, who published the following fragment of a description by one of his patients.

I don't see things as I used to . . . I see things devoid of substance. . . . They must be hallucinations and not real objects. . . . Things act only on my eyes, not on my brain. Doubtless I see everything, without doubt nothing is changed, except that things are not real. . . . It reminds me of the time when I had to take castor oil and some one would pinch my nose so I should not get the odor. I perceive things, but I have no sense of their taste. . . . When I did something too quickly, when I ran anywhere, I would suddenly stop, quite astonished, for my indolent brain had not been as quick as my legs; it had remained at the starting point and I was surprised to find that I had arrived. I had fallen from the moon and things no longer existed as they had. True, the appearance of things is just the same. I could describe them to you just as you would yourself, but what I see is only a play, a Punch and Judy show; it is clumsy, vulgar, unpleasant and, above all, false; it doesn't really exist. (Janet, 1921, p. 471)

This patient doubted not only the existence of objects but also their character. For example, she would look at her mother, recognize her, and then say that the woman she saw did not really exist. Sensory and perceptual experiences continued, yet their quality or value was altered.

An example of unreality feelings that have neither primary nor secondary sensory or perceptual attachments may next be cited. The wife of a musician who had been blind from infancy wrote William James concerning a peculiar and repetitive experience which had troubled her husband. In part, her letter read as follows.

Mr. P. has all his life been the occasional subject of rather singular delusions or impressions of various kinds. . . . Being totally blind, his other perceptions are abnormally keen and developed, and given the existence of a rudimentary sixth sense, it would be only natural that this also should be more acute in him than in others. One of the most interesting of his experiences in this line was the frequent apparition of a corpse. . . . At the time Mr. P. had a music-room . . . where he used to do severe and protracted practice with little interruption. Now, all one season it was a very familiar occurrence with him while in the midst of work to feel a cold draft of air suddenly upon his face, with a prickling sensation at the roots of his hair, when he would turn from the piano, and a figure which he knew to be dead would come sliding under the crack of the door from without, flattening itself to squeeze through and rounding out again to the human form. It was a middle-aged man, and drew itself along the carpet on hands and knees, but with head thrown back till it reached the sofa, upon which it stretched itself. It remained some moments, but vanished always if Mr. P. spoke or made a decided movement. The most singular point in the occurrence was its frequent repetition. He might expect it on any day between two and four o'clock, and it came always heralded by the same sudden cold shiver, and was invariably the same figure which went through the same movements. . . .

Mr. P. has no memory whatever of sight, nor conception of it. It is impossible for him to form any idea of what we mean by light or color, consequently he has no cognizance of any object which does not reach his sense of hearing or of touch, though these are so acute as to give a contrary impression sometimes to other people. . . .

The figure never produced the least sound nor came within a number of feet of his person, yet he knew that it was a man, that it moved, and in what direction, even that it wore a full beard, which like the thick curly hair, was partially gray; also that it was dressed in the style of suit known as "pepper and salt." These points were all perfectly distinct and invariable each time. If asked how he perceived them, he will answer he cannot tell, he simply knew it, and so strongly and so distinctly that it is impossible to shake his opinion as to the exact details of the man's appearance. (James, 1890, pp. 323–324)

This is certainly an experience of unreality without any ordinary sensory content. There is no reason to question the sanity of this person. The key phrase in the present citation is, "When asked how he perceived them . . . he simply knew." In other words, the experience simply stood as "real," without any attending explanations or references to a physical or physiological basis.

An example of the difficulty experienced by a deranged patient when disturbing perceptions intruded into his process of thought can be illustrated by an excerpt from the account of a man who suffered acute delirious episodes for several weeks before he recovered his mental equilibrium. In his account of the beginning of his illness he described the following incident.

It seemed to me that the space [vacant seat in a railway coach] was filled with a cane and umbrella rack, and that the handles and tops of these articles sprouted out . . . exotic plants and flowers. Oh, they were beautiful and fragrant! And yet I could not crowd out the lurking suspicion that there was something wrong about the whole matter. This idea haunted me through the whole period of my trouble—that even what I saw that was unreal, and that pleased me, was *not right*. My mind was constantly engaged in a brisk and earnest argument on a thousand points that every passing phantasy raised; and yet there was a strange and almost overpowering impression that all I saw was real. This conflict seemed to mark the boundary lines that divided sanity from insanity. To me this strife was one of the most unpleasant features of my trial. It was kept up in a thousand ways, until I was restored to soundness of mental health. (Anon., 1857, p. 166)

It seems evident that this man was distinguishing real from unreal by a judgmental process where to his mind unreal was *not-right*. One supposes that he meant that part of his sense-perceptions did not agree with his common-sense criterion of rightfulness. A cane and umbrella rack could be real, and right, but umbrella handles sprouting exotic plants, that was not-right, and thus cast doubt on what he thought he saw. The need to test each passing perception or idea for its reality was a disturbing procedure. In brief, this excerpt is an illustration of the difficulty some patients report as part of their attempts to make intellectual judgments that involve reality–unreality.

Difficulties in Distinguishing Real from Unreal

An interesting account written by a sane, healthy, and educated psychologist, Dr. Eleanor Rowland, illustrates further aspects of these reality-unreality judgments. Dr. Rowland had the physiological oddity of being able to sleep with her eyes partly open.

It has been my life-long habit to sleep with my eyes half open. I do not know whether the eyes are shut during the night and only open when morning approaches, or whether they are open all during the sleeping state. . . . However firmly the lids are drawn over the eyes on going to sleep, they fly back again until half the eye is left uncovered, and the retina is thereby exposed to stimulation as at any time during the waking life. . . .

The situation with which I am familiar, is as follows: The process of waking is often very gradual, and passes through a characteristic stage. In this period, I am still asleep, with no motor control whatever, but with sensory processes apparently in every way as complete as in the waking state. I see the room with perfect distinctness, although I do not believe that the eyes move. I see the chairs, the books, and the window, and often wonder why it is that all connection with my motor apparatus is lost, and why with my utmost efforts to move and the feeling that I *am* moving, my eyes inform me that I am all the time perfectly quiet. Sometimes I know that I am asleep, and simply wait patiently to wake up. Perhaps nothing is more curious in the whole experience than this waiting, in complete possession of my senses, for a return of motor control. Suddenly I am awake and can move, but I do not see the room a particle more distinctly than I have been seeing it for some time. . . . It often happens that dream persons issue from behind a real door, a dream hand moves along the real wall, and a dream figure sits upon the real bed. Since my vision is so accurate, I can not reassure myself by being certain that I am asleep. Nor am I in a slumber deep enough to accept any dream that comes without comment. My reasoning powers are active at such times, and I commune thus with myself: "No one can have cpened the door, for you know you locked it." "But I see a figure distinctly standing at my elbow, and it has knocked on the door twice." "You are probably asleep." "How can I be? I see and hear as distinctly as I ever do." "Why then don't you push the figure away?" "I will. Here I am doing it." "No—you are not doing it at all, for you can see that you have not moved an inch." "Then I am asleep after all—the figure is not there, and I need not be afraid of it." Sometimes this logic is sufficient and the dream vanishes; but at other times it continues, and I must go through the argument afresh, or perhaps sink into a deeper sleep where I do not dream at all.

Sometimes in place of real hallucinations, the dreams are only illusions or misinterpretations of visual sensations. I remember an instance not long ago when I was camping with several friends . . . where our clothes were hung on pegs in the wall at the foot of the beds. My friends and I were lying on four cots facing the wall, and on four pegs hung dresses surmounted by a hat. The sun shone into the room early, and I lay contemplating the wall as I slept. The clothes upon the pegs were transformed into a loose-jointed old lady attempting to hang herself. With perfect distinctness I saw the sun streaming in upon the rough boards and the low roof, and with equal distinctness the old lady was strangled on every nail, lurching from peg to peg along the wall, while I was a horrified, but helpless spectator. In a flash, however, the old lady became a hat and dress, while the rest of the scene remained unchanged. I have tried to determine whether I was in point of fact deceived by these hallucinations, or whether in the background of my consciousness I have known all the time the difference between reality and illusion. Certainly in some cases I have known the difference enough to question the presence of the dream figures; but whether it was because I distinguished between the two types of perception, or only that I questioned the reality of persons who would not ordinarily be in my room, I can not feel certain. . . .

The next question was whether the other senses, especially hearing, remained as acute as vision; but since there was nothing to listen to, I began, as I confidently supposed, to sing and heard my own song distinctly. Suddenly, however, came the indefinable change that told me I was awake. The sound vanished, and I found that I had not been singing. My mouth was so tightly closed that I could not have been doing so. Moreover, I could *hear* that I had not been singing, and should in any case have roused my neighbor in the next room had I been making the noise I supposed I had. (Rowland, 1909, pp. 353–356)

A major point of interest suggested by this description is the elaborate mental process in which Dr. Rowland had to indulge in order to distinguish between sensory reality and unreal dream states. She could tell the differences, but only after much testing. Since sleeping with her eyes open had characterized her existence over many years, one might have expected that her experiences would have in time furnished sufficient criteria to make the discriminative process an easy one, which obviously it was not. One's ears are always open, so to speak, and it might be expected that she would have had no difficulty in distinguishing real singing from illusory singing. This account seems to indicate that the feeling of reality when one is asleep differs sharply from the feeling when one is awake.

Dr. Rowland's difficulty may be compared to the same type of difficulty experienced by a patient who attributed his mental collapse to physical exhaustion.

The mental symptoms only occurred upon the very eve of my losing touch with reality. . . . I left my desk in the immense reading room of the British Museum [and] I was unable to find it again, or to remember where I had been sitting. . . . [He described the mental state in which he found himself in the following way.] The borderland state . . . is a very strange one, in which reality and unreality are strangely mixed. I did not once think that anything was wrong with me, only that something was very wrong with other people. Phobias and delusions crowded in upon one. Above all, one's thoughts and dreams are real, and all else seems remote and artificial. Then, paradoxical as it may sound, there is a kind of rare sanity in insanity. For if sane, one is sensitive to impressions, one is doubly sensitive to them when intellectual checks and reasoning inhibitions are absent. The whole universe is, as it were, inverted, and instinct rules supreme; and one reacts very strongly to those who are about one—almost as if one could see into their very souls. Pagan people, of course, respect the insane believing that they are living in another world; and many Christian people have a religious theory of insanity. (Anon., 1925, p. 346)

There is an obvious distinction between the description of the psychologist who slept with her eyes half-open and the account of this mental patient who was faced with a somewhat similar mental problem. The patient was quite willing, so to speak, to accept an inverted universe. His thoughts and dreams were *real*. His dream states felt real. There was no need for him to test each new feeling state. He was willing to accept insanity in place of sanity. Another patient described this experience by saying, "When part of the world is unreal, everything seems unreal."

Unreality Associated with Mystical Experience

For some persons the experiences of unreality either are, or become, closely akin to mystical experience. Mystical states are often characterized by the person's identification with the divine and his sharing, in part, its ineffable quality. The experience of unreality may similarly be associated with supernatural and invisible powers.

For example, Hahnenfuss, a psychotic patient, during an acute period of his illness wrote at some length about his general philosophy of life and explained how his illness had changed his viewpoints. He was particularly concerned with religious concepts and with ideas on the nature of reality.

It seems as if all people were one picture and only an illusion which is perceived in the scattered multitude. . . . There is no reality, but only the spirit. For that which is material no one knows, but what spirit is, no one doubts who has experienced it. The whole connection which holds this breathing spiritual world together is the bond of harmony. . . .

But why do the *remembrances* return and why is one remembrance *reality*? Every reality, however, is basically only a *possibility* and as such again only a remembrance. For there is no singular act with eternal meaning or worth in this unborn earthly condition; consequently every reality is a copy, an act of *anamnesis*. It is not conceivable that we experience things for the first time, we have rather already seen everything of which we are conscious, although we possibly never become conscious of this fact. The greater the clearness of the experience, the deeper the remembrance of the past, and therefore also the greater the joy. Recognition of a once perceived image gives joy; the clearer the act of recognition, the greater the joy. Herein lies, in case a proof for this is necessary, the deeper cause for the maze of our life on this earth. But it is not only valid for the recognition of outward things, but for the processes of consciousness especially for the perceptive faculty. Where this remembrance is *no longer* necessary or is *not yet* present, there is either *heaven* or *hell*. As long as we require the symbolism of *matter*, we are not in the realm of the true being; but that matter is reality for us, that is our fault. Only when we experience *singly* do we stand on the ground of the true being, but then forms of thought are no longer necessary for us. (Beringer and Mayer-Gross, 1925, pp. 212; 214–215)

Hahnenfuss found himself in a confused, troubled world, complicated by voices that claimed to be divine. These voices turned his thoughts to problems of good and evil and led him to question which of his own "remembrances" were actually real and which were imaginary or dreamlike. He tried to determine the qualities that made perception seem real. He mentions clarity, depth, and joy of experience as the outer concomitants that add to the reality of the "remembrance." But he finally concludes that the truth of acceptance or absence of "remembrances" is a matter of heaven or hell, that is, of good or evil. This does not seem to be very different from the mental problems commonly mentioned in reports of mystical experience, particularly when the person tries to reconcile his enveloping divine experience with his experience in the everyday phenomenological world.

During the course of her illness, Maude Harrison was certain that nothing around her in the world was real. She was convinced that the everyday world had been inverted and that newspapers, radio, and the remarks of people were all part of a gigantic hoax to spread throughout the world the knowledge of her enormous sinfulness. She had not been a particularly religious person before her illness, but religious thoughts now became part of her innermost thinking, possibly because of the messages that the voices conveyed to her.

Religious life in the midst of lunacy is far from an impossibility. Let the profane make the obvious comment, if they will. In the New Testament devils were cast out from people who knew that they needed casting out. There are devils, and devils-rage, melancholy, *accidie* (which is colourless indifference to all delights, all duties), *poltergeist*, the merry spirit, delusions, inversions, and I suppose perversions of all kinds. . . .

Accidie, or sloth, I suffered once in my life, after great anguish of heart.

I preferred the anguish. A priest to whom I once talked gave me the Church's name for my malady. He was intensely sorry for me, and his final words were "Good-bye, you know you have a difficult journey ahead of you" . . . This clergyman, an old friend of my family rather than a friend of my own, came into my head one morning with such force that I wondered if I could write to him, and ask him if I were not a real mental patient in a real mental hospital. This idea excited me so much that I walked into the wrong dining-room for breakfast. (Harrison, 1941, p. 135)

She did not write to the priest, but several days later she met the hospital chaplain and asked him whether he believed that anyone was past praying for. He told her "No," but that he had met many who thought they were past prayer and asked her to come to the hospital church services. Unfortunately, she thought that he was nothing but an actor and not a real priest. She summarized her feeling-state at this part of her illness as: "I know that I am acting a lie and acting in a lie, but I cannot get outside the lie."

For some patients experiences of unreality and mystical experiences become so intertwined that it is difficult for the sufferer to be certain which is basically the more potent.

Melancholia and Unreality

Another variety of the experience of unreality is that which seems to grow out of melancholia and nervous exhaustion. W. E. Leonard described a period during phobic neurosis when he suffered from unreality feelings.

For a year now I experienced attacks of acute melancholia . . . usually two or three times a week . . . from about eleven to two in the day. . . . All values dropped out . . . One power only remained—the *will*-to-live . . . *One* power? No, *two*. *Reason* remained . . . Without the will-to-live and without reason it would have been suicide. . . . As little can I explain the state of diffused unreality, similar to the melancholy but without the melancholic tone, which was intermittent for the first two years; describable as simulating the queer feel of the daylight world to one who had been without sleep for two or three nights. (Leonard, 1939, pp. 330–331)

Leonard's state of unreality resembled, in a sense, the unreality Maude Harrison described in the excerpt just cited. For both patients the unreality experience was associated with anguish and depression. In neither patient was there a true exhaustion, either physical or mental. Rather, the unreality experience was associated with an exhaustion of will. Later in his account, Leonard expressed the idea that his feelings of unreality might somehow be reverberations of vague, displaced memory traces that were akin to mystical thoughts.

Schizophrenia and Unreality Experiences

Unreality experience is a prominent symptom more clearly expressed by schizophrenic patients than by any other diagnostic group. These experiences are not unmixed with other derangements of mind, but the schizoid patient gives expression to these complaints in a peculiar fashion of his own.

Hackett included in his autobiography, *The Cardboard Giants*, a self-analysis of his unreality experiences, which he said afflicted him during his childhood. However, his descriptive analysis is phrased in rather unusual imagery. In the following excerpt he is trying to relate the nature of his mental state to a sympathetic physician.

It was just that sometimes I had a terrific sense of unreality. Suddenly I found myself in the present and all the immediate cords to the present had been severed. Like when someone wakes up in a strange room. Except that I had lived in the room for months. I often felt dazed. Or I awoke with a mood upon me as though I had dreamed something that disturbed me but did not remember what it was. Like a song going through your mind without any association with words or memory. Until you locate it in your own memory it is a disturbing thing to you. Then when you remember the words to the tune or make some association with it the whole thing is no longer important. I think that this feeling of time passing suddenly is one of the most disturbing of all. You are young . . . you are old . . . and there is nothing in between. . . . The strange feeling of wondering . . . and the feeling of unreality, perhaps you are not really there at all and the feeling that the whole thing is familiar as though you have been there is some previous life.

I remember when I was a boy of four having the same feeling. I remember standing in the driveway beside my house in the rain; standing and watching the rain run down the driveway, walking and getting a sudden chill and the feeling that I had been standing watching the rain before in some previous existence. Another thing is the feeling that my mind has three compartments, as though I were operating on three levels of awareness. At one time I have a flood of memories in my mind and an awareness of the thing to say, the "hello" section and the "it's a nice day" section and the awareness of present objects in the room and beyond all this a feeling of a cosmic awareness as though I were somehow in tune with the generations of men before me. It is this cosmic awareness that makes me feel the things in which most men place their interest are unimportant . . . Everyone possibly feels as I that there are open wires in his mind and that from these wires comes a stream of consciousness over which he has no control. (Hackett, 1952, pp. 51–53)

Hackett told how, from time to time since childhood, he had had an "idea" that he had been under the control of an evil *"Mind,"* which seemed to him to be, in one way or another, the essence of threatening danger. When Mind possessed him he was in terror and lost almost all of his will power. He said that at such times he had feelings of unreality.

He phrased the feeling as, "Perhaps you were not really there at all." The unreality experiences appeared whenever Mind was in control. At such times his thinking became disconnected, so that he only partially understood what people said to him and he also felt that people were all leagued against him. His sense of the passage of time became defective. He found himself filled with painful dread and anger. He lost knowledge of where he was and what day it was. And yet Hackett could recognize his loss of self-control and mental confusion during such periods. The peculiar element he emphasized in his description of the feeling of unreality was that associated with the distortions in his knowledge of the passage of time.

Another peculiarity of unreality experience may be drawn from the report of a young man who had sought medical help because of "peculiar thought disorders." He was said to be introspective, to suffer from obsessive thoughts, and to talk to himself even when other persons were present. He described his tendency to group people and concepts into unusual categories as follows.

At times when my condition gets very bad, my mind seems to become split off into compartments so that my concepts of the world and the people I know seem peculiarly artificial. The people in my uncle's office become all "Oriental businessmen" even if they have nothing to do with the East. Whatever there is about them that does not fit into this concept is blocked out of the picture. They lose, in other words, all their individuality; they lose, in fact, everything that does not fit into the artificial category in which I have put them. Whatever seems out of place in this artificial picture I am not able to think of as real. Similarly for other people, I put them in groups, according to certain qualities that are strangely significant for me and I am unable to see the real individual differences among them that are far more important and that would at once be apparent to any normal mind. Accidental similarities are all that strike me in this state. When added to this there is a dimming of my vision, the effect is to make the world at such times almost totally unreal." (Arieti, 1950, p. 291)

In this case the blockage was intellectual and selective, rather than complete and emotional. He said that he was to an extent still aware of the ordinary reality of his environment. The patient's description implies that he was in part deluded by his thought processes, and one may surmise that his feelings of unreality resulted partially from the dissociation in his thinking.

In his attempt to gain some degree of self-control Peters commented on his unreal experiences rather oddly.

I insisted upon some base of reality, and curiously enough there was a projection, a shape which I could fasten upon. I had been frightened of it at first, and now I could hold to it and look at it, even finding some comfort in the fact that there was one thing I knew . . . the fact of my own fallibility. I knew that I knew nothing, and knowing nothing is part of the cement in the foundation. (Peters, 1949, p. 184)

This certainly constituted an intellectual defense against his feeling of losing reality, without being either a description or an explanation. He had experienced the feeling of loss of reality. Now he was no longer clear in his own mind concerning what was real and what was unreal; he felt that all experience had to be examined since he no longer knew anything for certain. This is not an uncommon psychotic process, but the way in which he described it is unusual.

The most vivid and moving description of the experience of unreality that I have encountered is the one given by Renee in her *Autobiography of a Schizophrenic Girl*. I have cited excerpts from this autobiography in previous chapters to illustrate the role of unreality, as well as other disturbing experiences at the beginning and during the course of her psychosis. It will be recalled that Renee first complained about unreality at the age of five. Since the experience disturbed her so markedly, I will present further examples. At the age of twelve, the following incident occurred.

One day we were jumping rope at recess. Two little girls were turning a long rope while two others jumped in from either side to meet and cross over. I was seized with panic; I did not recognize her. Though I saw her as she was, still, it was not she. Standing at the other end of the rope, she had seemed smaller, but the nearer we approached each other, the taller she grew, the more she swelled in size.

I cried out, "Stop Alice, you look like a lion; you frighten me!" At the sound of the fear in my voice which I tried to dissemble under the guise of fooling, the game came to an abrupt halt. The girls looked at me, amazed, and said, "You're silly—Alice—a lion. You don't know what you're talking about." Then the game began again. . . . But actually, I didn't see a lion at all; it was only an attempt to describe the enlarging image of my friend and the fact that I didn't recognize her. (Sechehaye, 1951, pp. 4–5)

Although the feelings of unreality always terrified her, when the attack ended she could put it out of her mind. As she grew older, and while in secondary school, the attacks of unreality and the terror became more frequent, vivid, and disturbing. For example, she told of the unreality feeling on another occasion, while she was in a schoolroom of her elementary school.

In these disturbing circumstances I sensed again the atmosphere of unreality. During class, in the quiet of the work period, I heard the street noises—a trolley passing, people talking, a horse neighing, a horn sounding, each detached, immovable, separated from its source, without meaning. Around me, the other children, heads bent over their work, were robots or puppets, moved by an invisible mechanism. On the platform, the teacher, too, talking, gesticulating, rising to write on the blackboard, was a grotesque jack-in-the-box.

And always this ghastly quiet, broken by outside sounds coming from far away, the implacable sun heating the room, the lifeless immobility. An awful terror bound me; I wanted to scream. On the way to school in the morning at seven-thirty, sometimes the same thing happened. Suddenly the street became infinite, white under the brilliant sun; people ran about like ants on an ant-hill; automobiles circled in all directions aimlessly; in the distance a bell pealed. Then everything seemed to stop, to wait, to hold its breath, in a state of extreme tension. . . . Something seemed about to occur, some extraordinary catastrophe. An overwhelming anxiety forced me to stop and wait. Then, without anything having actually changed, again realizing the senseless activity of people and things, I went on my way to school. (Sechehaye, 1951, pp. 10–11)

At the age of seventeen she developed tuberculosis and spent several months in a sanatorium, where the attacks of unreality were not quite so frequent. However, when she returned home and resumed her domestic duties, together with her school work, her attacks became exaggerated in frequency and duration. At the age of eighteen she was placed under the care of a psychoanalyst. In spite of the psychotherapeutic effort, her mental illness became so acute and her behavior so bizarre that it was deemed necessary to place her in the locked ward of a mental hospital. Here she remained for a time in a catatonic state and out of touch with her surroundings. On one occasion, after her analyst had visited her in the hospital and attempted to "make contact" she experienced a lucid interval that she described in the following way.

I realized that my perception of things had completely changed. Instead of infinite space, unreal, where everything was cut off, naked and isolated, I saw Reality, marvelous Reality, for the first time. The people whom we encountered were no longer automatons, phantoms revolving around, gesticulating without meaning; they were men and women with their own individual characteristics, their own individuality. It was the same with things. They were useful things, having sense, capable of giving pleasure. Here was an automobile to take me to the hospital, cushions I could rest on. With the astonishment that one views a miracle, I devoured with my eyes everything that happened. "This is it, this is it." I kept repeating, and I was actually saying, "This is it —Reality." (Sechehaye, 1951, pp. 79–80)

Renee's account does give certain glimpses of the nature of the experience she called unreality. For her, it was a unique experience that came and went without any particular sensory or perceptual basis in environmental circumstances. On many occasions the experience was accompanied by, or associated with, fear, anxiety, and terror. She tried to regain her familiar contact with reality by performing accustomed acts, but this was not always successful. Concurrent with the unreality experience was the appearance in awareness of delusional ideas. For example, the schoolhouse became an army barracks and the children turned into prisoners who were compelled to sing. As we have said, even stranger was the fact that her visual and auditory perceptions of the immediate world around her seemed to alter completely. Visually, her world became an illimitable vastness with brilliant light, where everything seemed smooth and glossy. People seemed to swell and grow in size, yet they did not become gigantic. Sounds were heard distinctly, but they were detached from their proper source and were essentially meaningless. She felt she was behind a glass wall that cut her off from the rest of the world. So far as she was concerned, she did not think that she was insane or even sick in the usual sense of the word. She knew only that suddenly she had found herself transported into a strange, cubist, brilliant, mechanical world of unreality and that the experience filled her with terror.

The inner life of the schizophrenic patient is confused, tumultuous, and frightening. The survey that I have made of autobiographical accounts indicates that three or four experiences are commonplace. These patients usually hear voices and may have long lapses of conscious memory; they often experience a profound difficulty in distinguishing reality from unreality; and they may experience perceptual distortions.

Drug-induced Unreality Experiences

In previous chapters I pointed out that it has been very difficult or impossible to induce psychopathological states in otherwise normal persons by drugs or by alteration of environmental circumstances. There is a vast difference between the experience of an unhappy, frustrated, or even drugged normal person and the account of the truly psychotic or neurotic patient. In 1958 the experience of a normal man who suffered from acute asthmatic attacks and who had inadvertently treated himself regularly with a nasal spray of "spoiled" adrenalin was reported by Osmond. This was based on a series of letters and interviews that he had had with the person in question. In his description, this man made the following points.

I have always felt myself to be a normal individual—unneurotic and with a zest for living. It was therefore quite a shock to me to find one day that I suddenly became an individual who: (1) saw the world as through a distorted glass—I sought to interpret the visual distortions as being due to strange mental processes; (2) became quite anxious and depressive; (3) had compulsive thoughts; and (4) began to doubt myself and my sanity. I became quite panicky for I had never experienced anything even remotely like these feelings. They were alien to me and I had nothing to compare them to. . . .

I remember groups of people bothering me. I felt that there was something distorted or different appearing about them. This was not localized to any one person. There was a strangeness about seeing groups of people which had a somewhat frightening effect on me. I noticed distortion in many things, some animate and some inanimate. As far as the animate subjects went, it did not seem to me that women looked strange but it seemed to me that the faces of the men particularly had a different sort of appearance than I had ever seemed to have noticed before. I can't really explain it, except to me, it seemed sort of distorted. . . .

They were people who were very familiar, who I had seen all the time and never thought a thing about. I had seen them all my life, some of them. There were no distortions previous. All of a sudden, they appeared strange to me. There wasn't a strangeness, such as two heads and four arms; it seemed to be some strangeness that was inherent in what I was seeing and yet nothing that was recognizable as to being that different to me in their appearance and this is what bothered me. All of a sudden if I saw horns growing out of their heads, I don't think I would have been nearly as worried. I would have known that I had gone stark raving mad. . . . (Osmond and Hoffer, 1958, pp. 303; 308–309)

The description of unreality that this man has given may be compared to those given by psychotic patients. His visual world became unfamiliar and, although he did not specifically use the word *unreality,* his description of the alteration in the meaning of his environmental world is quite similar to the accounts written by schizophrenic patients.

Depersonalization

Closely akin to the experience of unreality is the experience of depersonalization. It may be that the distinction between the two is only that depersonalization consists of unreality experiences which are somehow referred to the immediate person or personality of the experiencer. However, distinctions seem possible among the descriptions—as, for example, between those that emphasize the phenomena of unreality, and the experiences related to the loss of one's body or loss of feeling that go with ordinary previous experience.

In order to secure a better knowledge concerning the nature of depersonalization among normal persons, Roberts collected accounts of such experiences from a group of students about twenty-one years of age. He first gave a lecture to the students in which he described as clearly and vividly as he could the various phenomena of depersonalization. He then passed out to each student a questionnaire in which the questions implied that these experiences were commonplace. Each questionnaire had a blank page on which the student was instructed to provide an account of his own experiences of depersonalization, if he could do so. Of the 57 students, 23 gave positive reports of having had such experiences. The following is a typical positive report, written by a young woman aged 19.

The most unusual occasion when this occurs is when I am out of doors. The last time was within the last month or so. I was in Nottingham with a friend and suddenly as we were walking along, I seemed to be completely apart from myself. I felt that I was somewhere above looking down on the scene of which I was a part and yet not a part. I was walking and talking, as though automatically. I couldn't feel any movement and yet I knew that I was walking.

Everything appeared to be of little importance any more. The experience on this occasion lasted for at least five minutes, but time as far as I remember passed as usual. We crossed the road, and although my legs moved with the motion, I felt that my brain had gone somewhere else and from there was just watching me.

I was completely unable to tell whether I myself was still present or whether I was the part which had gone. In short there were two different beings, the one watching the other.

The experience disappeared as suddenly as it had come and once again I felt complete. (Roberts, 1960, p. 481)

This description is certainly very similar to the accounts of depersonalization that have been written by mental patients. The way in which this young woman worded her description does not imply that she considered the experience to have been either unusual or particularly disturbing. The fact that about 40 percent of this group of normal students related what seemed to be true experiences of depersonalization is not surprising. In previous chapters we have seen evidence that many varieties of unusual experiences occur much more frequently in normal persons than most physicians and psychiatrists would have thought possible.

Margiad Evans, the poetess, described at some length the feelings of depersonalization that were associated with her epileptic seizures.

When [the seizures] have happened to me while crossing a room I have, if I may so illustrate it, left myself on one side and come to myself on the other, while feeling an atom of time divided the two selves, as the room might divide the figures of myself, supposing any one could create two figures of me. And this is important to the story, because "the two figures" idea became so strong later and so haunting just before each major fit that I had later, that I was afraid of there being, or there being danger of being, a real split in me. It took me a whole year of suffering and possibly a dozen major fits, to disentangle myself from the terror of mental disorder, and to discover by hard meditation the true state I was in during that dreaded moment of double bodiedness. (Evans, 1952, p. 40)

The depersonalization (or double-personality) feeling, engendered during the epileptic seizure, depended on the time lapse of awareness during the seizure. Her normal stream of thought, conscious of her location on one side of the room, was blotted out during the interval during which her motor action caused her to walk across the room—thus when she regained consciousness she was not where she remembered she had been. There was no inner conscious appreciation of the time lapse, but there was an appreciation of the change in spatial bodily arrangements, which indicated to her that something had occurred. The recognition of something wrong in the perceptual world undoubtedly gave rise to the feelings of anxiety, terror, and personal unreality.

A young man who suffered from the speech and motor handicaps of congenital bilateral athetosis, a neurological condition that may exist without mental derangement, had completed his college education and was earning his livelihood by doing library research. He recounted how he at times suffered from a combination of an experience of unreality and depersonalization. He characterized such episodes as "spells," and described them in the following way.

The spells of unreality come on very irregularly and as far as I can discover, bear no relation to work, current activities, diet, or any other immediate factor. . . . All of these spells . . . follow a fairly definite pattern. One of the more recent ones was as follows: . . . I was working for several days in a university library. . . .

On this and the previous day, I had been occupied with routine bibliographic work that required rather close attention but no special effort. . . . About 4:30 P.M. . . . the spell began as is usual with a certain vagueness in comprehension of the material I was handling—a sort of half-conscious wondering as to exactly why I was doing it . . . I began to feel unusually weary, not exactly sleepy and drowsy, but it took a certain amount of effort to follow the printed material. A little while later I began to wonder what day of the week it was, followed by a certain amount of confusion, and an element of fear that . . . I would do something wrong . . . which would make me ridiculous . . . so I put away my things and started for my hotel. . . . I was almost obsessed by a fear of forgetting the number of my hotel room, or possibly even the hotel itself. . . . I had the feeling of not recognizing buildings, people, or streets . . . I feel isolated, a complete stranger, and always have the sense that I am acting completely from habit; for example, if asked the name of an individual, a building, or some other common thing, I simply would not be able to give the answer. . . . On the way down to the hotel, I had stopped to look at an afternoon paper to reassure myself about the day of the week and the date of the month . . . [which] only intensified the feeling that the most minute things I do must be figured out as separate intellectual problems. However, after getting to my room, I lay down [until] . . . about 6:30 [when] the feeling of strangeness—of separation from the world, of uncertainty about the date and place of my current activities . . . gradually passed away. (Brock and Wiesel, 1942, pp. 144–145)

He said that there were several features which commonly marked the experience; a feeling of being cut off, a feeling of uncertainty about time, and a feeling of an inability to respond intelligently. The spells were always associated with a great deal of fear, tension, and apprehension. He said that such a spell was in no sense a feeling of a change in his personality, but rather, a terror that he might lose his own personality.

None of the three citations regarding depersonalization thus far cited was associated with either neurosis or psychosis. In Chapters 5 and 16 I cited a portion of the autobiographical account description of a surgeon who had suffered from profound anxiety neurosis during a tour of military duty. He described his feelings of depersonalization as follows.

One can't go on being frightened for ever, and depersonalization set in. This, again, is difficult to describe to others. One might best illustrate it, perhaps, by saying that it was a feeling of anonymity. I remember that I felt it all the time, and very acutely at some times. It was all so odd. I might be having a conversation with a friend or eating a meal, yet without any sense of my own identity or indeed of any identity. At such moments I sought other human company desperately, for if others recognised me and knew my name and treated me as a person, then I must exist. . . . But the depersonalisation became worse and worse, and there was an acute stage when, after three nights without sleep, a fundamental separation seemed to have taken place from the world that other people inhabited. After that I continued to live, talk, and act, but I felt like a walking ghost. I *was* in limbo. Everything seemed to happen at one remove. (Lancet, Editors of, 1952, pp. 85–86)

He had stated earlier that the acute anxiety neurosis had overtaken him suddenly and continued unabated for many months. Then the nature of the anxiety changed and depersonalization became the leading complaint. He remarked that in spite of the strange feelings "there was one in my mind who observed my derangement with detachment and with sanity, and I think this is what sustained me." In other words, the EDITOR process recognized the dissociation of consciousness; part of his consciousness remained on guard, in charge of ordinary activity and in contact with reality. For this surgeon the experience was not a dulling or distortion of bodily sensory experience, but a feeling of separation of part of his consciousness from reality, which increasingly deprived him of contact with the world about him, so that his true personality was "at one remove" from the rest of the world.

A psychotic patient on the road to recovery gave the following more bizarre and somewhat symbolic account of the change in his personality.

In relating my history I am conscious of the fact that it was only part of my present self which experienced all of this. Up to December 23, 1901 I cannot characterize myself with the self of today. The former self now appears to me like a small dwarf which is lodged in me. It is emotionally unpleasant and painful for my feeling of existence to depict the experiences up to that time in the first person. I can do it by the use of remonstrances and in that I am conscious of the fact that the "dwarf" ruled until that day and then lost his role. . . . In the summer of 1901 my consciousness became vague . . . I could not accept the objections from my surroundings that I would only imagine these things: I could not find any relationship between representations and my perceptions, not even now. Representations appeared to me as if they did not take up any space, as if they remained as faint images in my brain or behind my eyes. Whereas I had perceptions from an outside world which however did not have any relations to the world of the senses. Even later in the ordinary world there existed for me yet another with its particular space and my consciousness moved it well in one direction or the other. (Schwab, 1919, pp. 5–7)

The explanation offered by this psychotic patient condensed his former self or personality into a dwarf, which he said was all that remained of what had been his former ordinary self. The dwarf was now repudiated and the patient insisted that it was best ignored or forgotten, for the hallucinations and delusions which had bedeviled his former self were so real that they caused him to reorganize himself as a new person. Then somehow this new personality had difficulties in finding adequate relationships between his new perceptions and the representations of older ideas and memories. As he said, he was no longer his old dwarf self, but a new and confused person who could not quite recognize and organize the world about him. This variety of depersonalization is more a symbolic and confused recognition of a changed status than a unique experience of depersonalization or unreality.

A newly hospitalized psychotic patient gave the following account a few days after her acute episode had somewhat ameliorated. She said that she had awakened suddenly in the middle of the night with the feeling that her body was numb and that she had been cut off from her surroundings. The following day things around her seemed cloudy and unreal.

I feel as though I'm not alive—as though my body is an empty, lifeless shell. I seem to be standing apart from the rest of the world, as though I'm not really here. Is there something wrong with my ears? I hear you clearly, yet your voice sounds far away—distant and unreal. Whatever has deadened my feelings had deadened my hearing, too. It's the same with my eyes. I see but I don't feel. I taste but it means nothing to me. I'll eat anything you put before me. We had walnut cake which I normally adore—but it might have been a piece of dry bread. I eat, not for pleasure, but only to live. Perfume doesn't smell pleasant any longer. I'd have no preference for the smell of these roses over the smell of the cabbage cooking. (Bockner, 1949, p. 969)

From this description, it seems that the depersonalization grew out of a diminished or distorted sensory and emotional state. Under normal conditions her self-identity had always been anchored on the sum of her sensory and emotional experience. When these aspects of her inner life became absent or dulled, she felt that she was standing apart from her person; that her real body existed only as an empty, lifeless shell.

Each of these descriptions of depersonalization, whether given by a normal person, a neurological patient, a neurotic, or a psychotic patient, has had a common element: a split or distortion in the ordinary self-image. Each reporter has spoken of one part of his mind (the EDITOR) standing off and observing the rest of his mental life wandering into new and strange courses. The circumstances in which these splits within the self-image occurred, the length of time of the experience, and the frequency of such episodes, differ, and the differences probably account for the various meanings that each individual associated with the experience. The experience may be placidly accepted, it may lead to a certain amount of mental confusion, or it may be overlaid with extreme fear and terror. It even may lead to a denial of one's usual self-image and the attempt to reconstruct a new personality. The self-recognition of the split in one's stream of conscious thought is the basis of the experience that is called depersonalization.

DISCUSSION

Clearly, the unreality experiences that have been described by different persons have differing contents and meanings. From the accounts I have cited, it is apparent that the term *unreality* has been attached to a variety of phenomena. Some of the different uses may be listed as follows: (1) Unreality occurs when there is an additional distorting quality in perceptual experience; (2) Unreality is used as a term to describe a fogging or dulling of perceptual experience; (3) Unreality is a quality dependent on some associated hallucinatory experience; (4) Unreality is a quality of experience that differentiates dream states from waking states; (5) Unreality depends on the quality of doubt attached to uncertain memories; (6) Unreality refers to an attribute or quality of mystical experience; (7) Unreality is a feeling that is attached to or gives rise to delusional states; (8) Unreality is a state that results from a dissociation of consciousness; and (9) Unreality is an abnormal mental state that is induced by the administration of certain drugs. One might expect to find the term *unreal* attached to events or perceptions that are unfamiliar or to a misinterpretation of sensory experience. Actually, one seldom finds such a usage. Probably when unfamiliar events of this sort did occur, they were mentally explored and then characterized in an acceptable manner regardless of fact, leaving only those that defied reasonable characterization to be termed unreal.

Many who have had the experience either of unreality or of depersonalization have said that their mental life seemed to proceed in a dissociated fashion consisting of two or more streams or layers. An even greater number of persons have commented on the experience of having one part of the mind (the EDITOR process) observing the remainder, which seemed to rush on uncontrollably. This mental splitting is not in itself felt to be unreal; the unreality is attached to the recognition by the EDITOR of the fact that the confusion cannot be justified or understood.

Usually, the unreality is said to have the quality of an unpleasant, intrusive experience. The unreality colors, so to speak, both the fragmented streams of consciousness and the EDITOR process. The whole unreality experience may disappear just as suddenly and mysteriously as it first appeared.

This unpleasant, intruding unreality experience has a pervasive quality that elicits belief and conviction. In this respect, the experience is comparable to an auditory hallucination, to a feeling of delusional persecution, or to the mystical character of religious experience. The unreality experience is beyond voluntary control, so that reasonable arguments or distractions do not lend it any rationality. Since unreality phenomena do have these qualities of conviction and are so pervasive, they may strike at anyone's feeling of certainty of his own sanity. If these experiences are continued for several days, the person is forced to question and to doubt the validity of his own remembrances. Then he recognizes that he cannot be certain, even in his own mind, whether this or that remembrance is true or fictitious. Stated in a different way, the unreality experience casts grave doubt on one's own reference system of truth and fiction. Every man erects during his lifetime many reference standards, which he uses to determine whether his observations are real or unreal. He has found that persons who have an undue number of doubtful private experiences may arouse the suspicions of others. Hence the intrusion of unreality feelings, over and above their own inherent disturbing effects, is terrifying in that it is directly perceived as pertinent evidence of one's own possible insanity.

Many individuals have spoken of perceptual disturbances that are associated with the unreality experience. Commonly mentioned features of such sensory distortions are; (1) loss of three-dimensional space perception so that the visual world seems flat; (2) changes in the vividness of experience, making the visual world become brighter or dimmer; (3) changes in the auditory experience, so that sounds become either deafening or remote; and (4) narrowing or fluctuating of the focus of attention.

It is interesting to note how various persons guard their mental integrity when trying to overcome the effects of unreality experiences. Some insist on precise temporal localization, some memorize poetry and occupy their minds by repetitions of such material, some attempt to fix their minds and attention on objects or persons that are undoubtedly real, some keep themselves busily occupied, so endeavoring not to "think," and so on. None of these measures is very effective because of the pervasiveness of the unreality experience. The penetration is facilitated by the weakness of will and the blurring of mental discriminative processes. The unreality, lack of will power, and feeling of stupidity may overwhelm the person so that subsequently only a dreamlike, mystical, or trancelike state may constitute the fragmentary recall that may be retrieved.

So far as one can judge from the autobiographical accounts, the major basis for the distinction of depersonalization phenomena from unreality experience is that the phenomena refer, or are referred, to the immediate personality of the experiencer. The distinction between "myself" and "not-self" occupies the center of the mental confusion and the splitting of the stream of conscious thought.

There is no adequate explanation for the symptoms and experiences of unreality. These, like many other experiences that are called psychopathological, remain a puzzle to the person because he has no common ground on which he can communicate the experience to his fellowmen. It is in a sense paradoxical that nothing can be more real than the experience of unreality and nothing more personal than the feeling of depersonalization.

With perfect insight there is recognition of the abnormality through which the patient has passed.
(*MacCurdy*, 1925, p. 439)

CHAPTER 18

Insight

INTRODUCTION

The concept of *insight* has several different meanings and usages in psychology and psychiatry, none of them clearly defined. For example, in introspective psychology, insight means the direct and immediate apprehension of meanings or general truths. In gestalt psychology, insight refers to the sudden apprehension of meaning without reference to previous experience (the so-called *a-ha* experience). In modern psychiatry, the term insight has a rather special meaning, in that it refers to the level of the self-knowledge or self-understanding which the patient has of the abnormal mental phenomena from which he is, or has been, suffering. If, for example, a patient recognizes that his overwhelming fear of crowds exists only in his own mind, he is said, by psychiatrists, to have insight; while, on the other hand, if a patient believes that his body and mind are under the control of a devil, and that he has been changed into a new and strange person, he is said to have little or no insight. The degree to which a mentally disturbed patient comes to understand the nature and meaning of his own mental state is a psychiatric measure of progress toward recovery; that is, of increased insight. Psychiatrists use the word insight in two ways, as a measure of the progress from psychosis to sanity, and as an indicator of the difference between neurosis and psychosis.

Any person who finds himself in psychotic mental turmoil has little or no ability to perceive (or conceive of) an objective reality that exists outside his own disturbed consciousness. For such a distraught individual the passing of events is too rapid, too intense, and too self-involved to allow enough time for even a crude distinction between the phenomena of his own present existence and those that occurred during his previous sane existence, to which he had learned to attribute the quality of objective reality. Because of the intensity and rapidity of what seems to be a new class of phenomena, there is no opportunity for a thoughtful evaluation. The immediate phenomena in the psychotic patient's mind have become so unpleasantly overwhelming and demanding that the ordinary intellectual, emotional, and volitional characteristics which seemed to the sane mind real and objective are hopelessly confused. Even when the acute phase of the psychotic episode has passed, the changes in memory traces are so marked that the convictions set up during the episode still govern the mind and the patient has no insight into his mental status. One patient wrote after her recovery, "I could not bear reality. I turned my back on reality. Insanity is turning away from the truth because you cannot bear it. All insanity is jumping from the frying pan into the fire. I jumped." Psychiatrically speaking, this patient had lost insight, but regained it during recovery.

That patients retain their insight during acute neurotic episodes can only be interpreted by saying that the overwhelming fear and loss of voluntary self-control do not seriously impair their intellectual processes. The self-recognition of one's actions and behavior continues in the memories so that insight, psychiatrically speaking, is unimpaired.

What standards or criteria of reality can or does the deranged patient utilize in his attempt to cope with the varied confusions in which he finds himself? What do various patients have to say about insight? What are some of the mental mechanisms that patients utilize in acquiring or denying the questions that have to do with their apprehension of reality?

"I Was Insane"

Some patients, either suddenly or gradually, accept the idea that they are, or have been for a period of time, insane. Having accepted this idea, the patient feels no further need to question the phenomena presently occupying his mind. He is free to accept or deny the memory traces of his past "sane" existence. Ideas he had learned to reject when sane are now accepted without question. "I am insane; I am no longer responsible; my real and present problem is how to recover my mind and how to avoid losing it again." In essence, this acceptance of the fact of a lost mind implies that some sort of a discriminative process has been in action so that portions of one's past experience are now denied or obliterated from the rest of one's memories. Having come to this conclusion, he need not seek further explanation or rationalization of his memories of past events.

For example, an anonymous physician (writing in the third person) who gave an account of his psychotic experience, said as follows.

A——— began to weary of his imprisonment in the small room. He at times thought himself to be Daniel in the lions' den, though he did not appear to think it necessary to account for the absence of the lions. He began to try and puzzle out where he really was, and the reason for it. His thoughts began to get more lucid, and he appears to have been allowed more freedom in the garden. Suddenly, when walking there, the explanation dawned—he had been off his head and was in the asylum at R———, a place he had occasionally visited before his insanity. After this, his delusions dropped away, and he was shortly after discharged and sent to England. He suffered greatly from depression, and was actually neurasthenic for the next three years, passing through a period of great mental distress. This seemed due to the fact that, though sane, his full faculties only gradually returned. He was incapable of sustained thought, and had to give up the practice of his profession. (Anon., 1917, p. 574)

It should be noted that this patient's sudden insight ("the explanation dawned") into his delusions did not immediately end his mental distress nor clarify his delusional ideas. Other patients have commented along similar lines. We usually find that the histories of their lives are as follows: (1) sane and normal, (2) overtaken and overcome by peculiar feelings, ideas, and doubts, (3) mind possessed by delusional systems, (4) some insight gained ("I am insane"), (5) mental and physical feelings of exhaustion, (6) gradual return to physical and mental health and full insight.

Dr. Gaupp published the account of a murderer whose illness proceeded roughly along the sequence of event just listed. He became mentally disturbed and developed a system of delusional ideas. In this deluded state he murdered his fiancée. While awaiting trial, he wrote as follows.

Thus, I became convinced that my deed was a result of my diseased mental process of development and that it happened in a false world of experience. Today, this conviction is firm and incontrovertible. No one but me is guilty for this terrible deed; it was the deed of a severely ill, desperately acting individual who looked for a way out and at the same time gave free play to his feelings of hate. After the deed I was ready to accept death as the punitive answer of the community and as salvation. Today I would suffer it with consciousness of my guilt. . . . Once is not never; this truth I have taught to my students and must now myself experience it in a horrible manner. I have no illusions about my future. Before me stands as naked fact: You have murdered a young, human child, a student, who still had a whole, rich human life before her; you have plunged into deep sorrow a family which has never harmed you and have caused it an irreplaceable loss; you have injured and harmed the community. . . . Therefore, I do not know how I can make reparation for that which has happened. (Gaupp, 1942, p. 786)

It is not common for an individual who has suffered from persecutory delusions to gain as much insight as this account suggests. Police authorities would probably say that a statement of this sort was no more than a sympathy-getting device, and that there was no evidence of real insight or remorse.

The way in which the "I was insane" mechanism operates was told more explicitly by Hackett. It will be recalled that Hackett's basic delusion was that his life had somehow come under the influence of an evil cosmic Mind. This is illustrated by the following excerpt.

[The other patients] were talking and I did not listen to them. I watched the red-hued sky and the sun slipping behind the distant hills.

"Strange, that in the evil cosmic scheme the Mind allows beauty?"

I must have interrupted them. There was a silence and then Dolan spoke. He had stopped rocking in his chair. He looked at me intently.

"We thought you had some of that cosmic baloney in your head. Listen, Paul, I've been in these places three years. Jack's been in about the same. We know we've been sick and we can see it in someone else. I can tell by the way you walk, the way you look around a room. Look at your eyes in the mirror. I can have you talk to ten guys here that have cosmic knowledge. Look, we don't care how far out in left field you are, but to see someone doing just what we used to do, that's the trouble. Your're sick and this is a hospital and it's a good one, but you have to know you're sick and stop thinking that cosmic junk. Every time it comes in your head, think of something else." [In spite of remarks of this sort that both patients and physicians made to him and that might have been expected to have resulted in some insight, his deranged condition continued. Cosmic evil might be crazy, but he could not reject the idea. However, insight was gained later and in a somewhat different fashion.]

Then one night, I sat sleepless on the edge of my bed and thought about Marie and our love and the terrible burden she had carried and I knew I had to get home. It was as if that night I became aware of her position for the first time . . . I could see her during the happy times when she thought I was better, when I first got a privilege card, or on my first visit home. . . . But most of all I could see her facing an endless soul-draining procession of small problems mixed with great ones: . . . taking care of the three children, trying to meet the mortgage payments on the house and handle money, which always confused her, going to Mass in the morning before the children woke, sitting at night reading psychology books trying to find the answer . . .

No one could survive such a strain for too long. If she had been in the hospital and I were home, I knew I wouldn't have survived a month. I must have thought of these things before but only as a part of some self-destroying depression. Now the depression did not come; only a certainty that I could get out if I tried hard enough. (Hackett, 1952, pp. 63; 300–301)

In this account, the gaining of insight was not a direct change in Hackett's internal self-recognition, but rather, an indirect result of his growing concern for the welfare of his wife and children and his general responsibilities in the outside world. The personal problems of his own depression, his delusions and hostile rages, became quite secondary to his realization of the effect that this psychosis had had, and was having, on his wife and family.

In previous chapters I have given examples of experiences of both lucid intervals and the recovery of sanity. Lucidity and recovery are not necessarily equivalent to the gaining of insight nor does the acquisition of insight, in itself, bring about recovery. It has frequently been said that the aim of psychotherapy is the acquisition of personal insight. Insight may occur but it is certainly no guarantee that the period of psychopathology has ended.

"Can My Experiences Be Attributed to Physical Illness?"

Mental illness is so frequently associated with physical illness that many patients cannot determine what the relationships between their physical and mental distress may be. A common variety of acceptable self-explanations (or rationalizations) for psychopathological experiences is to say that some physical illness was the real basis for the mental disturbance. The psychotic pain, distress, false ideas, distorted perceptions, and so on, are said, by analogy, to be symptoms of mental weakness in the same way that physical distress, pain, and so on are symptomatic of bodily weaknesses. Actually, such an analogy on the part of a patient, is not, in itself, evidence of insight or self-understanding. An example of this type of explanation may be drawn from the autobiography of the Rev. William Walford, who suffered throughout most of his adult life from melancholia. Late in life he had a remission from his depression, during which period he wrote as follows.

It will not appear surprising that, after the singular and remarkable detail that has been given, I felt a great wish, if possible, to ascertain the cause of nearly fifty years' intense suffering through which I had passed. While, indeed, under the great force of my sorrows, I was evermore induced to regard them as arising from mental and spiritual causes, quite independent of any bodily disease; yet as soon as my recovery was confirmed, I strongly suspected this notion was incorrect, and some recollections of former years led me to the conclusion that it was quite unfounded. My natural temperament had ever appeared to me to be more of the sanguine than the saturnine species, so that whenever I possessed myself sufficiently to consider the case impartially, I imagined that somewhat superinduced, and not native, was the source of my melancholy despondency. (Walford, 1851, p. 372)

He went on in his speculation concerning the basis of his melancholia, considering the fact that he had been plagued with severe headaches most of his life. He thought it possible these headaches had been caused by a head injury he had received in infancy, and that they were probably the responsible factors for his melancholia. While this variety of speculation of course did not constitute insight, at autopsy some evidence was found of possible earlier skull and brain injury.

Renee, a young woman who underwent an acute psychosis marked by feelings of unreality, fear, and compulsions, together with both acute physical and mental pain, wrote during a period of remission that partial self-realization dawned on her as follows.

Little by little, meanwhile, I began to see the pain as a natural phenomenon belonging to reality and no longer deriving from a magical origin. And the oneness of my body and myself was conclusively accomplished. . . . Reality became more real, more rich, and I more social and independent. Now I can accept [my analyst] in her own right. (Sechehaye, 1951, pp. 105–106)

Although it is commonplace for patients to arrive at an explanation of their abnormal experiences in terms of a distinction between events in the physical or bodily world, the distinction, as such, does not constitute more than partial insight. Blaming the trouble on physical illness does permit the patient to become reconciled with some part of his mental turmoil, but it is not as effective for an adequate life adjustment as is the direct discovery and acceptance of the general proposition, "I was insane."

"The Lunacy Was My Own Fault"

Some patients, recalling all too vividly the awful experience through which they have passed, conclude that in some way they permitted themselves to be overwhelmed, either by their own imagination or by unknown powers or forces which they should have been able to resist. For example, a recovered patient wrote to Dr. Schwab as follows.

I believe that I have called forth the illness myself. In the attempt to penetrate the ulterior world, I encountered its natural guardians, the embodiment of my own weaknesses and errors. In the beginning I regarded these demons for lower form inhabitants of an ulterior world, which could use me as a plaything, because I entered these regions unprepared and lost my way there. Later, I regarded them as fragmentary parts of my mind (emotional forms), which existed freely around me and nourished themselves on my feelings. I thought that everyone else also had them but did not perceive them because of protection and happy deception of the personal feeling of existence. I conceived of the feeling of existence as an artificial product of memories, thought complexes, etc., an outwardly gilded chrysalis in which nothing essential lived. (Schwab, 1919, pp. 15–16)

He continued by saying that in his desire to bring himself closer to the higher, more spiritual things of life, he allowed and encouraged his own mind to become thin, weak, and porous. This permitted the demons (evil thoughts) to gain ascendancy over his mind, which in turn led him to decide that he must die. He attempted self-starvation, an ordeal which convinced him that the demons were like his own body; they could not survive without nourishment. Having come to this conclusion, he said that he was able to strengthen and unify his mind so that he now gained a more rational outlook on life. It is difficult to decide whether amidst all the symbolism and obscurities of his thinking there was any insight, or whether the symbolism merely covered over a fundamental psychotic confusion.

Graves, who suffered from repeated periods of mania and depression during much of his adult life, wrote as follows in trying to sum up and understand the effect of the repeated and prolonged episodes of psychopathology through which he had lived.

I am inclined to think now that the surrender to delusion—though shamefully great—drops in degree with repetition. The actual phases of manic activity have shortened and lessened. Of course, it is difficult for me to see now how I have ever departed from the norm in conduct and thought. In a way, the great fear of insanity which I used to have has disappeared—I have taken the worst of damage which seems to be possible for me. Nevertheless, the fears and the life-loathing which replace its vogue are none the less serious. Insofar as enjoyment of existence goes, I think I have increased insight to the point that will make such enjoyment nearly impossible. My feeling at the present moment is that never again could such a seizure take me—but the fear is of the lethargy, the life distaste, and the distance for the limited, hazardous, and probably painful life prospect which still remains. It seems to me that perfect apprehension of reality resumes rather quickly; and that there always exists enough insight for me to know that when my outlook is roseate and optimistic, I am probably on the verge of distortion. . . . And of course, now I consider that it couldn't happen again. (Graves, 1942, p. 691)

Essentially, Graves pointed out that although he had repeatedly surrendered to delusion, each successive attack had been less complete and insight had always been regained at the time of each recovery. But he still admitted to the possibility of being overwhelmed again by psychosis, in spite of all his prior experiences and hard-gained understanding of himself.

If a patient takes the attitude that he allowed himself to be overcome by lunacy and that he should have had the strength of character to resist, his attitude is, of itself, somewhat insightful, but it will not necessarily deter further episodes, nor really give any fundamental understanding of the mental processes that marked the period of lunacy.

"The Episode Seems Unreal and Had Best Be Forgotten"

Realization on the part of the experiencer that the period of mental pathology was somehow unreal and unnatural, and that no one, except himself and possibly his doctor, is interested in what happened, represents a frequent expression of partial insight. Usually this realization is accompanied by the opinion that the sooner the whole period is forgotten, the better it will be for all concerned. For example, a patient who recovered after insulin coma therapy wrote to his doctor as follows.

The landlord was not on the government payroll. That's an error on my part. . . . It's not normal to hear voices. Something must have been radically wrong with me . . . I know now that I can't read other people's minds. That's foolish . . . The wires had nothing absolutely to do with me. No sane person would believe in such things. I must have been mistaken about the signals. I was so sensitive at the time that I observed such things and thought they were all meant for me and of course, I realize now that I said so many ridiculous, fantastic things. It was all my imagination, insane impressions, I can understand. The whole thing seems to me now to be a dream and I want to forget about it and not talk about it, that is, except with you so that I can get it all clear. I might as well face it. Of course my mind was working in the wrong way. I was completely gone, completely out of my mind. I am so grateful and thankful that I have found myself. I really wouldn't want to live if I had to go through that state again. I think the [insulin] coma did wonders for me. (Milici and von Salzen, 1938, p. 665)

A report of this sort indicates that the person is attempting to repudiate and obliterate his own experience. He tells himself that part of his life experience, as he recalls it, was ridiculous, fantastic, and insane, and the sooner he can erase the entire episode from his mind the better for all concerned. Such an attempt indicates a rather realistic and rational variety of insight. A difficulty may arise later if there is a recurrence of the symptoms that were just denied without any actual understanding.

"Doubtful Insight"

Some persons who have lived through a prolonged period of psychopathological experience find great difficulty in repudiating the delusions that grew out of their experience. This is particularly true in persons whose experience has been, to some degree, of a paranoid nature. Dr. Peterson's patient, from whose long autobiographical statement I quoted in Chapters 5 and 8, wrote of the years of his greatest mental aberration.

Here I come to more debatable territory, on which I and the rest of the world have until this present been at variance. I will, in deference to the other side, make use of the word *believe* in stating facts drawn from the region of my memory lying within this shadowy world. I will be permitted to say, therefore, that I *believe* that after settling down in the [asylum], my brain was, by the gradual progress of events occurring naturally and according to the ordinary laws of human affairs, drawn into relations to the living actors around me, of an altogether unexampled kind—at all events different from anything plainly recorded in the annals of past ages. I *believe* that the final result of such relations was the superinducing of a state of mental intercommunication through the medium of my sense of hearing. (Peterson, 1889, p. 220)

It is apparent that this patient remained convinced of the reality of his hallucinatory and delusional experiences. In spite of his suffering, of the evident disbelief on the part of all other persons with whom he had associated, and all the simpler explanations that others had urged on him, he continued in his paranoid convictions, insisting on the truth of his private experiences.

Some patients while in a confused phase of their psychosis will give evidence, during the course of a single interview, of irregular changes in their level of insight and self-understanding. As Dr. Lewis' patient shows, some of his thoughts indicated self-understanding, but these comments were mixed with others which seemed clearly delusional.

I thought I heard voices saying always the same thing, wondering whether I was a Jew, or whether I was a fool. It worried me. There have been days lately when I have felt these voices. I seem to hear some sort of a voice calling in the distance. I have often thought they were obsessions, which I had thought myself into: that I was looking out for the voices. I could never really realize the truth . . . My nerves were in such a bad state that I really could not, what shall I say, couldn't find the mental background to force these obsessions out of my head. I think I'd call it "Verfolgungswahn" [state of persecution]. . . . I thought people from the boat had come along and told that story that I was a Jew and I was a fool. I never knew whether that was an obsession of mine or whether it actually existed. . . . This morning I felt as if I was hypnotized. . . . The man in the next bed. I thought it was him and then I thought he had changed completely, then I thought "Oh yes it is," but in a minute I thought, "No it couldn't be. . . ." My illness is purely mental. (Lewis, 1934, p. 346)

Evidently, this patient was in an unclear and confused state of mind, as though he were only partially awake, or partially in contact with reality. He was uncertain of his sensory experiences and feelings. He was unsure whether he heard voices or not, or if he did, what the voices meant. Certainly he was unable at the time to find satisfactory reference points on which to anchor any idea of reality in his stream of consciousness.

In his autobiography, *The Mind in Chains,* Moore described his final interview with his physician at the time he was discharged from the hospital. It is an interesting example of doubt tinged only slightly with insight.

He didn't ask me any questions which I could not truthfully have answered the same way upon my admission a year and a half before. His most awkward question was this: "You do realize now that you were mentally ill when you came here, don't you?"

"That depends upon how you define mental illness and where you draw the line. I can see how others must believe that I was that way."

That was my answer then, and it is still the same today. I was never "insane." As to my having been "sick," I cannot say that I really was; nor can I say that I was not, either. I still do not understand it. I still wonder what really happened. (Moore, 1955, pp. 302–303)

In contrast to Moore's doubt we have seen that Schreber was able to draw up legal documents in the conviction that they were sufficiently lucid and cogent to convince the judges of the Court of Appeals that he should be released from the custody of the hospital. Moore had reservations about his "insanity," but Schreber's remarks at the end of his *Memoirs* were written with "absolute certainty."

I have by *no means exhausted* the experiences and supernatural impressions I received during almost seven years of nervous illness; but I think I have rendered sufficient of the circumstances to allow an understanding of my religious views and to explain certain peculiarities of my conduct. It only remains for me to say a word about the future.

"What will come of this cursed affair?" and "What will become of me?" . . . such are the questions which have for years been spoken into my head by the rays in endless repetition; even if they rest on falsifications and do not render *my* own thoughts, yet they give a hint that even God is aware of a thoroughly mismanaged affair. . . . My own conception is as follows. It is of course impossible to predict with certainty what will become of me or in what way one can guide back into normal channels the circumstances contrary to the Order of the World in which God apparently finds himself towards the whole earth in consequence of my nerves' attraction. . . . All I can say with absolute certainty is something *negative, namely* that God will never succeed in his purpose of destroying my reason. (Schreber, 1955, p. 211)

From these concluding remarks it is quite evident that Schreber was completely convinced of the meaningfulness and reality of his psychopathologic experiences. There is no evidence that Schreber gained any insight or self-understanding. In fact, the Appeal Court held that he was still in a psychopathological state at the time he requested discharge. It ruled that his delusions and lack of insight did not constitute a danger to Schreber himself, to his family, or to the general public. In other words, the court held that psychopathology was not necessarily incompatible with permission to circulate freely in society.

Custance based a personal philosophical system on his experiences during mania and depression. His system, or "theory of actuality," was less complicated by mysticism than were some of the explanations offered by other patients (for example, Schreber). The insightfulness of his theory may be judged from this excerpt.

I am certainly not "certifiable" now, whatever I may have been when I was actually certified . . . Why not? I am really just as "mad" as ever. The difference is apparent rather than real. I just do not appear to be "mad," that is all. Certainly the apprehensions of the manic consciousness are as it were further away from my "field of vision"; they have receded into deeper layers of my "Unconscious." But they are there, and I know that they are true, in so far as there is such a thing as "truth" at all. As I have said, I go on acting upon them all the time, though I take care to do so in a way which is in accord with commonsense "reality." When I am in any way manic, however, I find this difficult. To some extent I am in another world, on another "plane of Actuality," and I cannot make proper contact with my fellow-creatures. They cannot understand me and I cannot understand them. (Custance, 1952, pp. 208–209)

Of his theory of actuality Custance wrote that it was all organized and ready in the back of his mind, beautifully reasoned, with a whole string of quite irrefutable proofs attached. But, he said, this theory persisted perversely in flickering and twinkling at the end of distant vistas of thought. When he attempted to write it down and then to read it later, he could barely make head or tail of it and its appalling egocentricity "nearly made him sick."

As near as one can understand, Custance held that actuality (a word meaning almost the same as reality) exists in depths (or layers) in man's consciousness. Attached to ordinary conscious experience are different layers of actuality. During periods of involuntary imagination that mark abnormal mental states, the level of actuality varies. The amount of actuality of the lunatic is different from that of sane persons around him. Actuality differs for each individual as he passes from normality to mania or to depression. The essential difference between Custance-sane and Custance-mad was in the level of actuality of his mental life. This theory constituted a basis of insight and self-understanding for Custance.

Relation of Insight to Psychotherapy

An axiom of present-day dynamic psychotherapy is that one of its aims is to make it possible for the patient to gain insight, that is, to reach an understanding of his own conscious and unconscious motivations which are responsible for his mental symptoms and problems. The patient is encouraged to report in an undirected, uninhibited fashion anything that comes into his mind. The therapist refrains from praise or blame and tries on occasion to suggest possible connections among the patient's various remarks. If the patient accepts the suggested connections, he may gain understanding or insight; if he rejects the connection nothing is lost. In this way it is possible for the patient to gain, slowly but surely, some insight into his mental difficulties.

Portions from Jane Hillyer's account of her experiences during an acute psychosis, which lasted more than four years, have been cited in previous chapters. After her recovery she placed herself under the care and guidance of a psychotherapist. She commented on the results growing out of the therapy as follows.

For three years I talked, unburdened every fear, every horror, every despair, that I had been conscious of and many that I did not know, save as they *affected me emotionally*. A certain concrete terror of early childhood was "excavated." In itself it proved to be unfamiliar, but the emotion of which it was the hidden center was as old as I, as new as yesterday.

At last it was done. . . . It was all commonplace and human. I became to myself not so much an individual as a mere unit in a species—and not a very exciting one either. Emotional reactions had become very largely subjected to reason. What the [Doctor] finally succeeded in doing—in a word—was to make me feel with my mind, not to think with my feelings. The relief was indescribable. (Hillyer, 1926, p. 189)

Generally speaking, persons who recover from schizoid episodes such as Miss Hillyer's are mentally "scarred"; that is, some of the peculiarities of the experience remain with them and intrude in the subsequent mental life. They do not have the strength that permits a long self-study or a deep analysis of their private mental life. That such an analysis together with the attendant insight can occur, as Miss Hillyer reported, is as unusual as it is interesting.

A social worker who had had considerable psychotherapeutic treatment prior to her illness finally developed an acute psychosis. She later wrote that during the period of her illness she tried to reassure herself on the basis of her previous psychotherapeutic experience.

This was my problem in a nutshell. There was a part of myself that had not been trustworthy, attributes which I had not liked, and which had to be eradicated. I was by no means rejecting myself completely, for incorporated into that self were all the values I cherished most. My feeling for nature, art, and science, and my general love of life seemed to be entirely in harmony with my value-system and inseparable from it. I became aware during my first illness of the tremendous debt which I owed to the past. (Anon., 1955, pp. 680–681)

In spite of the self-knowledge gained from prior therapy and special training; in spite of the insight which she felt she had, the pathological state continued. She heard voices, saw visions, and experienced delusions. Over a period of four years she had three psychotic episodes, each lasting a month or more. Remission from the first attack was attributed to sodium amytal treatment; from the second, the remission was said to be spontaneous; and the third was attributed to electric convulsive therapy. For this patient "insight," such as she had, did not seem to have played any role in the onset, course, or recovery from the illness.

Leonard, who suffered from a severe neurotic phobia throughout most of his adult life and who was treated by several therapists, made the following comments.

The discovery of the subconscious past and of its dynamics and organization down to the shifting present which it forever overtakes has had for my intellect the objective interest in personality as unitary and in life as a self-creative plot; and something of this I have perhaps been able to share with the reader. But the new and awesome subjective feeling thereby engendered I cannot share. (Leonard, 1939, p. 422)

He held that the self-knowledge of the remembrances of forgotten fears that acted as basic motivations in his phobia, which he rediscovered during therapy, were interesting and gave him some insight and understanding, both of himself and of his relations to others. However, the intensity of the feelings that overwhelmed him remained a private experience that was beyond self-control, and the insight brought no relief from the panics.

In contrast to the experience of Leonard, a woman who suffered from a somewhat similar phobic neurosis from the age of twenty-five to fifty-five, and who finally came to depend largely on her own self-analysis, summarized her recovery as follows.

So, bit by bit, fragments from my unconscious were torn from their moorings, and I saw them for what they really were. As my explorations continued, their hold was lessened until at long last my unconscious gave up its secrets in floods of associations. (Anon., 1952, p. 168)

During the course of her thirty years of phobic neurosis this woman had been treated by at least eight psychiatrists, had been in five clinics or hospitals, and had resorted to Christian Science. Her basic problem was fear of daylight. She dared not venture out of a darkened room during the day, since if she did she went into a panic, fearful of what daylight might reveal. Of her self-analysis she wrote as follows.

One thing I learned from conducting my own analysis was that no amount of knowing about a fear or talking about it will make the slightest dent in it. One has to live through each fear as it arrives, and, moreover, one has to do that again and again until the particular subject becomes threadbare.

Only then does it release its hold. Often when I thought I was done with one of them, it reared its head again. Thus the absolute necessity for feeling my fears through was made apparent; just thinking or knowing about them would not suffice. (Anon., 1952, p. 177)

Perhaps the failure of other individuals to achieve recovery from neurosis through the gaining of some degree of insight lies in the circumstance this woman has related: that insight alone was not enough; the fear-producing situation has to be lived through time after time until it finally loses its ability to produce terror.

Miss Dearborn, who suffered from an acute psychosis for which she was treated by intensive psychotherapy for some time without any beneficial results, was finally treated with electric convulsive therapy followed by intensive psychotherapy, after which she made a partial recovery. She published, later, an account of her psychotic experiences that included the following observations.

One interesting result of persistent work to this end is shown in the phenomenon of subjective voices, which I have been distinctly hearing during all the period of convalescence, and even currently. These voices come from nowhere, and are not related to my conscious thoughts. They are much nearer to sensory impacts, however, than are unvoiced thought-words, for they have actual sound, although entirely within my own mind. The fact that I recognize them as entirely within myself distinguishes them from the auditory hallucinations of the psychotic, for the latter believes his "voices" to be issuing from someone near him in his surroundings. These of mine have always been recognized as products of my own mind. (Dearborn, 1950, p. 116)

Whether this distinction between two varieties of auditory hallucinations had been suggested to her by someone else or was an original idea is not apparent. In any event, there is no evidence that would indicate that such an idea has any basis in fact. It certainly does not indicate any degree of insight.

An anonymous surgeon who suffered from a phobic neurosis wrote as follows.

Growth of insight has helped me greatly. If psychology didn't cure me it gave me some idea of how the mind works to avoid, and protect itself against, painful thoughts. I understood this and applied it personally as soon as I could. Now, like others who are disabled, I have my methods. The essentials are my few safety depots—people or places. The safety radius from them grows longer and longer. I am still claustrophobic; that rules out underground trains for me, but I use the District Railway. I find it difficult to meet relations and childhood friends, and to visit places where I lived or worked when I was very ill. But I have learnt to make short visits to give me a sense of achievement and to follow them when I am ready for it by a longer visit. (Lancet, Editors of, 1952, p. 82)

The testimony of this physician, like that of practically every other person who has been assisted by psychotherapy, is that the self-understanding and insight which had been gained made it possible to live *with* the disabling effect of the phobia, the anxiety, the obsession or the voices, but that insight, of itself, does little or nothing to end the complaint. The testimony of one of the persons cited above, that one has to live through the phobia again and again until the particular subject becomes threadbare, seems significant. Each particular fear may be disclosed and exhausted, but all too often a new fear (or other symptom) somehow comes to replace the one that has been extinguished. Insight in the form of self-understanding assists one in bearing the burden of each new symptom but it does not prevent the appearance or the discomfort of further painful experiences.

DISCUSSION

Insight is an elusive concept that conveys different meanings to different persons. In one sense, it is used to characterize the reactions of one person as his behavior is related to many other persons. In another sense, *insight* is used to describe the mental status which results when an individual changes his interpretations of his experience so that his new interpretation comes to agree with the conventional standards of the group of which he is a member. The word *insight* is also used as a way to describe the phenomenon of sudden understanding or reorientation. In this sense, insight has a unique mental character—the *a-ha* experience, or a "Now I see it; why didn't I see that before," experience.

The psychiatric concept of insight has attained a certain usefulness in the present-day considerations of the phenomenology of psychopathology. If a person has been overwhelmed and mystified by his own mental experience then the achievement of insight or self-understanding does in some persons seem to alleviate or even end the confusion and turmoil that have marked the pathology.

The autobiographical accounts indicate that a sudden reorientation, in which a complete change of interpretation of private experience occurs, is a rather uncommon event following a severe mental illness. The self-descriptions of an insightful change for the better indicate that it is usually a gradual process. I have classed these processes under several descriptive titles. The first ("I Was Insane") consists largely of rejection and repudiation of one's past private experience. The second ("Physical Illness") partakes largely of a process of rationalization. The fourth ("Unreal") is usually one of obliteration and putting remembrances out of mind, and the last ("Relation to Psychotherapy") is the acceptance by the experiencer of some other person's suggestions or explanations. To these we added a group of statements ("Doubtful

Insight") made by persons whose insight or self-understanding seemed largely composed of the presence of doubts.

The evidence I have assembled indicates that recovery from psychopathological experience is often attended by some degree of self-understanding and insight, but I have found nothing to indicate that insight, of itself, necessarily brings about recovery.

Part of the difficulty growing out of any use of the concept of insight derives from the fact that the term *insight* means several things to the experiencer and something still different to observers. It is difficult for one who has never experienced a particular variety of psychopathology to understand the nature of the experience itself, let alone the process of gaining an appreciation and self-understanding in re-evaluating the abnormal experience. Insight in this sense is related to particular and peculiar phases in an individual's life; that others fail to understand them is not remarkable.

And God said unto Moses, I AM THAT I AM; and he said, Thus shalt thou say unto the children of Israel, I AM hath sent me unto you.

(Exodus III : 14)

CHAPTER 19

Various Peculiarities

INTRODUCTION

In addition to the wide variety of peculiar experiences that have been detailed and considered in previous chapters, there still remain several other oddities reported by several different patients which have caught my attention. These oddities might have been included under one or another of the chapter headings that have been utilized, but when that was attempted each peculiarity seemed to lose part of its essential character. Hence, I have assembled and present this collection, treating each variety as though it was separate and unique.

"I AM"

Several times I have run into the phrase I AM in describing some phase of the psychopathological experience, usually in reference to religious experience. For example, Christopher Smart, who succumbed to a "religious mania," wrote while he was in a madhouse between 1756 and 1758 a long poem entitled, "A Song of David," which has long been considered one of the poetic masterpieces of the eighteenth century. One verse of this poem is as follows:

> Tell them, I AM, Jehovah said
> To Moses; while earth heard in dread, . . .
> All Nature, without voice or sound,
> Replied, "O Lord, THOU ART."
>
> (Smart, 1910, p. 502)

Obviously this "I AM" refers to the Biblical verse from the book of Exodus. In similar fashion, Rickman in 1841 published an autobiographical account of the periods of insanity that he had spent in several asylums. This account, which he wrote in blank verse and entitled "Madness or the Maniacs' Hall: A Poem in Seven Cantos," included one verse that ran as follows.

> Jesus! who didst all prophecy inspire!—
> "Ere Abraham was, I AM,"—could Godlike say . . .
>
> (Rickman, 1841, p. 139)

Most of Rickman's poem consists of an account of his experiences together with his recommendations for better care and treatment of the insane.

Perceval told of the following incident.

> I walked about Dr. F.'s ground and plantations, crying out at every carriage I saw, that it was my mother's; to every young female that she was one of my sisters, and calling aloud by inspiration, "I am the lost hope of a noble family—I am ruined! I'm ruined! I'm lost! I'm undone! but I AM the redeemed of the Lord; I AM the redeemed of the Lord Jehovah supremely omnipotent, and of the Lord Jehovah . . ." The above sentences were given to me to repeat, laying a stress on the word "am," of which sentences I now see the beauty and the connexion, though then I cried each out, separately, timidly, and undecidedly. (Perceval, 1838, p. 123)

These sentences he continued to call out even though he was beaten and misused by the attendants for his noisy public behavior. He recalled these incidents as having occurred during his acute insanity. He said that it seemed to him that the words were given to him by divine orders as part of the ritual of his trial for redemption.

Schwab published the autobiographical account of a schizophrenic patient that was written in an attempt to clarify the events that occurred to him during his psychosis. He stated that in order to maintain his control over the demoniacal voices he found himself forced to pronounce inwardly phrases such as the following.

"*I am*" (thereby I tried to feel the new and not the old ego).

"*I am* the absolute" (I referred to the bodily development, I did not want to be God myself).

"*I am* the mind, not the body."
"*I am* the one present in everything."
"*I am* the enduring" (in reference to the fluctuations of my physical and spiritual life) or I used only single words like: "strength," "life." (Schwab, 1919, p. 13)

He went on to say that the best protection against intrusive thoughts was obtained by saying or thinking short sentences and these sentences must always be in his mind and ready for utterance. Over time the sentences became part of a protective ritual.

Miss Dearborn published an account of her psychotic experience, of which the following is a part.

In the hospital, it was an obsession, yes; but reminding ourselves that the word "Jehovah" means "I AM," we here read an experience of childhood which accounts for such an extreme vagary: When in school at about 11 years of age, on some of my visits to the lavatory, I would repeat in my mind a magic formula, namely, "I *am*, but I *am*, but I *am*" . . . just those three words, over and over again. This, repeated during the toilet function, had the effect on me of carrying me right out of myself, so to speak; it brought on an ecstasy, in the original sense. I felt "other-worldly," lifted into another person who stood there strong and inspired. (Dearborn, 1950, p. 92)

It is difficult to guess whether or not these accounts constitute a ritual-like trend that has some common basis in psychopathological experience. It is odd that these instances did occur so widely spaced in time and place and for both sexes (Smart, English, 1756; Perceval, English, 1838; Rickman, English, 1841; Schwab, German, 1919; Dearborn, American, 1950). In each instance a somewhat different explanation was offered. If a generalization is possible, the most obvious would be that I AM was part of a ritual of reassurance; a means of reassuring oneself that despite the feelings of unreality and outside control that one's own personal existence continues and cannot be doubted since God's name could be appealed to.

Phrases, Metaphors, and Neologisms

Not too different in these ways in which the phrase I AM was used are the uses of many other phrases, parts of sentences, and neologisms that are repeatedly used by patients in fashions that seem to others to be quite senseless. Sometimes these have been thought by the patient to partake of the nature of a ritual, others have been thought to be nonsensical but were repetitiously imposed by the voices, still others had made sense to the patient at one time or another but the sense had faded and the phrase lingered on in his mind like an endlessly re-echoing sound. For example, a few samples from the many recorded by Perceval as having been imposed on him are as follows.

"I recollect amongst other instances of my memory failing me, and of accusations being made of me in consequence, in a similar manner, that I one day heard, and was desired to sing, and to apply to myself these words:
"I'd be a butterfly born in a bower,
Kissing all buds that are pretty and sweet."
Here I paused—I heard no more, I was desired to open my mouth in faith and go on—but I could not recollect the remainder of the song. Then different spirits suggested to me words, with which I was not satisfied, and amongst others—
"But I would not be a little idle thing,
Sitting here all day to do nothing but sing."
I have to observe, that although I had heard the song "I'd be a butterfly" before my illness, I do not recollect ever having committed it to memory, or being very familiar with it; therefore to have remembered the concluding verses could not naturally be expected of me, but would in a manner have been a gift. I bought the song since my liberty to see what were the other verses. Many persons have the gift of an extraordinary memory—they will hear a sermon and go away and repeat it word by word. I question now whether this is not in consequence of the machinery of the mind being in this respect, in them, in perfect order, and whether this power is not latent in all men, but disturbed through passion—through the mind being ill-regulated—perhaps through organic disease. (Perceval, 1838, p. 302)

Further in his account Perceval gave a much longer list of phrases which he heard or which were "put into his mouth." The tone of the voices which he "used to be made to fancy that he heard" were, he said, very beautiful and musical, like the tones of angels. Following are some of the fragments of speech that had been addressed to him, and that he was prompted to repeat continuously.

Keep rising—keep rising to heavenly places,
In the power of Louisa's glory. . . .

I am risen to heavenly places
In the power of the Lord Jehovah. . . .

The time of the trial of the time of the trial,
And the trial of the time of the trial of the time,
And the trial of the time of the time of the trial. . . .

To be hacked and hewed,
And manacled and brewed
In a manner most distressing . . .

I could if I would, and I would if I could,
I can if I will, and I will if I can. . . .

It will be so, and it won't be so,
It shall be so, and it shan't be so. . . .

I am joyful, cheerful, happy, grave and gay,
In the knowledge of the LORD my REDEEMER. . . .

CHRIST HALLELUJAH! is your cue—
CHRIST HALLELUJAH! is for you—
If you'll prove faithful to your cue—
Not otherwise.
(Perceval, 1840, pp. 320–323)

Perceval speculated at some length over these fragments of verse that the voices had so often directed him to repeat, frequently during inappropriate circumstances. Among other possible explanations, he was of the opinion that psychotics are apt to mistake a poetic train of thought for an attempt to explain reality. He also noted that such persons may mistake a spirit of humor, which may have become attached to some action, for a spirit of sincerity. He said that he had always been fond of music, and that before his illness he could sit and enjoy in his imagination the music of brilliant orchestras and bands, and although he did not understand how music is written, he often dreamt musical airs which he thought were original. During the month before the onset of his acute disturbance, he had spent several days visiting in a Scottish community where a religious revival was being held and where members of the congregation had "spoken with voices," that is, had arisen in church and spoken in whatever way they alleged God directed them to say. He commented that undoubtedly the Almighty has the power to make a man utter sentences of either a reasonable or unreasonable nature in words the speaker is unable to comprehend. The gift of tongues mentioned in the Scriptures *may* therefore not be altogether false, but rather the Lord's message may have been turned to folly and nonsense by the disingenuousness of the speaker who delivered the holy message. In brief, he said that the Lord had placed holy messages into his mouth, but that he in his imperfect state of mind did not understand and could not deliver them sensibly.

In Chapter 6, which dealt with hallucinations, I cited several of Schreber's examples of the fragmented phrases that he heard repeated day after day and that he said he had previously experienced as complete ideas. For example, "I shall," was incomplete for "I shall have to think about that first." Condensations of this sort may be even further developed into new words (neologisms). For example, the following neologisms, together with their definition or association supplied by the patient for each item, were recorded by Dr. E. L. Bryan.

Bouw	Mrs. B. is the right hand bouw of those who use the crocodile machine . . .
Li M. A	"Limed from the presence of Almighty God"
Oster Ostetter	"It's a state right, a virtue right" . . .

Mutterlies	"The years go by controlled by spirit of previous mutterlies, doctrines slightly mutual, can't control" . . .
Commotional	Used in referring to hallucinations . . .
Visioned	"I rather visioned, reviewing things" . . .
Because trust Cox	"Because it is the very highest lawyer" . . .
Hubbled	"Means pulling like somebody pulling down something"

(Bryan, 1933, p. 593)

The invention of a neologism, or unusual word, by any patient is largely an individual matter. The word may have been coined by the patient to designate a new or unique feeling or experience; it may have been provided by, and explained to, the patient by his illusory voices; or it may be a condensation of several common words that when combined lose their original meaning. Whatever its basis, the occurrence of these interpolated neologisms adds to the general confusion on the part of the observer when he attempts to understand the patient's subjective experience. To the untrained observer, a conversation with a psychotic who uses many neologisms only serves to convince him further of the patient's essential insanity.

In addition to the nonsensical quality of the patient's speech, enhanced by the intrusion of neologisms, some patients also make use of certain unclear metaphors that further add to the obscurity of the meaning. For some patients, this otherwise normal process becomes eccentric, blurred, and confused. Following is an example of this deviation collected by Dr. W. L. Woods.

One young woman spoke of the light that was taken away.
"What did you say about the light?"
"I was referring to the spiritual or sex life. I think its the same thing and if it's killed there is no after life. Dead. It goes out of the body and the body is nothing but dead."
"How is the sex life the same as the spiritual?"
"In the Catholic Church man and wife is the same as Christ is to the Church; that is spiritual life." (Woods, 1938, p. 304)

Another investigator, Dr. E. F. Sharpe, gathered the following list of loose expressions that are to some degree intelligible.

"I've wandered off the point and can't find it again."
"I've lost sight of what I came for."
"It's the way I set about things that's wrong."
"When I wander off the point bring me back to it."
"When I do anything I seem to have my eye on something else all the time."
"I am distracted because the tail of my eye is on something else." (Sharpe, 1940, p. 205)

If one recalls, then, that the verbal productions of many deranged patients contain metaphors, neologisms, rhymes, and condensations, together with whole portions of bizarre material attributed to auditory hallucinations, one realizes that the peculiarities of a disturbed person's speech contribute to the difficulties he may have in conveying knowledge to others.

Feeling of Unnatural Personal Power

As we have seen, it is fairly commonplace for mentally ill persons to claim that they have lost their ability to exercise self-control; that they have come under a variety of outside controlling influences; that they are overpowered by evil influences acting on them from without, and so forth. More rarely will a patient state that he has come into possession of some new and unnatural personal power with which he can influence and control the behavior of other persons or of external events. (I do not consider here those persons who believe that they have been given a divine power which enables them to convey God's messages to others.) These unnatural personal powers are usually said to be magnetic, telepathic, hypnotic, or the function of a strong personality. They are frequently used as self-protection against some unspecified influence or as a device to save others from an imaginary evil. Dr. Pollack published the case of a young female patient who insisted she could control others by projecting her personality.

I had always projected my personality and their personality fell so that I could see their psychic energy. I'd shoot out my energy and prevent them from falling. I was doing that to him. He was thirty-two and married. He smiled and finally accepted the situation. I was facing him and there was a channel between us. When two people think of the same thing at the same time there is a shudder or a shiver in me. I knew if such a thing happened in a person he would have control of the situation and could do what he wanted. I was afraid as I didn't know him that he would control my personality. I'd always controlled that with women and still wanted to with men. (Pollack, 1937, p. 347)

In this instance the patient implied (but did not state) that her projection was a form of sexual attraction with which she could draw or repel the love which other persons might feel for her.

Peters told how, while acutely disturbed, he developed the grandiose notion that he could control the thoughts and behavior of others by sending out a radar beam which he activated by staring. He described it as follows.

What weapon did I have against a whole hospital? My eyes. I wondered if I still had that beam in my eyes. Wherever it had come from, whatever it had been, I knew that I had had it and that it had been effective. Did I still have it? Come on, radar, I said to myself, and put my hands on my chest. I could feel the warmth growing inside me again. That was good. All I had to do was to get it into my eyes. I began to glare at the man opposite me, and I could feel my face reddening. He stopped eating and put his hands on the table. "What are you looking at?" he asked.

I did not answer him, but continued to stare into his face. I could feel the fear coming out of him. It was still there. I looked away. I had nothing against him. Would it affect other things besides people? Doors for instance? Could I burn my way through a door with it? I'd have to try that. But then what? Escape? I looked down at my clothes. Anybody would know in a minute that I had escaped. That's why they dressed you in blue of course. . . . Perhaps I would have to do with it with people. After all, my radar beam (thank God for it!) had got me to see Dr. Matthews and then out of the pack room, and it had been powerful enough to keep those men away from me and get me out of wet sheets. Maybe all I had to do was to stare people into doing what I wanted. (Peters, 1949, p. 135)

Peters' delusion of power had developed in a rather peculiar fashion. He was greatly attracted to the sun and felt that he could draw energy from it, which he could store in his solar plexus and use to stare at others and defend himself. His concentrated glare did in fact seem to frighten other patients and the attendants. He was at times dimly aware of the fantastic nature of his delusion but it worked to his satisfaction.

A not uncommon delusion of personal power frequently centers around ideas of telepathy or telepathic control. For example, Graves wrote as follows.

I was possessed by the notion that "communication" from an unknown external source was affecting me, and that a generally "unknown force" was being applied. . . . I [could not] agree to my own insanity, to the possession of any psychosis, because I clung to the demonstration that my normal, prosaic but quite sensitive mentality was subject to physical and aimed intrusion, and that other people could be made to feel the impact of the force if I worked out the principles of its application. . . . I meant that if I were fully informed as to the method of electrically projecting thought, and adequately armed with implements developed for the purpose, it would be possible for me or any other operator to influence the thinking of susceptible people. This was the delusional idea at its tritest. Speculating, I had accepted the conclusion that there was a sort of radio transmitting center . . . so that if trained and placed in the operator's position, I or anyone else might operate it. Just normal goofiness. (Graves, 1942, pp. 440–441)

Very often these beliefs in the capacity to affect events or persons at a distance are associated with schizophrenic delusions; Graves' notion, however, was only an outcome of his manic excitement. We notice in his last sentence quoted above that he later depreciated the idea as "normal goofiness," but the rest of his account does indicate that during the more acute phase of his illness he took the idea seriously.

Delusions of unnatural personal power are paradoxical from the outsider's point of view. The explanation offered by the patient is very frequently quite plausible if one grants him his basic assumptions. The patient says, "I feel that I have acquired some great new power. Where it came from, why I was selected, and what the ultimate aim of the power may be I do not know. I *feel* that this is true and and I *know* that I cannot resist, modify, start, or stop the power. The new power has possessed my mind." Since he cannot recall having ever before had such conscious thoughts, ideas, and feelings and never wished to have them, he is convinced that they must have been imposed on him from the outside. From scraps of childhood "folklore" and in the absence of any rational basis he resorts to such irrational explanations as spiritual possession, hypnosis, and telepathy. Even normal people may entertain the notion that if they stare fixedly at someone else, they will gain that person's attention. When a disturbed person attempts it, for whatever reason, he notices that his staring makes others uncomfortable. He fails to comprehend the implications of the fact that he is in a mental hospital where others, as well as himself, live through purely subjective experiences for which they are seeking explanations. His staring may be thought by others to come from the "Evil Eye" or to be the threatening action of a madman. In a hospital ward of actively disturbed patients one can hardly expect an atmosphere of mutual trust and confidence. The peculiar behavior of patients around him acts to reenforce the explanations that the patient develops in order to account for his own bizarre experience.

It may be noticed that the patient frequently uses qualifying phrases when speaking about the influences which he feels govern him. For example, "I had heard a great deal about . . ."; "He was stated to have been . . ."; "It was further asserted . . ."; "I have listened carefully . . ."; "As has been intimated . . ."; when used in introducing the subjective descriptions of delusions and hallucinations, lead an outsider to wonder whether the sufferer is quite as certain of the accuracy and meaning of his unique experience as he implies that he is.

Predictions and Coincidences

In several autobiographical accounts I have found clear statements to the effect that the patient had a firm conviction of his ability to predict and influence future events. Furthermore, these patients often believe that many of the events which occur in their lives are part of a large plan or system which some outside power is operating for their detriment or benefit. Another aspect of such delusion is a belief in their own ability to bring about changes in their surroundings. In this connection, Schreber wrote as follows.

God also regulates the weather; as a rule this is done automatically, so to speak, by the greater or lesser amount of heat emanating from the sun, but He can regulate it in certain ways in pursuit of His own purposes. . . . I wish to mention this at the outset—the weather is now to a certain extent dependent on *my* actions and thoughts; as soon as I indulge in thinking nothing, or in other words stop an activity which proves the existence of the human mind such as playing chess in the garden the wind arises at once. To anybody who is inclined to doubt such a fantastic statement, I could almost daily give the opportunity of convincing him of its correctness, as in fact I have recently convinced various people. . . . The reason for this is simply that as soon as I indulge in thinking nothing God, presuming that I am demented, thinks he can withdraw from me. (Schreber, 1955, p. 47)

Not only was Schreber convinced that his thoughts allowed him to control the weather but, as he says later, he was likewise certain of a direct spiritual connection between God and himself which could bring the soul of any person, living or dead, to him and thus enter into direct communication with all souls.

An extraordinary account is given by Lang of his own experiences of prediction and telepathy and their effect on his thinking.

A special phase of the verbal production of foreign ideas which deserves attention, is the appearance of anticipations, *i.e.*, the prediction of external events by the thoughts-out-loud. While this phenomenon has been rare, it has taken place with sufficient frequency to have had a marked effect upon my ideas. To give an example: in mid-May, 1930, the thoughts-out-loud stated something like this, "Remember the name ———— ————, she lived near you once. You will read about her death in the newspapers soon." Approximately two weeks later I did read about the death of a person of the exact name given whose address showed that she lived near where I had lived eight months previously. Another type of anticipation which proved accurate three times out of four appearances, was the prediction of the terminal game of the consecutive winning streaks of professional baseball clubs. A third type has been the forecast of the availability at the public library of popular books which have previously been unavailable.

It is impossible not to be influenced by the experiencing of such phenomena. Regardless of their social evidential value, they represent to the person who experiences them, proof of contact with some agent possessing sources of information broader then those of any factor of the human organism. The nature of his experience of the prediction satisfies the standard of proof of the individual to whom it occurs. To deny it, he must deny all the other data of his experience with which the prediction is inextricably interwoven. He cannot escape their implications. (Lang, 1938, p. 1092)

Although none of the specific and confirmed instances of prediction cited by Lang and other patients is, taken singly, too startling, the cumulative effect, as Lang points out, becomes so impressive and convincing to the patient that he "cannot escape their implications."

Maude Harrison offered a somewhat different description and explanation of these prophetic phenomena.

One of the great games that mental patients play is called coincidence. It is a silly game, but we can't stop playing it. As soon as nothing has a meaning everything has a meaning. Spinners Lake [the title of her book], as a name, was a hit at spinsterhood and my wish to die, if need be, even by drowning. I thought that I was the only patient who had had this bright idea, and was astonished when I found that other women's brains had wandered round it too. (Harrison, 1941, p. 129)

Miss Harrison also believed that some of her troubles were due to her cowardice in facing earlier problems in her life. The idea of cowardice became symbolized in her mind by the concept lemon. Hence whenever lemon-candy, lemon-colored clothing, or lemon served with the fish course would appear, the instance served to fit her claim of a systematic plot of persecution directed toward her life and well-being. Her axiom, "As soon as nothing has a meaning, everything has a meaning," sheds a great deal of light on psychopathological experience.

Davidson also discussed his experiences with similar predictive phenomena. In his case these were closely associated with visual illusions.

There were a good many small paths about the asylum grounds . . . Anyone using these was completely shut out by houses, walls, or hedges from the sight of anyone in the house until he actually . . . came on this main path. Several times I noticed watery-looking bodies float down from the sky and coincide or intermingle with various people instantly they appeared in view, so that as soon as I saw one of these vaporous bodies float down I knew someone was coming before they themselves appeared in sight. I remember remarking it to some of the attendants . . . I do not think these delusions were caused by any good influence—just by my wandering mind and, perhaps, some spirit in possession of it. (Davidson, 1912, p. 66)

Here we are offered a different explanation of the occurrence of this phenomenon, "just my wandering mind and perhaps some spirit in possession of it." Yet he very often experienced apparently prophetic delusions and it never occurred to him to deny their actuality.

Similar prophecies played such a leading role in Perceval's psychosis that he made use of their fallibility in convincing himself of his questionable mental state. He developed his criterion in the following way.

When I had been thus far freed from my delusions, and delivered from a blind and superstitious respect for the mental phenomena by which I had been hitherto influenced and misguided—the voices directed me to declare that I was of sound mind . . . But I now no longer obeyed their word, and I was so scrupulous, that I could not seriously claim to be considered of sound mind so long as there were any phenomena remaining, the faithfulness of which I had not tested, and the source of which I had not discovered. I have mentioned that I used to see visions; these visions were sent to me, as I imagined, to guide my conduct and that of others . . . Had I been at liberty I might very soon have brought one of these visions to a test, but being confined I adopted this plan. My youngest brother lost a favourite terrier bitch, and when I heard of it I was grieved . . . this took great possession of my thoughts . . . Soon after this I saw a vision of an inn and a turnpike-gate, and I was made to understand, that such a place was connected with the loss of the dog; I wrote to my brother then a description of the places as seen in the vision; supposing he would recognise them, having been there, or having seen them in his neighborhood. He replied that he had no recollection of such a place. From this I knew that I had been deceived—and concluded that this species of mental phenomena also was not to be considered as any unerring guide. (Perceval, 1840, pp. 325–327)

In spite of Perceval's claim that he tested all forms of supernatural phenomena before accepting their truth or untruth, even after his release from custody he still maintained many delusional beliefs, holding them to be true despite everything his family and medical advisers might have said to the contrary. Originally he had invariably accepted all the statements and directions made to him by the voices and spirits no matter how fantastic the performance required. He was, as he said, of a skeptical turn of mind, but since he had been assured by the voices that the orders were merely part of a divine trial of the worthiness of his soul, he followed their directions blindly. When finally he received one day a neutral message regarding his brother's pet, information that was not confirmed, he could at last begin to doubt the veracity of not only this vision, but a great deal of the supernatural information he had received prior to that time.

Two years after the appearance of *Wisdom, Madness and Folly,* Custance published a second book, called *Adventure into the Unconscious.* This volume differs rather markedly in content from the one I have quoted thus far. At the time of writing his second work, Custance had recovered from his acute mania but still clung to some of his psychotic convictions. He now believed that by following the directions and signs given by his unconscious, he could predict coming events more accurately than he could by sheer chance. As an example, he claimed that he could guess whether traffic lights would be red or green at the precise moment of his approach. The following is a rather curt but fascinating description of this process, taking place during a trip made by Custance to a neighboring market town.

Went to Melchester, tested technique of guessing on the basis of indications (a) in mind, (b) in exterior world,

Guess 1 (a)   that first lights would come green for me as I got there. Right within thirty yards.

2 (a)   that there would be parking space on left opposite auctioneers. Right wthin ten yards.

3 (ab)   that lights into Market Place would be red. Right.

4 (*ab*) that lights out of Market Place would be green. Right . . .
5 (*ab*) that lights opposite Close would be green. Right.
6 (*a*) that would pass car immediately opposite inn at All Saints. Right.
7 (*a*) that would pass lorry ahead in Downley without hurrying. Right, lorry stopped in Downley.
8 (*a*) that would pick up man beyond Downley. Wrong. Man asked for lift in Downley. (Custance, 1954, p. 142)

Custance gave further examples of this obsessive mental game and remained convinced that if he gave thought to almost any problem, however simple, his unconscious mind would give him an answer that would enable him to correctly predict the outcome of future events. Once when opening the Bible at random, his eyes fell on Ezekiel 1:20, and he found there an idea that satisfied him. The passage read: "Whithersoever the spirit was to go, they went, thither was their spirit to go; and the wheels were lifted up over against them: for the spirit of the living creature was in the wheels." Even this complex verse afforded him, after a rather involved interpretation, an explanation that he considered very lucid.

There is no way of ascertaining the exact meaning or significance of the various prophecies and coincidences with which I have dealt in this section. To say that they express unconscious wish-fulfillments is to beg the question, since we are left with no more insight than before. As we have seen, in each instance the particular individual was convinced that he was under the control of an outside force greater than himself. As Lang pointed out, the person cannot doubt the evidence of his own senses. It seems plausible that every human being has a tendency to believe in "magic," so that when confronted with mystical and prophetic experiences, any but a clear, critical, and skeptical mind would indeed accept "magic" as a plausible explanation. Obviously this is accentuated in the case of an emotionally disturbed and confused individual, since he is often unable to differentiate the probable from the improbable. As a consequence, he will regard simple coincidences as determined by supernatural powers that he at times even bestows on himself.

Nudity

A type of antisocial behavior commonly observed in large mental hospital wards, but often neglected in treatises dealing with psychopathology, is that of stripping and exposing oneself in the nude. I have gathered a sample of autobiographical accounts referring to this rather casual type of behavior, reported by patients suffering from a variety of mental illnesses. What they all have in common is a haphazard attitude or, at most, the suggestion that the act seemed to satisfy certain impulses or commands which implied freedom, particularly freedom from guilt and fear. The following excerpts are illustrative.

It was so warm outside that I took off my shirt and the sun felt good on my chest and back. I stood in the middle of the lawn, turning and turning. Why did people wear clothes? Even when they were warm, when they went swimming, they always wore something. Not to protect. No, to hide. Hide what? Shame. That's all it was. If no one wore clothes, no one would be ashamed. Simple. Take off my clothes. Everybody take off their clothes. I took off my pants. Warm all over now. No clothes. Naked. The only thing they wanted to hide was sex. Why? All the men were the same, all the women were the same. What was there to hide? Nothing hidden, no secrets; no secrets, no excitement, no suspicion. No excitement and suspicion, no fear. (Peters 1949, pp. 7–8)

On one of these occasions I contrived to get out of my bands and I undressed, and ran naked, by order of the voices I heard, into a small yard attached to our prison, singing, in Portuguese. (Perceval, 1840, p. 299)

Exercising their asserted Divine Authority, the thoughts-out-loud demand that I take off my clothing and go around in the nude. The halaffective tone of intense trust and belief continues. Despite this feeling of trust, my self dislikes the command. (Lang, 1939b, p. 198)

Only once did I premeditate and attempt to execute my design of escape by stripping myself stark naked in the garden, imagining that just then I had measured the height of the wall and could calculate on the certainty of my success. (Symons, 1930, p. 53)

It seemed to me that [they] would be more active supernaturally than anyone else. I was in the nude. That was the end of one set of symbolism. I was nude when I had finished the symbolism in the bed, and I got on to the floor. (Rows, 1914, p. 197)

Marthe took off her clothes too. She stood without embarrassment small and white . . . Why are you undressing out here? said Miss Wade, have you no decency at all standing there naked like that? . . . She floated away from Miss Wade . . . She whirled in a black volcano and began to dance. (Coleman 1930, pp. 101–102)

When my father was in the hospital I would come out of the bedroom without any clothes on. My mother said, "Haven't you any shame?" (Milici and von Salzen, 1938, p. 64)

None of these incidents suggest that the patient's motivation was connected with a tendency toward exhibitionism. If any deliberate ideation or motivation underlay these episodes, other than a symbolic expression of a wish for freedom, such is not evident.

Staring at the Sun

One of the strangest kinds of behavior that I encountered in my review is that of staring directly at the sun over prolonged periods of time. Not only do these patients report that they are not dazzled or blinded by this dangerous act, but they say they derive pleasure from it. Schreber wrote as follows.

Even today the sun looks different to me than before my illness. Her rays pale before me if, turned toward her, I speak with a loud voice. I can look into the sun unperturbed and am dazzled only very little, whereas in days of health, I, like other people, would have found it impossible to look into the sun for minutes on end. (Schreber, 1955, p. 126)

Schreber's physician confirmed his statement.

On the one hand the reaction against the hallucinations became increasingly noisy and intense, in the garden the patient used to stand for a long time motionless in one place, staring into the sun, at the same time grimacing in an extraordinary way or bellowing very loudly at the sun with threats and imprecations. (Schreber, 1955, p. 269)

Schreber wrote that the sun symbolized God and hence when he looked at it he was looking directly at God, and even the actual appearance of the sun had changed since before his illness.

Peters' autobiography, *The World Next Door*, is prefaced by the following statement, "This book is based on actual experience." In his record he makes much of the fact that he could look directly at the sun without flinching. His discovery of this ability was significantly associated with the onset of his illness. During the acute phase of his psychosis he would stare at the sun for long stretches to reassure himself of the fact that he was Jesus Christ and to gain strength for his "radar control" of others. Relevant excerpts from his account follow.

Reflection of the sun? I looked again. It was yellow! "I can look right into the sun." I said, astonished. . . . I looked back at the sun. That was better. "You know what I mean." There were whispers in the room behind me. Then another voice: "Are you cold?" I was cold, but I didn't mind as long as I could see the sun. . . .

It [the sun] was high in the sky and only by leaning against the wire and looking almost straight up, could I look full into it. It felt very warm and pleasant, even with the wire pressed against my face. . . . I kept my eyes upon it, looking directly into the circle of bright light in the cloudless sky, and closed my ears to the sounds around me. Only faintly was I aware that people were walking behind me and talking to themselves or each other. . . .

I turned my head and looked directly into the face of the sun, stared at it a moment, and then looked back at my hands. No doubt about it, I could look directly into the sun. In fact, I liked to look at it. Wasn't that unusual?

"Can you look directly into the sunlight?" I asked the man in the staw hat. "What do you think I wear sun glasses for?" he asked. "Nobody can look at the sun without blinking or wearing glasses." "I can," I said and looked into it again. . . .

As my mother approached, her eyes upon me, I looked up at the sun. I forced my eyes open to it, but they blinked in pain. I could not look at it any more. I could not go back. (Peters, 1949, pp. 4; 122; 129–130; 362)

Other than warmth and a source of energy for his "radar beam," the sun had no special symbolic meaning so far as Peters reported. When he recovered and left the hospital, he found that he could no longer gaze fixedly at the sun.

With respect to the subject of our present discussion, the author of *An Autobiography of a Schizophrenic Experience* wrote as follows.

Light symbolism was a dominant feature of the first illness. The sun was the mystical symbol of life and of truth, particularly intellectual illumination. The sunlight was dazzling and blinding—prolonged exposure was dangerous. I felt I had been subjected to an excess of light—that what I was enduring was the utmost violation, an "intellectual rape," the rape of the mind by truth. (Undoubtedly there was some displaced sexual content in this image.) In spite of my sense of danger, I could hardly believe that the truth could hurt me. I would stare at the sun, trying to see how long I could do this without blinking. I was also afraid that my eyes would be damaged by the light and that I would become blind. (Anon., 1955, p. 688)

It must be noted that staring directly at the sun causes physical damage to the tissues of the eye. If one brings a beam of sunlight to a sharp focus by a small lens on the bare skin of any portion of the body, it is easy to blister and burn the skin. Similarly the lens of the eye brings the sunlight to a focus on the retina and should likewise result in a burnt spot on the retina. In normal human experience even short glances at the sun are followed by troublesome afterimages that may persist for hours or days. That many patients are able to stare at the sun unperturbedly is not indicated by the autobiographical accounts I gathered. If this oddity were commonplace, it would have been mentioned by previous observers. It would be interesting to investigate this peculiarity further to find how many persons are able to stare directly at the sun and if so what physiological mechanisms make it possible.

That the moon may be related in some way to insanity is an ancient belief, as evidenced by the word *lunacy*. I have not found, however, any autobiographical account in which the moon was mentioned in terms more significant than simple observations of the scenic view in the moonlight. The sun, though, did figure in many reports in other ways than the being-stared-at phenomenon. To cite but a single reference from the many referring to sun-symbolism, I quote the following from Custance.

The sun came to have an extraordinary effect on me. It seemed to be charged with all power; not merely to symbolise God but actually to be God. Phrases like "Light of the World," "the Sun of Righteousness that setteth nevermore" and so on ran through my head without ceasing, and the mere sight of the sun was sufficient greatly to intensify this manic excitement under which I was labouring. I was impelled to address the sun as a personal God, and to evolve little rituals of sunworship. (Custance, 1952, p. 18)

In many other cases the sun-symbolism was part of a complicated nightmare-like delusional system in which this celestial body became identified with ancient Gods.

Crying; Bellowing

Another oddity in the material utilized is that of crying or bellowing. In many ways these occurrences resemble epileptic seizures, except that they were never accompanied by loss of consciousness. Even after Margery Kempe's recovery from the acute phase of her psychosis, she continued to be preoccupied by religious thoughts and desires and made pilgrimages to various English shrines. Shortly after, she determined to make the great pilgrimage to Jerusalem, and, once there, when at the Mount of Calvary, she had the first attack of crying. She wrote about these attacks, speaking of herself in the third person as was her custom.

When they came up on to the Mount of Calvary, she fell down, because she could not stand or kneel, and rolled and wrested . . . spreading her arms abroad, and cried with a loud voice as though her heart burst asunder . . . And this was the first cry that ever she cried in any contemplation. And this manner of crying endured many years after this time . . . The crying was so loud and so wonderful that it made the people astounded unless they had heard it before, or unless they knew the cause of the crying. . . .

First when she had her cryings in Jerusalem, she had them often, and in Rome also. And when she came home to England, first at her coming home, it came but seldom, as it were once a month, then once a week, afterwards daily, and once she had fourteen in one day, and another day she had seven, and so on, as God would visit her, sometimes in church, sometimes in the street, sometimes in her chamber, sometimes in the fields, whenever God would send them, for she never knew the time nor the hour when they would come. And they never came without passing great sweetness of devotion and high contemplation. And as soon as she perceived that she would cry, she would keep it in as much as she might that the people should not hear it, to their annoyance. For some said that a wicked spirit vexed her; some said it was a sickness; some said she had drunk too much wine; some banned her; some wished she was in the harbour; some wished she was on the sea in a bottomless boat; and thus each man as he thought. . . .

And therefore when she knew that she would cry, she kept it in as long as she might, and did all she could to withstand it or put it away, till she waxed as livid as any lead, and ever it would labour in her mind more and more till the time it broke out. . . . then she fell down and cried wondrous loud, and the more she laboured to keep it in or put it away, so much the more would she cry, and the louder. (Butler-Bowdon, 1936, pp. 107–109)

Margery Kempe's story leaves no doubt that she did actually suffer from an acute psychotic episode from which she later "recovered." Her subsequent history indicates that she was an unstable person, frequently in trouble with both the religious and civil authorities of her day. She mentions in her essay that some of the common people with whom she came in contact doubted her sanity. Certainly outbursts of screaming or crying, as just described, would lead almost anyone to doubt the person's mental state.

The attacks of crying just described greatly resemble the fits of bellowing discussed by Schreber in 1903.

Much greater nuisance is caused by the states of bellowing which regularly accompany the withdrawal of the rays. Naturally I consider it beneath my dignity to have to bellow like a wild animal because of miracles enacted on me; furthermore the bellowing itself when repeated leads to equally painful concussion of the head. Nevertheless at certain times I have to allow the bellowing as long as it is not excessive, particularly at night when other defensive measures like talking aloud, playing the piano, etc. are hardly practicable. In such circumstances bellowing has the advantage of drowning with its noise everything the voices speak into my head, so that soon all rays are again united. This allows me to go to sleep again or at least to stay in bed in a state of physical well-being. . . .

The attacks of *bellowing*, although not completely gone, are less severe, particularly because I learnt to counteract them successfully when they might be a serious nuisance to other people. . . . Therefore bellowing does not occur as long as I count continuously. This is particularly important at night because with bellowing precluded by counting I usually achieve sleep, and when I do waken I soon fall asleep again. This success cannot always be achieved. It is not easy for a human being to count for hours. Therefore even if by counting continually for some time I cannot fall asleep and I stop counting, at that very moment the bellowing miracle commences and when frequently repeated in bed becomes unbearable. . . . By continual counting I can also prevent bellowing almost completely in public places, in the theatre, in an educated environment, etc., or during pauses when not carrying on a conversation aloud. . . . But while going for walks along country roads, through open fields, etc., I make things easy for myself when no one else is about. I simply let the bellowing happen; sometimes it continues for five or ten minutes almost without interruption, during which time I feel physically perfectly well. . . . A witness of such bouts of almost continuous bellowing would however hardly be able to understand the connection and might really think he is seeing a madman. (Schreber, 1955, pp. 227–228; 247)

The medical reports to the court, which are included in Schreber's *Memoirs,* confirm and amplify the facts of the bellowing spells. He was very noisy, particularly at night, so much so that he had to be removed to a distant and secluded room in order not to disturb other patients and persons living in the vicinity of the asylum. It should be noted that both Kempe and Schreber did attempt to control their frequent outbreaks but were unable to do so, and also that neither offered an adequate rational explanation for this particular behavior.

DISCUSSION

The oddities that have been the subject of this chapter are no more peculiar than many of the facets of psychopathological experience I have already mentioned. Some of these phenomena have been touched on at some length by previous investigators. For example, delusions of power or of evil, rituals, and metaphors have all been commented on previously, though some of the other oddities have escaped any particular emphasis.

The idea of coincidences and ability to predict the outcome of future events is a paranoid-like symptom—the remark we have seen "As soon as nothing has a meaning, everything has a meaning," or similar statements, probably serving as a satisfactory rationalization to many patients.

Whether the phenomena of "I AM," the desire and ability to stare at the sun, bellowing and crying, and the like, are actually no more than coincidences to be expected when reading approximately five hundred different accounts of psychopathological experiences, is impossible to decide. It would certainly be worthwhile to survey the populations of large mental hospitals in order to find out more about their frequency and the meaning, if any, that patients attach to these phenomena.

The principal problem of psychotherapy is—the therapist.
(Prinzhorn, 1932, p. 338)

CHAPTER 20

Therapy and Therapists

INTRODUCTION

Much, but not all, of the source material I have utilized was written by persons who had at one time or
another been institutionalized for nervous or mental
illness. In general, these persons were informed that
they had been confined because they were sick, and it
had been feared that their continued freedom might
prove dangerous both to themselves and to others.
They were also told that the doctors, nurses, and attendants in charge of each patient all hoped to assist
each patient to the restoration of his health and mental
equilibrium. I have reviewed and cited numerous instances of the onset of psychopathological experiences
that led to hospitalization where the patient stated
that he did not realize either his own mental status or
the purpose of his hospitalization. Many patients were
convinced that they had been illegally imprisoned by
the police or incarcerated in order that they might be
tormented by the Devil; others were possessed by
some equally fantastic idea. In far too many instances,
doctors and attendants were quickly identified by the
patient as jailers whose actions and intentions had no
apparent connection with his welfare.

The attitude that most mental patients have held regarding the treatment they have received is condemnatory. After regaining sanity, most persons remember that during the acute period of their illness they had been fearful, excited, angry, confused, uninhibited, lonely, distrustful, and disturbed. In many instances they recalled that they believed that they were under the control of supernatural forces or that they had been instructed directly by some divinity to behave in certain peculiar ways. No doctor, nurse, or attendant seemed in the patient's eyes to have tried to understand their complaints, their experiences, or their beliefs. Rather they were admonished by such statements as, "Be quiet," "Take it easy," "Obey the rules," or "Do what the doctor says." An endless number of patients have written that no one seemed interested in their particular personal problems, so that most of the time they felt acutely neglected and rejected. Consequently, their resentment of the physicians' lack of interest and concern seemed to them to be both rational and well justified. However, during lucid intervals or after complete recovery, some of the patients may have been able to comprehend the circumstances which had given rise to their hostility, so that these individuals were able to change their attitudes and to reappraise both the therapy and the therapists. On the other hand, all too many recovered patients have continued to insist that they had been unjustifiably illtreated.

Ordinarily, any person when physically ill will seek and accept medical assistance. After listening to the person's complaints and account of his symptoms, the physician usually prescribes medication and therapy, while telling the patient something about the basis of his difficulties and reassuring him that his health will soon improve. Similarly, though in different context, if a person has violated the ethical or moral code that guides his behavior, he may confess his "sins" to his spiritual advisor, who will recommend penance and subsequently grant him absolution. In general, however, the mental patient does not voluntarily call upon either a physician or a priest, and if he does do so, he seldom receives what *he* considers to be adequate assistance in dealing with his basic troubles. As a result, the individual patient finds himself increasingly overwhelmed by the turmoil of his inner experience and more and more at a loss because of the un-understood or misunderstood responses of those from whom he sought help.

Since psychopathological events are usually unique and unexpected in any person's experience the afflicted person is all too apt to conclude that never before has any other person been similarly afflicted. Likewise, since both his behavior and personal reports are not commonplace or part of the everyday knowledge of most people, the sufferer's abnormalities do seem novel to the public at large, while in actuality, all the phenomena involved are as old as the history of mankind.

An excerpt from Burton's *Anatomy of Melancholy* will illustrate the point that there is nothing new in either the pathological experience itself or in the quality of advice that the sufferer may expect to receive from others.

We should moderate ourselves, but we are furiously carried, we cannot make use of such precepts, we are overcome, sick, distempered and habituated in these courses, we can make no resistance; you may as well bid him that is diseased not to feel pain, as a melancholy man not to fear, not be sad. . . .

Thou thinkest thou hearest and seest Devils, black men, &c. 'tis not so, 'tis thy corrupt phantasy, settle thine imagination, thou are well. Thou thinkest thou hast a great nose, thou art sick, every man observes thee, laughs thee to scorn; persuade thyself 'tis no such matter: this is fear only, and vain suspicion . . . . Rule thyself then with reason, satisfy thyself, accustom thyself, wean thyself from such fond conceits, vain fears, strong imaginations, restless thoughts. . . . Do that voluntarily then which thou canst do, and must do by compulsion. . . .

If then our judgement be so depraved, our reason overruled, will precipitated, that we cannot seek our own good, or moderate ourselves, as in this disease commonly it is, the best way for ease is to impart our misery to some friend, not to smother it up in our breast; canker thrives and flourishes by concealment, etc., and that which was most offensive to us, a cause of fear and grief, another hell; for grief concealed strangles the soul; but when as we shall but impart it to some discreet, trusty, loving friend, it is instantly removed, by his counsel haply, wisdom, persuasion, advice, his good means, which we could not otherwise apply unto ourselves. . . . The simple narration many times easeth our distressed mind, and in the midst of greatest extremities; so divers have been relieved, by exonerating themselves to a faithful friend; he sees that which we cannot see for passion and discontent. (Burton, 1927, pp. 470–472)

Burton's book went through many editions and translations during the first two hundred years after its publication. Later its style became quaint and its fashion of expression unfamiliar, and today only scholars know of its existence. It was the greatest text on mental hygiene and psychotherapy the world knew in the seventeenth and eighteenth centuries, and its loss of popularity was a loss to civilization.

It is always difficult for an outsider to understand exactly what happened to a person who has become mentally disturbed and what is true or false in the accounts of the patient and of those who have charge of him. One must realize that it is all too human to recall and "expose" injustice, whereas fair, intelligent, sympathetic treatment is taken for granted and very seldom receives mention in a published record. If some of the excerpts that have been cited or that follow appear to be misrepresentations conceived by a deranged mind, it should be pointed out that such material does have a positive value, in that it is illustrative of the wide variety of events which were, in the patients' eyes, unhappy mistakes. Hence, they may serve as a caution to future therapists and assist them in achieving a better understanding of the inner life of the mental patient.

At the start of any patient–therapist relationship there is usually a period during which there is a mutual attempt at understanding and evaluating the other's personality. The institutionalized patient is distrustful, hostile, overly sensitive, suspicious, and confused. Only rarely has such a patient sought out a therapist; usually he has been coerced into the so-called therapeutic relationship. Mental patients are often described by outside observers as egotistical and apathetic. Since these two attitudes have received frequent comment from both patients and the therapists, I will consider them more specifically.

Egotism

The outstanding egotist among mental patients is commonly said to be the neurotic. Leonard observed as follows.

So too the psychopathologists make egotism the chief of the neurotic's stigmata; whereas the neurotic may be preoccupied with himself, in the same way as a man with cancer in the stomach—each has himself forced upon himself in pain. Or in the same way, for that matter, as the man whose golf is going to pieces—each has an absorbing problem of immediate personal concern. Egotism is often enough a genuine neurotic symptom, but is quite as often only the inevitable preoccupation with pain and with the problem of getting rid of it. . . . The psychoanalysts in discussing neurotics sometimes forget very elementary data of everyday human nature . . . and [are] unaware that perhaps my first-hand experience of fifteen years may itself be as significant for truth as his own ready-made terminology and stereotyped thinking. (Leonard, 1939, p. 177)

One suspects that these charges of neurotic egotism derive from two (or more) circumstances. In the first place, the patient has usually dealt with many physicians and it has often been intimated to him that the basis of his complaints is totally imaginary. Hence, his attitude towards any new therapist is apt to be one of skepticism and arrogant defiance. Second, it is often true that the symptoms from which the patient complains are physiologically impossible, causing the physician to become impatient, whereupon the patient insists even more vigorously on his *malaise.* Most neurotic patients do give the impression of an exaggerated self-centeredness, but this tendency is not restricted to neurotics. Sick persons generally manifest exceeding egotism and self-reference.

Apathy

The confused, semistuporous, mentally ill person often fails to react adequately to requests, directions, or commands that are made by the hospital personnel. Such a patient often appears to be dull and apathetic.

In spite of this outward appearance, internally the patient's feelings may be those of excessive sensitivity. This opposition between feeling and expression led Perceval, who had himself been in a confused, stuporous condition for more than a year, to make the following comment.

The lunatic doctors appear to think that patients do not *feel* their position: now, I know that many lunatics are extremely sensitive to ridicule; this sensitiveness is, indeed, one of the phenomena of an unsound mind; and I know that lunatics are very much pained and embarrassed by exposure under their misfortune, and I suspect that this is common to all. But they are not able to bear up against the feeling, and therefore fly for relief to boisterousness and impudent boldness, or sink from it into an apathy and passiveness, which is supposed to betray absence of feeling, when it really betrays incapability to meet such feeling. (Perceval, 1840, p. 286)

Another way of describing the patient's sensitivity and the physician's lack of understanding was expressed by one woman as follows.

I had to tell you [the doctor] things by doing them instead of talking, because I didn't dare let you know things about me. I was sure you would turn things against me and use what I said to hurt me. Also, no one ever paid attention to what I asked for, but they usually did react if I did something. I wanted terribly for you to help me, but I had to be sure I could trust you. We . . . say and do a lot of stuff that is unimportant, and then we mix important things in with all this to see if the doctor cares enough to see them and feel them. . . .

Patients kick and scream and fight when they aren't sure the doctor can see them. It's a most terrifying feeling to realize that the doctor can't see the real you, that he can't understand what you feel and that he's just going ahead with his own ideas. I would start to feel that I was invisible or maybe not there at all. I had to make an uproar to see if the doctor would respond to me, not just his own ideas. . . . (Hayward and Taylor, 1956, pp. 214; 215)

Evidently, this patient had been noisy and assaultive rather than quiet and mute, yet the same basic sensitivity and distrust on her part, as well as comparative ignorance on the part of the physician, operated here as they do in many instances.

The rather common feeling on the part of the mental hospital patient with respect to the physician's lack of genuine concern and understanding has led several patients to write directions as to how a mental patient should behave while in the hospital.

Advice from the Insane to the Insane

Davidson, whose *Remembrances* are singularly free from reproaches or animosity, made the following comment relevant to how a patient should guard his conduct in a mental hospital, basing it on his own experience.

Some time after this, it struck me that it was dangerous to make any reference or quotation in such a place, for you run the risk of being considered as imagining yourself to be the author or character referred to. On the other hand, you must not keep quite silent and refuse to answer questions, or you are melancholy, perhaps suicidal, or even homicidal. If you talk, you are talkative and excitable; if you pay no attention to what is going on round you, you are sinking into idiocy; if you carefully look about you and take an interest in everything, you are inquisitive and meddlesome; if you sit still, you are comatose; if you take much exercise and feel happy in spite of your surroundings, you are unduly elated; and if you whistle or sing, you are marked down as a candidate for a violent ward. If, however, you don't show to a marked extent any of the above symptoms of insanity, which the attendants are told to watch for, you are a practically hopeless case, needing the most careful watching, for you are a patient so determinedly and wickedly insane and maniacally cunning that you are able to successfully conceal your insanity. . . .

I have since realized that [this was] a plausible perversion of the truth; that mental experts have many other ways of coming to a conclusion which the untrained layman cannot hope to understand. Moreover, if a man behaves and talks in a very abnormal manner, he must be shut up, and no man is to blame; but he sometimes finds it hard, even when he is all right, to persuade experts that it is so. (Davidson, 1912, pp. 180–181)

The first of these paragraphs is truly representative of the dilemma that faces many hospitalized patients. Actually, each mental patient must solve these problems for himself. That such dilemmas are solved and without very much guidance by ordinary physicians is shown by the second paragraph above.

Custance, who had been hospitalized several times, also recorded some of his thoughts on the behavior and predicament of hospitalized mental patients.

They are told, if they seem to harbour resentment against the hospital or any of the authorities responsible for their treatment, that this resentment is a typical sign of "delusions of persecution", the commonest of all delusions in asylums. In order to prove their fitness to be let out, they "repress" or in the most fortunate cases succeed in "suppressing" their resentment. It disappears into their Unconscious; they really do "forget it" as they are generally expressly urged to do. . . . [Elsewhere in his autobiography he wrote as follows.] Why then have the doctors changed their minds about me? Why do they think I am "sane"? The answer is quite simple. Yielding to the persuasion of my wife, I agreed to crawl to the doctors—no milder word meets the case—to say nothing about any grievances I may have, and to give the impression that I am quite satisfied with my own treatment. With the exercise of a modicum of self-control and of all my powers of dissimulation, I have shown myself a model patient, and am now getting my reward.

"Sanity, normality," in mental treatment today, seems to be largely synonymous with submission to Authority with a big A. The obedient "lunatic" has a reasonable chance of securing his release; the defiant "lunatic" has none.

No matter how much injustice or ill-treatment a patient in a Mental Hospital may have suffered—and a modicum is inevitable even in the best-run and most humane—the wise man endures it in silence. Complaints and appeals are practically useless, as I have learnt from bitter experience; they only make matters worse.

Furthermore, while a golden rule is never to complain at all, a silver rule is this: if you must complain, stick strictly to your own case. To complain about the treatment of others is sheer madness and is regarded as such. Anybody in a Mental Hospital who suffers—as I unfortunately am apt to do—from the horrible delusion that his neighbour is a concern of his and that when he sees others stupidly or unjustly treated he should do something about it, is asking for trouble. (Custance, 1952, pp. 117; 226–227)

These cautionary remarks by Custance must be understood with a certain amount of reserve. One must remember that the mental patient does not see the world with normal eyes. It is, however, true that in place of the confidence and trust which should exist between patient and physician, doubt and distrust frequently exist on both sides, and it often is very difficult to decide in which direction the truth may lie.

Perceval, who was very resentful of the treatment he received from both attendants and doctors while in the asylum, recorded his opinions and several incidents that are pertinent to the present discussion.

The question, then, lies between the power of the patient to endure, and the power of the quack to break his spirit. The latter is shamefully uncontrolled by law, in consequence of the very generous, legitimate, and simple confidence placed by chancellors, magistrates, and law-officers of the crown in the humane, and tender, and scrupulous doctor. I have proved that the power of the patient is equal to that of the oppressor. But in this contest, when the patience and fortitude of the first is exhausted, look to it if the stamina of the constitution—if those foundations of sound health, are not undermined or broken through, on which, with respectful and natural treatment, cure, *perfect cure*, might have been established, and good citizens assured to the state; not those patch-up pieces of work called healed patients, now returned to the world. . . .

Mine was not a solitary instance. Another patient, who seldom or never spoke . . . opened his lips, to my astonishment, and declared that when he first came to the asylum, whilst sitting one evening in the parlour wherein we were, he rang the bell, or called for a candle for another gentleman, when the servant came up, and, grossly insulting him turned him, too, out of the room, and sent him to bed; since which, says he, I have never opened my mouth, except when absolutely necessary. . . . The only resource for the pride of many men is in a stubborn silence, and outward indifference. (Perceval, 1838, pp. 146–147)

Perceval's remarks and observations are not exceptional. The hospitalized psychiatric patient all too often bitterly resents the attitude and treatment he receives from the physicians, nurses, and attendants. From his viewpoint, he has been deprived of his freedom; he is to all intents and purposes held in confinement and subjected to a variety of indignities, even physical torture, without ever being given any rational explanation for this treatment. In spite of his bizarre verbal productions and disturbed outward behavior, the patient frequently does retain a fair amount of lucidity and has a real basis for the resentment he feels. The fact that any person has been adjudged insane should never be allowed to detract from his dignity as a human being.

Trite Phrases

Another source of irritation encountered by most persons who suffer from any variety of psychopathological experience is the trite phrases of advice they receive during their everyday contacts with friends, relatives, strangers, doctors, attendants, and even therapists. These bits of advice have usually been suggested by one or another acquaintance early in the history of the patient's illness and were found by him to be of no avail. The phrase *forget your troubles* is an example. Leonard commented on it as follows.

One often heard the easy and fatuous comment: "forget your troubles; be interested in somebody else beside yourself, and you'll get well." Let me set down the following for *science:* since early last summer I have been *daily* preoccupied with the affairs (physical and spiritual) of . . . the most interesting and appealing and desperate case of helplessness, gifts, and misfortune I've ever known . . . to the *exclusion* of myself. And it's made NO difference in my neurosis. . . .

Those friends who say I don't want to get well irritate me—but why? The irritation need be no proof that they've hit a subconscious truth. They irritate me because they have such an easy time of it—because their wisdom is so ready and so cruel, for it *really* implies *blame* (it is, too, a washing their hands of the necessity of concerning themselves further about me). The psychoanalyst [similarly] makes it too easy for himself and his own human fallibility who can always retort upon his patient—especially a patient who is objective and informed and scientifically schooled—"Your very doubts as to my statements veritably prove the truth of my statements." . . . There remains the possibility of such a thing as an objective scientific discussion . . . even between the patient and his physician. Let it be appreciated as a scientific fact that I have *perpetually* hoped, have perpetually striven in the conviction that psychoanalytic effort would bring possible results. . . . The continuation of the neurosis is NOT due to a negative attitude. (Taylor and Culler, 1929, pp. 368; 388)

Phrases like "forget your troubles" imply that the patient could, by taking stock of his situation, ignore or stop the inner turmoil, when a large part of the patient's mental distress actually grows out of the fact that he *cannot* control his mental processes.

To this same category of trite phrases belongs the familiar advice, *stop worrying.* William James (who suffered from depressed episodes himself) wrote on this point as follows.

When you find a man living on the ragged edge of his consciousness, pent in to his sin and want and incompleteness, and consequently inconsolable, and then simply tell him that all is well with him, that he must stop his worry, break with his discontent, and give up his anxiety, you seem to him to come with pure absurdities. The only positive consciousness he has tells him that all is *not* well, and the better way you offer sounds simply as if you proposed to him to assert cold-blooded falsehoods. "The will to believe" cannot be stretched as far as that. We can make ourselves more faithful to a belief of which we have the rudiments, but we cannot create a belief out of whole cloth when our perception actively assures us of its opposite. The better mind proposed to us comes in that case in the form of a pure negation of the only mind we have, and we cannot actively will a pure negation. (James, 1902, pp. 211–212)

Not only are these trite phrases irritating because the sufferer realizes his inability to accept the advice, but they exasperate the patient since they further confirm his inner experience by demonstrating that neither the amateur nor the professional advisor really comprehends the true nature of his mental difficulties.

Another trite phrase that annoys the bewildered patient is the glib remark, "*You'll have no troubles if you obey the rules.*" This suggestion is expected to reassure the patient once he is in the hospital. Davidson received this advice and acted on it, with the following result.

At last I ventured to tell one of the doctors at dinner that the necessity for compliance with all the "rules of the place" had been continually impressed upon me. He replied that it was, indeed, very necessary. I then told him, what was the truth, that I was very anxious to get a copy of the rules in order to study them carefully, and could he oblige me? He looked at me as if I was deliberately trying to insult him, and angrily replied that there were no rules.

I was surprised and taken aback, for I had no idea that there was not such a copy as I wanted; and I remarked that in any place or club where there were rules to be obeyed, they were printed and hung up, or copies were obtainable by all the members. . . .

I then continued that insanity was not confined to the patients, for to impress upon a man the necessity for observing all the rules of a place, and then to tell him there were no rules, or, if there were, to refuse him a copy of them, was not sensible.

His reply was to request me to mind my own business, and not to be insulting. (Davidson, 1912, p. 255)

This incident illustrates both the literal-mindedness of the patient as well as the doctor's lack of understanding of the attempt this patient was making to regain his status as a normal person.

To our list of trite phrases could be added, "It's all in your imagination," "Face reality squarely," or "Stop being such a baby." In any event, such comments or well-meant advice, which seem like obvious good sense to most outsiders, serve only to make the patient even more wretched, as well as to convince him that the person offering the advice does not and probably cannot comprehend the true nature of his troubles. These same "helpful" ideas have occurred to most patients with mental troubles very early in the course of their disturbance. Each idea was tested and found to be useless, and then very quickly became a source of irritation whenever it was reheard.

Psychiatry, or the practice of psychotherapy, has never attracted any considerable fraction of medical practitioners into the art and practice of mental medicine. In general, most men who have practiced hospital psychiatry during the past centuries have not been well grounded in such knowledge of either organized psychology, or with such common-sense skill in management of patients as was available. The approach of the well-qualified physician to the troubled and confused psychiatric patient has, with some notable exceptions, not been one designed to establish sympathy or confidence on the part of the patient. The autobiographies of mental patients are documents that, when taken seriously, must have discouraged many a physician who may have read even a sample of them. The following is an example.

The lunacy trade (with marked and fine exceptions, of course) [is especially open] to the doctor who is no good for any other "specialty," and knows he is not. His province is the unknown; the law works for him; he is in charge of a certain number of unfortunates, whom others—not he—have pronounced "mad"; he argues, when he argues at all, backwards. He has not to say to his patients, "Your words and thoughts are inconsecutive, your eye is wandering, etc.; therefore you are 'mad'"; but, "You are mad; therefore your words and thoughts are inconsecutive, and your eye is wondering." This argument has been absolutely used in that shape with me; and I leave honestly to judge what the effect was. . . .

I was relegated to the care of a good-natured young village medico, with about as much knowledge of the buildings of the brain, I should think (and small blame to him), as of Cambodian architecture. He was a kindly fellow, and did all he could . . . I am consoled by thinking that I must have been of great value to him in his studies, as he was trying his "prentice" hand in "nervous" cases, to which he suspected himself of a call . . . I was fully convinced that I was the wickedest man that ever lived, and even in my illness rather triumphed in the fact after the fashion of Topsy. . . .

Looking back from my present vantage-ground, and conscious of never having wittingly harmed anyone, I cannot imagine why I arrived at so desperate a conclusion. I must have tried that poor young doctor sadly; for I never spoke of anything but my sins and ailments. . . . For my sins, to deal with which he felt to be outside his province, he sent to the clergyman of the village locality, who fled after five minutes' discourse; and, as I have learnt since, with a good sense for which I shall ever mentally thank him, wrote to some of my relatives to tell them to send me "home" at once—dear, good, blessed old word that it is—and save me from doctors as soon as might be. They preferred [to send me to] an "asylum." (Merivale, 1879, pp. 33–38)

This patient, who was evidently a journalist, and who concealed his own identity by signing himself *A Sane Patient*, was indeed biased. He waved aside all his own accounts of his aberrant behavior and experience, by ridiculing the physicians and attendants who had been charged with his care. He never faced the facts and consequences of his own mental derangement, nor had any physician ever conveyed to him any evidence that he, the physician, understood or recognized the mental turmoil he underwent.

I have encountered accounts in which the therapist appears, as in the following excerpt, to provide an impression of almost complete quackery insofar as the patient is concerned.

In almost all my own experiences, and in some others of which I have personal knowledge, there was a definite procedure: (1) You are very ill. (Arousal of fear!) (2) Your life can't be much good to you. (More fear!) (3) You have been from doctor to doctor and the medical profession can't help you. (Only too true, but not for the reason implied.) (4) I am the only person who can help you. (The arrival of the father-saviour on to the stage with its "set" of confirmed despair—a fascist technique!) (5) If you trust me completely, follow my instructions implicitly, I shall make you well. (The appeal, here, to the "child" cast out by other father-figures, and to the child's guilt at being ill. If it obeys, it shall be "forgiven" and all will be well.) (6) The not-to-be-broken law—a very strict schedule, for instance, especially as to diet. If one jot or title be disregarded the whole procedure breaks down, providing a good get-away for "Dad." I remember that once the "magic" didn't work because I had gravy with my meat! (7) Renunciation. Something pleasant—tea, coffee, sweets, meat—is given up; this sacrifice representing to the unconscious mind a freely accepted punishment for the guilt of illness, which will then be remitted. (Stuart, 1953, p. 92)

It is apparent that the woman who wrote this account in 1953 was well versed in psychiatric jargon and had been exposed to many medical advisors. This citation actually constitutes a succinct statement of many of the things any person who attempts to do psychotherapy should carefully avoid. No one item in her list is particularly unwise but the resulting combination presents overwhelming evidence of therapeutic incompetence.

Distrust of a therapist, with pertinent evidence supplied for it, was recorded by "Miss O'Brien" (1958). She had had several unfortunate encounters with psychiatrists including a Freudian, for whom any breakdown in mental or emotional machinery could be traced only to one cause. The therapist told her that her sex life was not sufficiently full. She was told that at her age she should have had a hundred and twenty-five affairs. She tried to calculate one hundred and twenty-five on a yearly basis but says she was unable to cope with arithmetic. The turning point from illness to recovery did occur while "Miss O'Brien" was under the care of this analyst, but, as far as she was concerned, she did not consider that anything her analyst had done or said had any connection with her recovery. She spoke of the analyst's efforts as verbal sparring, which had been very difficult for her and likewise must have been very difficult for the analyst. She felt that her recovery could in no sense be attributed to the guidance which any therapist had given her. This consideration leads us to the topic of psychotherapeutic failures.

Psychotherapeutic Failures

Only a very few published accounts of psychotherapeutic failures, written by either the patient or the therapist, can be found. In a field as ill-defined and uncertain as that of psychotherapy some statements of what *not* to do, rather than what to do, should be of value in guiding therapists in the direction of more effective procedures. The following account was given by a patient whose troubles seemed to have increased during therapy.

Throughout most of the period of therapy I had a desire to impress my therapist and to win her approval. I went out of my way to take pains with my dress and personal appearance when I saw her. Later on, I began to feel that my point of view was changing, that my values were different from hers, and that there was no longer as much common ground for discussion. I also felt I knew myself better than she knew me. I was failing to communicate a good many of my half-formed thoughts about myself, partly because of limitations of time, and partly because these thoughts were not fully clear even to myself. At this point I was no longer able to obtain emotional support from the transference relationship. (Anon., 1955, p. 679)

This account was published after the patient had recovered from two acute psychotic episodes that had started while the patient, a psychiatric social service worker, had begun to receive psychoanalytic treatment. The essence of her report was that the therapist had little or no knowledge of her mental problems or the emotional turmoil she was undergoing.

Another account of a psychotherapeutic failure may be drawn from the *Autobiography of a Schizophrenic Girl*, where Renee discusses the kind of treatment her analyst (Mama) had employed during the first phase of the psychotherapy.

I was glad that Mama changed her method at the end of the first year of analysis. In the beginning, she analyzed everything I said, my fear, my guilt.

These investigations seemed to me like a bill of complaints, quite as though in looking for the cause of feelings, they became more at fault and more real. As if to say, "Find out in what instances you are guilty, and why." This for me was proof that the guilt existed, that the System [delusions] was really there since one could find the reason for its actions. From these sessions I went home more unhappy, more blameworthy, more isolated than ever, without any contact, alone in my unreal world.

But after Mama sat down beside me, talked to me in the third person and especially seemed to understand without looking for causes at all, how relieved I was! She alone could break through the unreal wall that hemmed me in; she alone kept me in contact with life.

Unreality finally reached such a point that Mama herself could no longer make contact between us. For some time I had been complaining bitterly how I suffered because of it. (Sechehaye, 1951, pp. 33–34)

Renee, in continuing her account, detailed how the distortions of her perceptual world and the system of delusional ideas came to occupy her mind so completely that she lost all contact with her therapist.

The more conventional form of analytic therapy is one which encourages the patient to talk as much as possible about his inner life, while the analyst attempts from time to time to call the patient's attention to the probable relationship between parts of his self-revelation, so that the patient may become conscious of the source of his disturbance. If the patient is mentally intact and possesses the inner strength that this kind of self-analysis demands, then much can be accomplished and new synthesis achieved. But if the pathological mental process is one that of itself tends toward mental fragmentation, if there is a "weakness of intellect" and the patient is completely overwhelmed by feelings of guilt, anxiety, and self-punishment, then such self-analysis may hasten the mental disintegration.

Still another comment on a therapist's mistakes was given by Mary Jane Ward in *The Snake Pit*. At the time of her recovery she wrote as follows.

Well, the hell with my subconscious. What I'm interested in is getting the old conscious to working again. You know, maybe my subconscious did cook up something like Dr. Kik said, but if it did I'm sure it was for a novel. I always did have a secret, anyhow I hoped it was a secret, ambition to write tripe. . . .

It isn't that I don't appreciate all you did, or tried to do, Dr. Kik, but there is a sympathy in this other man (one of the asylum doctors) that you lacked. You had pity and interest but this new one has an intuitive understanding and a willingness to admit that a problem is solved even when he does not understand what the problem was or how it was solved. Or this is what I think; this is what I hope; this is what my intuition told me. (Ward, 1946, pp. 257; 264).

Mrs. Ward had had many hours of psychotherapy under the guidance of Dr. Kik. Her condition had become progressively worse, ending in a stuporous catatonia. Finally she was treated with electro-convulsive therapy, which started a process of recovery. As she regained her "lost mind" she had only patches of uncertain memory that were related to any of the therapeutic sessions, or, indeed, little recall of much of the experience that had led to her hospitalization and treatment.

For the most part, anyone who attempts to do psychotherapy with mentally disturbed patients can only guess as to why he succeeds, and will almost never understand why he fails. From the autobiographical accounts, it does not seem that a knowledge of the source of the illness is particularly helpful to the recovery of the patient or the success of the therapist. What the patient most desires and appreciates is some evidence that the therapist has an emotional sympathy with his inner problems. The understanding of the physician need not be marked by any ready knowledge of the sources of the patient's turmoil or by any agreement with the patient's delusional convictions. It is enough for the patient to feel that the outsider appreciates the fact that he is suffering and stands by ready to render whatever assistance may be possible. One patient expressed this feeling in the following way.

Meeting you made me feel like a traveler who's been lost in a land where no one speaks his language. Worst of all, the traveler doesn't even know where he should be going. He feels completely lost and helpless and alone. Then suddenly, he meets a stranger who can speak English. Even if the stranger doesn't know the way to go, it feels so much better to be able to share the problem with someone, to have him understand how badly you feel. If you're not alone, you don't feel hopeless any more. Somehow it gives you life and a willingness to fight again. (Hayward and Taylor, 1956, p. 221)

This excerpt constitutes, so far as the therapist is concerned, a tribute of the sort not frequently found in published records. It seems to me that a distinction in therapeutic approaches may be made among those groups of persons who are suffering from psychopathological complaints: (1) persons with mild troubles or characterological difficulties; (2) persons whose complaints are fairly clear-cut and for whom an effective therapy is known; (3) a third group where there is no doubt of the mental disturbance and no known specific therapy. For the first of these groups, psychologically oriented counsel or therapy is probably the most effective procedure available at present. For the second group (largely made up by manic, depressive, epileptic, and paretic patients) the appropriate physical therapy should be initiated as rapidly as possible. For the third group there is no substitute for "tender loving care." All too frequently, therapists forget that, so far as the inner life of the sufferer is concerned, ill-chosen words can be more injurious than any drug or any surgery.

How Much Should the Therapist Tell the Patient?

One of the oldest continuing debates in the practice of medicine is concerned with the general question of how much information the doctor should disclose to the patient. At one extreme of the argument are those practitioners who maintain that a patient should never be told more about his state of health than a kindly but authoritative reassurance that he can trust the medical skills and art that are being made available to him. At the other extreme are those who insist that a full disclosure of all the factors concerning the illness should be made available to the patient, particularly if the patient asks for the information. This problem, on which medical opinions are so divergent, becomes acute when a physician is treating mentally disturbed persons, especially where there is from the start considerable doubt in the therapist's mind about the nature of the entire process. No generally accepted answers to the questions posed by the patient is possible in such cases. Seemingly, the circumstances of the instant, plus the personal relationship that has been established between therapist and patient, will determine the former's course of action. (The first working rule for many physicians under these circumstances seems to be, "You will get into fewer difficulties if you say little or nothing." The second rule is, "Be evasive but never give a direct lie as an answer.")

To illustrate this serious therapeutic dilemma more clearly, let me compare an instance in which a truthful and direct answer was devastating to the patient, in contrast to one when a direct answer helped the patient. In considering the first incident it is easy to comprehend where the therapist—evidently a well-trained, competent man—made his mistake. In answering a direct question he made a realistic, honest remark, but its emotional impact was beyond the intellectual strength of the sufferer, a phobic neurotic. The excerpt is from the *Autobiography of David*—from which I have already drawn material.

In writing what follows, I shall endeavor to be scrupulously careful, for I know how easily proportions might be lost in this matter, involving, as it did to me, the great tragedy of my life.

I had already heard in a vague way of psychoanalysis and complexes, but so far had consulted no medical practitioner who specialized in the subject. I looked forward to the interview with hope, as the final effort that would break the shackles and set me free. . . .

I was tense and alert; I had come to a clinic where the treatment of functional nervous trouble was a special study. There was the prestige of the doctor's name, and the impressive atmosphere. . . .

I then described my symptoms and what had happened, and ended by saying that my progress had been steadily upward. "I have been getting on so well," I said, "that I feel that someday I shall waken up to find that my fears have dropped from me like a cloak." . . . I paused and waited for a reply.

Quite gently, but firmly, in tones that sounded to me like the tolling of a funeral bell, he replied: "I have never heard of such a thing. We may ameliorate the symptoms in two years. We may effect a cure in three."

I was speechless. *Incurable*, perhaps! Anyhow, no certainty of a cure! Two or three years of uncertainty with the menace of ultimate failure hanging over my head! I felt like a man who has clambered up on to his knees with infinite difficulty and is then struck down, just as he seemed to be gaining his balance. (Raymond, 1946, pp. 111–112)

It is easy to say that this therapist should have realized that any patient who has described a deep, widespread phobia of long standing, who thought that he had made some progress in achieving self-control, deserved sympathy and support, not a statement of prognosis, however true. It may be true that the therapist was more interested in the particular therapeutic method he advocated than he was in David's problem. In any event he completely misjudged the effect that his opinion would have on this patient.

In contrast to the disastrous effect of this straightforward answer, the following incident, recounted by Hackett, shows that a different patient under different circumstances could and did benefit by a direct answer to a direct question.

I decided to see the doctor and to face the thing squarely and find out what was wrong and how long I would be here and what would happen to me. . . . That morning, I talked with Dr. Edwards. It was a quiet conversation but when I finished I knew that I was facing a struggle more deadly than any in my delusions. As I sat across from the doctor, I asked for it straight, as one old soldier to another, what was the matter with me and what were my chances.

He took his time answering and then he said, "Probably I should ask you what you think is wrong and drag out this session, but you ask for it straight and I'll gamble with you on it. We think you are sick and have been sick a long time. It probably started in the service but the seeds were there. The service was ripe soil for mental sickness. Officially your diagnosis is paranoid schizophrenia which makes you a tough bird to handle. I don't care what they call it, the name is just a name. It's a severe emotional break with reality. I've seen them get better and have helped some get better. It will be the toughest fight you could face. . . . What you face is this: probably two or three years of the depression and anger and breaks with reality. It may be less. During this time you will be locked up in here for the most part. You have to choke down the anger and survive the depression and live with the others during this time. When it is done and you're ready to go home, you have to face getting a job after being in an institution and you have the social adjustment which will last a lifetime. That's it as straight as I can make it. Now, what do you want to do?"

"What can I do, Doc? If you told me it was a cancer what could I do.

I'd make the best of it and follow the bouncing ball. Well, where do we go from here?"

It was a nice military statement, full of the old school try, and as I said it, I meant it and I could not have known that the fury and anger would grow so intense that I would hold my hands behind my back to keep from choking someone or the depressions so deep that any end, any sleep, would look like a God-given release, and that I would feel such sympathy for the others with me that I would rather remain with them than live in the society outside. All these things I did not know as I listened to the doctor in the heat of the August afternoon. (Hackett, 1952, pp. 120–122)

There are not too many accounts illustrative of the effects of straight-from-the-shoulder information. That its effect may be either crushing or strengthening is evident. Certainly both of these citations suggest the need for caution in placing the plain, blunt truth of the probable outcome of treatment at the disposal of the mental patient. If the therapist is not too certain about either the basic trouble or the probable outcome, the need for caution grows even greater. As many of the citations given in this chapter—and in previous chapters—indicate, patients greatly resent the fact that they are deprived of their liberty and restricted in their activities. They also resent the obviously evasive replies their doctors give them. Time after time they compare their lot with that of criminals who are held in jails on an indeterminate sentence. They emphasize that the way they are, or have been, treated convinced them that both the doctors and attendants behaved as though the patients should be punished rather than medically treated.

In an autobiographical account entitled *Inside the Asylum*, the author (Vincent) relates the difficulties he faced due to his marital impotence. In addition, he endured many other hardships, which arose from his enrolling himself as a conscientious objector during World War II, his inability to earn decent wages, and his involvement with nonconformist religion. Finally, in despair and deeply depressed, he applied voluntarily for admission to a County Asylum. Of this venture, he wrote as follows.

It is with almost unspeakable gratitude that I write of the medical treatment which I myself received. It is difficult to write adequately of this part of my life. The medicines, drugs and injections no doubt contributed to my recovery, but the thing to which I looked forward with eagerness was the analytical interview with the doctor which took place every two or three days. For the first time in my life I felt that I was in the presence of someone who completely understood. Furthermore, while I was with the psychiatrist I had the strange feeling that my individual welfare was the only thing that mattered to him. These interviews, together with the medical treatment, continued for about two months. Then the doctor told me that he was going to try hypnotic treatment, after which I was to go home for thirty-six hours only. Despite the confidence of the psychiatrist, and the trust which I placed in him, I may be forgiven for having my doubts as to whether, after six years of sexual impotence, any treatment would be successful.

The week-end when I was to go home was arranged, and an hour before my wife was due to fetch me I was taken into a room where everything had been arranged for my comfort, even to a warmed and scented pillow on the bed upon which I was to lie. The doctor gave me an injection in each arm and warned me that they would make me drowsy. He then assured me of my ability to have sexual intercourse. He did not induce a state of deep hypnosis which he said was unnecessary. All this seemed so simple that I could hardly believe in its efficacy. My wife came for me and escorted me to the bus. I gradually became more drowsy and had difficulty in walking. We had to transfer to a train and in the carriage my chin kept drooping forward on to my chest. When we arrived at our own station we were faced with a two mile walk. I felt quite incapable of the effort but I stumbled along, from time to time leaning against the stone wall to rest.

At last I was home, and the house seemed to wear a new and brighter aspect than when I had seen it last. In accordance with the doctor's instructions my wife and I went at once to bed. I was still drowsy. My wife was not looking forward to what was to come, and six years of inforced abstinence were not the best preparation. But the attempt was successful. The ecstasy of that hour cannot be described. Again and again, during that weekend, my wife and I were in each other's arms. My honeymoon had at last arrived. I went back to the hospital with a new song in my heart. The terrible look of strained anxiety had for the time left the face of my wife, and once more we kissed each other farewell at the hospital doors, this time in a spirit that was full of hope. A week or so later, the doctor told me that he could do little more and, almost reluctantly, I left the building where my life had been re-shaped. (Vincent, 1948, pp. 100–101)

Unfortunately, this improvement in his marital sex life did not carry over to an improvement in the other life adjustments that he had to make. He found that to his former problems was now added the stigma of having been mentally ill. The fact that he had been a mental hospital patient was now added to the reproaches of being a pacifist, a religious nonconformist, and a general ne'er-do-well. After several months his wife found his sexual advances unbearable so that he felt once more rejected and depressed. The most that Vincent had gained from the psychiatric therapy was a temporary relief from impotence. For this relief he eventually paid the price of increased personal rejection and social disapproval, so that, in this sense, the psychotherapy was of doubtful value.

The Protection of the Patient

In general, most recovered patients will agree that during the acute phase of their illness they should have been protected against the violence of their own acts, as well as of the acts of others. But all recovered patients agree that the doctors and attendants should have behaved in a fashion that indicated some degree of sympathy with those under their care. Mental patients bitterly resent any interpretation of their behavior which implies that their condition deserves blame or reproach. Like all human beings, the patients desire praise and resent receiving any obvious moralizing. This point clearly was stated by Grace Stuart.

> Often in those days I wanted to cry out: "I am doing more than my best. Please say that you believe me." I took too long to learn that the crying-out is never worth it—never! Too long to learn that those who do not already understand can never be told. That, not only for people who live in my particular private world, but for all of us, there will only be a few real friends, and that we shall be fortunate to have those few. (Stuart, 1953, p. 59)

I said earlier that mental patients are generally considered by outside observers to vary between overemotionality and apathy in their relations to others. Those who are in charge of the care and treatment of acutely ill mental patients too often tend to disregard the patients' behavior and remarks. The sympathy and patient care that each individual seeks are all too often met with casual rejection.

In connection with the general protection offered by society to the mental patient, Davidson made the following observation after he had recovered from his second illness and had been discharged from the hospital.

> No one but a madman wishes to put insanity upon a pedestal. If a man behaves in an abnormal manner an asylum is the best place for him, and he should be put there without any delay whatever; otherwise, he may ruin or disgrace his family. The customs and conventions of this country are against even amiable and harmless lunatics wandering about at large, trying to teach and partaking of mixed hospitality. In a sinful world, how can men judge between amiability and erotomania? The stupid prejudice and ignorance with which all forms of mental disturbance are regarded by the public, and the stigma that attaches to the idea of insanity, are the main obstacles to immediate and necessary seclusion in every case. (Davidson, 1912, p. 288)

It is not common to find this degree of social awareness on the part of a recovered mental patient. If the patient has paranoid tendencies he usually bitterly resents his deprivation of liberty and freedom of action, and even after amelioration, such a patient is not apt to agree that the incarceration was really beneficial as far as he was personally concerned. That society does attach an odious stigma to the fact that a person has been psychotic must be deplored. But it must also be recognized; it cannot be evaded.

DISCUSSION

This collection of autobiographical excerpts bearing on therapy and therapists indicates that the experiences of the patient provide but few suggestions for novel or positively oriented therapeutic procedures. Patients obtain little direct help or self-enlightenment from any of the medical or pastoral psychotherapeutic procedures that are ordinarily followed, particularly during the acute phases of the disturbances. In fact, most patients are inclined to resent the psychotherapeutic efforts employed in most mental hospitals, saying that they are worthless and "cruel." They do appreciate "tender loving care," understanding, sympathy, and a modicum of praise. On the other hand, persons who suffer from the milder neuroses, "personality disorders," "troubled mind," or from certain obscure psychosomatic disorders, often do accept and seem to derive some benefit from a psychodynamically oriented treatment. This limited acceptance does not often characterize those who have suffered from a real psychotic disturbance.

This last observation is, of course, not relevant to the basic truth or rejection of psychodynamic theory, any more than a patient's acceptance of the "germ" theory is relevant to his treatment of, let us say, appendicitis. Such objections do indicate, however, that acceptance of the theory on the part of the patient is not a necessary condition for obtaining successful results with psychodynamic methods, especially during the acute phases of a truly psychotic disturbance.

Why the simple fact of telling one's troubles to a sympathetic listener will ease the distressed mind is a question that has been considered many times, but remains essentially unanswered. An attempt is made to clothe one's frightening, unreal, and bewildering experiences with words; that these words enable a discreet listener to understand one's suffering does, in part, make one's fears easier to bear and the turmoil easier to resist, and this remains as true today as it was in Burton's times. It is as though words can condense all the vague, chaotic feelings into a somewhat organized cognitive pattern; but, even so, the control and relief depends largely on the quality of the words employed. Words may heal, words may kill, but in either event the effect partakes of magic.

There is often a certain wry humor in the statements mental patients have made concerning the therapy to which they have been subjected. There can be no doubt of the realistic shrewdness and basic honesty of the patients who made these evaluations, no matter how insane they may have been at one time or another. I have cited many examples of confused thinking, feelings of unreality, and delusional ideas—in brief many examples of the patient's mental disturbance. But one is often sharply impressed by the realistically sagacious remarks made by the same patient.

One of the problems which face every therapist is that of informing the patient directly, completely, and honestly concerning his own belief and opinion relevant to the patient's condition, as opposed to indirect evasions coupled with vague reassurances. Seemingly, only long years of dealing with sick people can furnish a basis for judging whether to disclose facts partially or completely, or to evade, as many as possible of the patient's pertinent questions. The contrast in responses to directly answered questions, which was illustrated in several excerpts in the present chapter, poses the problem but does not provide a solution.

The more the therapist knows about the patient's unusual experiences, feelings, and ideas, the more effectively can he say, "I know; I understand," and if his manner and conversation seem to confirm his words, then the patient may find some comfort in his evident understanding. But if the patient acquires the notion that the therapist is unaware or has little understanding of the nature of his problems, then no matter how erudite the therapist, the patient is apt to reject and resent almost any effort on the part of the therapist to be helpful.

Although most mental patients deprecate the ineffective psychotherapeutic attempts made on their behalf, they all agree in stating that a real complaint can be directed toward society in general. They especially resent the social attitude which holds that insanity is sufficient and satisfactory evidence of the truth of the allegations of sin and evil. They further resent the idea that this concept of sin is not only attached to the individual but is extended to his relatives and friends. All therapy could be somewhat more rational if it were not complicated with this sort of prejudice and bias.

I have read a good deal, since my last lesson [hospitali-zation] about insanity, and the different forms of it; and other people know a great deal more about it, both from a physical and a psychological point of view, than I do. There are very great mysteries lying behind it and an asylum is a good school for those who cannot learn in any other.

(*Davidson*, 1912, p. 290)

CHAPTER 21

The Philosophy of Insanity

INTRODUCTION

The title of this chapter was suggested by a short auto-biography called *The Philosophy of Insanity* first pub-lished in 1860 (and reissued in 1947) by a "Late In-mate." Custance entitled his autobiography, *Wisdom, Madness and Folly: The Philosophy of a Lunatic.* Schreber's *Memoirs*, Davidson's *Remembrances*, and Graves' *Eclipse of a Mind*, as well as a hundred or more additional autobiographies, all touch on the meaning, causes, and consequences of the neurotic or psychotic experience. General agreement as to the *context* of these individual accounts is the most any outsider may hope for. In the present chapter I will, for the most part, limit myself to statements that were intended to characterize the essence and meaning of an overt neurosis or psychosis.

Sample Characterizations of Psychotic and Neurotic Experiences

It is clear from much of the material cited in previous chapters that there is no simple descriptive statement which can encompass the experience characteristic of psychopathology. Yet there is obviously a very human desire to try to compress the essence of pathological experiences into an explanatory nutshell, so that sufficient and relevant information may then be conveyed to others or recalled by the person himself at some later date. The following group of excerpts constitute a random collection of such attempts.

Being crazy is like one of those nightmares where you try to call for help and no sound comes out. Or if you can call, no one hears or understands. You can't wake up from the nightmare unless someone does hear you and helps you to wake up. (Hennell, 1938, p. 221)

And sometimes it is like a big, threatening obstacle. But you have to put up with it. You think: "Isn't there something the doctor can cut away?" It is like a monster, it is like a growth. It presses down on you. It mocks you. It exhausts you. It makes your thoughts go spinning around like a squirrel in a cage, and it wears you out just as going around in a circle physically would wear you out. "If I could only press a lever to stop this whirring," you say to yourself. (Krauch, 1937, pp. 95–96)

The loneliness of the insane! The insane are surely the most lonely people in the world . . . from the very nature of their illness the insane are shut out from all communication to others of what is happening to them. . . . A great gulf separates each and all of the patients: they wander round and round, shut off completely from one another, unable to explain themselves or their actions . . . and to this is added the last cruelty . . . the suffering of the insane arouses quite often a feeling of revulsion—so morbid, so full of the strange and unknown is it. (Raymond, 1946, pp. 152–153)

No one who has not been deranged, can understand how dreadfully true a lunatic's insane imagination appears to him, how slight his sane doubts. (Perceval, 1838, p. 55)

Madness, like melancholy, *is* self, and almost every mental patient thinks that everything that happens is directed against himself or herself. Exceptions are those arresting and extraordinarily beautiful characters who, even in their insanity, find spiritual life, and those lesser, yet lovable people whose evil spirit is nothing worse than a poltergeist (Harrison, 1941, p. 39)

But how impossible, how futile, to try to put any of the diverse horrors of a neurosis into words. Words—that is *all* they are, when set down on paper, just words. Words lacking the peculiar connotation of sick, blind terror with which every real neurosis is fraught; wording lacking, I fear (or should I rejoice?) the power of transmitting even a vestige of that emotion over onto their readers. Only those who have gone through it, can know; the others, the untouched, will have to accept it on faith as truth—dark truth. (Pierce and Pierce, 1929, p. 54)

Each of these statements is different and yet there is a similarity among the characterizations—a similarity which is largely in the common attempt to find words to convey to the uninitiated an idea of the fearfulness of the experience. Additional statements could have been selected that would have been similar, but mere quantity would not have helped to clarify the point at issue. Characterizations of this sort do not lend themselves to logical or easy generalizations. Madness is not an imaginary thing to the sufferer; it is reality itself. Each individual is particularly impressed by one aspect of the experience, more than he is by some other. But above all it is agreed by the sufferers that the experience is rarely pleasant, and that it is difficult to define.

Excerpts of the sort listed above are illustrative, but none is particularly relevant to any potential central meaning of the experiences of insanity. Before we consider this central topic, there are certain areas of difficulty that must be set forth and evaluated, particularly the problems that surround the phenomena of (1) unreality, and (2) volition. Also puzzling are the processes that may be involved in (3) religious and mystical experiences, and finally, the phenomena underlying (4) rationalization, and (5) obliteration. If these topics can be organized and brought into focus, then perhaps we may be able to evaluate more adequately some of the philosophies of insanity that various patients have formulated.

Difficulties Arising from the Experience of Unreality

The material presented in earlier chapters showed that the experience of unreality is only in part to be identified with mental derangement; that is, feelings of unreality may occur in the life of anyone, whether sane or insane.

I have cited at some length the accounts of several persons who had been specifically disturbed by the confusion resulting from their inability to distinguish between reality and unreality. Perhaps the most vivid descriptions dealing with feelings of unreality were those that Renee recounted in the *Autobiography of a Schizophrenic Girl*, which were cited in previous chapters.

An excerpt from Lara Jefferson's autobiography, *These Are My Sisters*, may serve to further illustrate this particular difficulty.

I cannot escape it—I cannot face it—how can I endure it.
The whole thing is a dream and a nightmare. No doctor ever stood before me and told me that I would shortly be incurably insane unless I learned to think differently. Oh, I am sure it is all just a dream. Presently, I shall wake up and be oh, so relieved—to know that this has all been a dream. Then it will be only funny—and I can recall with humor the odd sensation I had on finding that a crazy woman had moved into my body. A crazy woman who had

no sense at all, and who refused to be governed by reason—who acknowledged no law higher than her own whim—and who had no fear of anything. I shall shortly awake and remember how frail my strength felt and how helpless I was in trying to budge her gross and unseemly proportions. Dreams seem quite real as you dream them, but how quickly they pass; when I awake I shall be able to laugh at this nightmare. For that is what this great skinned horse is— somebody's nightmare.

She is not real—she is not I—I never saw her before I dreamed her. I am dreaming her now. If am not dreaming her—then someone else is. And presently they will wake up and this whole thing will dissolve into the night— where nightmares go on waking. Oh, it is all a dream—a delusion—a nightmare. Nothing is real. Everything is a wild toss of hallucinations of one kind or another about one thing or another. All this other raving and howling going on around me—will not someone come and awaken me—so that I may go free? (Jefferson, 1947, pp. 19–20)

Miss Jefferson had been placed in restraint because of her extreme destructiveness, assaultiveness, and noisiness. During one of her quiet periods, the doctor informed her that unless she regained her self-control, she would have to be transferred to a building for incurable cases. I gather from her own words that she was not sure of what constituted her "real self." Was it the screaming, mad, psychotic personality, the personality who had experienced the many insoluble problems that finally brought her to the hospital, or was it a new self, reborn and free from both old memories and present turmoil? For as long as the dreamlike and dissociated state continued, Miss Jefferson was in no condition to offer any report of material that would be relevant to the core of the psychotic experience. Her autobiography as a whole is a meaningful document, but the manifestation of her split personality, her uncertainty as to the nature of reality, and the periods of complete lack of contact with her environment do present difficulties in the evaluation of her history that cannot be overlooked.

Difficulties Arising from Disorders of Volition

In earlier chapters we have seen that the one factor which will generally lead a patient to conclude that he is, or has been, insane is the self-recognition of his loss of responsibility. Subjectively, this loss is related either to lack of will or to the feeling that conative functioning has been overwhelmed by the intrusion of external forces which prevent the exercise of normal control. Apparently, when the objective evidence of the consequences of his own actions or ideas is indisputable, then the person becomes aware of his state and is led to say, "I was not responsible; I was insane." If the feeling of irresponsibility includes some awareness of evident contradiction between the internal and external world, so that at least part of his behavior becomes attributable to some volitional defect, the person convinces himself of the dubious nature of his sanity.

Such a situation presents a special problem in any attempt an outsider may make when attempting to evaluate patients' reports concerning the subjective meaning of their experience of derangement. The report made by an insane patient often casts doubt on his judgment and memory, strongly suggesting that both may be false or distorted. A sane person is reasonable; an insane person is unreasonable—at least, this is the common-sense social distinction made by the general public. The following citation may serve as an illustration. During the weeks prior to his hospitalization for a psychosis, the famous Russian dancer, Nijinsky, had started to keep a diary in which he recorded, among other things, some of his ideas concerning life and death. He realized that his mind was not functioning adequately, yet he could not believe that he, Nijinsky, could be actually mad.

People think that without intelligence a man is either insane or a fool. An insane person is a person who cannot reason. A lunatic does not realize what he is doing. I understand my good and my bad actions. I am a man who has reason. In Tolstoy's book a lot is explained about reason. I read this book and therefore know what it means. I am not afraid of intelligent people. I am strong because I feel all that is said about me. I know that they invent all sorts of things to calm me. The doctors are good. My wife is also a good woman, but they think much too much. I am afraid for their intelligence. People went mad because they thought too much—I am afraid for them, they think too much. I do not want them to become insane; I will do everything to make them healthy." (Nijinsky, 1936, p. 178)

Nijinsky wrote this passage after his wife and several doctors had tried to get him to consent to enter a hospital where he might receive treatment for his mental and emotional turmoil. Evidently, he was at least partially aware of his derangement, but had retained sufficient intellect to permit him to doubt whether he was in fact insane.

To illustrate a later period in the course of the psychotic process, another excerpt from the account of Miss Lara Jefferson is relevant.

I must have had a fair share of intelligence, or I could not have conducted myself according to the rules as long as I did. . . . But now I cannot conduct myself as the rules set forth because something has broken loose within me and I am insane—and differ from these others to the extent that I still have sense enough to know it; —which is the mark of spectacular intelligence—so they tell me.

"Here I sit—mad as the hatter—with nothing to do but either become madder and madder—or else recover enough of my sanity to be allowed to go back to the life which drove me mad. If that is not a vicious circle, I hope I never encounter one. But today the circle had stopped chasing itself long enough to drop me somewhere along the unmarked line between stark lunacy and harmless eccentricity. The latter is as near to normal as I ever hope to get.

I am not relying on my own opinion in that matter. The doctor was just through now and flattered the extent of my intelligence and education by discussing with me in some longhandled, technical words I suppose were the labels for my phobias. (Jefferson, 1947, pp. 12–13)

Miss Jefferson had said earlier in her account, "I know I cannot think straight—but the conclusions I arrive at are very convincing to me." She then characterized her state in terms of the excerpts given above, which might have been labeled as a lucid interval. A few paragraphs further on in her narrative she wrote, "It is just up to me—the power of the life within me." She has acknowledged both her inability to think adequately and one of the consequences of that inability—madness. She believed that somehow she must restore her sanity from within herself. Where shall any psychotic individual find the inner strength and will to re-create sanity out of madness?

Doubts Arising from Mystical Experiences

One of the marks of mystical experience, either sane or insane, is the person's conviction of the truth of his experience and its meaning. It is this inner conviction of unmistakable truth which we must now consider. The certainty that marks a paranoid delusion in the mind of any psychotic is a conviction beyond the comprehension of the outside observer. The difficulties in belief really become appalling when we wish to evaluate the meaning which a mystical experience conveys to the mind of the lunatic.

In his treatise *The Psychology of Religious Mysticism* Leuba dealt with the relationship between religious mystical ecstasy and ecstatic experiences not necessarily of a religious nature.

Whether they belong to the religious life or not, these raptures, or psychical storms, break out suddenly and overcome the subject. He feels as if in the hands of an external power, and he interprets what happens to him, in accordance with the custom of the time and his own private knowledge. These wonderful experiences include indescribable impressions, designated by the term illumination or revelation. Their traits—suddenness, unexpectedness, passivity, illumination, ineffability—therefore, are not characteristic of religious life alone.

In many cases these psychical storms have no conscious cause. Neither perception, nor idea, nor emotion brings them about. They break out suddenly, as of themselves. . . . These phenomena have unconscious causes which may be sufficient in themselves or which may need supplementing. The facts seem to warrant the further conclusion that the unconscious causes are organic. . . .

In the instance of mystical ecstasy, consciousness had no share in the production of the primary, the immediate experience; Christian beliefs intervened only after its experience. But they transfigured it by putting into it a divine meaning. In this ethical-minded person, the rapture became a powerful source of moral energy. (Leuba, 1929, pp. 216–217)

Leuba's conclusions were drawn only after he had exhaustively examined the phenomena of mystical ecstasy as they had been reported by epileptic patients, religious leaders, poets, and psychotics. He pointed out that the onset of the mystical episode is characterized, first of all, by a storm of physical events which involve the pulse, breathing, and muscular contractions. This over-all physical disturbance carries with it a momentary wave of unconsciousness. The mystical state becomes part of conscious life by means of a secondary feeling of belief that may have divine significance and the potentiality of acting as a powerful source of moral energy.

Another excerpt may be added as an illustration of the mystical feeling and its effect on the will to believe. It is quoted from the epilogue of Nijinsky's diary and was written before his final committal to a mental hospital.

I want to cry but God orders me to go on writing. He does not want me to be idle. . . . I do not know what to write, but God wishes me to . . . I am a simple man who has suffered a lot. I believe I suffered more than Christ. I love life and I want to live, to cry but cannot—I feel such pain in my soul—a pain which frightens me. My soul is ill. My soul, not my mind. The doctors do not understand my illness. I know what I need to get well. My illness is too great to be cured quickly. I am incurable. My soul is ill. . . . My body is not ill—it is my soul that is ill. I suffer, I suffer. Everyone will feel and understand. I am a man, not a beast. I love everyone. I have faults. I am a man—not God. I want to be God and therefore I try to improve myself. . . . I am a man. God is in me. I am in God. I want Him, I seek Him. . . . I hope to improve myself. I do not know how to but I feel that God will help all those who seek Him. I am a seeker, for I can feel God. God seeks me and therefore we will find each other. (Signed) God and Nijinsky. (Nijinsky, 1936, pp. 186–187)

This final statement and plea for understanding with which Nijinsky ended his diary conveys the essence of the difficulty which will be encountered by an outsider who attempts to grasp the meaning a psychotic patient attaches to his mystical or religious experiences.

The Mental Processes of Rationalization

The question of the role played by rationalization in the recollections of the inner mental life of deranged patients has been raised at various points in the foregoing chapters. This process must be reconsidered, particularly since it has become apparent that two different meanings and usages have become attached to this concept.

The term rationalization (or rationalism) as it is used in philosophy and theology serves to describe the theory that *reason* is the source of a knowledge superior to both sensory perception and mystical revelation. William James spoke from the philosopher's standpoint in the following way.

Nevertheless, if we look on man's whole mental life as it exists, on the life of men that lies in them apart from their learning and science, and that they inwardly and privately follow, we have to confess that the part of it of which rationalism can give an account is relatively superficial. It is the part that has the *prestige* undoubtedly, for it has the loquacity, it can challenge you for proofs, and chop logic, and put you down with words. But it will fail to convince or convert you all the same, if your dumb intuitions are opposed to its conclusions. If you have intuitions at all, they come from a deeper level of your nature than the loquacious level which rationalism inhabits. Your whole subconscious life, your impulses, your faiths, your needs, your divinations, have prepared the premises, of which your consciousness now feels the weight of the result; and something in you absolutely *knows* that that result must be truer than any logic-chopping rationalistic talk, however clever, that may contradict it. (James, 1902, p. 73)

The concept of rationalism is opposed to the concept of mysticism employed in the realms of philosophy and theology. Rationalism makes all things mental the subject of reason. And yet, as James points out, the rational side of human experience does not necessarily provide any inner certainty concerning one's subjective experiences.

In current psychiatric theory the concept of rationalization has been given a special meaning. Here the word is used to designate an unconscious process that supplies the practically universal human need for personal explanations or theories that will account for the meaning of one's actions and experiences. One's consciousness, by virtue of the action of the ego process of rationalization, attempts to disguise the demands from both the unconscious and the superego so that the unverbalized and undifferentiated primitive drives may be successfully adapted to the facts of external reality. This function of the ego is developed automatically and without very much conscious direction or awareness. Since unusual or psychologically overwhelming experiences may, at times, intrude into one's awareness, rationalization is one of the major processes whereby the ego defends itself against the force of unconscious demands.

To common-sense speculation of the everyday mind nothing seems more self-evident than the fact that part of one's mind (the EDITOR process) is engaged in a process of noting and sorting perceptions, and arranging incoming impressions so that they agree with the memory traces of past experience. The EDITOR function is a special aspect of the stream of thought. The EDITOR function may be likened to watching the play of lights and shadows on a screen or mirror. During observation, the EDITOR function may be scanning closely and in sharp focus or it may be more or less out of focus. The record produced by the EDITOR process may constitute either a clear and well-organized moving trace of events and ideas, or it may be confused and disorganized. Generally speaking, the EDITOR process provides a pleasing, organized record while a disorganized or confused record must be reorganized through the mechanism of either rationalization or obliteration. The EDITOR process does seem to select or obliterate portions of the record, this process of editing being only partially conscious. If part or all of the EDITOR process record is noted in a fashion which can be neither ignored nor approved by the Self, the event will be recollected as having been involuntary and beyond control. If the EDITOR process can organize and incorporate the elements or events of the moving record without too much difficulty so that it becomes part of a usual and meaningful pattern, the recollection is later incorporated as a remembrance that is real. If the passing experience is scrambled, fragmentary, or internally contradictory, then that period is classified by the EDITOR process as probably unreal. If, in the process of observing, organizing, and reporting, the EDITOR function is left with partially organized components that seem to be part of a properly organized record of events, ideas, and memories, such components become recognized as either rationalization or as memory elements that were thrust into focus by some outside power.

Time after time a normal individual will report with seeming certainty and belief that some experience has occurred which seems unbelievable to other persons. It then follows that this experience must be explained, that it must be made believable, usually by the mechanism of rationalization. In many instances, the EDITOR process neither has nor can it find any immediate rational explanation for certain experiences. For example, the EDITOR function can find no basis in any rational external circumstances to account for either the perception or the memory traces that would justify some instance of an undue and overwhelming feeling of grief and anxiety. Hence, the EDITOR process attaches itself to some trivial element that does exist in the store of memory traces, or to some partially associated ideas or to some mostly forgotten but still available perceptual elements, and utilizes some one or more of these devices to "explain" as much as possible of the entire picture, thus making total experience at least partially rational. In general, the normal EDITOR function is not too critical or exacting during such an evaluation. Hence, an outside observer often wonders how such a process of rationalization can be credited, forgetting that it is the normal individual's accustomed last line of defense against the admission of chaos or, even, insanity.

It is this conflict between an absolute certainty of knowledge and an inner certainty of the verity of the circumstances that have operated in one's external environment that is the crux of the patient's personal problem of sanity versus insanity. It is this normal process of rationalization that slips out of control during a period of insanity. The feelings of fear and desolation, of loss of self-control, and the knowledge that one's behavior has gone beyond possible rationalization, mark the psychotic period. When sane, one can at least rationalize one's behavior. When insane, the process of rationalization becomes devoid of belief, becomes illogical and fantastic. Others cannot accept the "explanations" offered and the sufferer finds himself in an inner turmoil where his convictions and his self-explanations take on a strange kaleidoscopic quality.

An instance that Perceval recorded as having occurred during one of the nights early in his psychotic episode illustrates this point.

I say this was indeed a trial of my faith, in two senses, for it was a trial of the strength of my delusion, and of my reasonable understanding: of my real faith, which I then called human fear; and of my false faith, which I then called trust in God. It is contemptible and ridiculous, but when night came and I had to decide, I split the difference by taking half the dose [of medicine] that my physician had ordered me. The truth is, that I doubted my delusions, and I doubted my physician. (Perceval, 1838, p. 36)

This account does not typify the delusional beliefs (false faith) that soon came to dominate Perceval's mental life during the more acute phase of his illness, nor does it typify his even stronger religious beliefs and convictions that were maintained for many years after his release from custody. This excerpt is an example of the in-between hazy state of mind that is sometimes evident at the start of a psychosis.

To summarize, there is a difference between the role of rationalization in the mental processes of the sane man and its ineffective action in the mind of an insane person. The sane man seizes on some obscure line of reasonable fact and inflates it, so to speak, using it as a last line of defense. The insane individual can offer only a confused account of his thought processes, which he is certain have been thrust into his mind by outside forces, usually some supernatural power that has invaded and taken control of his mind, body, and soul.

Obliteration or Active Forgetting

Obliteration is evident in the reports of some persons who have suffered a period of derangement. It may be illustrated by the following excerpt.

I did lose my mind—people do. I don't think it would be particularly interesting to anyone beside my friend the doctor—how I did, and why. Suffice it to say that I do not remember being taken to a hospital, nor did I recognize I was in one for eight months. I lived in an Alice-in-Wonderland sort of existence in a world of my own hallucinations, travelled in many lands, and had so many vivid experiences that when I did get well, I don't see why I wasn't a complete wreck. (Anon., 1940, p. 811).

While such an account does not provide the slightest opportunity for anyone to gain any knowledge of the phenomena that were characteristic of the psychosis, obliteration does seem to offer one of the best possible means for an adequate personal adjustment following such an episode.

A second example, somewhat more informative as to the process involved, is taken from a letter a woman wrote, three months after leaving the hospital, to the physician who had treated her.

Now the thing which strikes me with force is that I've used a mind, brain, and intelligence, which has been given every possible chance of being good as anyone else's in such a stupid way that it just walked off on its own and caused a whole lot of unnecessary trouble. To counteract the effects of this realization I've spent a lot of time trying to instill into myself a quiet, cool and courageous way of looking at the future, and I have a happy feeling that this will carry me through without any more serious breaks. (Fraser and Sargant, 1940–1941, p. 145)

Whether or not a person can assist in his own recovery by voluntarily declining to recall the episode, and instead try to cultivate a quiet, courageous attitude towards life and its problems, is a debatable point.

Judging from the autobiographical material that has been reviewed in the present study, it would appear that the number of instances in which obliteration of remembrances has been mentioned is small. It is more usual for ex-patients to insist that the subjective account of their private experience is correct, truthful, and relatively complete. If others disagree with their recollections, that disagreement is regrettable but immaterial. The outsider's doubts do not compel, so far as patients are concerned, any readjustment of personal memories and beliefs.

The process of active forgetting results in selective remembrance. Since the patient can then make available only a small fraction of the total mass of experience this probably results in biasing the relative meanings of material that patients chose to report, and on which we have had to base our comments and conclusions.

Difficulties Inherent in the Organizing of Subjective Material

There is no method whereby either the person who has described his own experience or any outside observer can be certain of the objective truth of a mental patient's description. The only way to approach objectification has been to depend on the similarity of the content of the reports of many persons.

When experience of a deranged person is related as though it had been forced on the patient by supernatural or unnatural agencies, he usually disclaims responsibility for the thoughts, ideas, and actions that bear such a connotation. When deranged experience is of a mystical or religious nature and meet James' criteria of ineffability, transiency, passivity, and noetic qualities, the experiencer is generally convinced that the experience was unique and cannot be reported in ordinary language. Such experience carries for each individual the quality of deep truth and a conviction of its continuing supernatural authority. In contradistinction to mystical experiences stand the mental processes of rationalization and rationalism. Rationalization seems to be a common mechanism of a disturbed but still normally functioning mind.

The Meaning of Neurotic Experience

To the outsider, the markedly neurotic person seems to be self-centered, immature, and grossly egotistical. He seems to be continually preoccupied with his own troubles and complaints, difficulties that seem to the outsider to be imaginary. The person's inner experience, however, denies these outward appearances.

We have repeatedly quoted from Leonard's *The Locomotive-God*, which is essentially an autobiography of his phobic neurosis. His self-analysis, in addition to ideas gained from external medical and psychological counsel, led him to the conclusion that the essence of his neurosis revolved around the continuation of his childhood fears of the Loco-motive-God; the locomotive being a symbol of God and God's wrath. In conclusion, he wrote as follows.

If the crowning irony of my lifelong adventures with the Locomotive-God is the fact that I have gained my knowledge of him, as it would seem, only at the tragic expense of a still greater surrender to his power as Lord of Fears, I still cannot honestly conclude this book in defeat before him. He has been Lord of my Fears; but he has not been Lord of my Life . . . He had disturbed my temper and my emotions, but they were and are mine, not his . . . He had not unmade my essential temperament and character . . . He had not undone the aboriginal instinct to know . . . he has not undone the instinct to create . . . The only primary experience is experience with energizing consciousness, one's own consciousness. And through such an experience with what for me must be ultimate reality—I mean boldly with my own mind even in its strange disturb-ance—as I have had particularly in these four years, I feel that it is there that the pulse and breath of the universe may be best surmised . . . out of which too [come] all the religions. . . . The end of the human being is a being that most fulfills the implications of human nature: energy unfolding into ethical forms and organized thought. . . . From any but this point of view my own life remains frustration. (Leonard, 1939, pp. 424–425)

To the outsider the basis for Leonard's overwhelming phobic neurosis might have been imaginary but not so for him!

One of Karen Horney's patients wrote a long letter describing her many years of neurotic experiences. In part, she wrote as follows.

Suddenly vistas spread out and out to the sky, and all came together at my feet. Was it possible that I had touched the key to the universe—the key which every man carries so nonchalantly in his pocket? Instantly I knew in my bones, and by grief itself, that I had discovered the very core and essence of neurosis—my neurosis and perhaps every neurosis. The secret of wretchedness was SELFLESSNESS! Deep and hidden, the fact and the fear of not having a self. Not being a self. Not-being. And at the end—actual chaos. (Horney, 1949, p. 5)

We have to observe that the basis of her difficulty was not really selflessness but fear, particularly fear of not having a self; indeed, the very lack of one. At the center of every self-description of a phobic neurosis there invariably is found a statement of a feeling of fear—an unjustifiable and unreasonable fear. The problem of the patient has always been that of ascribing some meaning or reason to the fear. This woman's phobia was a fear of not-being—that is, of death without a life after death.

Prior to the period of psychoanalytic speculation autobiographical accounts of prolonged neurotic experience are neither common nor illuminating. Dr. Margaret Cleaves published in 1910 The Autobiography of a Neurasthene, which is a subjective account of the years of suffering following her having "sprained her brain." She was a practicing physician thoroughly imbued with the medical ideas current at that period. She rarely permitted herself the privilege of even speculating about the nature of her mind or her mental processes. Yet one chapter of her book was devoted to a description of her psychic processes. She said that she believed in the possibility of psychic communication between minds. This she thought could be accomplished by means of D'Albe's concept of "psychomeres" consisting of a variety of "mental" X-rays.

This is the only theory in regard to life after death, which has ever appealed to me. Its ability to appeal depends upon its physical basis. There should be nothing sad about this dying, it is after all part of living and no thought could be more beautiful, more satisfying than that my radiant energy will live in the "psychomere"—saturated atmosphere above us. . . . To follow . . . further is to pass into a state of transcendant radiance, for after thirty thousand years of this existence in the soul-saturated atmosphere [there is] a further transformation into a state of existence suited to the environment which is to be found in interplanetary space, implying . . . the final cosmic union of all souls and ages. . . . There is a natural desire for immortality inherent in all of us. In the natural processes through which our bodies pass when they are no longer needed, there is a transformation of energy which should it seems to me yield satisfying content as to immortality. . . .

The habit of introspection by the varied mental cults is unwholesome. . . In all my hard and bitter experience I have recognized this, but with the conditions of my life it could not be helped. I have rarely given up to this side of the question, but have always resolutely set myself to work to fill up the chinks with some change of occupation, even though within my four walls, in order to prevent the extreme of unphysiological conditions. (Cleaves, 1910, pp. 210–213)

Cleaves' autobiography of her "sprained brain" is a long history of fatigue, frustration, and fear. She resisted the tendency, as she says, to admit into her thoughts the direct acknowledgement of the fact that fear might play a role in conscious life. This defense broke down on those occasions when acute panic made her daily activities impossible. Only in one chapter of her book does she provide a glimpse of her more intimate psychic life and her speculations on the nature of her mind and the problems of immortality. The excerpt above was quoted from this chapter and shows that she was preoccupied by the problem of the possible survival of her soul for thirty thousand years.

The last three excerpts, as well as other accounts written by neurotic patients, all indicate that the core of the neurotic experience is fear of chaotic death, that is, death without chance of immortality. The fear is so intense that it acts to overwhelm both intellectual and volitional processes. It is in no sense a normal fear, but a *dreadful* fear which is basically a fear of death and of the loss of one's individuality and immortality. There is probably a phenomenological difference between dreadful neurotic fear and the fearfulness of the psychotic patient. Admittedly this difference is a matter of speculation not subject to direct proof. I have attempted to be guided by the actual content of the patient's published autobiographical accounts. One has to resist one's inclination to interpret conjecturally or theoretically the statements set forth by these writers; one should be biased *not* to read personal speculations into the published source material.

The Core of Psychosis

Custance theorized at length on the topic of the philosophy of lunacy. The following selection is a series of excerpts from his earlier book.

One of the most striking features of the views which impelled themselves upon me in the course of my illness is their similarity to those professed by mystics of all ages and peoples. . . . I only want to show that the similarity irresistibly suggests a common origin. The mystic insight seems generally to begin with a sense of a mystery unveiled, of a hidden wisdom now suddenly become certain beyond the possibility of a doubt. . . . In admitting this, I know that I am laying all that I write open to the criticism that is, in the useful term of the psychologists, a mere "rationalization." It can be said that I am simply finding reasons for what I believe, or what I want to believe. . . .

It is, I think, arguable that "rationalization" is one of the principal methods by which the human mind works, and one productive of results if logically and conscientiously pursued. In other words there is little objection to intuitively or instinctively feeling the truth of a theory or system of thought and then setting out to prove it, provided that facts are not distorted to fit the theory. The objection becomes even less valid if the original springs are frankly admitted. And in my own case I can perhaps claim that frankness could go no further than to show how my ideas, for what they are worth, are derived from a period of what is technically known as insanity. . . .

But by accepting the principles of the Philosophy of the As If, by admitting that we "know" nothing for certain, that "reality" always eludes our grasp, but that for purposes of practical action we must set up fictions, or postulates, or hypotheses, and act "as if" they were true, merely judging by practical results how near to the "truth" we have got, life becomes comparatively simple.

If, therefore, I say, as I do say, that I postulate (and have postulated since well before I was first thought to be "mad" that there is a God, that all the experiences through which I have passed, am passing, and must pass are experiences sent by Him for my especial benefit, that it is His Will that I should endure them and that if I will accept His Will and learn all I can from them I can achieve many of my most cherished ambitions. . . . I cannot possibly be accused of being "mad" for that reason . . . my determination to act "as if" there were a God has shown me that for me there really is a God, or rather that there is something or somebody in the Universe . . . which acts on my consciousness as a "God" might be expected to act.

Nothing is more infuriating for a mental patient in the grip of overwhelming inner experiences arising out of his Unconscious than to be told that they are merely the result of his "illness," or "madness." His whole being rises up in revolt against the very idea, and all the innumerable defensive mechanisms of the human psyche, such as rationalization, are immediately brought into play. The natural result is to make the patient in his innermost soul want to be "insane," since he is led to believe that "sanity" involves the rejection of inner experiences to which he has become deeply attached.

In this sense I have no hesitation in saying that I myself want to remain "insane." I have not the slightest intention of returning to "sanity" if that means rejecting my own inner experiences. . . . Only if I accept my experiences, my manic consciousness, *in toto* and resolutely adapt them to "reality," does it seem to me that there is any hope of a permanent cure. (Custance, 1952, pp. 21–22; 23; 120; 243)

Custance was convinced of the ultimate reality of the revelations and convictions that had come to him during his periods of mania and depression. The manic excitement and confusion, the overwhelming shadow of impending Divine judgment, all convinced him that he was one of God's children. For Custance, the meaning of his insanity was that lunacy was the way in which God had revealed Himself to him.

An insightful account relevant to the meaning of the inner mental life of the melancholic patient may be drawn from the autobiography of the Rev. William Walford. He felt keenly the reproach that had been urged against his complaints, particularly since he was a man of God and a student of theology. He wrote as follows.

Ignorant, prejudiced, and irreligious men are frequently guilty of ascribing such a derangement as that which I have described, to false conceptions of the nature of religion, and the extravagances of heated and fanatical imaginations—the results of puritanical or methodistic representations of Christianity. By such means they endeavour to discredit all serious and spiritual piety, and to justify their own careless and wicked disregard of it. In the instance which this memoir offers to observation, it is plain and undeniable that the dejection, melancholy, and excited apprehensions of misery, present and future, would have agitated any individual whatever, religious or irreligious, who should have suffered from physical injury a similar disturbance of nervous and mental health. (Walford, 1851, p. 200)

Walford was convinced that his generally poor physical condition was the result of a brain injury acquired during infancy. His melancholia represented God's visitation on him to humble his spirit. It was thus a mystical experience and as such accounted for at least the greater part of his mental torture.

I have repeatedly drawn excerpts from the autobiography of Davidson, who characterized himself as a religio-maniac. His comments on other people's opinions and on his own convictions concerning his mystical experiences and the meaning of his insanity may be illustrated by the following excerpts.

I know that there is a fearful condemnation of idle and filthy dreamers; but accusers should be certain that their epithets are just. . . . But a careful perusal of Church doctrine and of Holy Scripture corresponding with internal evidence, make me know that I am right; for the thing was *unsought* by me, and it caused a turning, and gave me faith, and a chance of salvation, and showed me in what frightful danger I had been. . . . Also that this is the last genuine message from the right quarter of the spiritual world . . .

If any man thinks that I acted and spoke in the earnest and dramatic manner in which I did, not under compulsion, but from a desire to be made a spectacle, causing amusement, or because I was anxious for another sojourn in an asylum, he is very greatly mistaken. If the thing is out of my own mind, there is nothing in it; if it is not, and very clearly not, it is important. A man's death and everlasting destiny is very important to himself, and, once he has been thoroughly awakened and alarmed, he will take great care. As far as I can see at present, if a man says anything earnestly, and under very apparent compulsion from an unseen power, he is mad; if he says it very quickly and gently, he does not mean it; and if he writes it all out, he is inventing it.

No one could shrink from notoriety and ridicule more than I do. . . . I record the facts, however, truthfully, as they happened. I have been a coward all my life, and the greatest act of faith and penance I have ever made is to do this, and determine, if need be, to face the music.

I have come to the conclusion that my guardian in the Australian asylum was exactly the very person I thought he was the second time I set eyes on him, and that he said he was. . . . It is quite certain that Almighty God Himself, before the incarnation of His Son, appeared at times upon the earth in a human form. (Davidson, 1912, p. 271–272; 277–278; 267; 269)

The second time that Davidson had set eyes on his asylum guardian in Australia, he had asked the attendant whether he was God, Himself, and not a man at all. The guardian had replied, "I suppose I am," adding that in the hospital Davidson should call him J————. In trying to sum up his disturbed experiences, Davidson gave a list of reasons for his certainty that God in the guise of an attendant had been at his side and guided him during the dark days of his hospital stays. Davidson was convinced that the meaning of his own days of lunacy depended on God's intent to show him the errors he had made, and so ultimately to convey, through Davidson, God's last message to a sinful world. In brief, Davidson remained convinced that he had experienced an actual mystical revelation.

In several previous chapters reference has been made to an autobiography that Peterson quoted from extensively. The patient, it will be remembered, had provided a long and detailed account of the development of his paranoid state. This patient also traced the course of his mystical revelations.

I would think of the Bible, go and open it at haphazard, and just where my eye fell there was a passage that showed me *myself*. . . . The most perfect identity of all is to be found scattered through the Psalms (from which he quoted several pages) . . . I do not intend to appropriate the spirit of these passages, or to make their language my own, but quote them thus collectively as an evidence of fact. . . . Can it be that the same thing that has happened to me has befallen another in ages long past, and that these are the traces of it? . . . The signs are too many and too evident to permit me to doubt that my destiny is bound up with the religion of the world. . . . I will not waste time in useless discussion, but start with the assumption that it is God's will that I should give the world my opinions. . . . Was it not the confidence of Jesus in the book spoken of above that made him say he knew the Father, when contending with believers in personified derangement? . . . I find an application for the tower of Babel in my own insane history. I expect a confusion of the speech of the old sects to ensue likewise. . . .

Israel is held responsible for the destruction of the heathen and their idols. I conceive that I am the Lord's instrument for the completion of this work, and that I have been shown these signs in the law that my hands may be strengthened. I cannot shut my eyes to the fact that I have been made the world's sin-offering." (Peterson, 1889, pp. 216–219)

This is an account of mystical, religious revelation that had developed out of a long history of distorted feeling states, of mystical predictions, of visual and auditory hallucinations; all of which finally developed into delusions of persecution. The patient's own account of his life experiences and peculiar intellectual processes is quite clear and cogent. The seemingly fallacious conclusions which he drew from these experiences and the philosophical meaning which he attributed to his disturbance were likewise explicitly stated.

In his autobiography *The Witnesses*, Hennell presents the story of his prolonged period of derangement, from which obviously he had not fully recovered at the time the book was written. The following are some of his ruminations and rather dramatic postulates.

We lived in several different lives: three, I should say. First, the unreal one wherein we ate and wore our boots; second, the collective night life, wherein guards and inmates were together engaged in worship, in seeking journeys and encounters, through strange chambers, now beset by demons and spirits, now among the hushed mazes of the dead. Thirdly, the life of solitary, supreme experience, where a vision being worked up for, as to a climax, would be vouchsafed marvellously yet momentarily—seeming almost always to be betrayed by an involuntary movement of the brain, to some spiritual enemy who was ever on the watch. Indeed, there needed no speech for spiritual communion. The thoughts of those who lay near by were heard, audibly and continually. . . . Powers, indeed, spoke through one, as with their own voices, independently of one's conscious will: their words came at moments of crisis, and were the fewest and strongest that could rightly direct the interested. . . .

For there is no absolute distinction between madness and sanity, apart from a man's work and social relations. Sanity has an active duty and function: to think and to do appropriately to the purpose of one's life, and to act consistently in its fulfilment. Nevertheless, there is no standard purpose in all men's lives, though men may share common necessities, and may have individual requirements, which each ought to seek for himself. But beyond this, to postulate that all men should be sane, and should give up experiences and certainties which are not allowed by the supervising class, is simply to sterilize life. And if men who are placed in charge of these "insane" grow even less sane themselves, through believing in the insanity of others, then they may not uncharitably be classed with the unselfish pioneers of research, who by the effect of their experiments to cure others have themselves become incurably afflicted.

[After he left the hospital he reported as follows.] A park-walker thus accosts me: "You will think me mad, I dare say, when I tell you I had the privilege of shaking hands with the Creator two years ago in Suffolk." "I do not think you mad," is my reply. "For I had an experience, about as long ago, which is no easier for other people to believe," and with that the subject is dropped, with a good enough understanding on both sides.

We live in a world of dual beliefs that cannot be made to agree, and most are content to cover the difficulties of life with the conventions of polite ignorance. . . . In truth, madness is the illusion; and those systems to which there seems to be madness are themselves deficient, incomplete: whether they are upheld by doctors, patients, or the subscribing public. Those who make loudest claim to discern and determine insanity in others are the surest lunatics. All, all are beginners; there are specialists and professors, but there are no professional adepts in wisdom. (Hennell, 1938, pp. 132–133; 228–229; 238–239; 249)

Hennell had many hallucinations and delusions and steadfastly maintained that his experiences were real and palpable. He was deeply convinced of the all-important meaning of his mystical experiences.

At this point I quote from the Rev. A. T. Boisen, who experienced one or more brief, but acute, schizophrenic episodes, which he described in some detail as follows.

The disturbance came on very suddenly and it was extremely severe. I had never been in better condition physically; the difficulty was rooted wholly in a severe inner struggle arising out of a precocious sexual sensitivity, dating from my fourth year. With the onset of adolescence the struggle became quite severe. It was cleared up on Easter morning in my twenty-second year through a spontaneous religious conversion experience which followed upon a period of black despair. An impulse, seemingly from without myself, bade me not be afraid to tell. I was thus set free and given a new start in life. Two years later came a relapse into the land of bondage and then a desperate struggle to get free again. Following a decision to give up the teaching of languages, in which I was then engaged, and to enter upon the profession of forestry, there came a love affair which swept me off my feet and sent me forth on the adventure which has resulted in this book. This love affair was on my part a desperate cry for salvation. It led to my decision to enter the Christian ministry. . . . The call to a church was slow in coming. . . . While waiting I decided to write out a statement of my religious experience, such as I had been required to do when I was a candidate for ordination. I became much absorbed in the task, so much so that I lay awake at night letting the ideas take shape of themselves, as I frequently do when I am writing. This time the ideas carried me away. First of all came the thought that I must give up the hope which meant everything to me. Following this there came surging in upon me with overwhelming force a terrifying idea about a coming world catastrophe. Although I had never before given serious thought to such a subject, there came flashing into my mind, as though from a source without myself, the idea that this little planet of ours, which has existed for we know not how many millions of years, was about to undergo some sort of metamorphosis. . . . In the wake of this idea followed others. I myself was more important than I had ever dreamed of being; I was also a zero quantity. Strange and mysterious forces of evil of which before I had not had the slightest suspicion were also revealed. I was terrified beyond measure and in my terror I talked. . . . I soon found myself in a psychopathic hospital. There followed three weeks of violent delirium which remain indelibly burned into my memory. . . . Then I came out of it much as one awakens out of a bad dream. (Boisen, 1936, pp. 2–3)

Boisen's relatives were told by the hospital doctors that his diagnosis was catatonic dementia praecox and that they felt that there was no hope for his recovery. However, he did improve rapidly; he interested himself in his surroundings; he worked willingly on tasks given him by the hospital authorities, and he was finally discharged from institutional custody several months later. During the following five years he engaged in specialized graduate studies in a theological seminary, attended courses in the graduate school of Harvard University, and became a psychiatric social service worker at the Psychopathic Hospital. Finally he was appointed as a research investigator and a member of the multi-disciplinary team that spent several years making an intensive study of chronic schizophrenic patients at the Worcester State Hospital. The findings of the various groups of investigators were later published during the 1930's. In 1936, Boisen published *The Exploration of the Inner World: A Study of Mental Disorder and Religious Experience*, in which he reported the data he had gathered from more than 173 patients. Of particular interest for our present purpose is his final chapter, "In Conclusion," in which he states his philosophy of insanity, the product of both his own inner experience and of his intensive study of chronic psychotic patients.

Once more I am concerned less about myself than about those without whom life is valueless to me. All this I see not as a mere intellectual proposition. I feel it as a grim and awful reality. It is brought back to me with particular vividness in a Statement of Belief which marks the transition to the definitely abnormal condition. This Statement of Belief may serve to suggest the central thesis to which we have been led by this inquiry. . . .

A STATEMENT OF BELIEF

I believe in the Love which came to my rescue on that Easter morning long years ago, the Love that has pitied my weakness and borne with my failures and forgiven my sins, which has lighted the way through the dark nights of despair and has guided me through the awful wilderness of the insane where the going is difficult and very dangerous. I believe that this Love is one with the God who through all ages and among all races has sought to make himself known to the children of men.

I believe that this God was once perfectly revealed in the life and character and teachings of Jesus of Nazareth. His patience with our shortcomings, his compassion upon our infirmities, his unfaltering faith in men, even in his enemies, and his method of dealing with them, not through force but through the power of love, culminating in his death upon the cross, where he died, the just for the unjust, the perfect for the imperfect, the strong for the weak.

(At this point the abnormal condition began.)

And this process has been going on for nineteen centuries. The strong have been giving themselves for the weak and the perfect for the imperfect. Thus a crossing process has resulted. The divine has in consequence been coming into the world disguised in ugliness, crippled by disease, shackled by sin, and impotent with weakness.

I believe that the weak and the imperfect should no longer accept this sacrifice, but that they should be willing now to give their lives, the imperfect for the perfect, the weak for the strong, that the divine may be freed from its prison-house of deformity and may be able to come into the world in beauty and power and not in disguise. Then may the reign of love replace that of brute force and ruthless competition, where survival goes to the strong and to the merciless. And even as the divine has pitied our weakness and loved us in our imperfections, the weak and the imperfect should take pity on his suffering and impotence.

(End of Statement of Belief.)

It will be noted that the first part, while written under strong emotion, follows more or less conventional lines. It came as the result of considerable reflection and had been worked over several times. At the point where the definitely abnormal condition begins, there came a sudden invasion of something quite foreign to all my previous thinking and reading. It came surging in as from an outside source and I wrote down what came to me just as rapidly as I could write, feeling myself merely a passive instrument. Ideas followed each other in rapid succession, ideas that were strange and terrifying and utterly unheard of. These ideas carried conviction with them. They had to do with that which was beyond the range of normal vision and they shattered completely the foundations of my accepted system of beliefs.

The nature of that experience of mine has, I think, been somewhat clarified through this inquiry. It has been shown that it does not stand alone but belongs to a group of experiences which are characterized by the same general constellation of ideas. It has been shown that these experiences are essentially purposive. They are attempts to solve difficult personal problems and tend either to make or break. Among the hospital cases we have found a large proportion of the acutely disturbed who went to the back wards as hopeless wrecks. We have found others, not a few, who emerged from these experiences freed from malignant sets and attitudes and with their problems largely solved. We have found that these acute disturbances which can be observed in any mental hospital bear a striking resemblance to certain types of religious experience. This experience of mine, mental disorder of the most profound and unmistakable variety, was yet for me religious experience in that it brought with it a correct solution of a very difficult personal problem, the solution which is embodied in this Statement of Belief. It was a solution which came automatically through the spontaneous resolution of the subconscious elements that were present, just as previously all my major decisions had been made automatically, although without any such profound upheaval.

Our inquiry has shown furthermore that back of the more constructive solutions resulting from these acute upheavals is a common basic experience. In my own case the basis of the solution lay in the giving up of a hope on which I had staked everything, so that to give it up was for me as the giving up of life itself. So far as I have been able to determine, some renunciation equivalent to the experience of death is characteristic of other acute upheavals. Such experiences may then be looked upon as attempts, sometimes more and sometimes less successful, to eliminate that which is blocking development and preventing the achievement of some higher level of adjustment. They would thus be attempts to carry through the principle enunciated by Jesus of losing one's life in order to find it, of giving up some lesser good or some conflicting desire in order to make possible an integration on the basis of loyalties and values which are regarded as supreme. It is apparently for this reason that nearly always in such experiences there is the sense of being identified with some great superpersonal Being. Those who pass through such experiences may and usually do feel their own infinite littleness. At the same time they also feel themselves one with God or with Christ or with whatever other symbol of the collective they may have chosen. And standing on the threshold of the mysterious and limitless unknown, face to face with the stern realities of death and life, they become profoundly concerned over the fate of the group or race. (Boisen, 1936, pp. 295–298)

This concluding statement of Boisen's probably comes as close to an adequate summary of the personal meaning of psychosis as anyone will ever be able to make. As stated, Boisen had himself lived through an acute psychotic episode. He regained his sanity and then secured an almost ideal advanced educational training for the investigation which he had the opportunity to make. He did investigate carefully and individually a large group of psychotic patients, securing further information concerning the inner life of many psychotic persons who had undergone experiences quite similar to his own. In his conclusions, Boisen stated that the psychotic experience is akin to one of an intense religious nature. An impression as of an invasion of an outside power (Divine force, God) overwhelms the mental life of the individual. The power conveys utter conviction, demanding and obtaining the renunciation of all personal desires so that each individual accepts a new and unique purpose which guides him.

In conclusion, I would venture that the basic personal experience in neurosis is the overwhelming of the self by an irrational and dreadful fear. A common core of neurotic panic is the fear of death and the eternal loss of one's soul.

The basic personal experience in a psychosis is very similar to a mystical ecstasy during which the person is carried along without regard for his old hopes and aspirations by what appears to him to be an external influence that seizes control of his mind and convinces him of the peculiar importance of his condition. If of a religious turn of mind this may take the form of divine revelation and be so vivid that he is fully convinced that he is the last person who will ever be summoned to serve as the messenger for divinity.

Obviously the sufferer's opinion as to the "cause" of his disorder has no necessary relation to scientific or medical causes, but what we have been concerned with in this book is the patient's view of his condition—not the doctor's. Furthermore, while the patient's condition is bound to be different as the result of different scientific causes (and thus in different diagnoses) this is of little concern to the patient and anyway to enter into *that* subject would require another book!

In the preceding pages one cannot but be impressed by the bewildering disorganization of the thought processes as the afflicted sufferers have struggled to express themselves. If these pages have imparted to the reader some degree of familiarity with the actual phrases used, with the obstruction of thought and its turnings, turbulence and distortion, and, above all, with the frankness and sense of urgent validity that characterizes mental disorder, my purpose may be considered to have been accomplished.

References

Alper, T. G.   1948   An electric shock patient tells his story.   *J. abnorm. soc. Psychol.*, 43:201–210.

Anderson, E. W.   1938   A clinical study of states of "ecstasy" occurring in affective disorders.   *J. Neurol. Psych.*, 1 (N.S.):80–99.

Angyal, A.   1936   Phenomena resembling lilliputian hallucinations in schizophrenia.   *Arch. Neurol. Psychiat.*, 36:34–41.

Anon.   1846–1847   Illustrations of insanity.   *Amer. J. Insanity*, III:342–344.

Anon.   1849a   Supposed demoniacal possession.   *J. psychol. Med.*, 2:462–468.

Anon.   1849b   Details sur l'établissement du Dr. Willis pour la guérison des alienes.   *Ann. med-psychol.*, 1:380–390.

Anon.   1850a   The Ohio lunatic asylum.   *J. psychol. Med.*, 3:456–490.

Anon.   1850b   Confessions of a patient after recovering from an attack of lunacy.   *J. psychol. Med.*, 3:388–399.

Anon. (R.F.)   1850c   Supposed demoniacal possession.   *J. psychol. Med.*, 3:262–268.

Anon.   1850d   Autobiography of the insane.   *J. psychol. Med.*, 3:40–54.

Anon.   1854a   A chapter from real life, by a recovered patient.   *The Opal*, Utica, 4:48–50.

Anon.   1854b   Spiritual pathology; or the autobiography of the insane.   *J. psychol. Med.*, 7:356–385.

Anon.   1855   *Scene from the Life of a Sufferer: Being the Narrative of a Residence in Morningside Asylum.* Edinburgh: Royal Asylum Press.

Anon.   1856a   Insanity—my own case.   *Amer. J. Insan.*, 13:25–36.

453

454———References

Anon. 1856b Practical insanity. *The Opal*, Utica, 6:73–87.

Anon. 1857 Cases illustrating the pathology of mental disease. *Amer. J. Insan.*, 14:159–171.

Anon. 1858 A singular case of insanity. *J. psychol. Med.*, 11:490–493.

Anon. 1917 Insanity from the patient's point of view. *J. ment. Sci.*, 63:568–575.

Anon. (Vincent) 1919 Confessions of an agoraphobic victim. *Amer. J. Psychol.*, 30:295–299.

Anon. (J.S.C.) 1925 The mental patient as he feels himself. *J. ment. Sci.*, 71:346–347.

Anon. (An Ex-Patient) 1931 The asylum environment. *Brit. J. med. Psychol.*, 10:344–364.

Anon. (E. Thelmar) 1932a *The Maniac*. London: Watts.

Anon. 1932b *I Lost My Memory: The Case as the Patient Saw It*. London: Faber & Faber Ltd.

Anon. 1940 Insulin and I. *Amer. J. Orthopsychiat.*, 10:810–814.

Anon. 1947 *The Philosophy of Insanity*. New York: Greenberg.

Anon. (Mrs. F.H.) 1952 Recovery from a long neurosis. *Psychiatry*, 15:161–177.

Anon. 1954 Leucotomy. *Lancet*, 1:1232–1233.

Anon. 1955 An antobiography of a schizophrenic experience. *J. abnorm. soc. Psychol.*, 51:677–689.

Arieti, S. 1950 Autistic thought. *J. nerv. ment. Dis.*, 111:288–303.

Baillarger, M. 1856 La théorie de l'automatisme étudiee dans le manuscrit d'un monomaniaque. *Ann. med-psychol.*, 2:54–65.

Balleine, G. R. 1956 *Past Finding Out*. New York: Macmillan.

Beers, C. W. 1908 *A Mind that Found Itself*. New York: Longmans, Green.

Benson, A. C. 1912 *Thy Rod and Thy Staff*. London: Smith, Elder.

Beringer, K., and W. Mayer-Gross 1925 Der Fall Hahnenfuss; Ein Beitrag zur Psychopathologie des akuten schizophrenen Schubs. *Z. Neurol. Psychiat.*, 96:209–250.

Berry, C. S. 1916 Obsessions of normal minds. *J. abnorm. Psychol.*, 11:19–22.

Blalock, J. R. 1936 Psychology of the manic phase of the manic-depressive psychoses. *Psychiat. Quart.*, 10:262–344.

Bockner, S. 1949 The depersonalization syndrome: Report of a case. *J. ment. Sci.*, 95:968–971.

Boisen, A. T. 1936 *The Exploration of the Inner World*. Chicago, Willett, Clark.

Boisen, A. T. 1942 The form and content of schizophrenic thinking. *Psychiatry*, 5:23–33.

Boisen, A. T. 1947 Onset in acute schizophrenia. *Psychiatry*, 10:159–166.

Bond, E. D. 1917 A study of self-accusation. *Amer. J. Insan.*, 74:169–184.

Brock, S., and B. Wiesel 1942 Derealization and depersonalization: Their occurrence in organic and psychogenic states. *Dis. Nerv. Syst.*, 3:139–149.

Brown, H. C. 1937 *A Mind Mislaid*. New York: Dutton.

Bryan, E. 1933 A study of forty cases exhibiting neologisms. *Amer. J. Psychiat., 13:*579–595.

Burnham, W. H. 1903 Retroactive amnesia:Illustrative cases and a tentative explanation. *Amer. J. Psychol., 14:*382–396.

Burton, R. 1927 *The Anatomy of Melancholy.* (Ed. F. Dell and P. Jordan-Smith) New York: Farrar & Rinehart.

Butler-Bowdon, W. 1936 *The Book of Margery Kempe.* London: Jonathan Cape.

Cary, J. 1958 *Art and Reality: Ways of the Creative Process.* (Edited by Ruth N. Anshen) New York: Harper.

Channing, W. 1892 The evolution of paranoia: Report of a case. *J. nerv. ment. Dis.: 19:*192–214.

Clark, R. A. 1946 Cosmic consciousness in catatonic schizophrenia. *Psychoanal. Rev., 33:*460–504.

Cleaves, M. A. 1910 *The Autobiography of a Neurosthene.* Boston: Badger.

Clevenger, S. V. 1890 Heart disease in insanity and a case of panphobia. *Alien & Neurol., 11:*535–543.

Cohen, F. 1956 The relationship between delusional thinking and hostility: A case study. *Psychiat. Quart., 30:*303–321.

Coleman, E. H. 1930 *The Shutter of Snow.* New York: Viking.

Conklin, E. S. 1925 Photographed lilliputian hallucinations. *J. nerv. & ment. Dis., 62:*133–140.

Courtney, J. E. 1901 Dangerous paranoiacs: With autobiography of one. *Alien. & Neurol., 22:*139–149.

Cowper, W. 1816 *Memoir of the Early Life of William Cowper, Esq.* (ed. 2). London: Edwards.

Cullerre 1886 Des perversions sexuelles chez les persecutés. *Ann. med-psychol., 3:*210–231.

Custance, J. 1952 *Wisdom, Madness and Folly.* New York: Pellegrini & Cudahy.

Custance, J. 1954 *Adventure into the Unconscious.* London: Christopher Johnson.

Dahl, R. 1959 *Breakdown.* Indianapolis: Bobbs-Merrill.

Davidson, D. 1912 *Remembrances of a Religio-Maniac.* Stratford-on-Avon, England: Shakespeare Press.

Dawson, W. R. 1909 An autograph account of a case of sane hallucinations due to alcohol and atropin. *J. ment Sci., 55:*711–726.

Dearborn, E. M. 1950 Time out for death. *Psychiat. Quart., 24:*89–123.

Devine, H. 1921 An expiation process in a case of schizophrenia. *J. Neurol. Psychopath., 2:*224–248.

Dewey, R. 1896 Report of a case of "dreamy mental state." *J. nerv. ment. Dis., 24:*763–769.

Diaetophilus (K.W.L. v. Drais) 1798 *Physiche und Psychologische Geschichte seiner Siebenjahrigen Epilepsie.* Zurich: Orell Füssli.

Diethelm, O. 1930 Disturbance of vision and consciousness in petit-mal attacks. *Hum. Biol. 2:*547–554.

Downey, J. E. 1905 Normal variations in the sense of reality. *Psychol. Bull., 2:*297–299.

456———References

Dumont, C. 1865 *Testament Médical.* Paris: Delahaye.

Efron, R. 1956 The effect of olfactory stimuli in arresting uncinate fits. *Brain,* 79:267–281.

Eliot, T. S. 1936 *Collected Poems, 1909–1935.* New York: Harcourt, Brace.

Evans, M. (Williams, P.) 1952 *A Ray of Darkness.* London: Arthur Barker.

Farrar, C. B. 1911 Documented delirium. *Amer. J. Insan.,* 67:571–586.

Ferriar, J. 1813 *An Essay towards a Theory of Apparitions.* London: Cadell & Davies.

Fischer, F. 1929 Zeitstruktur und Schizophrenie. *Z. ges. Neurol. Psychiat.,* 121:544–574.

Flint, E. N. 1893 A case of paranoia. *J. nerv. ment. Dis.,* 20:567–578.

Fodor, N. 1945 Emotional trauma resulting from illegitimate birth. *Arch. Neurol. Psychiat.,* 54:381–384.

Forel, A. 1937 *Out of My Life and Work.* New York: W. W. Norton.

Fraser, R., and W. Sargant 1940–1941 The subjective experiences of a schizophrenic illness: Personal records written at the end of the illness by some patients who were treated with insulin. *Character & Pers.,* 9:139–151.

Freeman, L. 1951 *Fight against Fears.* New York: Crown Publishers.

Freeman, W., and J. M. Williams 1953 Hallucinations in Braille. *Arch. Neurol. Psychiat.,* 70:630–634

Freyberg, H. 1901 Ein Fall chronischer Paranoia mit Ausgang in Heilung. *Allg. Z. Psychiat.,* 58:27–60.

Gaupp, R. 1942 Zur Lehre von der Paranoia. *Z. ges. Neurol. Psychiat.,* 174:762–810.

Gesell, A. L. 1905 A case of symbolistic writing with senile delusions. *Amer. J. Psychol.,* 16:519–536.

Glauber, I. P. 1949 Observations on a primary form of anhedonia. *Psychoanal. Quart.,* 18:67–78.

Graves, A. 1942 *The Eclipse of a Mind.* New York: Medical Journal Press.

Griesinger, W. 1871 *Die Pathologie und Therapie der Psychischen Krankheiten* (ed. 3). Braunschweig.

Grover, M. M. 1931 Report of cases of folie á deux. *Psychiat. Quart.,* 5:307–311.

Hackett, P. 1952 *The Cardboard Giants.* New York: Putnam.

Hallett, J. (Ed.) 1714 *The Life of the Reverend Mr. George Trosse.* Exon: Richard White.

Hamilcar, M. 1910 *Legally Dead.* London: Ouseley.

Harrison, M. 1941 *Spinners Lake.* London: Lane.

Haslam, J. 1810 *Illustrations of Madness: Exhibiting a Singular Case of Insanity, and a no less Remarkable Difference in Medical Opinion: Developing the Nature of Assailment, and the Manner of Working Events; with a Description of the Torture Experienced by Bomb-Bursting, Lobster-Cracking, and Lengthening the Brain.* London: G. Haydon.

References———457

Hayward, M. L., and J. E. Taylor 1956 A schizophrenic patient describes the action of intensive psychotherapy. *Psychiat. Quart.* 30:211–248.

Hennell, T. 1938 *The Witnesses.* London: Davies.

Heveroch, Dr. 1913 Über die Störungen des Ichtums. *Z. ges. Neurol. Psychiat.,* 19:422–496.

Hillyer, J. 1926 *Reluctantly Told.* New York: Macmillan.

Horney, K. 1949 Finding the real self. *Amer. J. Psychoanal.,* 9:3–7

Hughes, C. H. 1885 Borderland psychiatric records, continued. *Alien. & Neurol.,* 6:84–86.

Jackson, J. Hughlings 1889 On a particular variety of epilepsy ("intellectual aura"): One case with symptoms of organic brain disease. *Brain,* 11:179–207.

James, W. 1890 *The Principles of Psychology* (Vol. 2). New York: Holt.

James, W. 1902 *The Varieties of Religious Experience.* New York: Longmans.

Janet, P. 1906 On the pathogenesis of some impulsions. *J. abnorm. Psychol.,* 1:1–17.

Janet, P. 1921 A case of sleep lasting five years with a loss of sense of reality. *Arch. Neurol. Psychiat.,* 6:467–475.

Janis, I. 1950 Psychological effects of electric convulsive treatment. *J. nerv. ment. Dis.* 111: 359–379; 469–489.

Jayson, L. M. 1937 *Mania.* New York: Funk and Wagnalls.

Jefferson, L. 1947 *These Are My Sisters.* Tulsa: Vickers Publ. Co.

Juan de la Cruz (St. John of the Cross, Juan de Yepes) 1953 "Dark Night of the Soul," in *The Complete Works of St. John of the Cross* (trans. and ed. E. A. Peers). London: Burns Oates and Washbourne.

Kampmeier, A. 1907 Confessions of a psychasthenic. *J. abnorm. Psychol.,* 2:112–122.

Karinthy, F. 1939 *A Journey Round My Skull.* London, Faber and Faber.

Karpman, B. 1953 Dream life in a case of hebephrenia. *Psychiat. Quart.,* 27:262–316.

Kindwall, J. A., and E. F. Kinder 1940 Postscript on a benign psychosis. *Psychiatry,* 3:527–534.

Knight, P. S. 1827 *Observations on the Causes, Symptoms, and Treatment of Derangement of the Mind, Founded on an Extensive Moral and Medical Practice in the Treatment of Lunatics. Together with the Particulars of the Sensations and Ideas of a Gentleman during Mental Alienation, Written by Himself During His Convalescence.* London: Longmans.

Krauch, E. 1937 *A Mind Restored: The Story of Jim Curran.* New York: Putnam.

Lancet, Editors of 1952 *Disabilities and How to Live with Them.* London: Lancet.

Lang, J. 1938 The other side of hallucinations. *Amer. J. Psychiat.,* 94: 1089–1097.

Lang, J. 1939a The other side of hallucinations. *Amer. J. Psychiat.,* 96: 423–430.

Lang, J. 1939b The other side of the affective aspects of schizophrenia. *Psychiatry,* 2:195–202.

458———References

Lang, J. 1940 The other side of the ideological aspects of schizophrenia. *Psychiatry,* 3:389–393.

Lennox, W. G., and S. Cobb 1933 Epilepsy. *Arch. Neurol. Psychiat.,* 30:374–387.

Leonard, W. E. 1925 *Two Lives: A Poem.* New York: Huebsch.

Leonard, W. E. 1939 *The Locomotive-God.* New York: Appleton-Century.

Leroy, R. 1922 The syndrome of lilliputian hallucinations. *J. nerv. ment. Dis.,* 56:325–333.

Leuba, J. H. 1929 *The Psychology of Religious Mysticism.* London: Kegan Paul.

Lewis, A. 1934 The psychopathology of insight. *Brit. J. med. Psychol.,* 14:332–348.

Lippman, C. W. 1953 Hallucinations of physical duality in migraine. *J. nerv. ment. Dis.,* 117:345–350.

Lombard, E. 1923 Quelques impressions après une commotion. *J. Psychol. norm. Path.,* 20:651–654.

Ludlow, F. 1868 *The Opium Habit.* New York: Harper.

McCall, L. 1947 *Between Us and The Dark.* Philadelphia: Lippincott.

Macalpine, I., and Hunter, R. A. 1956 *Schizophrenia, 1677: A Psychiatric Study of an Illustrated Autobiographical Record of Demoniacal Possession.* London: Dawson.

MacCurdy, J. T. 1925 *The Psychology of Emotion: Morbid and Normal.* London: Kegan Paul.

Mann, F. W. 1890 Alcoholic hallucination. *Amer. J. Insan.,* 46:439–450.

Manning, H. 1882 Moral insanity: Case of homicidal mania. *J. ment. Sci.,* 28:369–372.

Mayer, E. E. 1911 A case illustrating so-called demon possession. *J. abnorm. Psychol.,* 6:265–278.

Menninger, K. 1954 "We hardly know we are alive." *Bull. Menninger Clinic,* 18:17–18.

Menninger, K. A. 1924 Paranoid psychosis with uremia. *J. nerv. ment. Dis.,* 60:26–34.

Merivale, H. 1879 *My Experiences in a Lunatic Asylum.* London: Chatto & Windus.

Milici, P. 1937 Graphocatharsis in schizophrenia. *Psychiat. Quart.,* 11:44–73.

Milici, P., and C. Von Salzen 1938 Situational schizophrenia. *Psychiat. Quart.,* 12:650–668.

Millingen, J. G. 1840 *Aphorisms on the Treatment and Management of the Insane.* London: Churchill.

Minkowski, E. 1926 Bergson's conceptions as applied to psychopathology. *J. nerv. ment. Dis.,* 63:553–568.

Moore, W. L. 1955 *The Mind in Chains.* New York: Exposition Press.

Nicodemus (pseud. for M. Channing-Pearce) 1942 *Midnight Hour.* London: Faber and Faber.

Nijinsky, R. (Ed.) 1936 *The Diary of Vaslav Nijinsky.* New York: Simon & Schuster.

Nolan, M. J. 1928 Hallucinations and sanity. *J. ment. Sci.,* 74:49–58.

Nunnally, J. C., Jr. 1961 *Popular Conceptions of Mental Health.* New York: Holt.

O'Brien, B. 1958 *Operators and Things: The Inner Life of a Schizophrenic.* Cambridge, Mass.: Arlington.

Oliver, J. R. 1928 *Fear: The Autobiography of James Edwards.* New York: Macmillan.

Osmond, H., and A. Hoffer 1958 The case of Mr. Kovish. *J. Ment. Sci.,* 104:302–325.

Owens, E. ("North 3–1") 1929 *Pick up the Pieces.* New York: Doubleday.

Pastorelli, F. 1936 *The Glorious Bondage of Illness.* London: Allen & Unwin.

Perceval, J. 1838 *A Narrative of the Treatment Experienced by a Gentleman During a State of Mental Derangement, Designed to Explain the Causes and the Nature of Insanity.* London: Effingham Wilson.

Perceval, J. 1840 *A Narrative of the Treatment Experienced by a Gentleman, During a State of Mental Derangement, Designed to Explain the Causes and the Nature of Insanity.* London: Effingham Wilson.

Peters, F. 1949 *The World Next Door.* New York: Farrar Straus.

Peterson, F. 1889 Extracts from the autobiography of a paranoiac. *Amer. J. Psychol.,* 2:193–224.

Pierce, S. W. and J. T. 1929 *The Layman Looks at Doctors.* New York: Harcourt, Brace.

Pollack, B. 1937 Schizophrenic thought. *Psychiat. Quart.,* 11:337–355.

Prince, M. 1912 A clinical study of a case of phobia. *J. abnorm. Psychol.,* 7:259–276.

Prinzhorn, H. 1932 *Psychotherapy.* London: Cape.

Rathmell, T. K., and K. M. Corrin. 1940 Retrospective study of a case involving homicide. *J. nerv. ment. Dis.,* 91:316–322.

Raymond, E. (Ed.) 1946 *The Autobiography of David* ————. London: Gollancz.

Reid, E. C. 1910 Autopsychology of the manic-depressive. *J. nerv. ment. Dis.,* 37:606–620.

Ribot, T. 1914 *The Psychology of Emotions.* New York, Scribners.

Rickman, E. S. 1841 *Madness or the Maniac's Hall: A Poem, in Seven Cantos.* London: Smith Elder.

Roberts, W. W. 1960 Normal and abnormal depersonalization. *J. ment. Sci.,* 106:478–493.

Rowland, E. H. 1909 A case of visual sensations during sleep. *J. Phil. Psychol. sci. Meth.,* 6:353–357.

Rows, R. G. 1914 The importance of disturbances of the personality in mental disorders. *J. ment. Sci.,* 60:192–224.

Rutherford, M. 1885 *The Autobiography of Mark Rutherford.* R. Shapcott (Ed.). New York: Dodd, Mead.

Rychlinski, K. 1896 Ein Fall hallucinatorisch-periodischer Psychose. *Arch. Psychiat. Nervenkr.* 28:625–639.

Santayana, G. (Ed., L. P. Smith) 1920 *Little Essays.* New York, Scribners.

Schreber, D. P. 1955 *Memoirs of My Nervous Illness*. (Ed. and trans. by I. Macalpine and R. A. Hunter). London: Dawson.

Sharpe, E. F. 1940 Psycho-physical problems revealed in language: an examination of metaphor. *Int. J. Psychoanal., 21*:201–213.

Schwab, F. 1919 Selbstschilderung eines Falles von schizophrener Psychose. *Z. ges. Neurol. und Psychiat., 44*:1–20.

Sechehaye, M. 1951 *Autobiography of a Schizophrenic Girl*. New York, Grune and Stratton.

Sidgwick, H. 1894 Report on the census of hallucinations. *Proc. Soc. Psych. Res., London, 10*:25–422.

Smart, C. 1910 "A Song to David." *Harvard Classics, 41*:496–510.

Southcott, J. 1801 *The Strange Effects of Faith with Remarkable Prophecies*. Exeter, England: Brill.

Spencer, H. 1878 Consciousness under chloroform. *Mind, 3*:555–558.

Starobinski, A. 1921 Un cas de psychose maniaque dépressive a un jour d'Alternance. *Ann. med. -psychol., 1*:344–347.

Stengel, E. 1943 Further studies on pathological wandering (fugues with the impulse to wander). *J. ment. Sci., 89*:224–241.

Straus, E. 1938 Ein Beitrag zur Pathologie der Zwangserscheinungen. *Mschr. Psychiat. Neurol., 98*:61–101.

Stuart, G. 1953 *Private World of Pain*. London: Allen & Unwin.

Sullivan, D. J. 1948 Insulin subshock (subcoma) treatment of psychoses and psychoneuroses. *Arch. Neurol. Psychiat., 59*:184–214.

Sullivan, H. S. 1927 The onset of schizophrenia. *Amer. J. Psychiat., 7*: 105–134.

Swedenborg, E. 1839 *Concerning the Earths in Our Solar System which are Called Planets*. Boston: Clapp.

Swedenborg, E. (translated by Bush, G., and Smithson) 1883 *The Spiritual Diary*. London: Speira.

Symonds, J. 1895 *John Addington Symonds, A Biography, Compiled from His Papers and Correspondence by Horatio F. Brown*. London: J. C. Nimmo

Symons. A. 1930 *Confessions: A Study in Pathology*. New York: Fountain Press.

Tanner, A. E. 1907 An illustration of the psychology of belief. *Psychol. Bull., 4*:33–36.

Taylor, W. S., and E. Culler 1929 The problem of The Locomotive-God. *J. abnorm. soc. Psychol., 24*:342–399.

Traherne, T. 1910 *Traherne's Poems of Felicity* (ed. from the ms. of H. I. Bell). Oxford: Clarendon Press.

Turnbull, R. C. 1921 A case of catatonia. *J. Neurol. Psychopath., 2*:154–158.

Upham, T. C. 1849 *Life and Religious Opinions and Experience of Madame de la Mothe Guyon* (Vol. 1). New York: Harper.

Vincent, J. 1948 *Inside the Asylum*. London: Allen & Unwin.

Walford, W. 1851 *Autobiography of the Rev. William Walford*. London: Jackson & Walford.

Ward, M. J. 1946 *The Snake Pit*. New York: Random House.

Weickhardt, G. D., and K. H. Langenstrass 1947 Psychosynthesis of amnesia. *J. nerv. ment. Dis., 105*:238–254.

Winkler, W. 1948 Das Oneiroid (zur Psychose Alfred Kubins). *Arch. Psychiat. Nervenkr., 181*:136–167.

Woods, W. L. 1938 Language study in schizophrenia. *J. nerv. ment. Dis., 87*:290–316.

Zeifert, M. 1940 Metrazol remission in severe obsession-compulsion neurosis of five year's duration. *J. nerv. ment. Dis., 92*:290–301.

Zubin, J. 1948 "Objective studies of disordered persons." Chapter in T. G. Andrews: *Methods of Psychology*. New York: Wiley.

Indexes

Diagnostic Index: Editor's Comment

Considerable caution is necessary in presenting "auto-biographical" psychotic material for scholarly study. Public interest in this subject has created a demand for such material in the publishing world, and there is scarcely a periodical or publisher, however remote from the scholarly field, which has not brought out some alleged autobiographical item, and the more livid and sensational the better. Professor Landis and I have both exerted ourselves to prevent any of such more or less frankly fraudulent material from finding its way into this book and I know of no item appearing here which was produced for the primary purpose of financial profit.

A second problem which arises is that of diagnostic classification. It should be apparent that not every patient who believes he has been diagnosed as having a particular type of disorder really knows what his medical attendants think. Thus the patient's own classification of his case may be something less than accurate. It has also been necessary to provide the reader with some means of knowing what cases from a much earlier period would be considered to be today. Only a practical-minded and thoroughly experienced psychiatrist is in a position to prepare such a classification and I am happy to have been able to persuade Humphry Osmond, the Director of the Bureau of Research in Neurology and Psychiatry of the State of New Jersey, to do this.

Doctor Osmond's classification covers most of the cases mentioned in the book in a very practical manner. It must be borne in mind that many of these cases exhibit secondary or atypical features, which while familiar enough to clinicians may throw off the inexperienced reader. Thus, Peters, whom Osmond classifies, quite properly, as a schizophrenic also exhibits a form of behavior (sun gazing) which is occasionally encountered in cases of convulsive disorder. This "staring into the sun," as it has been called by Landis, is a form of bemusement in which photic driving may play a part. Aretaeus (fl. first to second centuries A.D.) of Cappadocia commented that convulsive seizures could be precipitated by contemplating a running stream, rolling wheel, or spinning top (C. C. Mettler, 1947, *History of Medicine*. Philadelphia: Blakiston; see page 512). Patients with convulsive disorder sometimes are under the *compulsion* to induce attacks by producing similar flickering phenomena by standing in the sun and blinking the eyes or by waving something between the eyes and sun. Robertson (*Brain*, 1958, 77:232–251) describes several such cases. The following relates to a thirty-year-old woman with grand mal seizures.

The patient herself said that these attacks only occurred when she was out in the sun and that she knew it was the sun that did it. She felt that she must look at the sun which made her eyes blink, and meanwhile she felt peculiar. If she continued for a long period, a prolonged attack of unconsciousness tended to occur. She could stop the blinking if she wished. When asked why she did not always stop it, she replied that she did not know; and then added that sometimes when she was a bit upset or excited she hadn't the same control over herself.

The phenomenon is also seen in persons with petit mal.

A man of 18 years stated that, during the last eight years, he has been unable to stop himself looking at the sun. The sun seems to attract him, and he blinks because it is so bright. Every time, and as soon as he goes outside on a sunny day he looks up at the sun and blinks. He feels dazed and is not fully conscious for a second, then his mind comes back again. He stops if he is speaking but is able to pick up the trend immediately. He adds that when he goes into the sun, thinking of anything, the light blinds him and puts him off his thought for a moment. He has been aware that his eyes were closed for a brief interval when crossing a road, but he knows where he is in his memory, and can walk with his eyes shut. Once he was knocked down, quite unexpectedly, by a motor-car.

The similarity between such a situation and self-stimulation with implanted electrodes is fairly obvious. Patients of this variety are familiar to nearly every psychiatrist who has a wide hospital experience. Sometimes such patients say they are trying to "move the sun," and the cases often represent transitional states between convulsive disorder and schizophrenia.

Something of the nature of the compulsive urge that may be experienced was explained by another patient with petit mal, as follows.

When the sun is out, or if I am near a window, I am tempted to wag the hand. I try not to, but there is a kind of nitch in my mind that makes me do it. I try to think of something to do to keep my mind off it. Sometimes I remember after taking my hand up once, and try to stop it. At other times it just goes on. If it goes on for too long I can't stop and this might lead to a turn. I don't feel uncomfortable if I stop it. It isn't pleasant to do it, but I just can't help it. I suppose that I have got into the habit of doing it, and cannot stop. I am so used to doing it that I cannot think whether I want to do it or not. When I look at the sun, it seems to pierce the right eye and touch a nerve or something, and I feel as if I want to do it. My mind goes blank for a second or so after longer waves.

The influence of the sun on other neurologic disorders such as headache—or more specifically, migraine—is also well known and it is of some interest to observe that not only does migraine still play a prominent (and complex social) role in practices on the Côte d'Azur (and recently the Costa Brava) but its descriptions form a constant feature of Mediterranean medical writings from pre-Hippocratic times onward.

It has obviously been impossible for Dr. Osmond to consider all such variations and there is no inconsistency in encountering petit mal features in a basically schizophrenic individual. Dr. Osmond comments, with regard to his index which appears below, as follows.

It is a pleasure and an honor to have been invited by Professor Mettler to make a small contribution to the late Carney Landis' great book. It is also a responsibility, for Landis assembled this work with the skill that those who knew him will find familiar, and generally speaking the descriptions of the sick people which he adds to their own narratives require no glossary from me or anyone else. However, Professor Mettler felt that an auxiliary index, giving a rough and ready but contemporary classification wherever this is possible, might help readers unfamiliar with such obsolete terms as frenzy or monomania, or such near-dead ones as neurasthenia.

It is necessary, however, to recognize the limitations of contemporary psychiatric classification. Are we to use the single psychiatric illness covering all sorts of conditions of mental affliction that Menninger has been advocating in recent years, or the seventeen or more varieties of schizophrenia that Kleist and his followers find so useful?

There is nothing new about this kind of disagreement, since the classifiers and unifiers in medicine have been disagreeing steadily since

Sydenham's time over three hundred years ago. The detailed categories of illnesses, marshalled in genera, subgenera, species, and subspecies, were challenged and sometimes temporarily eliminated by the grand generalizings of men like Brown, Stahl, and Broussais. Psychiatric classification still has many uncertainties, but we do have illnesses where natural history, presenting symptoms, outcome, and treatment seem to differ considerably from each other, and as this book shows us so clearly, these illnesses have remained very similar from century to century. Evidence is slowly accumulating that there are underlying physiological disturbances in at least some of these conditions which account for the psychosocial disruption they produce and which results in much suffering for patients and families.

I shall use the following crude but useful classification without apology, for it works well in clinical practice where many more refined ones fail.

1. *The Schizophrenic Psychoses:* In these illnesses changes of perception and thinking often precede and determine the mood change. They have been recognized for hundreds of years, as Thomas Willis' excellent description in *De anima brutorum*—written in the latter half of the seventeenth century—shows, "For these kinds of brains, like distorted looking glasses, do not rightly collect images of things, nor truly object them to the rational soul"—we might use the word project today, or perhaps display.

2. *The Affective Psychoses:* Illnesses which are characterized by alterations in mood of a long-sustained kind, and often of a marked intensity. This mood-change does not usually seem fully appropriate to the patient's circumstances. Depression (melancholy) and elation (mania) are familiar examples of this—although apathy is frequently seen and irritability may be more evident than high spiritedness. These illnesses, too, as Carney Landis' book shows, have been recognized for centuries.

3. *The Psychoneuroses:* States of anxiety and all-encompassing fear, which may be accompanied by phobias, compulsions, hysterical conversion symptoms, psychosomatic symptoms, and so forth. They also have a very long and respectable history.

4. *Epilepsy and similar convulsive states.*

5. *Toxic confusional states* of a variety of kinds, usually associated with alcoholism.

6. *Mixed or unusual syndromes,* such as the effects of cerebral tumor, cerebral hemorrhage, migraine, concussive states, intoxication with adrenalin derivatives, and so on. It will be noted that the dementias, the slowly or rapidly deteriorating illnesses produced by brain damage of a variety of kinds, are hardly represented at all here for the very good reason that these accounts are written by the sick people themselves and demented people are seldom able to write a greal deal or very coherently.

I have arranged the cases in three main categories: Category A, where the main classification is fairly unequivocal, although the subcategories, such as paranoid, or hebephrenic schizophrenia, are always questionable and involve a matter of opinion; Category B, in which the diagnostic classification is much less certain because the samples are too small or the information may be somewhat unclear; and Category C, which includes those cases in which I have not attempted to make a diagnosis because this is either inappropriate, such as in the cases of St. John of the Cross and Swedenborg, or there just are not enough data.

Princeton, New Jersey   HUMPHRY OSMOND, M.R.C.S., L.R.C.P., D.P.M.,
July 1964   F.W.A. Director, Bureau of Research in
Neurology and Psychiatry

Index of Cases by Diagnosis

Leroy 1922, 118

CATEGORY C

No diagnosis has been attempted. The data supplied are either inappropriate or insufficient.

Balleine 1956, 131
Berry 1916, 336
Burnham, 1903, 217
Cohen, 1956, 320
Conklin 1925, 119

Downey 1905, 352
James 1890, 355
Juan de la Cruz 1953, 309
Leuba 1929, 436
Rickman 1841, 391
Roberts 1960, 367
Rowland 1909, 356, 357
Stuart 1953, 419, 427
Symons 1930, 403
Swedenborg 1839, 1883, 126
Taylor and Culler 1929, 416

Diagnosis of Cases

Alper 1948, Schizophrenia, paranoid
Anderson 1938, Affective psychosis, manic
Angyal 1936, Schizophrenia (paranoid?)
Anon. 1846–1847, Schizophrenia, acute
Anon. 1849a, Schizophrenia, paranoid
Anon. 1849b, Affective psychosis, manic-depressive, circular type
Anon. 1850a, Schizophrenia, acute
Anon. 1850b, Schizophrenia
Anon. 1850d, Psychoneurosis, phobic, obsessive
Anon. 1854a, Schizo-affective psychosis
Anon. 1854b, Epilepsy? Cataleptic seizures
Anon. 1855, Toxic confusional state, delirium
Anon. 1856a, Schizophrenia (acute?)
Anon. 1857, Schizophrenia, acute
Anon. 1858, Affective psychosis, manic
Anon. 1917, Schizophrenia, acute
Anon. 1919, Psychoneurosis, phobic state
Anon. 1925, Schizophrenia, acute
Anon. 1931, Schizophrenia, acute
Anon. 1932a, Schizophrenia, acute
Anon. 1932b, Amnesia (origin unclear)
Anon. 1940, Schizophrenia, undifferentiated

Anon. 1947, Affective psychosis, depression (with agitation)
Anon. 1952, Psychoneurosis, phobic state
Anon. 1954, Uncertain. ?Chronic anxiety state
Anon. 1955, Acute Schizophrenia: onset
Anon. 1956b, (?) Schizophrenia, paranoid
Arieti 1950, Schizophrenia, acute
Baillarger 1856, Psychoneurosis, obsessive compulsive? Pseudoneurotic schizophrenia
Balleine 1956, ?
Beers 1908, Schizo-affective state
Benson 1912, Affective psychosis, depression
Beringer and Mayer-Gross 1925, Schizophrenia, acute
Berry 1916, Normal subject. Fixed ideas
Blalock 1936, Affective psychosis. manic-depressive, circular type
Bockner 1949, Affective psychosis, depression
Boisen 1936, Schizophrenia
Boisen 1942, Schizophrenia, acute
Boisen 1947, Schizophrenia, acute onset. Schizophrenia, paranoid?
Bond 1917, Schizophrenia, paranoid
Brown 1937, Affective psychosis, depression
Brock and Wiesel 1942, Bilateral athetosis (depersonalization in)

Bryan 1933, Schizophrenia (paranoid?)

Burnham 1903, No diagnosis attempted (*jamais vu*)

Burton 1927, Affective psychosis; depression

Butler Bowden 1936, ?Schizophrenia

Channing 1892, Schizophrenia (paranoid)

Clark 1946, Schizophrenia, catatonic

Cleaves 1910, Psychoneurosis; chronic anxiety state. ?Pseudoneurotic schizophrenia

Clevenger 1890, Psychoneurosis, phobic state

Cohen 1956, Diagnosis unclear

Coleman 1930, ?Schizophrenia (too little information)

Conklin 1925, No diagnosis possible

Courtney 1901, Schizophrenia, paranoid

Cowper 1816, Affective psychosis, depression

Cullere 1886, Schizophrenia, paranoid

Custance 1952, Affective psychosis, (circular). Manic and depressive.

Dahl 1959, Affective psychosis, manic

Davidson 1912, Schizophrenia, acute, onset

Dawson 1909, Toxic confusional state (post alcoholic)

Dearborn 1950, Schizophrenia (paranoid)

Dewey 1896, Epilepsy. ?Uncinate seizure.

Devine 1921, Schizophrenia, acute

Diaetophilus 1798, Epilepsy (idiopathic), grand mal

Diethelm 1930, Epilepsy, petit mal

Downey 1905, Introspective psychologist

Dumont 1865, Toxic confusional state, (delirium)

Efron 1956, Epilepsy, uncinate seizure

Evans M. 1952, Epilepsy (symptomatic), grand mal (associated with slow-growing glioma)

Farrar 1911, Toxic confusional state (alcoholic delirium)

Ferriar 1813, ?Schizophrenia, acute (too little data)

Fischer 1929, Schizophrenia, acute

Flint 1893, Schizophrenia, paranoid

Fodor 1945, Schizophrenia, acute

Forel 1937, Cerebral hemorrhage

Fraser and Sargent 1940–1941, Schizophrenia acute, onset

Freeman 1951, Psychoneurosis with psychosomatic disturbance

Freeman and Williams 1953, Schizophrenia, paranoid

Freyberg 1901, Schizophrenia, paranoid

Gaupp 1942, ?Schizophrenia, paranoid

Gesell 1905, Schizophrenia, chronic, dementia.

Glauber 1949, Psychoneurosis, chronic anxiety state; ?schizophrenia, pseudoneurotic

Graves 1942, Schizophrenia, affective

Grover 1931, Schizophrenia, paranoid (*folie à deux*)

Hackett 1952, ?Schizophrenia, acute onset

Hamilcar 1910, Uncertain. ?Schizoaffective psychosis

Harrison 1941, Schizophrenia, acute

Hallett 1714, Schizophrenia, paranoid

Haslam 1810, Schizophrenia, paranoid

Hayward and Taylor 1956, ?Schizophrenia

Hennell 1838, Schizophrenia, paranoid

Heveroch 1913, Schizophrenia, acute

Hillyer 1926, Schizophrenia, acute

Horney 1949, Psychoneurosis, phobic anxiety type

Hughes 1885, Affective psychosis, depression

Jackson 1889, Epilepsy, petit mal

James 1890, Blind Man. No psychosis.

James 1902, Affective psychosis, depression

Janet 1906, ?Alcoholism

Janet 1921, ?Schizo-affective psychosis

Jayson 1937, Schizophrenia, paranoid

Jefferson 1947, Schizophrenia, paranoid

Juan de La Cruz 1953, Affective psychosis, depression; mystical experience

Karinthy 1939, Cerebral tumor

Karpman 1953, Schizophrenia, hebephrenic

Straus 1938, Psychoneurosis, obsessive compulsive type

Stuart 1953, Not enough to go on

Sullivan 1927, Schizophrenia, acute

Sullivan 1940, ?Schizo-affective state

Swedenborg 1839, 1883, No diagnosis made

Symons 1930, ?

Taylor and Culler 1929, No diagnosis made

Turnbull 1921, Schizophrenia, catatonic

Upham 1849, Affective psychosis, depression

Vincent 1948, Psychoneurosis, chronic anxiety state?

Walford 1851, Affective psychosis, depressive

Ward 1946, Schizophrenia, paranoid

Weickhardt and Langenstrass 1947, Psychoneurosis, ?hysteria with amnesia (too little data)

Wickler 1948, Schizophrenia, acute onset

Woods 1938, Schizophrenia, ?hebephrenic

Zeifert 1940 ?Psychoneurosis, obsessive compulsive

General Index

477

General Index———479